The Sea
Off
Southern California

An oceanographer's typical view of the ocean—cable coming out of the water. Black-footed albatrosses are interested spectators.

John Wiley & Sons, Inc. ——————— **New York**

London

The Sea

Off

Southern California

A

MODERN

HABITAT

OF

PETROLEUM

K. O. Emery

PROFESSOR OF GEOLOGY
UNIVERSITY OF SOUTHERN CALIFORNIA

TO **Professor Francis P. Shepard,**
WHO AWAKENED MY INTEREST IN THE OCEAN,
AND TO **Captain Allan Hancock,**
WHO PROVIDED THE MEANS FOR FOLLOWING
THAT INTEREST.

Preface

During the last 120 years more than 2500 scientific articles have been published on various aspects of the sea floor, the water, and the marine life off California (Terry, 1955). Beginning about 1920 the average annual number of articles has risen from 10 to 150, owing to increased awareness of the ocean and its resources. Altogether these publications have brought the state of knowledge of the submerged area off southern California to a very high level as compared to that of any other area of the ocean having a similar size and complexity. The present knowledge has arisen through the efforts of many workers and, although certain fields of investigation have largely been confined to marine research organizations such as the Allan Hancock Foundation at the University of Southern California and Scripps Institution of Oceanography at La Jolla, other organizations have contributed. In view of the large number of articles having limited objectives, the abundance of unpublished material, and the rapidly increasing interest in marine studies and in recovery of offshore petroleum, it seems desirable to bring much of this material together in a single volume. Such a summary of information may prove helpful to other investigators working in this region. Knowledge of the interrelationships of geography and processes off southern California may also serve as a guide to what may be expected in other less well-known regions of the sea floor.

Some idea of the complexity of the marine environment is given when we realize that topography, for example, is interrelated with structure, lithology, sediments, life, and water movements. Structure has exerted a major control on topograpy through block faulting and regional warping, but the shelves along the mainland and islands were cut by waves. Erosion by boring organisms has aided the waves, particularly in shallow water. Locally, resistant rocks have remained as headlands, stacks, and small submerged hills. Thick layers of sediments have smoothed the floors of basins and prograded shores. The sediments themselves consist of rock debris, organic materials, and precipitates from water, and all are deposited in topographic traps where rate of deposition exceeds rate of erosion by water movements. The remains of organisms that live in the water are deposited with other sediments at favorable topographic positions. After compaction to rock, some of this organic matter is yielded as petroleum, which can then be recovered economically where the rocks contain reservoir sandstones of favorable structure and water depth.

The immediate concern of oil geologists is that of locating favorable sites of accumulation of petroleum, but a thorough understanding of petroleum includes background information on the manner of deposition and alteration of organic materials. Accordingly, an attempt will be made to describe the basic environmental factors of the region and to relate them to each other and, whenever possible, to the general problem of origin and accumulation of petroleum, one of the most important resources of the region. In many respects the present sea floor basins are similar to ancestral forms of several basins which have become filled with sediments and are now rich oil-producing areas on land in southern California. The similarities were recognized by several workers at about the same time: Trask in 1932 for organic matter, Natland in 1933 for foraminiferal ecology, and Reed in 1933 for structural geology. Since the time of these early publications, much additional material has been uncovered.

Although the economic view is appreciated, the objective of this book is the integration of basic knowledge rather than the pointing out of prospective sites for mining or oil drilling. Little space will be used to describe methods of sampling because these are adequately covered in other works or can best be learned aboard ship.

Ideas presented in this book have evolved during a period of about twenty-two years through discussions with many workers, questions from students, and solitary musings. Special thanks are due Dr. Bruce C. Heezen for his critical review of the manuscript. To all others who have aided in one way or another, on land or at sea, the writer expresses his deep appreciation.

K. O. EMERY

Allan Hancock Foundation
University of Southern California
Los Angeles, California
November 1959

Contents

Physiography

Knowledge of the topography of a region is essential to an understanding of the environment and its processes. When topographic data are organized into physiographic units they become still more useful. In this respect the sea floor off southern California is better known than are most other parts of the ocean. Its basins, banks, and islands are essentially unique for the sea floor, and they really belong neither to continental shelf nor to continental slope nor to abyssal sea floor. Instead, they are similar to features of the nearby land area, which itself is unique in the world. Farther north and south of southern California both land and sea floor change to more typical forms. Although the region is of unusual physiography, its very complexity has resulted in a concentration of environments of such varied nature that elsewhere it would require long cruises to visit them. Since the detailed knowledge obtained off southern California can be extrapolated to more distant regions, this area might be thought of as a large model useful for easy testing of many ideas about general oceanic processes.

Exploration

The earliest explorations of the shores of southern California, lost in the mists of time, were doubtlessly made by primitive immigrants from Asia via Bering Strait. Their antiquity is shown by the finding of artifacts near the shores of former lakes, on the sea floor, and under soils that date from some unknown part of the Pleistocene Epoch, but probably from the last glacial age and possibly the preceding interglacial (Clements and Clements, 1953; Carter, 1957a). Radiocarbon dating of charcoal and bones from hearth sites on Santa Rosa Island (Orr, 1956) showed the presence of man in the area at least as long ago as $29,650 \pm 2500$ years. On the same island is the oldest dated midden of the West coast, 7400 years (Orr, 1958). No record remains of the explorations of these people other than what can be inferred from the distribution of debris and occasional tools which they left behind. On the mainland and most of the islands many bowls made of steatite quarried on Santa Catalina Island have been found, indicating that extensive boat travel and trading occurred during at least a late stage of the Indian culture. Indian canoes seen by the Spaniards in 1602 and 1770 were so well made and so seaworthy that they were given special mention in the diaries of Vizcaíno (Bolton, 1916, p. 87) and Fray Crespi (Bolton, 1927, pp. 34, 159).

Even more hazy is a record of a series of Chinese visits, possibly to western North America about 2250 B.C. This record, the *Shan Hai King,* was compiled by Emperor

1

Shun's Minister of Public Works, Yu. The evidence is primarily the possible identification of existing mountains, rivers, and dunes with those encountered during journeys tersely described in the old manuscript (Mertz, 1953). Possible support for some trans-Pacific trading and visiting in very ancient times is provided by certain similarities of sculptures, games, words, and useful plants in the Old and New Worlds according to some workers, among whom are Ekholm (1953) and Carter (1957b).

Also on uncertain ground is the story of a wandering band of Buddhist priests written by one of them, Hui San (Vining, 1885). According to his tale and those of several later Chinese, the land of Fu-sang located about 13,000 miles east of China was inhabited by people who could write and weave and used corn as a chief food item. Many topographic, cultural, and language similarities between the priest's story and Central America were described by Mertz (1953), who in addition interpreted the record as showing that the first landing of these Chinese visitors in A.D. 458 was made in southern California, precisely at Hueneme. Others, such as Goodrich (1938), find no justification for assuming early Chinese knowledge of North America, pointing out the absence of maps or references to maps of North America in pre-Columbian Chinese literature.

Of interest was the finding by Mr. Ralph Glidden, owner of a museum at Avalon, Santa Catalina Island, of the top half of a Chinese ceramic burial image at Empire Landing in 1922. The image was under an abalone shell, a typical Indian "treasure box." After studying a photograph of the image, Dr. T. Y. H. Ma of Taiwan University, Formosa, and his colleagues reported, "The preliminary judgment from only a black and white photograph is that it certainly is of Chinese origin. The workmanship shows that it could not be earlier than the Tang dynasty (A.D. 618–905) and it could not have been made later because such statuettes were not made so well after the Tang dynasty, when they began using paper or wooden figures for the same pur-

pose of accompanying the dead to burial. As to the possible time of bringing such a statuette to the American continent we must surmise that it was during the last days of the Tang dynasty when people were being massacred during the uprising of Huang Chao (A.D. 875–884) that someone just put out to sea in a junk to leave his destination to fate, just as people run out of the Iron Curtain now." There is no means of determining when the image arrived in California or even when it was buried, owing to incomplete observations when it was discovered. Conceivably, it was brought by a ship which Vizcaíno, during his visit in 1602 (Bolton, 1916, p. 85), was informed had been wrecked on the island a few years earlier. Also it could have been found by Indians in a wrecked junk bearing no living persons. Several such junks have been washed ashore in Alaska and Washington during historical times, two since 1900, and the same ocean currents still deposit Japanese glass fishing floats on the islands and mainland of southern California.

Although the concept is intriguing, more concrete data are needed before pre-Spanish visits to southern California of people other than Indians can be accepted. Nevertheless, the possibility of such visits remains. The uncertainty resulting from lack of adequate records is well exemplified in central America where the Maya god named Quetzalcoatl, the bearded visitor from across the ocean, has been variously identified as of Hebrew, Chinese, Greek, and Norse origin.

The earliest well-documented explorations are, of course, those by the Spaniards. A few years after Hernán Cortés took Mexico City, he crossed the Gulf of California to the tip of the peninsula to begin in 1535 the exploration of the coast to the north. By 1539 one of his captains, Francisco de Ulloa, had sailed to the head of the gulf, back to the tip of Baja California, and then part way up the Pacific coast (Wagner, 1937; Sykes, 1937). A second expedition under Hernando de Alarcón also reached the head of the Gulf in 1540. Their finds, shown on a map of 1542 (Fig. 1), were soon extended

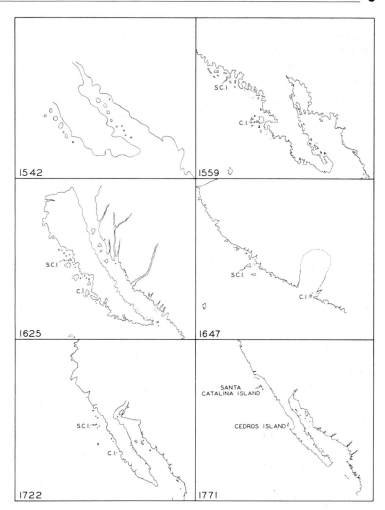

Figure 1. Early maps of California redrawn from photographs in Wagner (1937): 1542, Batiste Aganese's map, including Ulloa's discoveries of 1539. 1559, André Homem's planisphere, including discoveries by Cabrillo. 1625, Henry Briggs's map probably based on copy of chart by Fray Antonio de la Ascension. 1647, Robert Dudley's map. 1722, Joseph Nicholas Delisle's map, showing explorations of Kino and Consag. 1771, Miguel Castansó's map, including data of Portola's ships.

to southern California by another expedition under Juan Rodríguez Cabrillo (Bolton, 1916), sent out by the viceroy Antonio de Mendoza to find a route to China and possibly also to establish contact with Coronado in his search for the Seven Cities of Cibola. Cabrillo arrived at Santa Catalina Island, which he named San Salvador after one of his two ships, on October 7, 1542. Continuing up the coast, the expedition wintered on San Miguel Island where Cabrillo died. The next year under his successor, Bartolomé Ferrer, the ships reached Cape Mendocino in northern California before returning to Mexico.

The findings of Cabrillo's expedition are shown on a map of 1559, which is distinctly better than other maps of the region made during the following two centuries. In fact,

it was during this period that European map makers conceived the idea that Baja California was an island, an illusion that was not dispelled until Fray Eusebio Francisco Kino in 1699 and Padre Fernando Consag in 1746 repeated Ulloa's and Alarcón's explorations at the head of the gulf. Probably the island concept as well as the name arose because of the popularity of a Spanish romance called *Los Sergas de Esplandián* written by García Ordoñez de Montalvo in 1510. This was a tale of an island populated by Amazons, abundant in gold and gems, and ruled by the queen Calafía. Similarities, real and fancied, between this fabled land and the tip of Baja California led to the latter's being called the land of Calafía, or California (Stewart, 1945, p. 14).

Except for sighting of the islands by the

treasure galleons returning from Manila to Acapulco in 1565, 1605, 1606, and 1696 (Wagner, 1937) and stories of three shipwrecks in 1598, 1701, and 1754 (Coffman, 1957), the only known visitor to southern California between 1543 and 1769 appears to have been Sebastián Vizcaíno. Sent out from Acapulco to find refuge harbors for the galleons after their experiences with Francis Drake in 1578–1579 and with Thomas Cavendish in 1587–1588, Vizcaíno spent about two weeks during November 1602 in the region, repairing his ships at San Diego and visiting Santa Catalina Island (Bolton, 1916). Although he described the ports of San Diego and Monterey, settlements were deemed unnecessary, at least for the time being, because the galleons generally stood far out from shore at these latitudes and were running with scurvy-ridden crews downwind as fast as possible on the last part of the voyage to Acapulco. Vizcaíno, a merchant, made only a minor contribution to the knowledge of the coast and is chiefly distinguished for having changed the names of landmarks given by Cabrillo.

In 1769 a permanent settlement, a presidio, was established at San Diego by Gaspar de Portolá in an effort by the Spanish to offset the advances of Russians from Alaska, French from Canada, Dutch from the Cape of Good Hope, and British from Cape Horn. The two ships sent by Portolá completed the early exploration of southern California coasts and the accumulated findings are reproduced in a map of 1771. This map is accurate in detail, and it also corrected the errors of latitude and longitude that gave rise to the westerly coastal trend shown by earlier maps. To fix the hold of the Spaniards on California, other presidios were established at Monterey in 1770, San Francisco in 1776, and Santa Barbara in 1782, and El Pueblo de Nuestra Senora la Reina de Los Angeles de Porciuncula was founded in 1781. During the overland trip to establish Monterey Fray Crespi noted topographic details so carefully (Bolton, 1927) that, by using his diary as a guidebook, we can very closely follow his path from San Diego.

One of the first visitors to the newly founded towns was Captain George Vancouver who came during November 1793 to investigate the status of occupation of the region by the Spaniards. His is the first known oceanographic work—the failure to find bottom with several hundred fathoms of line just off the Palos Verdes Hills (Wilbur, 1954).

During the period of exploration and settlement little was learned of the sea floor until after California became a state in 1850. Beginning in 1851 lead-line soundings were taken by the U. S. Coast and Geodetic Survey in shallow waters of important bays, and a few soundings were made in deeper waters. In 1922 about 5000 well-distributed sonic soundings were made by the destroyers *U.S.S. Hull* and *Corry* off southern California and northern Mexico. Contours based on these soundings revealed a complex topography but left much to be desired, owing to poor position control. New and improved sonic surveys were made between 1935 and 1937 by the Coast and Geodetic Survey with positions obtained by a radioacoustic-ranging method. These brought the total number of good soundings in the area to about 500,000, of which nearly 300,000 are deeper than 300 feet, an average density of about 10 per square mile in deep water. On the basis of these soundings the 300-foot interval contours of Chart I were drawn by Shepard and Emery (1941). Very similar contours were drawn on U. S. Coast and Geodetic Survey Charts 5101 and 5202, which cover part of the same area. Since 1940 no general resurveys have been made, and the modifications discovered through local surveys which used recording echo sounders and radar have been so minor as to require no changes in the original contours.

General Description

The sea floor between the mainland shoreline and the continental slope off southern California is much more complex than typical continental shelves of most other areas of the world. For this reason it was named the continental borderland by Shepard and

Emery (1941) to distinguish it from ordinary continental shelves. Even casual examination of Chart I shows that the continental borderland is a checkerboard-like arrangement of high and low areas having a general elongation that ranges from southeast-northwest to east-west, more or less parallel to the topographic trends of the nearby land areas. Some of the topographic highs extend above sea level to form islands, whereas others rise almost to sea level, constituting banks, most of which are flat-topped. Still other highs are deeply submerged. Bordering the high areas are slopes that lead down into the adjacent deep areas formed by thirteen closed basins and several open but flat-floored troughs. Measurement of the total areas covered by the major kinds of sea floor features of Chart I shows (Table 1) that the flat basin and trough floors, the chief areas of sediment accumulation, comprise about 17 per cent of the total 30,370 square statute mile (78,580 sq km) area of the continental borderland. The remaining 70 per cent of the area consists of slopes, bank tops, and shelves, on all of which the accumulation of sediments is relatively minor. In the basin range physiographic province of eastern California and Nevada the percentages are reversed, with 30 per cent of the area being mountains and 70 per cent depositional areas. This reversal is the re-

sult of the abundance (30 per cent) of sloping fans and bajadas on the land area and their tendency to bury the lower parts of mountains.

Coasts

Raised Marine Terraces

Perhaps the best-known physiographic feature of the southern California coast is its series of raised marine terraces (Fig. 2) which rise in steps from the shores up the slopes of the nearby mountains. Widths range from barely perceptible to more than 5 miles. Slopes of the wider terraces are a fraction of a degree, but those of the narrower ones are only slightly gentler than the slopes of the steps that separate them from the next terraces.

The terraces were recognized by Blake (1856) and J. G. Cooper in 1863 (Lawson, 1893b) as raised shorelines, but later Davidson (1875) unaccountably ascribed them to erosion by glaciers moving parallel to the coast. Lawson, after a reconnaissance of the coast, vigorously defended the concept of ancient marine erosion. He and later Smith (1898, 1900) made aneroid measurements of terrace elevations on several islands and on the mainland and concluded that elevations of most terraces were too great for them to have been left exposed by with-

Table 1
Total Areas of Major Topographic Features of Chart I

	Square Miles	Square Kilometers	Percentage of Total Area	Percentage of Area of Continental Borderland
Mainland mountains	4600	11900	10.0	
Mainland basins and other depositional areas	4090	10590	9.0	
Islands	340	880	0.7	1.1
Mainland shelf	1890	4890	4.1	6.2
Island shelves	1390	3580	3.0	4.6
Bank tops	2420	6270	5.3	8.0
Basin and trough slopes and other deep irregular areas	19210	49700	42.0	63.3
Basin and trough floors	5120	13260	11.2	16.8
Continental slope	1960	5070	4.3	
Abyssal sea floor	4740	12320	10.4	
Total	45760	118460	100.0	100.0

Figure 2. Raised terraces of Palos Verdes Hills facing southeastward toward Palos Verdes Point. Compare with profiles of terraces in Fig. 8. Photograph by J. S. Shelton and R. C. Frampton.

drawal of sea water to form glacial ice; hence, at least the higher terraces must have been elevated by diastrophic movements. Lawson noted that many terraces are underlain by rocks of Miocene age and some of Pliocene age; thus, the uplift must have occurred in post-Pliocene time. Since the reconnaissance work of Lawson and Smith, no other writers have attempted a general analysis of the terraces; instead, they have confined their efforts to a detailed study of terraces in small areas or to brief description of terraces as incidental to quadrangle mapping of geology. Among the most thorough local studies were those of Davis (1933) at Point Dume, Putnam (1942) at Ventura, Woodring, Bramlette, and Kew (1946) at Palos Verdes Hills, and Upson (1951a) at Gaviota. Briefer reports of local terrace elevations have been given by Ellis and Lee (1919), Hoots (1931), Bremner (1932, 1933), Norris (1951), and others. Terraces farther south, in Baja California, have been briefly described by Beal (1948) and those farther north by other authors.

Each terrace is a feature of composite origin. The cut surface where visible is not horizontal but instead has a slope that indicates a period of slower-than-average rise of the land from the sea. Atop the eroded surface there is sometimes present a veneer a few feet thick of rounded pebbles and cobbles and of shells typical of shallow water. Many of the cobbles and some of the bedrock contain borings made by worms and various

mollusks before the terrace was raised. Covering these marine deposits are alluvial fans and other stream deposits that have filled in the angle between the wave-cut terrace and the ancient sea cliff at its back. This material reaches thicknesses of scores of feet, completely burying small terraces and softening the profiles of larger ones. The cover on the broad Linda Vista Terrace near San Diego is partly in the form of six subparallel beach ridges which rise as much as 100 feet above the general level of the terrace (Emery, 1950b).

Elevations of the erosional surfaces would be best for making possible correlations but exposures of it are rare. Published elevation measurements of the depositional surfaces are nearly worthless for comparing separate areas because most writers have reported only single elevations for the terraces, either that at the front or that at the back. These two elevations may differ by more than 100 feet. Both are higher than the original cut surface, the one at the back because of deposition of alluvial material, and the one at the front because of removal of the original seaward edge by both marine and nonmarine erosion. In order to secure comparable elevation data for many parts of the coast, the writer decided to ignore all past measurements and to begin anew, measuring with a sensitive altimeter the profiles of terrace series. These data are still too incomplete to provide a general picture, so instead elevations of terraces or of the alluvial cover atop terraces were estimated from contours of the new 7½-minute U. S. Geological Survey topographic quadrangles, on most of which topography was compiled from aerial photographs. Contour intervals range from 5 to 50 feet, with 20 and 25 feet the most common. The results were grouped for eight sections of mainland coast and for seven islands (Fig. 3), at all of which many terraces are present, some to elevations of more than 1500 feet above sea level. Some terraces are very certain; others that are narrow or highly eroded (such as those on Santa Catalina Island) may have been overlooked. Certainly, small terraces have been missed because of not being shown by the contours; for example, altimeter readings on Santa Barbara Island showed four small terraces

between 87 and 112 feet where contours indicate only one. Other terraces are buried under alluvial material, which itself is shown as a terrace. Considering the various uncertainties in the compilation, it is doubtful whether more than half the existing number of terraces were recognized, although probably all wide ones are included.

Among the most interesting physiographic problems of southern California is the question of the presence of raised terraces on Santa Catalina Island. Lawson (1893b) believed the island to be free of terraces and, therefore, to be an area of submergence, in contrast to San Clemente Island and Palos Verdes Hills where great emergence is shown by the high terraces. Some support to this belief is given by the drowned character of

Figure 3. Elevations of raised marine terraces as estimated from recently published contour maps of the U. S. Geological Survey. Numbers refer to the sections of mainland coast and islands in which all coastal quadrangles were examined. Thin vertical lines show the range of elevations that is included by contours in each section of coast; wide vertical lines indicate the elevations of individual terraces from the low seaward edge to the high alluvium-covered edge against the raised sea cliffs.

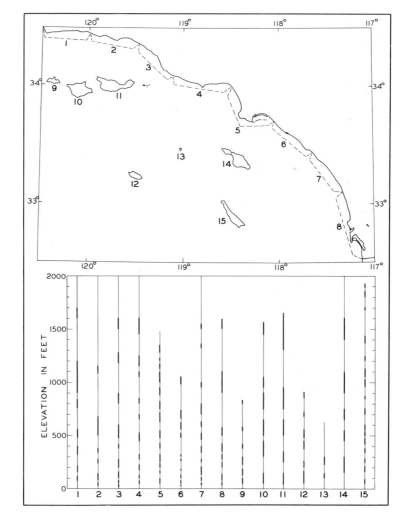

the isthmus which nearly separates the island into two parts. The recent contour maps of the island and examination from shipboard, however, suggest the presence of highly eroded terraces, mostly as ridges having sharp but nearly horizontal crests, particularly northwest of the isthmus. It is possible that terraces were cut on the island, but for some reason, such as greater age, are not as well preserved as elsewhere; if so, Santa Catalina Island may have had a history not greatly different from that of the other islands and coastal areas, a conclusion reached earlier by Smith (1933). Support for similarity of its late history is given by the presence of well-developed submerged terraces like those found elsewhere in the region; these will be described in a later section.

Terraces of adjacent coastal sections or of islands are commonly at similar elevations, but correlations cannot be made reliably for long distances on the basis of elevation alone, owing to known variations in the thickness of alluvial cover, in regional warping, and in local faulting. Because all or most of the terraces are of post-Pliocene age, a time too short for much evolution to have occurred, paleontology has proved of little or no value in the correlation of terraces. Radiocarbon measurements have yielded only minimum ages of cutting of the youngest terraces: greater than 30,000 years for the 75-foot terrace at Palos Verdes Hills (Kulp, Tryon, Eckelman, and Snell, 1952), greater than 29,650 years for the 25-foot terrace at Santa Rosa Island (Orr, 1956), and greater than 39,000 years for the 100-foot terrace at Santa Cruz north of Point Conception (Bradley, 1956).

If all the water now locked up in glaciers were to be released, the sea level would rise no more than about 200 feet, according to Flint (1947, p. 437). Most of the terraces thus require more than raised sea level to explain them; diastrophic uplift is necessary, and it is not difficult to believe this possible in such an unstable region. Some of the terraces lower than about 200 feet may be correlative in elevation with terraces elsewhere in the world if the rate of Late Pleistocene and Recent diastrophic movement has been

slow compared to the rate of sea level change. When more precise data are available, interesting comparisons might be made with the terraces lower than about 200 feet in Maryland (Shattuck, 1906), in Louisiana (Fisk, 1939), in Florida and Georgia (MacNeil, 1949), in the Hawaiian Islands (Stearns, 1935, 1945), and elsewhere in the world (Charlesworth, 1957).

Shoreline Classification

The total length of the shoreline in southern California is about 615 miles (990 km), as measured on the recent 7½-minute topographic sheets. More than half this length belongs to the islands where most shorelines are rocky and irregular. Along the mainland there are also many rocky shorelines, but straight smooth beaches are about five times as common. Close behind most of the sandy beaches are rocky cliffs; other beaches are backed by mud flats or broad lowlands. Because of the diverse nature of the shorelines, a concise summary of their characteristics can be formed only by grouping the various forms within the framework of general shoreline classifications. Only then can effective comparisons with other shorelines of the world be made. The classification outlined above and summarized in Table 2 is descriptive but gives little information on the dominant shore processes or on the past and probable future form of the shorelines.

Table 2

CHARACTERISTICS OF SHORELINES FACING
OPEN OCEAN (STATUTE MILES)

	Rocky	Sandy	
		Backed by Cliffs	Backed by Lowlands
Mainland	50	173	80
Islands	255	57	0.3

More information about shore processes is given when we translate the figures of Table 2 into energy characteristics—whether the shoreline is dominantly of erosional or depositional origin. All rocky shorelines (Fig. 4) are obviously erosional. Sandy

Figure 4. Irregular cliffed coast of Point Loma. Cretaceous sandstones and shales are overlain by Eocene shales and then by terrace alluvium. Note complex profile controlled by varying lithology and the presence of small sea caves, some with collapsed roofs. Narrow gravel beaches line indentations. The flat top of Point Loma is a marine terrace raised to about 350 feet above sea level and surmounted by a beach ridge. In the distance is North Island, the end of a long curved spit that encloses San Diego Bay. Photographed by R. E. Stevenson in 1952.

beaches backed by rocky cliffs (Fig. 5) are temporarily depositional because seasonal or longer-term deposition has built a barrier of wave-washed debris at the base of the cliffs; however, such shorelines must be considered erosional on a long-time basis if only because of the presence of the cliffs. Other sandy beaches that are backed by mud flats, alluvial fans, and deltas (Fig. 6) are clearly of depositional origin. Extending the classification, we can say that the erosional shorelines are retreating ones, whereas depositional shorelines are prograding. A minor rearrangement of the figures of Table 2 shows that 87 per cent of the shoreline of southern California (including islands) is erosional and only 13 per cent is depositional. These percentages are in agreement with what might be expected of the region with its precipitous coastal areas and low stream runoff. They lead to the obvious conclusion that the supply of debris to the present shoreline is

far less than the capacity of the ocean to transport it seaward.

Strict application of Johnson's (1919) emergent-submergent classification is beset with difficulties. These arise because the whole region has experienced great emergence, both diastrophic and eustatic, as shown by the widespread raised marine terraces; it has also undergone submergence chiefly eustatic, as shown by submerged terraces and by numerous estuaries that are filled with alluvium to depths now below sea level. Only the larger streams were able to cut valleys that later became drowned, owing to rise of sea level at the end of glacial times; smaller streams in this region of low rainfall could not cut deeply during the short time of glacially lowered sea level, so they were unable to add their evidence to the record of submergence. During the Pleistocene Epoch, as well as the present, most streams of southern California were in stages of geomorphic

Figure 5. Straight cliffed coast north of La Jolla. Eocene shales are overlain by terrace alluvium. The broad flat Linda Vista Terrace is for the most part between 300 and 400 feet above sea level. Note the straight cliffs, the wide sand beach at their base, the talus, and the highly dissected upper slopes. Photographed by R. E. Stevenson in 1952.

youth or early maturity and were able to cut only narrow valleys. These contrast with the wide valleys cut by the mature streams of the eastern United States which produced broad estuaries when they became drowned. Thus, the evidence of submergence in southern California is less obvious than that of emergence, but still it is sufficient to show that all the shorelines are compound, in the sense of possessing characteristics of both emergence and submergence. Even shorelines originally of neutral origin, such as the huge alluvial fan or delta at Hueneme and the fault scarp of San Clemente Island (Fig. 67, p. 78), contain evidence of submergence (small estuaries) and emergence (terraces), respectively, that require them to be classed as compound. In summary, if we consider the coast in the broad sense (adjoining belts of land and sea floor, and for lengths of 10 to 15 miles), we must classify it as nearly 100 per cent compound. The presence of both estuaries and raised marine terraces on the East and Gulf coasts of the United States also require these shorelines to be classed as compound in the broad sense. If, on the other hand, a restricted view is taken of the shoreline (omitting terraces and classifying short sections), it is often possible to determine whether the last major movement was emergence or submergence. This is the way in which Johnson's classification has generally been used on the East coast where the terrace record of emergence is less obvious than it is on the mountainous West coast. By this restricted sense of the classification, 5.7 per cent of the southern California shoreline is submergent in the youthful stage (estuaries), 7.3 per cent is emergent in youth (lagoons and offshore islands), 83.5 per cent is emergent in maturity (cliffed shores), and 3.5 per cent is neutral (fault scarp). Percentagewise, this breakdown is only slightly more divided than the 100 per cent compound classification, and it is highly subjective.

The shoreline can also be classified using Shepard's (1948, pp. 71–76) system, in which the first breakdown is youthful or mature, depending on whether the forming agent is nonmarine or marine, respectively. Under this classification only 3.5 per cent is nonmarine, the fault scarp of San Clemente Island. Of the remainder of the coast, 7.3 per cent has been straightened by deposition of sand beaches, 5.7 per cent has been straightened by deposition of offshore sand islands, 37.5 per cent has been straightened by marine erosion, and 46.0 per cent has been made irregular by marine erosion. Nearly five-sixths of the latter category belongs to the islands. For comparison, nearly the entire southeastern and Gulf coasts of the United States consist of shorelines straightened by deposition of sand beaches or offshore sand islands backed by mud flats. The difference between the two coasts is a reflection of the more mountainous nature of the California coast and its much smaller supply of sand relative to capacity of the ocean for redistribution.

In summary, it may be seen that Johnson's genetic classification does not work well in southern California because of the complex history of the region and the imperfect record of submergence left by smaller streams. Shepard's classification as an extension of pure description of the coast offers a break-down of the major type, erosional shorelines, into two major subequal classes, those that have been straightened and those that have been made more irregular by marine erosion.

Of interest is the fact that the two largest areas of depositional shorelines (Los Angeles and Hueneme) are backed by the two lowlands having the greatest agricultural production. Only the former has developed as the site of a large city, perhaps partly because it is the only one having a deep-water harbor, and this was built by sediments and man. The third and fourth largest areas of depositional shores, San Diego and Santa Barbara, are sites of less important agriculture and of cities, the first and larger of which has a deep-water port also bulit by sediments.

Erosional Coasts

Erosional coasts everywhere consist chiefly of sea cliffs. In southern California these cliffs vary in height from a few feet to more than 500 feet, with a mean of 75 feet for the mainland and 175 feet for the islands. Slopes range from overhanging to less than 45°,

Figure 6. Seal Beach just west of breakwater. The wide offshore sand island provided quiet water for the accumulation of fine marsh sediments. Highly meandering tidal channels are typical of such marshes. Note the shortening of crest-to-crest spacing of waves as they approach the beach and enter progressively shallower water. Photographed by R. E. Stevenson in 1952.

with higher cliffs being generally less steep than lower ones. The profiles are commonly broken into steps of varying steepness that are controlled by differences in lithology and structure. Other departures from simple slopes are common at the base where low rock platforms may extend as much as 100 yards seaward (Fig. 7) or where talus slopes cover the foot of the sea cliffs (Fig. 8). Boulder and gravel beaches locally skirt the base of the sea cliffs or of their talus slopes. It is estimated that talus covers the base of about 20 per cent of the coast having sea cliffs. Even where the base of a cliff is covered by talus, it is evident that shoreline erosion was active during the past and was responsible for the steepening of the cliff which even-

tually resulted in landsliding and deposition of talus.

The ocean washes continually against the base of some sea cliffs but is separated from others most of the time by the talus or by sand beaches. During single exceptionally large storms, or as the cumulative effect of a winter season of smaller storms, beaches are commonly narrowed by seaward transportation of sand. While the beach is absent or narrow, the ocean can do more erosion of the cliff than during the whole remaining bulk of the year. Thus, marine erosion is similar to stream erosion in that by far the greatest effect comes during short periods separated by much longer intervals of very slight erosion or even of deposition. When

Figure 7. Laguna Beach. Cliffs consist of Miocene schist breccia and basalt. The marine terrace is between 80 and 120 feet above sea level. At the base of the cliffs is a low rock terrace of the type sometimes known as a storm terrace. Note the pocket beaches, only one of which is at the mouth of a stream. Photographed by R. E. Stevenson in 1952.

Figure 8. Palos Verdes Hills viewed toward southsoutheast across Palos Verdes Point. Six raised terraces are easily visible, the lowest one clearly beveling deformed Middle Miocene siliceous shales at an elevation of 125 to 150 feet. Note the presence along most of the cliff of talus largely covered by vegetation. The ship is the *Gratia* stranded during a storm in 1932. Photographed by Fairchild Aerial Surveys in 1933.

the ocean can reach the sea cliffs, one of the most important processes by which it erodes is abrasion and impact by the stones that the water moves. The well-known rattle of a gravel beach is probably intensified to a roar when the ocean waves are large enough to move boulders against the base of a sea cliff. Such waves are infrequent enough in southern California to allow sharp-edged solution basins and pits to develop on boulders at the base of sea cliffs, yet movement of large boulders is noted on photographs taken several years apart (Fig. 9). Occasionally we can also find gravel and pebbles driven tightly into cracks of sea cliffs in such a way that it is clear that the driving force was upward. The ability of the ocean to throw stones is attested to by many records of broken lighthouse windows cited by Johnson (1919, p. 68) and Cornish (1912) and by the windows and siding of houses at Redondo, California, broken by stones thrown by storm waves (Fig. 10).

Stones up to 5 cm in diameter were seen to be thrown more than 100 feet through the air and over the Redondo sea wall in January 1953. Similar observations at the base of sea cliffs during storms are virtually impossible to make, so the role of abrasion must be based on indirect evidence. Such evidence as the presence at the base of cliffs of smoothly concave surfaces of hard unweathered rock and of deep potholes containing one or more tool stones are evidence of abrasion. Impact by rocks thrown against the cliff is more likely to be indicated by broken-off former projections.

Hydraulic action developed by sudden pressure of water against a sea cliff and by its rapid retreat is an erosional process that is very difficult to evaluate. However, it would seem to be the chief process that is capable of dislodging large blocks of rock near sea level. Certainly, it can be important only where rocks are jointed and are thus able to be removed in blocks. Even less

Figure 9. Boulders of Eocene sandstone 0.3 mile north of Scripps Pier, La Jolla. Pittings and stone lace have been developed by chemical and biochemical weathering. Difference in positions of boulders in July 1940 (top) and August 1956 (bottom) shows considerable movement by waves during this period.

capable of evaluation is the much quoted compression and expansion of air trapped in caves or open joints by rising waves. Where a small opening reaches to the ground surface, the compressed air forces water spray upward as a geyser-like spouting horn. More commonly, the compressed air drives the spray nearly horizontally seaward out of openings that have become filled with water.

Many examples of the latter form of air compression are known in southern California, and good spouting horns exist at one or two places on the mainland and on all islands except possibly San Miguel and San Nicolas. Spouting horns are spectacular, but they are by no means convincing evidence of the erosive ability of compressd air because many have lasted for at least several decades in the Hawaiian Islands and elsewhere in the world.

Wetting and drying action by water in and just above the intertidal zone is slow, but it accomplishes a large amount of erosion, particularly in southern California where many sea cliffs consist of sedimentary rocks. Prolonged soaking of shale in water is a well-known method of causing the shale to break down into its constituent particles. This action is probably not so much the result of dissolving of a cement as it is the result of base exchange, hydration, or swelling of the grains so that they become loosened and able to be washed away. For sandstones solution of calcareous cement is, of course, more likely. Exfoliation by formation of thin fragile scales is common and serves as an indicator of these processes. Expansion of scales and loosening of grains

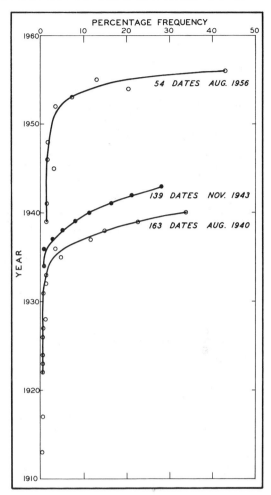

Figure 11. Frequency distribution of dates cut in Eocene and Cretaceous sandstone cliffs at La Jolla in 1940, 1943, and 1956. It appears that about 6 years are required for weathering to obliterate the dates. If the average depth of each is ⅛ inch, a rate of weathering of about 1 foot in 600 years is indicated. Numbers indicate total numbers of observations.

Figure 10. Wave damage to house at Redondo Beach. Photographed January 17, 1953, after a small storm.

by growth of salt crystals has been suggested in the literature, but neither field nor laboratory tests seem to support the suggestion. These processes operating in the intertidal and spray zones produce pittings in the rocks and also a general wasting away of the surface. The latter was estimated at about 1 foot in 600 years (Emery, 1941a) for sandstones at La Jolla on the basis of frequency distribution of dated inscriptions cut into the rocks (Fig. 11).

Biological activity in the intertidal zone is a much overlooked means of erosion. It takes place by both mechanical and chemical action. The most direct form is that of borings made by worms, pholads, chitons, limpets, and sea urchins (Barrows, 1917). Each of these animals bores or dissolves its way into the rock surface for protection, making a hole of characteristic shape during the process (Figs. 12–16). The mass of rock removed is unknown but very large, perhaps surpassing that of some of the more widely recognized processes of marine erosion. Borings are not restricted to soft sediments but have been found in gneiss, andesite, and chert. In shales near Point Fermin, pholads are especially effective, having bored so thoroughly that more than 50 per cent of the rock in specimens from many low-tide areas has been removed and much of the remaining rock between holes has been loosened to form gravel because of the joining of several adjacent holes. Many snails, although not borers, contribute materially to erosion of rocky shores through their activity in grazing for blue-green algae that grow on the rock surface. Their peculiar patterns of scraped trails are common (Seilacher, 1953), and sand excreted by the snails has proved on analysis to have the same grain-size distribution and mineralogy

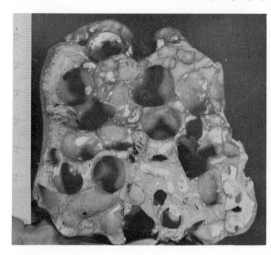

Figure 13. Miocene siliceous shale from Whites Point, Palos Verdes Hills, bored by pholads that make bottle-shaped holes which are larger at depth than at the entrance. Boring by the pelecypod is accomplished by mechanical twisting of the shell against the bottom of the hole, aided probably by biochemical action. Centimeter scale for comparison.

as the rock on which the snails grazed (Emery, 1946; North, 1954). North estimated the erosion by the snails at about 1 foot per 1200 years.

Indirect or biochemical erosion produces solution basins (Emery, 1946) which occur in limestone, sandstone (Fig. 17), and even basalt (Fig. 18) in southern California. These are shallow flat-floored pools having irregular outlines and usually steep walls. Some have raised rims, but most are surrounded by flat surfaces or by a miniature karst topography that is indicative of additional solution outside the pools. Solution occurs because the carbon dioxide liberated by the plants and animals living in the pool combines with the water to form carbonic acid. Enough carbonic acid accumulates at night, when none is used by photosynthesis, so that bicarbonate ion exceeds carbonate ion (Fig. 19). At the existing temperature, salinity, and pH the water can contain more calcium carbonate, bicarbonate, or borate than was originally present when the water entered the pool, so calcium carbonate is dissolved from the rock underlying the pool. Solution of calcium carbonate is also shown

Figure 12. Boulder beach at Whites Point, Palos Verdes Hills. The large block of Miocene siliceous shale under the hammer was rafted to shore by kelp, as shown by remnant of holdfast and by encrusting coralline red algae and bryozoans. Cup-shaped holes are the work of sea urchins which erode by moving their spines.

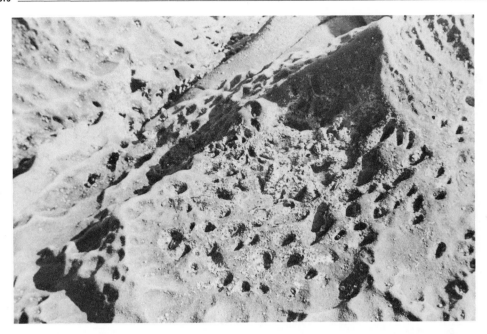

Figure 14. Cretaceous sandstone at Whale View Point, LaJolla, drilled by chitens that make elliptical hole by biochemical action. Photographed April 1943.

by the increased alkalinity of the water during the night. During the daytime, however, the plants require more carbon dioxide for photosynthesis than is produced by respiration of both plants and animals; therefore the total carbon dioxide content of the water decreases below that of the water which entered the pool. As a result of increased temperature, salinity, and pH, calcium carbonate is often deposited during the daytime. Calcium carbonate deposited from capillary films of water extending outward

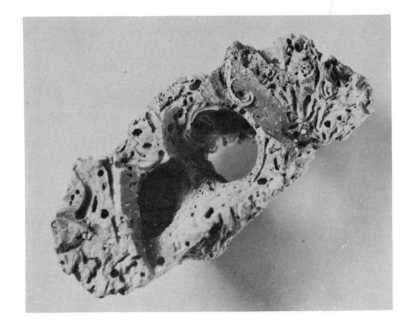

Figure 15. Miocene (?) limestone bored by worms from depth of 720 feet in San Pedro Sea Valley ($\times$ 1). Similar boring also occurs in shales from the intertidal zone.

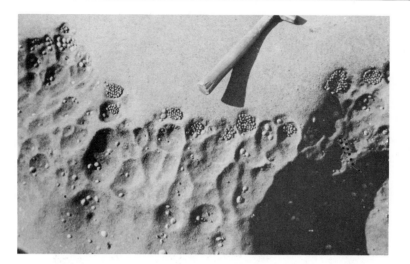

Figure 16. Cretaceous sandstone from Whale View Point, La Jolla, showing broad indentations made by biochemical activities and perhaps mechanical rasping of small snails—*Littorina.* Limpets lower in the photograph often make holes like those of chitens, but these particular ones have not done so. Photographed January 1944.

Figure 17. Solution basin in Cretaceous sandstone at Whale View Point, La Jolla. Basin is nearly flat-floored but has steep sides that are fluted. Small snails, *Littorina,* cluster in flutings. Algae present on the floor during winter are absent during summer. Biochemical studies show that solution of calcium carbonate cement occurs at night and deposition of calcium carbonate, mostly reinforcing rims, during the daytime. Photographed January 1944. Re-examination in August 1956 showed negligible change. From Emery (1946, Fig. 5).

Figure 18. Solution basins in Miocene basalt near Resort Point, Palos Verdes Hills. Basins are believed to form by biochemical methods like those in sandstone and limestone. Photographed May 1956.

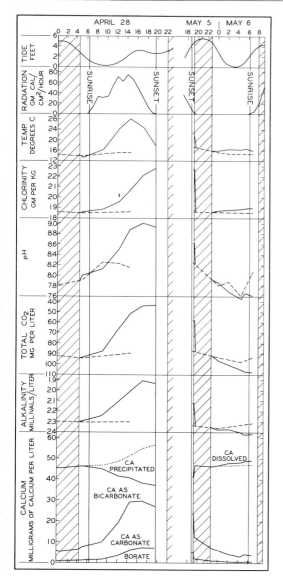

Figure 19. Diurnal variation of water characteristics of a solution basin in calcareous sandstone at La Jolla (Fig. 17). Dashed line shows data for water of ocean near the basin. Lowest part of figure shows the variation in calcium combined with carbonate, bicarbonate, and borate ions, as computed from measurements of temperature, chlorinity, pH, total carbon dioxide, and alkalinity. The dashed line indicates the concentration of this calcium if no solution or deposition of it had occurred. Cross-hatching shows times of flooding of basin at high tide. Redrawn from Emery (1946, Fig. 12).

from the pool locally strengthens the surrounding rock enough so that raised rims are left when the rock surface farther from the pool is eroded away.

Analyses made at Guam and Bikini (Revelle and Emery, 1957) show that the oxygen content of the water bears an inverse relationship to carbon dioxide, as would be expected from the processes of respiration and photosynthesis. The diurnal change of these ions and of pH occurs to a much greater extent in the tide pools than in the open sea because of the greater ratio of bulk of plant and animal tissue to bulk of water in the pools. With lateral enlargement several pools may join together; eventually their growth intersects a joint and the pools become drained. The process starts anew at a low point of the empty pool, so that by the time several generations of pools have existed much rock has been removed. Although large pools exist only on relatively flat surfaces, small thimble-like holes on near-vertical sea cliffs are occupied by a small amount of water and associated plants and animals; these are being enlarged by the same process. The great role of biochemical erosion is signified by the abundance along the shore of its products. Moreover, the organisms responsible for it work during the long periods of calm seas when many other erosional processes are inactive. The rate of deepening of the solution basins of La Jolla is estimated at 1 foot in 1000 years.

All these erosional processes are restricted to a zone only slightly greater than the range between low and high tide. None of them erodes directly the tops of high sea cliffs. Yet, they do cause the undercutting which finally results in landsliding of the whole sea cliff so that all the material of the cliff comes within reach of the ocean for comminution and redistribution. An examination of the coast mostly from shipboard showed the presence of landslides along at least 25 miles (40 km) of coast, about 40 per cent of the length of shore illustrated by Figure 20 and probably about 80 per cent of the shore frontage of all landslides in the entire region. The distribution shows little relationship to degree of wave exposure and only a moderate relationship to steepness of slope; therefore, we must infer that the major control is that of lithology and structure. For example, the largest slide known in the re-

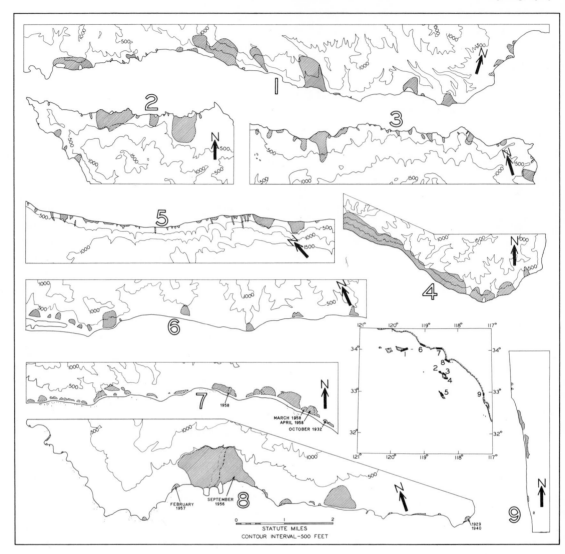

Figure 20. Areas of most abundant coastal landslides (cross-hatched areas) identified mostly from observations aboard ship. Section 7 mostly from field studies by Roth (1959).

gion, that near the center of the Palos Verdes Hills section, is neither steep nor much exposed; however, the Miocene shales of which it is composed dip toward the ocean and contain beds of bentonite which is slippery when wet. Most of them are rock slides or debris slides, according to Sharpe's (1938) system of classification.

Direct erosion at the shore cuts only a slot into the base of the sea cliff, so that for high sea cliffs the bulk of the rock is eroded indirectly by landsliding. This is analogous to erosion by youthful streams (Fig. 21) in which direct erosion by the stream is restricted to a downward direction and the bulk of the material that was removed to form the valley reached the stream by landsliding or slope wash. In addition to landsliding, much of the sea cliff face is removed by spray that is thrown against the cliff. During storms when great sheets of water drain down the face of the cliff, the runoff must be many times that from rain, and thus it must produce many times as much erosion.

In spite of the numerous methods by

which sea cliffs can be eroded, the erosion of rocks other than alluvium takes place exceedingly slowly in southern California. This has been shown by a comparison of old and new photographs of many sea cliffs (Shepard and Grant, 1947). Slowness of present-day erosion is also indicated by the presence of large talus slopes at the base of many sea cliffs (Figs. 5 and 8). Some of the slopes are fairly old, as indicated by the establishment of abundant vegetation on their surface. Shepard and Grant suggested that present slow erosion may be a result of a decreased rate of cliff erosion, owing to increased width of the cut terrace, to lower waves in recent years, and to long intervals between storms violent enough to erode the sea cliffs. The latter suggestion appears to be particularly plausible; however, one other possibility seems worthy of consideration: that the ocean cannot easily reach the base of the sea cliffs and their talus slopes since the 6-foot lowering of sea level about 3000 years ago (Kuenen, 1954; Cloud, 1954; Antevs, 1953). Other evidence of this lowering is presented in the tropics by a raised and now largely dissected reef level and by a nip commonly present about 6 feet above present sea level. In southern California it may be represented by the low rock platforms that are awash or are only a few feet above high-tide level and are cut across dipping beds of basalt, sandstone, breccia, and siliceous shale (Figs. 7, 22, and 23). Because

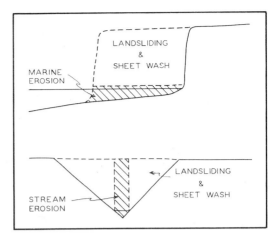

Figure 21. The amount of direct stream erosion during the cutting of a valley is small compared with the effects of landsliding and sheet wash; similarly, the amount of direct marine erosion during the cutting of a sea cliff is small compared with the effects of landsliding and sheet wash.

of their preference for very hard rocks, the low platforms are most common at rocky points between which marine erosion has removed areas of softer rocks and thereby produced irregular shorelines.

Low rock platforms are common throughout the world, but many writers (for example, Bartrum, 1935; Jutson, 1939) have ascribed them to storms, terming them storm terraces. They have reasoned that, because the low platforms are practically free of debris, they are being cut at the present time.

Figure 22. Low rock terrace ("storm terrace") in Miocene basalt sill near Resort Point, Palos Verdes Hills. White projections above basalt consist of more resistant siliceous limestone veins in basalt. Terrace extends about 100 feet to the left of the picture. Photographed May 1956.

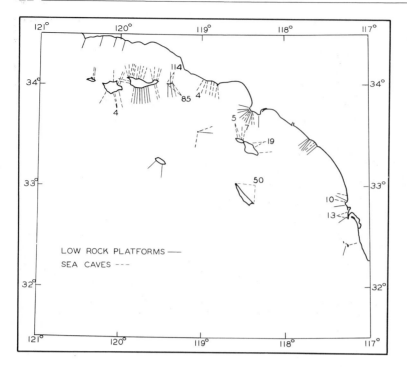

Figure 23. Distribution of some low rock platforms ("storm terraces") and of some sea caves.

During storms, waves wash across the low platforms removing weathered material and eroding fresh rock. In opposition, it should be pointed out that the stronghold of the concept of storm terraces is New Zealand, where at least two low terraces (at Wellington and Napier) are known to have been produced by earth movements associated with historical earthquakes. Moreover, it is difficult to see why storm waves, being larger than ordinary ones, should not erode deeper rather than shallower than usual. Certainly all storms do not have waves of the same height, nor do they occur at tides of the same height, so at best we would expect storm terraces to have profiles with outer edges that are convex upward. However, most low rock platforms in southern California and elsewhere have abrupt outer edges. In addition, in this area there are small offshore islands surrounded on all sides by low platforms having no difference in height on seaward and leeward sides. The height of these island platforms and of offshore platforms having no central island is about the same as the platforms fringing the nearby mainland sea cliffs. An alternate explanation, favored by the writer, is that the low rock platforms

indicate a recent eustatic lowering of sea level, supporting the evidence of the talus slopes. The low platform left by a drop in sea level can, of course be reached by storm waves and by spray, and so it is the site of solution basins and other forms of water-level weathering described by Wentworth (1938–1939) for the Hawaiian Islands. The fact that most of the low platforms and their adjacent sea cliffs of southern California consist of the hardest kinds of rock in the area, such as basalt, is more in line with inheritance from a time of higher sea level than with erosion by present-day storms.

An interesting feature associated with sea cliffs is the sea cave. More than 350 are present in southern California. All that have been inspected are localized along zones of structural weakness, faults or joints (Moore, 1954b). Waves have succeeded in abrading and prying away the rocks on both sides of the fault zones, widening the zones to form caves that are elongate into the sea cliffs. The comminuted rock debris is carried in suspension and solution out of the cave. Most of these caves are less than 20 feet long, but one extends nearly 600 feet into Santa Cruz Island (Fig. 24) (Emery, 1954a). The floors of the caves are as much as 50 feet below sea level, the depth being approximately proportional to the length of the caves. A large sea cave at Marineland in Palos Verdes Hills is dry and slightly above sea level; it probably was abandoned by the sea at the same time that a nearby low rock platform emerged. Other caves have collapsed roofs as at Point Loma or have developed into sea arches as at Anacapa (Fig. 25) and Santa Barbara Islands.

Depositional Coasts

In southern California depositional coasts consist chiefly of sand beaches. Mud flats are present in estuaries and lagoons but do not face the open sea and therefore are not considered in this discussion as a type of depositional coast. Gravel beaches are narrow, many are separated from the ocean by sand beaches, and with one major exception they occur at the base of sea cliffs from which they were mostly derived (Emery, 1955a). Because of these facts most gravel beaches in southern California are more indicative of erosional coasts than depositional ones. One gravel beach, however, forms a bar across the half-mile width of an estuary three miles north of Encinitas; thus it is part of a depositional coast (Fig. 157, p. 184).

About 30 per cent of the sand beaches of

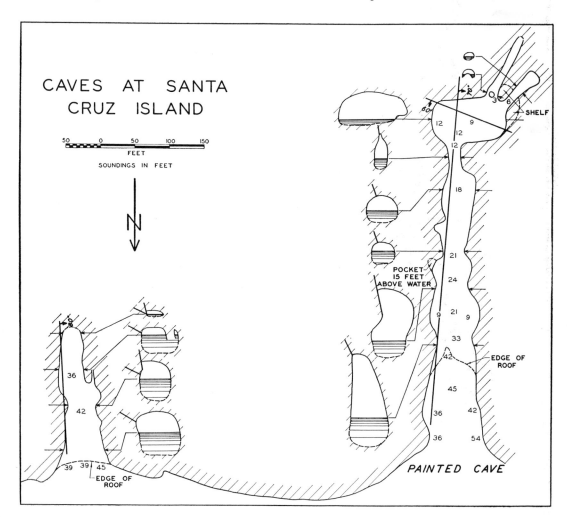

Figure 24. Sketch map of Painted Cave and a smaller one east of it cut through andesite and basalt near the northwestern end of Santa Cruz Island. The heavy straight lines mark the strike of faults along which the caves were eroded. From Emery (1954a).

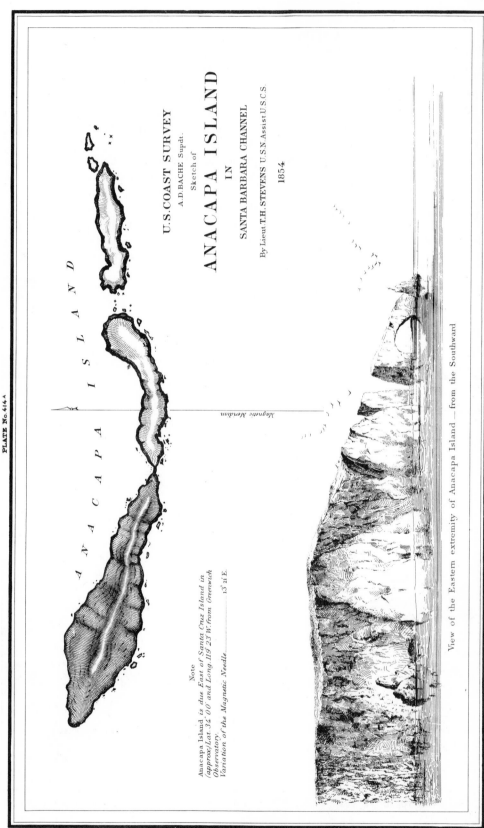

U.S.COAST SURVEY

A.D.BACHE Supdt.

Sketch of

ANACAPA ISLAND

IN

SANTA BARBARA CHANNEL

By Lieut.T.H.STEVENS U.S.N Assist U.S.C.S.

1854

Magnetic Meridian

Note

Anacapa Island is due East of Santa Cruz Island in
(approx)Lat. 34° 00′ and Long. 119° 23′W.from Greenwich
Observatory.
Variation of the Magnetic Needle ————— 13° 21′ E.

View of the Eastern extremity of Anacapa Island — from the Southward

Drⁿg by W.B.M⁄.Murtrie

Engᵍ by J.A.Whistler J.Young & C.A.Knight

Figure 25. Terrace and slope at Anacapa Island are being eroded away by 200-foot vertical sea cliffs. Many caves are cut along faults and joints in the volcanic rock. A fine sea arch about 35 feet high is a remnant of one cave. Etching was made by James Abbot McNeill Whistler during his brief employment by the Coast and Geodetic Survey.

the coast are backed by lowlands, mostly marshes or mud flats, such as those of Figure 6. These are the only truly depositional coasts of the region, ones which have prograded over a long period of years. According to Handin (1951, p. 6) one of them, the Santa Clara River delta near Ventura, prograded 580 feet between 1855 and 1933. Most large changes of other sand beaches during the last hundred years appear to have resulted from man's activities. The remaining 70 per cent of the sand beaches are at the base of sea cliffs in coastal areas that must be classed as of erosional origin over a long time span but depositional over shorter time spans when a wide sand beach is present. About a sixth of the latter occupies small coves in irregular rocky coasts; many examples exist along the shores of the Palos Verdes Hills, Laguna Beach, La Jolla, and most of the islands. These beaches consist largely of sediment derived locally from streams and sea cliffs, as commonly shown by great differences in texture and mineralogy of sand in adjacent coves. Movement of sand out of the coves is difficult because waves which enter the coves are refracted so that their crests are convex landward. The lagging ends produce longshore currents at both sides that drive sand toward the center of the cove. As a result, the coves are commonly lined with boulder beaches at the entrance that grade through gravel to sand beaches in the center. Because of their apparent isolation from other beaches, these areas are sometimes known as pocket beaches. Most beaches at the base of sea cliffs, however, are more or less continuous with those that are backed by lowlands. They also are of similar grain size and mineralogy; thus they are part of large units of sand having related sources and are in equilibrium with related forces at least throughout much of the year.

Sand reaches the beaches of southern California chiefly from streams and to a much lesser extent from erosion of sea cliffs and the sea floor (Fig. 26). Most of the sediment comes during large infrequent floods; for example, more than 7,303,000 cubic yards of sand was deposited at the mouth of the Santa Clara River and more than 6,000,000 cubic yards at the mouth of the Los Angeles River during the floods of March 2, 1938, according to surveys reported by Handin (1951, pp. 36, 44). The quantity of finer sediment carried seaward past these temporary deltas is unknown but was probably much greater than the quantity of sand deposited. The contribution by streams during years of ordinary rainfall is even less well known, no reliable figures for load near the mouths of streams being available. Existing information on stream contribution is based on rate of erosion of watersheds which, in turn, is inferred from the rate of deposition in reservoirs and flood debris basins in upstream areas. The finest material escapes these traps, and there is little reason to assume that all the coarse sediment which is trapped would have crossed the lowlands between the traps and the ocean.

A second method of estimating stream contribution has been that of measuring the rate of accretion behind breakwaters near the stream mouths, but of course little sediment finer than sand is trapped, and it is virtually impossible to separate the contribution of littoral drift from that of nearby streams. Although the amount is not well established, it is estimated that several million cubic yards of sediment are contributed annually by streams in the area of Chart I. It also seems evident that the greatest rate of contribution occurs in the middle part of the broad coastal embayment in the area reached by the largest rivers, the Santa Clara, Los Angeles, San Gabriel, and Santa Ana. These rivers together drain about half the total drainage area of 12,000 square miles (31,000 sq km) that borders the shore of southern California (Fig. 27).

Once on the beach, the sediment comes under the influence of waves. The constant movement eventually breaks up the grains, and the fine debris is carried seaward. Before being lost to the sea, the sand is moved along the shore for greater or lesser distances by waves. Where waves strike the beach diagonally, they run up the beach and down again at a point a few feet farther along the beach. As a result of this net longshore

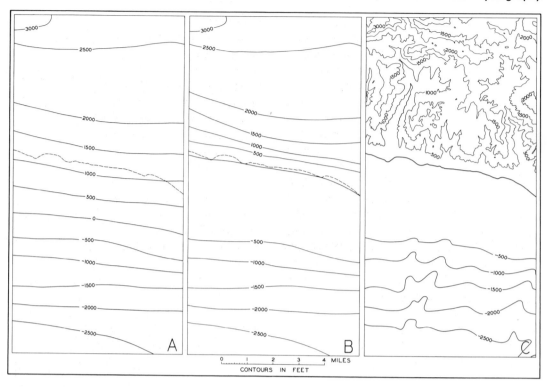

Figure 26. Portion of coast just west of Point Dume showing approximate relative effects of marine and stream erosion. C, present topography of land and sea floor. B, topography drawn by connecting seawardmost points of each contour of C. This eliminates the incisions produced by stream erosion. A, smooth topography drawn in by eliminating the wave cut the terrace B. This eliminates the effects of marine erosion and serves as a possible expression of the original structural topography.

Subtraction of the volume of rock below the contours of B from that below the contours of A shows that marine erosion removed about 3.6 cubic miles of rock from this area; subtraction of the volume of rock below contours of C from that below the contours of B shows that stream erosion subsequently removed about 5.5 cubic miles of rock. Thus, in this area streams have removed at least 50 per cent more rock than has marine erosion. Stream erosion prior to terrace cutting should further increase the role of stream erosion in comparison with marine erosion. In other portions of the coast having through-flowing streams, the role of stream erosion has been even greater than here.

water movement, some sand is transported along the beach. Because most of the waves in southern California come from the northwest during winter and from the west or southwest during summer, the sand contributed all along the mainland coast might be expected to accumulate in the central part of the broad embayment, between San Diego and Ventura, supplementing the effect of greater stream contribution in this area. This conclusion is supported by the fact that the beaches are more or less progressively wider going southward and eastward from north of Point Conception to Point Conception, to Ventura, to Los Angeles, and northward from Ensenada, Mexico, to San Diego to Los Angeles. In addition, since the winter waves are larger than the summer ones, we might expect the longshore drift to be predominantly southeastward, and again this belief is supported by the accumulation of sand against the north or west sides of nearly all groins of the coast. An eastward movement of sand at least between Point Conception and Santa Barbara is also shown by its mineralogy with respect to source areas (Trask, 1952). Local northward or westward movement of sand (Shepard and Inman, 1951*b*) results from irregularities of trend of the shoreline and from seasonal variations of wave direction.

Only minor leakage of sand out of the

area toward the south by littoral drift is suggested by data from a compilation of rates of accretion of sand behind breakwaters and groins (Handin, 1951; Johnson, 1956). The rate of transportation from the west toward the middle of the embayment is approximately three times that of transportation southward away from the middle (300,000 versus 100,000 cubic yards per year) as shown by Figure 28. These figures for rate of littoral transport are minimum ones because much sand probably bypasses the obstacles, particularly when the areas of trapping are nearly filled.

A large amount of sand may escape the beaches by leakage to deep water, counterbalancing the ultimate tendency of beaches to prograde the shoreline of southern California into a smooth broad curve.

Four submarine canyons (the Hueneme-Mugu-Dume group, Redondo, Newport, and Scripps–La Jolla) extend so close to shore that large quantities of sand moving along the beaches can be intercepted. Sliding of sandy sediment is known to have occurred at the heads of Mugu, Redondo, Newport, La Jolla, and Scripps Canyons, and large fans are present in deep water at the mouths of Hueneme, Mugu, Dume, Redondo, and probably Newport and La Jolla Canyons (Table 4, p. 47). Interruption of the littoral drift is also indicated by the scarcity of beaches in areas immediately east or south of the canyons—Santa Monica Mountains, Palos Verdes Hills, Laguna Beach, and La Jolla, respectively. Thus the submarine canyons appear to divide the region into five subequal and more or less independent beach units.

Sand moves seaward and landward across the beaches in areas that are free of canyons. The movements are periodic and produce cyclical changes in the profiles of beaches that have been measured for many years (Shepard and LaFond, 1940; Shepard, 1950b). Vertical variations of more than 10 feet (Fig.

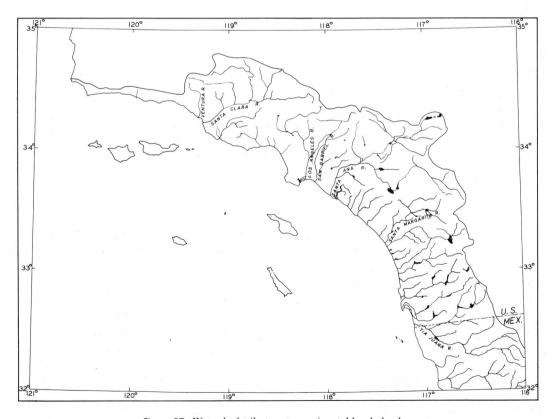

Figure 27. Watershed tributary to continental borderland.

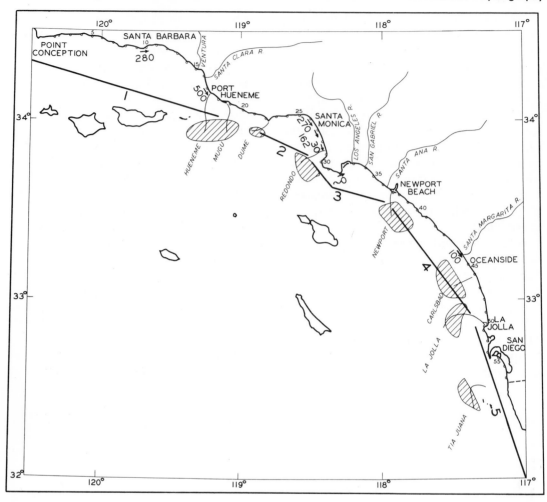

Figure 28. Rate and direction of littoral movement of sand along beaches, compiled from various sources, chiefly Handin (1951) and Johnson (1956). Rate is expressed in thousands of cubic yards of sand per year trapped behind breakwaters and contributed by streams. Bars divide the shore into five segments along which the beaches increase in width toward the southeast until ended by a submarine canyon which begins close to shore and ends in a submarine fan (cross-hatched areas). Small circles show the positions of beach sand samples collected November 23, 1956.

29) sometimes occur, and these are accompanied by variations in beach width of as much as 100 feet. The chief cycle is an annual one, which for most beaches of southern California results in a lowering of the level of the top of the beach during winter and a building up of it during summer. Sand carried seaward during the winter is deposited seaward of the breaker zone, so that that area is shallower in winter than in summer (Fig. 30). This cyclical change of profile is caused chiefly by the greater size of waves occurring during winter as compared with those of the summer, although seasonal differences in the direction of wave approach also plays a part, particularly for short beaches.

As shown by Grant (1943), waves of medium height approaching shore are able to lift sand of medium grain size as the crest approaches, transport it landward with the crest, and set it down as the crest passes on so that it is not carried seaward during the backwash of the trough. Large grains may not be moved at all, whereas small ones may be kept in suspension so that they are moved both landward and seaward, with the latter movement predominating, owing to the effect of the seaward slope of the bottom. It is evident that waves of medium size tend to build up the beach with contributions of medium sand if sand of that size is available. With larger waves the medium sand behaves as did the fine sand for the medium waves, so that the large waves erode the upper part of the beach, leaving only coarse sediment there. Rip tides or rip currents (Shepard, Emery, and LaFond, 1941) also shift sand seaward, particularly during winter when the waves that produce them are large. So much sand may be carried away that the beach becomes incised by channels several feet below the general sand level (Fig. 31). As the size and direction of waves change, the channels shift in position and size (Shepard and Inman, 1950, 1951b).

Another cycle of beach level, biweekly, has been related to the lunar tidal cycle by LaFond (1939b). Maximum erosion of the upper part of sand beaches occurs during spring tides when waves can effectively reach that part of the beach. During the intervening time of neap tides only the thin edge of waves can reach the top of the beach, and these redeposit there the sand which had been shifted to deeper water during spring tides. Variations of beach height are usually only a few inches, but these are known to and are taken advantage of by the grunion, a fish that flops ashore at spring tides and

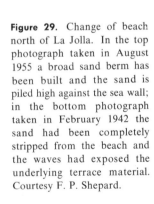

Figure 29. Change of beach north of La Jolla. In the top photograph taken in August 1955 a broad sand berm has been built and the sand is piled high against the sea wall; in the bottom photograph taken in February 1942 the sand had been completely stripped from the beach and the waves had exposed the underlying terrace material. Courtesy F. P. Shepard.

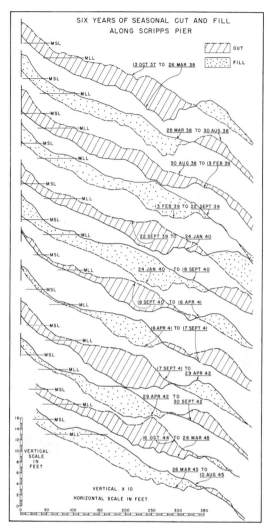

SIX YEARS OF SEASONAL CUT AND FILL
ALONG SCRIPPS PIER

Figure 30. Profiles showing winter and summer changes of the beach and shallow sea floor along the pier at Scripps Institution of Oceanography, La Jolla. From Shepard (1950*b*).

lays its eggs in the sand of southern California beaches (Fig. 127, p. 144). The incubation period of two weeks is just completed by the next time of spring tides when the eggs are washed free of the sand and immediately hatch. An error of a few days in the laying of the eggs would result in premature exposure and loss.

The analogy drawn in a previous section between marine erosion of sea cliffs and stream erosion of valleys has its counterpart (Fig. 32) for marine deposition of beach sands and stream deposition of flood plain alluvium. Again, however, we must think in terms of the horizontal changes by marine agents and the vertical changes by the streams. In other words, the planes of action of shore and stream processes are 90° apart. The long gradual slope of a stream at grade has its parallel in a long straight or broadly curving beach, along each segment of which the amount of sand entering from up-beach or up-current and from land exactly equals the amount that either is transported out of the segment over a long period of time in a down-beach direction or is lost to the open sea. Where the beach consists of fine sand, it is long and nearly parallel to the trend of wave fronts, and thus it is an area of only moderate or slow longshore drift. One composed of gravel is usually short and trends at a large angle to approaching wave fronts, whose fast longshore drift has winnowed away the sand. These relationships have their parallels in streams, wherein the segments having high velocity are floored by gravel (if gravel is available) and those having low velocity are floored by sand or finer sediments. In addition, the rocky points separating some beach segments are areas of high turbulence and little sediment, just as are waterfalls and rapids for streams. The great turbulence of winter storm waves which reduce the width of beaches also has its counterpart in the turbulence of flooding streams which places much of the stream bed in suspension and thereby temporarily reduces the thickness of alluvial fill in valleys. Estuary and lagoon fillings of mud accumulated in closed areas of quiet water and separated from the open ocean by baymouth bars have their parallels in muds that eventually fill lakes and then are covered by layers of sand.

Sediment supplied to the beach by streams ranges from fine- to coarse-grained. The fine-grained sediment is carried away in suspension by longshore currents and finally it diffuses seaward; the medium-grained sediment slowly moves along the shoreline by saltation, and the coarse may be left as a lag deposit. Trunk streams similarly dispose of sediment contributed by tributaries. Where streams or landslides contribute too much sediment to the beach for the waves to move immediately, a delta or bulge results; similarly, trunk streams may be dammed or shallowed by sediment from a tributary or a landslide. In both examples the effects are felt far up and down the beach and far up and down the stream.

If the gradient of the water surface of a section of stream having a flood plain is artificially reduced by the building of a dam, the water entering the reservoir builds a delta whose head extends the same distance upstream that the original valley was at grade. At the same time the water leaving the reservoir is underloaded so that it erodes the flood plain far enough downstream until its load again reaches capacity. If the downstream area was formerly at grade, the stream must incise a new valley all the way to its mouth. Thus, for a graded stream

valley the dam produces extensive deposition upstream and erosion downstream (Mackin, 1948; Gould, 1953). An exactly parallel series of changes occurs when a groin or breakwater is built across a beach that is in equilibrium with the environment. The sand that normally would pass through the area is dammed up by the structure so that prograding of the beach eventually occurs far up-beach. Sand down-beach from the groin continues its down-beach movement, but the structure built across the beach prevents the normal replenishment of this sand by more from up the beach; thus erosion occurs down-beach from the structure, at first close to it and then at a greater distance. This sequence of events has occurred after the building of practically every such structure across southern California beaches—Santa Barbara, Santa Monica, Redondo, Seal Beach, Mission Beach, and Camp Pendleton.

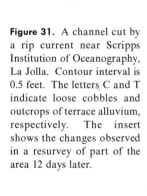

Figure 31. A channel cut by a rip current near Scripps Institution of Oceanography, La Jolla. Contour interval is 0.5 feet. The letters C and T indicate loose cobbles and outcrops of terrace alluvium, respectively. The insert shows the changes observed in a resurvey of part of the area 12 days later.

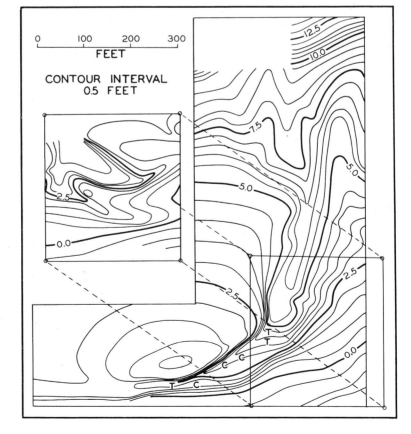

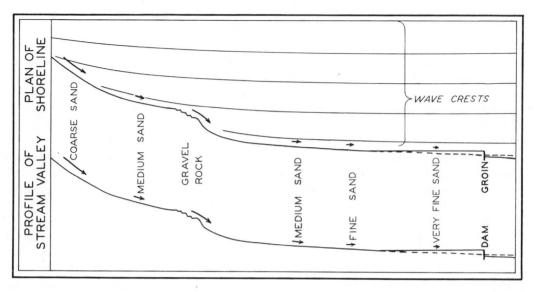

Figure 32. Topographic and textural analogies between marine and stream environments. Arrows show direction and relative velocity of water currents.

Shelves and Bank Tops

The mainland shore is bordered by a shelf which ranges in width from less than 1 mile to 15 miles and averages 4 miles. Maximum widths of more than 7.5 miles occur at four places: the United States–Mexico border, San Pedro Bay, Santa Monica Bay, and east of Santa Barbara. Although each of these areas is off the mouth of a main river of southern California, the greater-than-usual shelf widths cannot be the result of deltaic deposition because rocky bottom is abundant on each of the four shelves.

Shelves around the islands vary from less than 0.1 mile to 22 miles wide. Reference to Chart I shows that the shelves are narrowest around the eastern islands (San Clemente and Santa Catalina), are intermediate around Santa Barbara Island, and are widest around the five western islands. This variation in shelf width may be due to less exposure of the eastern islands to storm waves, aided by the presence of more resistant rock on the same islands.

The surfaces of flat-topped banks are similar to shelves, except that they lack a bordering land area. Widths range up to 8 miles but, unlike the shelves, they are limited by the width of the block that was truncated. Even so, most of the wider banks are west of the narrower ones, paralleling the distribution of island shelf widths.

Rocky bottom is present at many places on the mainland shelves, is even more common on the island shelves, and is most abundant on the flat bank tops. As shown by fathograms and photographs of Figure 33, rock bottom is usually marked by irregular projections above the general level of the shelf. The correspondence of very irregular topography with rocky bottom permits rapid identification of rocky areas on fathograms.

In addition to irregular rocky areas, the shelves and bank tops have a series of step-like terraces which are similar to those on adjacent land areas: The terraces are easy to recognize on sounding profiles made off rocky points of the mainland and on island shelves and across bank tops. On shelves bordering low depositional mainland coasts they are partly obscured by aprons of debris derived from land (Fig. 34). In such areas jet drilling through overburden (Thompson, 1957) or sonoprobe studies (Moore, 1957; Moore and Shumway, in press) have aided in the recognition of the terraces. Typical of the shelf profiles are those around the Palos Verdes Hills as shown by Figure 35. Profiles for other parts of the region are given by Emery (1958a). Several terraces can easily

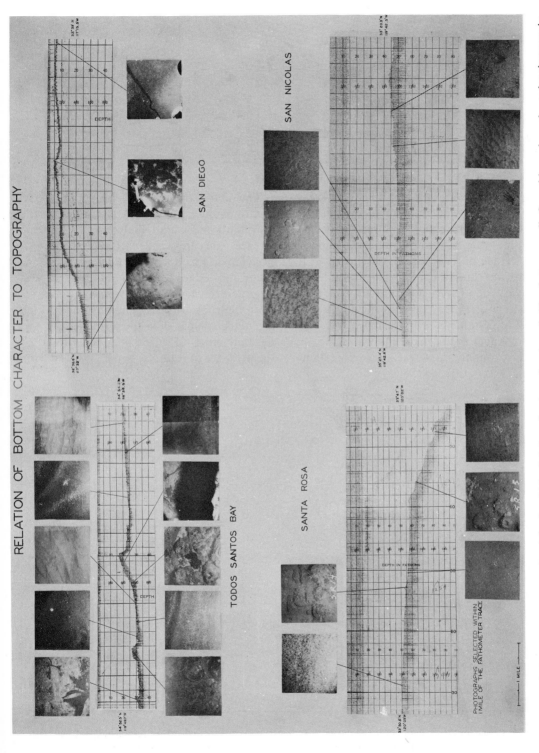

Figure 33. Fathograms across several mainland and island shelves showing minor irregularities that are usually floored by rock, as shown by photographs of the bottom, in contrast to sand which covers flat areas.

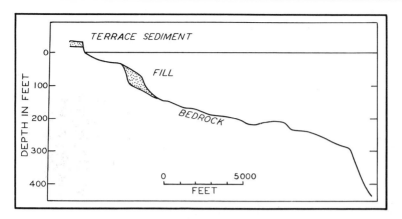

Figure 34. Profiles of sea floor near Santa Barbara showing masking of submerged wave-cut terrace by sedimentary fill. Adapted from W. C. Thompson (in Dietz and Menard, 1951, Fig. 10D).

be seen; however, correlation of terraces from one profile to another is difficult by mere visual inspection. A more satisfactory method is one in which the depth span of each terrace on each profile is shown by a wide vertical line (Fig. 36). Correspondence of terrace depths on adjacent profiles permits short-distance correlation with a fair degree of certainty. Correlation of most of these terraces from mainland to island or island to island, however, is less certain.

The abundant outcrops of sedimentary, metamorphic, and igneous rocks on the mainland and island shelves show that the terraces are erosional rather than depositional in origin, at least for the most part. At the outer edges of both submerged and emerged terraces, where sediment cover is thin, bedrock forms linear outcrops which are much steeper than the terraces that border both sides. Erosion is also indicated by the presence of rounded gravels derived from

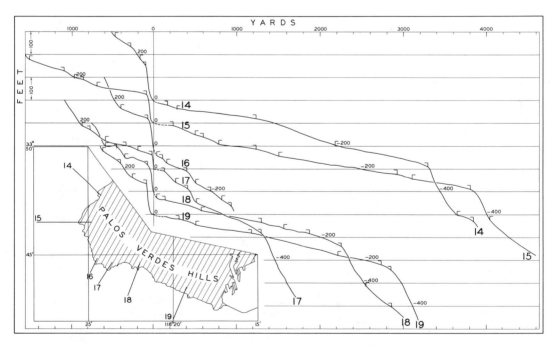

Figure 35. Profiles of the sea floor bordering the Palos Verdes Hills from shore to depths of several hundred feet. These were made from spot echo soundings taken about 60 feet apart, supported in part by recorded fathograms. Extension of profiles on land is based on published contour maps. The vertical scale is eight times the horizontal one. From Emery (1958a, Fig. 4).

local high areas that once were islands or stacks such as the center of Santa Monica Bay (Terry and Stevenson, 1957).

Multiple terraces at shallow depths occur elsewhere in the world—Japan, Guam, Australia, the Persian Gulf, Britain, and the Gulf and Atlantic coasts of the United States (Emery, 1958a). The shallowest terrace (50 to 60 feet) is even more widely known. This widespread distribution is strongly indicative of eustatic origin in relatively recent times. According to Flint (1947, p. 437) the lower-

represent separate glacial ages of the whole Pleistocene Epoch or whether they were formed during only part of this time.

The terraces that together make up the mainland and island shelves and the bank tops are wider and flatter than most of those now exposed on land. Many are between 1 and 5 miles wide, in contrast, for example, to the 0.1- to 0.5-mile width of the high terraces of the Palos Verdes Hills (Fig. 37) and of San Clemente Island. The greater flatness of the submerged terraces (usually less

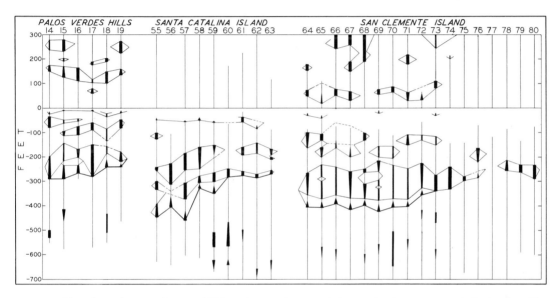

Figure 36. Elevations of terraces between 300 feet above and 700 feet below sea level at margins of Palos Verdes Hills, Santa Catalina Island, and San Clemente Island. Thin vertical lines show depths or heights that were sounded or shown on land contour maps. Wide vertical bars show depth ranges of individual terraces or relatively flat areas having definite landward and seaward edges; medium-width bars indicate terraces having less definite edges. Top and bottom limits of terraces on each profile have been connected by lines to show the lateral extent of terraces.

ing of sea level during the maximum extent of glaciers was about 400 feet, to a level slightly shallower than the deepest terrace off southern California and slightly shallower than Shepard's (1948, p. 143) figure of 430 feet for the average depth of the outer edge of the continental shelf around the world. The Pleistocene age of the terraces that is indicated accords with the fact that some of them, at San Pedro Bay and along the coast from Ventura to Santa Barbara, truncate structures in Pliocene shales. The question still remains of whether the shallow terraces

than 1°) as compared to the emerged ones (usually more than 3°) is a reflection of the lesser width of the latter as well as of their greater mantling by sedimentary materials. These differences may be expressions of repeated movements of sea level across the area, each time planing off more rocks to make the flat shelves, in contrast to single brief times of cutting of the very high and the very deep terraces. The small depth variation of the shelf-break and the fact that the shallow submerged terraces are present in areas where high terraces on land or very deep ones

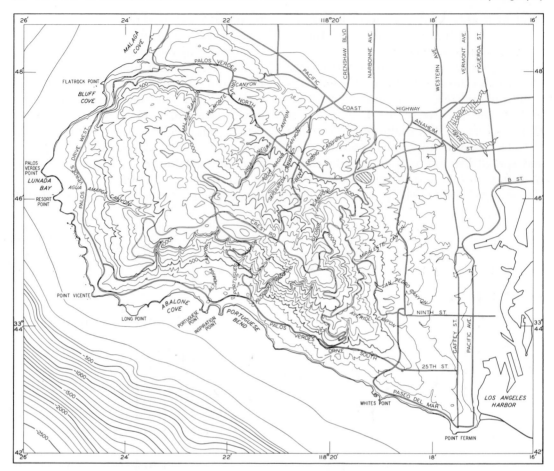

Figure 37. Contour map of Palos Verdes Hills and adjacent sea floor at contour interval of 100 feet. Note that this interval fails to reveal any except the widest raised terraces; in contrast is the great width of the mainland shelf, a composite of several terraces of slightly differing depths. Smoothly curving contours of basin slope beyond the shelf-break are partly due to the relative scarcity of sounding data on sea floor as compared to elevation data on land.

on the sea floor indicate much diastrophic movement suggest that the shelf terraces are younger than those of diastrophic origin. At Ventura (Putnam, 1942) the high terraces bevel strata that were folded during the mid-Pleistocene diastrophism, and at Palos Verdes Hills (Woodring, Bramlette, and Kew, 1946) fossils in marine deposits on the terraces indicate a Middle or Late Pleistocene date. In addition, stream channels cut as much as 230 feet below sea level at the present shoreline must have been correlative with the submerged terraces; these channels are eroded into Early and Middle Pleistocene strata in the Ventura and Los Angeles Basins and have been filled by later sediments (Up-

son, 1949; Crowell, 1952; Poland, Piper, and others, 1956). Thus, several lines of evidence indicate that at least in part of the area off southern California the submerged terraces are no older than Middle Pleistocene. Perhaps they were cut during the eustatic levels of the Wisconsin Age that correlate with the Iowan, Tazewell, Cary, and Mankato Subages (Flint, 1947, p. 212). In the Sierra Nevada also, several separate Wisconsin moraines probably are correlative with separate terraces of Mono Lake (Putnam, 1950). Several different eustatic sea levels have been suggested by Zeuner (Ericson and Wollin, 1956b) for subages of the Wisconsin. Thus, it is possible that the broad gently sloping shelves were cut by multiple lowerings of sea level during the Pleistocene, at least in some parts of the region, but that the present well-defined submerged terraces date only from Wisconsin time.

Some support for a Wisconsin age of terrace cutting is provided by lithothamnoid encrusting calcareous algae found in cores from depths of 334 to 387 feet just beyond the deepest terrace off the Palos Verdes Hills (Emery, 1958a). The present depth is too great for the algae to live today, considering the turbidity of the water; moreover, the algae occur in layers covered by as much as 10 feet of silt, sand, and clay. It is believed that they lived when the sea level was lower —probably low enough to have cut the deepest terrace. Radiocarbon ages of four samples of the algae show them to be 17,000 to 24,500 years old (Emery 1958a), presumably indicating a similar age for the deepest terrace. This makes the deepest terrace younger than the +75-foot terrace on the nearby shore, dated as older than 30,000 years (Kulp, Tryon, Eckelman, and Snell, 1952). Moreover, carbon-14 dates compiled by Shepard and Suess (1956) show that the sea level rose from minus 150 feet to the present position during the past 12,000 years, supporting the ages derived from the algal encrustations. Of interest here is the finding of nearly 700 stone mortars and a few metates and other artifacts in water 20 to 100 feet deep off Solano Beach, La Jolla, Point Loma, and Imperial Beach (Tuthill and Allanson, 1954), of at least one mortar off Santa Barbara (Wallace and Kritzman, 1956), and of one or two off Malibu and Redondo Beach (Conrad Limbaugh, personal communication). Although the mortars conceivably were carried out in boats and dumped, it is more probable that they mark village sites submerged beneath the post-Pleistocene rising sea level (Carter, 1955). If so, then many other sites remain to be discovered under the sea, and archaeologists must be prepared to take to the water.

The outer flat terrace differs from all the shallower ones in that its outer edge marks the depth of abrupt change of slope that has been called the shelf-break by Dietz and Menard (1951). This is the true edge of the shelf. If any of the terraces are correlatable over long distances, the one at the shelf-break is the most certain, owing to its ease of identification. Its depth ranges from about 250 feet near Los Angeles to about 480 feet far to the south and to the west. Contours of depth of the shelf-break in Figure 38 show a gradual deepening from northeast to southwest throughout the borderland. Variations in depth of wave base in the region are insufficient to account for the differences in depth of the shelf-break, for as pointed out by Dietz and Menard (1951) effective wave base is that depth at which energy begins to be transferred to the bottom and the wave velocity begins to decrease. For all practical purposes this depth is only about 30 feet. Instead, the depth variation must be taken as a measure of the extent of regional warping after the terrace was cut.

Although the shelf-break yields the most reliable information about warping of the coastal region, some additional information is provided by the shallower terraces. The outer edge of each terrace is shallower where crossed by profiles off most of the mainland and the nearshore islands of Santa Rosa, Santa Cruz, and Anacapa than where crossed by profiles off the outer islands and banks. Average depths for each terrace in both areas (Table 3) show that the difference in depth is progressively greater for deeper than for shallower terraces. In fact, the ratio of depth difference to depth offshore exhibits only a small range, 26 to 40 per cent.

Table 3

DEPTHS OF OUTER EDGES
OF SUBMERGED TERRACES, FEET

Terrace	Mainland and Nearshore Islands	Offshore Islands and Banks	Difference
1	30?	50?	20?
2	80	125	45
3	160	245	85
4	255	345	90
5	290	430	140

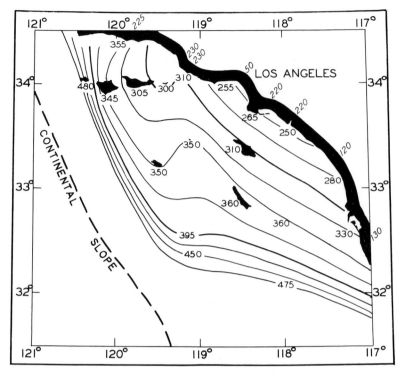

Figure 38. Depth distribution off southern California of the outer or lower edge of the terrace which marks the shelf-break (depth at which slope becomes markedly steeper than at any point closer to shore). The contour interval is 25 feet. Depths are based on average shelf-break shown by groups of detailed sounding profiles. Italicized numbers on the land side of the shoreline show depth in feet below sea level of alluvial fill in mouths of valleys. From Emery (1958a, Fig. 13).

Basin and Trough Slopes

The slopes that border the shelves and bank tops and lead down into the adjoining basins or troughs are commonly long and straight. Several are more than 50 miles long with curvatures or departures of less than 5 miles from being straight lines. Forming the largest irregularities of the basin and trough slopes are sharp and more or less right-angled offsets. Examples can be seen on Chart I opposite La Jolla, off Newport Beach, west of Santa Catalina Island, south of San Nicolas Island, and south and east of Sixtymile Bank. These offsets have much the aspect of cross faults. Topographic evidence suggesting fault origin of the slopes is provided by the straightness, height, and steepness of the slopes, the occasional presence of "sagponds" and offsets, and the general parallelism of the slopes to major known faults on the adjoining land.

Heights of the slopes range up to more than a mile above their bases. In general, the steep slopes of basins near the mainland have their bases near or even above the sill depth of the basin, but the slopes of basins farther from shore extend as much as 3000 feet below the sills; this, of course, is in response to the greater degree of filling of the basins closer to shore. The steepest portions with angles between 10 and 22° are commonly nearer the top than the bottom of the slopes. As shown by Figure 39, the mean of 239 measurements of basin and trough slopes of Chart I is 8°, considerably less than the steepness of the continental slope and of the sides of mountains located within the area of Chart I. Five slopes are steeper than usual (mostly 15 to 20°). These are the Coronado Escarpment off San Diego, the slopes that border the two long sides of Thirtymile and Fortymile Banks, and the ones that border the two long sides of Santa Catalina Basin. The base of each of these five slopes also makes a more abrupt angle with the basin or trough floors than does that of most other slopes of the region (Chart I). These facts suggest that the five slopes may have undergone more recent major faulting than the other slopes.

Detailed profiles of slopes (Fig. 40) reveal

them to be more irregular than can be shown by the contours of Chart I. Irregularities consist partly of uneven rocky bottom, as in the profile of the east side of Santa Cruz Basin (Fig. 41), partly of incomplete blanketing of sediment, as in the profile off Santa Catalina Island, and partly of sediment believed to have slid downslope to accumulate at the foot, as off the Palos Verdes Hills. Some step-like irregularities of the slopes may result from parallel splinter faults. Near the top of the slopes there commonly is seen a slight concavity that may represent the form taken by a terrace cut into a steep slope. At still greater depths of about 1800 feet the slopes commonly contain a slight nick. The frequency of its occurrence and the uniformity of its depth suggests an origin as a narrow terrace produced by eustatic lowering of sea level. However, such a lowering far exceeds the generally accepted maximum for the Pleistocene Epoch. For the present, the nick is considered an unsolved problem.

Close examination of Chart I shows that the slopes bordering the mainland shelf are commonly fringed at their bases by an apron that generally is lacking for slopes bordering islands and banks. Where sampled, this slope consists of sediment. A sequence can be set up of slopes that descend into small linear depressions similar to sagponds on land, through ones that have a small apron at their base to a larger apron, and finally to gentle slopes that appear to be aprons from top to bottom (Fig. 40). This sequence is exactly parallel to that for continental slopes proposed by Dietz (1952) as stages from initial, to early youth, late youth, maturity, and old age. In general, the slopes of greater geomorphic age border the mainland shelf; thus, the age corresponds closely to the availability of sediments for building up aprons. In addition to forming aprons, sediments may mantle the top of the slope, building it outward in areas where sediments are contributed to the ocean most rapidly. Detailed studies by Emery and Terry (1956) showed the presence of sediment at least 18 feet thick on a slope of 18° off the Palos Verdes Hills (Figs. 41 and 42). From many of the offshore slopes rock has been dredged, suggesting less mantling by sediment on slopes farther from the mainland source of sediment.

Irregularities are not restricted to features which parallel the slope. Others have been

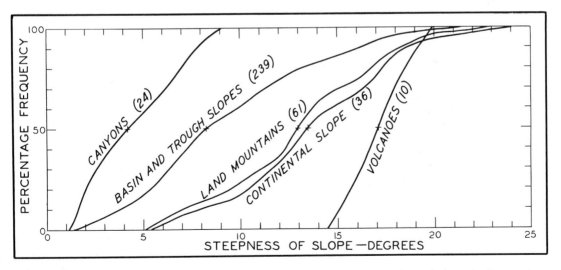

Figure 39. Cumulative curves of measurements of steepness of canyon axes, basin and trough slopes, land mountains, continental slope, and submarine volcanoes of Chart I. The number of measurements for each kind of feature is indicated in parentheses. Each measurement is that of the steepest 1500-foot vertical span of profiles spaced about 10 miles apart, except for submarine canyons for which profiles are closer.

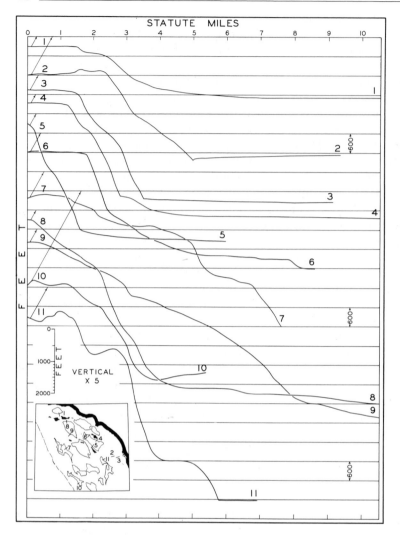

Figure 40. Comparison of several basin slopes at various distances from shore. Note that the base of some slopes is bordered by a trench and others by an apron. Still other slopes have intermediate kinds of bases. Vertical exaggeration—×5.

detected by fathograms run parallel to the slope. The smallest of these features have been termed sea gullies by Buffington (1951), who found them on slopes between San Diego and San Pedro. Subsequently they have been found on nearly every slope studied. Good examples exist off the Palos Verdes Hills where each sea gully was crossed by several fathograms (Fig. 43). Although not definitely established, it is believed by Emery and Terry (1956) that the sea gullies are elongate landslide scars produced by movement of sediment down the slope to the apron at the bottom. Cores in the slope encountered nothing but sediment, and the sea gullies have side slopes of the same steepness as the front of the basin slope into which they are incised.

Submarine canyons also cross the slopes and parts of the adjoining shelves. These features are much larger and more complex than the sea gullies and will be discussed separately in the following section.

Submarine Canyons

Characteristics

There are few physiographic features of the world about which more papers have been written and yet less is known regarding origin than submarine canyons. Nearly all that is known about them has been learned during the past 25 years. The effort to secure facts was headed by Shepard, who studied the California canyons principally,

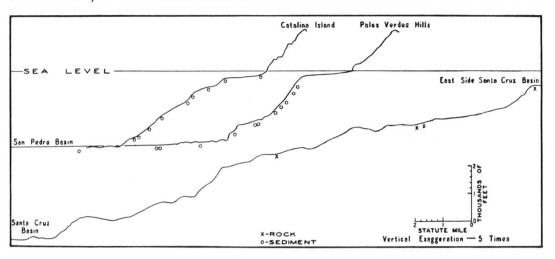

Figure 41. Composition and character of several basin slopes. Note that, although all these slopes are irregular, only one is immediately underlain by rocky bottom, and this one happens to be the gentlest slope. From Emery and Terry (1956, Fig. 7).

Figure 42. Photograph of upper part of basin slope off Palos Verdes Hills (lat. 33°41.1′, long. 118°20.3′, 957 feet). Camera is facing nearly parallel to slope and tilting 10° downward; the slope, thus, is at least 18° steep. Cores show the slope to be covered with a blanket of mud more than 18 feet thick. White light-scattering objects at left are small bathypelagic animals or grains of sediment—they are very commonly present near the bottom. (AHF 2102.)

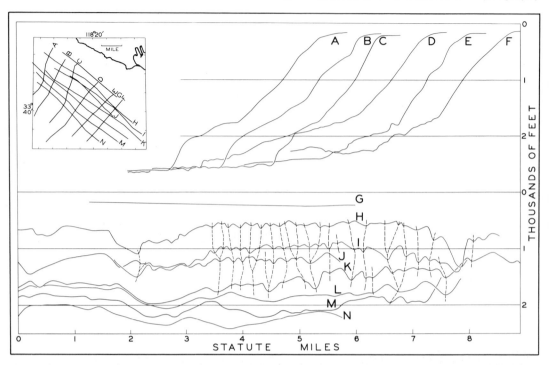

Figure 43. Profiles of slope off Palos Verdes Hills. Profiles A to F extend southwesterly downslope at approximately 1-mile spacing. Note the presence on each profile of the following zones: mainland shelf, smooth upper slope, undulating lower slope, and basin floor. Profiles G to N extend parallel to the slope at approximately one-third-mile spacing. The shallowest profile, of the mainland shelf, is very flat; those of the lower slope have broad gentle undulations. Dashed lines show possible connections of sea gullies. The broad sag in the middle left is a major indentation, atop which the small irregularities are superimposed.

summarizing most of his information in a mongraph (Parts III and IV of Shepard and Emery, 1941). His later papers have concentrated on changes at the heads of the canyons, on results of diving operations, and on hypotheses of origin. Most of the more recent work was done on La Jolla and Scripps Canyons. Thirteen canyons in southern California have been assigned names (Chart I). At least 19 additional canyons are present, but most of these are small in comparison with nearby named canyons (like those between Hueneme and Mugu Canyons and those near Newport Canyon) or are poorly known (like those northeast of San Nicolas Island). Of this total of 32 submarine canyons, 20 border the mainland, 10 border islands, and 2 are off submarine banks. There is no question but what others are present off islands and banks where the density of soundings is less than in areas near the mainland but where

existing soundings show some irregularities of the slopes. In fact, on the basis of these irregularities Ma (1952) drew courses for 120 submarine canyons in the area of Chart I. Doubtlessly, more canyons exist even near the mainland but are buried beneath thick sediments which locally mantle the slopes. Finally, there is probably a size gradation of canyons down to the scale of the smaller sea gullies discussed in the previous section.

Description of the physical characteristics of the submarine canyons is simplified by considering them in relation to the three environments that they cross, shelf, slope, and basin or trough floor. Far more is known of the canyons in the shelf environment than elsewhere, owing to ease of extrapolation of geological data from land, to certainty of positions, and to shallowness of water there.

Eight of the submarine canyons (including nearly all the named ones off the mainland) cross almost the entire width of the mainland shelf. Five others cross more than the outer third of the shelf. The remainder (all except San Pedro Sea Valley are unnamed and poorly known) make only small indentations at the edge of the shelves. Even though not all the canyons cross the shelves, there is no reason to believe that they did not formerly cross them. For example, jet drilling by oil companies has shown the presence of a narrow sediment-filled valley extending across the shelf from shore to the head of San Pedro Sea Valley. This is similar to the filled channel that extends from the delta of the Mississippi River to the head of a large submarine trough (Carsey, 1950), and it also is similar to the partly filled Hudson Channel which crosses the continental shelf between the mouth of the Hudson River and the head of the large Hudson Canyon (Veatch and Smith, 1939, Chart V).

In addition, records of wells on land have shown the presence of sediment-filled channels reaching the shore at points inshore of Hueneme Canyon, Santa Monica Canyon, Redondo Canyon, San Pedro Sea Valley, Newport Canyon, and Coronado Canyon (Poland and colleagues, 1945, 1948, 1956; E. J. Zielbauer and R. G. Thomas, personal communications), counterparts of features in New England and Australia (Flint, 1947, p. 447; Hack, 1957). Since the channels were cut 123 to 255 feet below present sea level, they doubtlessly extend seaward of the shore and may connect with the canyons. Similar channels occur at Oceanside and Goleta, where no canyons are known to cut the shelf; however, contours of the lower part of the trough slope off Oceanside are indented as though by a largely filled canyon, and the slope off Goleta is so gentle that a canyon could formerly have existed there and now be completely buried. Even where the canyons are open across most of the shelf, partial and at least temporary filling by sediments is shown by photographs (Fig. 44) and direct examination (Fig. 45) (Shepard, 1949; McAllister, 1957) of the bottom in Scripps and La Jolla Canyons and by observations of sliding of sediment at the heads of La Jolla, Scripps,

Newport, Redondo, and possibly Mugu Canyons (Shepard and Emery, 1941, pp. 94–103; Shepard, 1951*a*). Similar changes may occur at the heads of canyons located farther from shore, but the required precise navigation is impossible or at least impractical far from shore.

Canyons which reach close to shore have been found to have numerous tributaries, four for Scripps Canyon, at least seven for La Jolla Canyon, and four for Hueneme Canyon. Canyons such as Coronado, San Pedro, and Santa Monica, which head far from shore, are mapped on Chart I and elsewhere as having simple heads. The simplification is almost certainly a result of the difficulty and cost of obtaining accurate positions for detailed surveys. To illustrate, when detailed studies of the head of Santa Monica Canyon were required for construction purposes, a survey there showed at least three tributaries, although only one was known before. Similar accurate surveys farther along the valley walls would doubtlessly reveal the presence of many additional tributaries. This question of surveying accuracy and sounding density may have been overlooked by Crowell (1952) in his discussion of the restriction of tributaries to the heads of submarine canyons.

Profiles at the heads of the southern California canyons are steeper than farther from shore, with mean slopes at the head, middle, and end of 14.5°, 5.5°, and 4.0°, respectively, according to measurements by Shepard and Beard (1938). As Woodford (1951) pointed out, the slope at the head is far steeper than the slope at the mouth of the adjoining valley on land. Such a relationship is reasonable, of course, in view of the sediments that have filled the axis near sea level, alluviating the drowned valley on land and prograding into the part of the valley that remains submerged.

Some indication of the age of the canyons with respect to the shelf can be provided by an examination of the depth of the intersection of the side slope of the canyon and the surface of the shelf. This feature is similar to the shelf-break. If the canyons were cut after the shelf had formed, the canyon shelf-

Figure 44. Contact of sloping canyon fill with vertical north wall of Sumner Branch of Scripps Canyon. Note pholad borings in wall and eel grass in fill. Depth 100 feet. Courtesy of F. P. Shepard.

break would be progressively shallower as shore is approached, paralleling a profile of the shelf itself. If, on the other hand, the canyon were older than the date of cutting of the shelf, we would expect the waves entering an embayment of the lowered shoreline to have cut the shelf back along the sides of the canyon. The depth of the canyon shelf-break, thus, would be nearly uniform along the canyon. In other words, if the canyon were older than the shelf, the shelf could have been cut not only from its seaward side but also along re-entrants into it. Clearly, the only canyons that can provide such data are those that cross most of the shelf width, such as Redondo, Hueneme, and perhaps Coronado, Scripps, and Mugu. Only one special survey has so far been made in an effort to settle this question.

This one, at Redondo Canyon, showed a uniform depth of canyon shelf-break except at the head (Fig. 46); therefore, we might conclude that only the head of the canyon postdates the time of cutting of the shelf. Much more work should be done along this line in order to find the depth of the canyon shelf-break elsewhere and to learn the relation of the canyon shelf-break to the several terraces on the shelf.

The second portion of the submarine canyons is that which crosses the basin or trough slopes. North of Point Conception in California and elsewhere in the world this portion would correspond to the continental slope. If any canyons cross the true continental slope of southern California south of San Miguel Island, they have not yet been discovered. The slope part of the canyons is larger in cross section than near the head, but not in all instances is it larger than the canyon near the outer edge of the shelf. The large cross section is evidently a result of the deep cutting permitted the agents of erosion by the initial steepness of the basin and trough slopes. It has its counterpart on land in the large cross sections of stream valleys where they cross the emerged sea cliffs as compared to their small size at the back edge of the emerged flat terraces. Axial profiles of the canyons generally present a fairly smooth decrease of gradient from the head to the mouth, where the base level is the basin or trough floor—corresponding to the basin floor base level of valleys in closed basins on land like Death Valley.

Crowell (1952) commented on the possible significance of nickpoints in this portion of the canyon axis, but two factors make the existence of nickpoints exceedingly uncertain. One factor is the difficulty of recognizing in the field the deepest individual sounding on successive transverse sounding profiles. This difficulty is particularly great where canyons are deep and narrow and where audiovisual echo sounders are used (contours of Chart I were based entirely on such spot soundings made before the advent of automatically recording sounding instruments). The second factor is the uncertainty in positions. Errors due to both factors increase with depth and distance from shore, and the wonder is not that occasional unsubstantiated nickpoints remain but that more depressions and bars are not erroneously shown by the charts. This does not

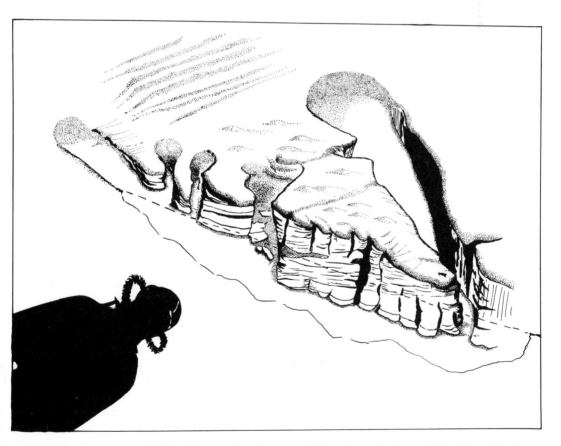

Figure 45. Sketch of head of Scripps Canyon. Based on many observations and photographs by diver. Nearly vertical walls consist of Eocene conglomerate and sandstone. Sediment on the floor has a steep slope and chokes tributaries. Kelp and other organic debris have accumulated in the sediment. Drawn by T. E. Mahnker, Jr. Courtesy of F. P. Shepard.

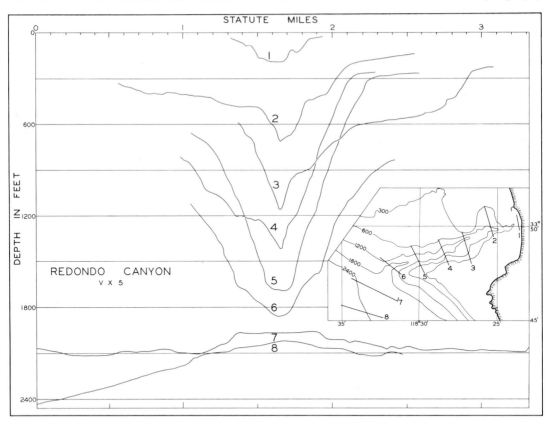

Figure 46. Cross sections of Redondo Canyon made from echo soundings at 60-foot intervals aboard *R/V Velero IV*. Note fan at mouth. Shelf-breaks of profiles 3, 4, and 5 are nearly uniform, suggesting at least partial planation of the shelf by wave erosion after the canyon was formed. Depths must be increased by 9 feet to correct for tide and keel depth of hydrophone.

mean that nickpoints do not exist but simply that few of those shown on charts can be considered as proven. The general lack of tributaries along this part of the canyons is also a reflection of the lesser density of soundings far from shore compared to those made nearer the canyon heads. As shown by Figure 1 and the accompanying discussion of Shepard and Emery (1941), the sounding density at the outer parts of the canyons may be more than an order of magnitude less than at the heads. For this reason, tributaries as large as Scripps Canyon could be completely overlooked if they occur 5 or 10 miles from shore. In addition, the front of the sound wave from the ship's echo sounder is an approximately spherical surface. At great depth, reflection of nearly all the sound from a fairly flat surface into which such narrow slot-like tribu-

taries may be cut would prevent the recognition of the tributaries. Again, we must consider the limitations of survey methods in comparing the characteristics of different portions of the canyons.

The outer part of the canyons, where they leave the base of the slope and debouch on the adjoining basin or trough floor, is even less well known than the other two parts, owing to greater distance from shore, greater depth of water, and smaller cross section of valley. In this area two forms are taken, constructional and erosional. The constructional form is that of a large fan; although it has been referred to during the past as a delta, the term delta implies a control by sea level, but sea level actually was probably not related in any way to the feature. Fans exist at the mouths of the Hueneme-Mugu group of five canyons and at Dume, Redondo (Fig. 47), Carlsbad, and Coronado Canyons. They are probably also present at Newport, La Jolla, and Catalina Canyons, but their form is less regular. For the above five best-known canyons or groups, the fans have volumes several times greater than those of the eroded canyons above them (Table 4). As will be discussed later, the basins contain large additional quantities of sediments derived from shallow water probably through the canyons. The excess of volume of deposition over the volume of erosion of areas that are submarine at present can be equated only with the erosion of presently subaerial areas, by littoral drift of sand intercepted by the canyon heads, or by shelf sand slumped down the sides of the canyons. Perhaps the presence of an especially large fan at the mouth of the small Carlsbad Canyon means that this canyon formerly extended to nearer the shoreline where it could intercept much of the littoral drift of sand south of Newport Beach. Filling up of its head may have allowed this drift to continue southward to Scripps and La Jolla Canyons.

Table 4

VOLUMES OF FANS AND CANYONS

	Cubic Yards, 10^9		Ratio of Fan to Canyon
	Fan	Canyon	
Hueneme-Mugu group	33	18	1.8
Dume	2.3	0.7	3.3
Redondo	20	11	1.8
Carlsbad	37	1.3	28
Coronado	22	7.8	2.8

The second, or erosional, form of the canyon extension beyond the slope is a long narrow channel which may cross the fans, as discussed briefly for Coronado Canyon by Emery, Butcher, Gould, and Shepard (1952). Detailed deep-water soundings revealed the presence of a "deep-sea channel" extending beyond the mouth of the main part of La Jolla Canyon and across at least part of the San Diego Trough (Menard and Ludwick, 1951; Shepard, 1951a; Buffington, 1952). Other such channels, mostly only 50 to 300 feet deep, 0.2 to 2 miles wide, and bordered by levees, have been described off Monterey Canyon by Dill, Dietz, and Stewart (1954), in the Atlantic Ocean by Ewing, Heezen, Ericson, Northrop, and Dorman (1953), and in the Indian Ocean by Dietz (1953). Detailed surveys would probably show that many such channels cross the floors of basins on which the submarine canyons of Chart I end. To date they have been found only at Coronado, Redondo (Fig. 47), Mugu, Hueneme, and possibly off San Pedro and Newport Canyons.

The age of the submarine canyons may be determined partly from the age of the strata which they cut (Emery and Shepard, 1945). La Jolla Canyon is cut partly through Cretaceous shales and sandstones (Fig. 48). La Jolla and Scripps Canyons are cut partly through Eocene conglomerates, sandstones, and shales. Coronado, La Jolla, San Pedro, Redondo, Santa Monica, Dume, Mugu, Tanner, and probably Santa Cruz and Newport Canyons are cut through Miocene shales, limestones, or basalt. San Pedro Sea Valley and Coronado Canyon are cut partly through Pliocene shales. According to Poland and his colleagues (Crowell, 1952), the heads of Newport, Redondo, and Hueneme Canyons are cut partly through Pleistocene clays, silts, sands, and gravels. Data of the same workers show that Hueneme, Santa Monica, San Pedro, Newport, and probably Mugu and San Gabriel Canyons have land extensions that have become filled with Recent gravels, sands, and silts of both marine and nonmarine origin. These stratigraphic relationships show generally older rocks occurring at progressively greater distance from shore and depth of water. In summary, where any data are available, the canyons are known to be cut through the strata of their particular area, and some are cut through strata as young as Pleistocene; thus, at least some of the canyons were cut at least in part in Late Pleistocene time.

Origin

The discovery of submarine canyons was reported somewhat earlier on the Atlantic

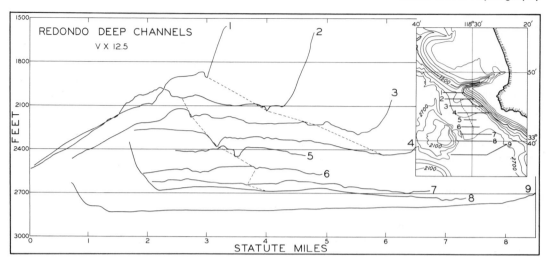

Figure 47. Detailed profiles across fan at mouth of Redondo Canyon, showing two deep channels extending across the upper part of the fan down toward San Pedro Basin.

(Dana, 1863, pp. 441–442) than on the Pacific coast of the United States, but description of the Atlantic canyons (Lindenkohl, 1885, 1891) and the Pacific ones (Davidson, 1887, 1897) was almost simultaneous. Immediately there arose conflicting opinions on their origin. During later years these opinions have been modified and new ones added at a rate exceeding the rate of accumulation of new facts about the canyons. It is noteworthy that few of the men who have written about this subject have taken either soundings or samples from the canyons. In the following pages no attempt will be made to exhaustively treat the morass of opinions of origin; this has previously been done by Johnson (1938–1939), Shepard (1948, pp. 207–251; Shepard and Emery, 1941), Daly (1942, pp. 111–157), Umbgrove (1947, pp. 120–139), and Kuenen (1950, pp. 480–531).

The general similarity of the submarine canyons to large youthful river valleys in plan, profile, and cross section led Dana (1890), Le Conte (1891), Lindenkohl (1891), Fairbanks (1897), and Spencer (1903) to consider them products of subaerial erosion during a brief time when local uplifts brought the continental shelf and slope high above sea level. Later, canyons were discovered elsewhere in the world (although nearly half the presently known ones are off the United States where marine surveying has been relatively intense), requiring something more than local uplift as an explanation. At this stage the opinions of origin progressed down two contemporaneous but separate paths: (1) subaerial erosion owing to world-wide causes and (2) submarine processes.

The world-wide distribution of canyons, the Pleistocene age of some of them, and the presence of some off mouths of large rivers naturally led to the hypothesis that they were cut by streams flowing across the former sea floor during the Pleistocene Epoch when much of the water that evaporated from the ocean was temporarily stored on land in the form of glacier ice. This hypothesis, advocated by Shepard in a long series of papers beginning in 1932, was so completely accepted by Veatch and Smith (1939) that in areas of their charts of the Atlantic continental slope where soundings were lacking they drew subaerial-type valleys with numerous tributaries to depths exceeding 1200 fathoms as the most probable topographic form. The hypothesis, however, is opposed by estimates (Flint, 1947, pp. 429–437; Kuenen, 1950, pp. 535–540) of much too small an ice volume and by the probable drastic biological effects that would have been produced by the resulting increase of salinity of the remaining ocean. The recently discovered deep-sea channels extending from the canyons would require almost complete loss of the ocean if they too were formed by subaerial processes. In an attempt to circumvent these difficulties, suggestions for removal of water have been based on continental flexure (Bourcart, 1938), sudden change of rate of earth rotation (Hess and MacClintock, 1936), and sudden changes in position of the axis of earth rotation (Ma, 1952). Each of these proposals has its own set of difficulties plus the common ones of wide distribution and great depth of the canyons.

Forming the second series of hypotheses are those based on processes that can operate below sea level. Perhaps the first one advocated was that of fault valleys (Lawson, 1893a; de Andrade, 1937). Although many submarine canyons (La Jolla, and possibly

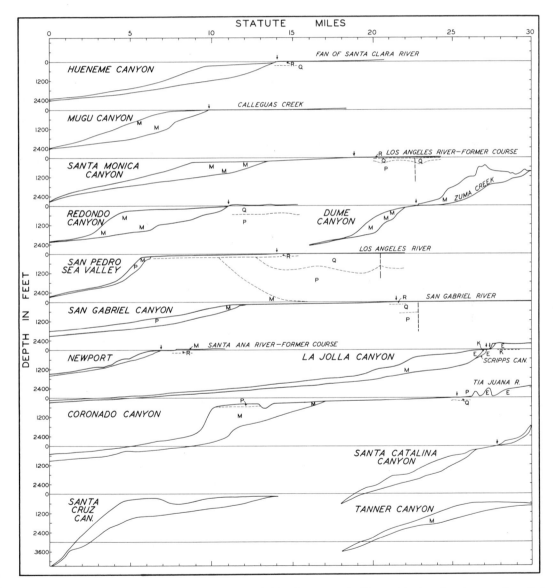

Figure 48. Profiles of submarine canyons of southern California compared with stratigraphy where known. Compiled from many sources. Symbols are as follows: arrow, shoreline; K, Cretaceous; E, Eocene; M, Miocene; P, Pliocene; Q, Quaternary; R, postglacial (on sea floor letters show sites of dateable rock samples).

San Pedro, Catalina, Santa Cruz, and Tanner, for example) follow the trend of faults known on land, they are not necessarily fault valleys any more than is the Grand Canyon of the Colorado whose course is partly controlled by preferred erosion along fault zones. Many other submarine canyons are transverse to general fault trends or are in areas of only slight faulting. Two other hypotheses, no longer requiring much discussion, are those of submarine spring sapping (Johnson, 1938–1939) and erosion by tsunamis (Bucher, 1940). The former is opposed by the continuous outward profiles, the rarity of canyons off limestone coasts, and the rarity of limestone and favorable structure in areas of abundant canyons, such as southern California. The latter, tsunami origin, is opposed by the abundance of canyons in nonseismic areas, in the lee of islands such as those off San Nicolas Island, and by details of their topography. Landslides, in the form of mudflows, have been proposed as an origin for the sea gullies of southern California (Buffington, 1951; Emery and Terry, 1956) and have been measured at the heads of La Jolla, Scripps, Newport, Redondo, and possibly Mugu Canyons as well as in others outside of southern California (Shepard, 1949, 1951a); however, it is difficult to conceive of them as the chief origin of entire submarine canyons owing to the continuous outward profile of the canyons and to their elongate plan, numerous tributaries, and varied kinds of wall rocks.

Davis (1934), recognizing the erosional character of the canyons, attempted to explain them through a seaward flow of bottom water created by the piling up of surface water against the coast by strong onshore winds. However, the water is so well stratified by density that return flow should occur at intermediate depths—at the top of the thermocline—just as it is known to do in fresh-water lakes (Mortimer, 1951).

Finally, there is the turbidity current hypothesis, proposed by Daly (1936) and extended by Kuenen in many papers beginning in 1937. According to this theory, during times of glacially lowered sea-level waves were able to attack accumulations of muddy sediment on the outer edge of the continental shelf, presumably forming a dense suspension which could flow along the bottom beneath clear surface water. In addition, sediment that accumulates from littoral drift at the heads of some canyons is known to slide periodically, and on sliding it may also be converted into a turbidity current. It is believed that such a heavy turbidity current may easily flow down a canyon and across the sea floor beyond its mouth. The presence of littoral sand was noted along the axis of Redondo Canyon by Ritter (1902) and in later studies of other workers. Extension of the turbidity currents beyond the mouths of canyons is believed by Ewing and associates (1953), Dietz (1953), Menard (1955), and others to have formed the deep-sea channels by eroding the channels and by building up the adjacent levees. Evidence for erosion of the canyons themselves by turbidity currents is not very convincing as yet, being based only on Kuenen's (1951) laboratory experiments and on the breaking of submarine cables by the currents (Heezen and Ewing, 1952).

In summary, it seems probable that at least the upper (less than 400-foot depth) part of the canyons was cut by subaerial erosion during times of glacially lowered sea level. The heads of many of the canyons, however, have been modified by deposition of postglacial sediments, accounting for the steep gradients at shallow depths discussed by Woodford (1951). The deeper portions of many canyons cannot be older than Miocene, the age of the wall rocks, yet it is not possible to make a clear-cut choice of a single agent of erosion. Perhaps several agents are responsible as long ago advocated by Smith (1902) and Ritter (1902) and recently reiterated by Shepard (1952) and Kuenen (1953a).

Basins and Troughs

Description

A basin in the usage of marine geology is a more or less equidimensional closed depression deeper than its surroundings. The lowest point on its rim is termed the sill; higher parts may be shallow banks or even islands. Curiously, each of four basins off southern California has two sills whose depths are within 200 feet of each other and another basin (West Cortes) has five sills within a vertical range of about 120 feet. No mechanism is known that can have caused these similarities, but it hardly seems possible that mere coincidence is involved. As shown by Table 5, the sills of the basins range in depth from 1560 to 6240 feet below sea level and the basin floors are 496 to 2892 feet deeper than the sills, or 2056 to 8436 feet below sea level.

Within the area of Chart I are twelve complete basins. A deep-area cut by the southern border was discovered to be the northern two-thirds of another basin (Fig. 49) by sounding and water sampling during 1952; because the work was done aboard *R/V Velero IV*, this basin was named Velero Basin (Emery, 1953). Two other relatively deep areas at the border of the chart south of San

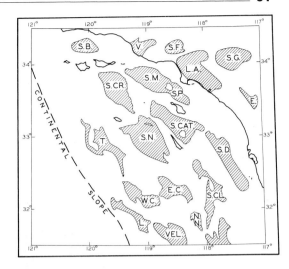

Figure 49. Outlines of present and former marine basins. Wherever possible the outline is at sill depth. Full names are given on Chart I.

Clemente Basin may be the northern ends of another basin, but this one has not yet been explored. In addition to these thirteen known basins, there is a fairly flat area un-

Table 5

BASIN STATISTICS

Basin	Number of Sills	Depth of Bottom, feet	Depth of Lowest Sill, feet	Difference between Sill Depth and Bottom Depth, feet	Area of Basin at Sill Depth, square miles	Area of Relatively Flat Basin Floor, square miles	Volume of Basin below Sill Depth, cubic miles
Ventura	1	0–400	0	0	0	270	0
San Fernando	1	500–1400	500	0	0	200	0
Los Angeles	1	0–500	0	0	0	980	0
San Gabriel	1	400–1500	400	0	0	600	0
Santa Barbara	1	2056	1560	496	255	420	11
Santa Monica	1	3078	2418	660	696	780	50
San Pedro	2	2994	2418	576	253	270	19
San Diego	1	3000–4500	4500	0	0	680	0
Santa Cruz	1	6450	3558	2892	687	280	210
Santa Catalina	2	4452	3222	1230	826	690	103
San Clemente	1	6912	5958	954	575	480	29
San Nicolas	1	6012	3630	2382	1027	370	231
East Cortes	1	6492	4644	1848	407	240	52
No Name	2	6282	5094	1188	118	30	10
Tanner	1	5088	3822	1266	487	200	44
West Cortes	5	5892	4470	1422	388	250	38
Velero	1	8436	6240	2196	506	220	101
Long	2	6360	5568	792	320	210	15

derlain by thick sediments and nearly surrounded by ridges and hills known as the
San Diego Trough. In all probability this is
a basin that has become filled to overflowing
with sediments. Several other filled basins
may be present (between Oceanside and
Santa Catalina Island, 20 miles west of Des-
canso Point, and 30 miles west of San Nicolas Island), but the evidence for them is less
definite. Four basins on land represent a
further stage of filling by sediment because
they have become filled to above sea level.

Altogether, there are eighteen known basins within the area of Chart I. These can
be grouped into parallel belts progressively
farther seaward as follows: (1) Ventura, San
Fernando, Los Angeles, San Gabriel; (2)
Santa Barbara, Santa Monica, San Pedro,
and San Diego; (3) Santa Cruz, Santa Catalina, San Clemente; (4) San Nicolas, East
Cortes, No Name; (5) Tanner, West Cortes,
Velero; and (6) Long. In general, the basins
along each belt become deeper to the southeast. This arrangement of basins is followed
by Table 5, in which the dimensions are from
physiographic, but not necessarily structural,
data. Areas of the basins at their sill depths
range from 118 to 1027 square miles. The
volumes range from 10 to 231 cubic miles
and total 913 cubic miles (3790 cu km), but
this is only about 5 per cent of the total volume of water atop the continental borderland.

Examination of Chart I shows that several
of the outer basins are compound, that is,
they enclose several areas much deeper than
their surroundings on the basin floors: San
Clemente, East Cortes, West Cortes, and
Long. The basins having the flattest floors
are among those closest to shore: Santa
Monica, San Pedro, San Diego, Santa Catalina (Fig. 50). Minor irregularities characterize the basins at intermediate distance:
Santa Cruz, San Nicolas, San Clemente, and
Tanner. The flattish submarine basin floors
beyond the foot of the basin slopes have a
total area of about 5120 square miles, about
60 per cent of the total area of deep flat portions of Chart I (Tables 1, 5) and about 78
per cent of the total area of the basins at
their sill depths. For the nearshore basins

the area of flat floor exceeds the area at sill
depth, whereas for offshore basins the area
of flat floor averages about half that at the
sill depths. Thus, the basins present a gradual shallowing (both absolute and with respect to their sills), a broadening, and a
smoothing of irregularities from far offshore
to nearshore (Fig. 51). The trend is continued by the basins on land, except for the
effects of stream erosion along their inner
margins. This trend of characteristics of
basin floors strongly indicates progressively
thicker fills of sediments in basins closer to
shore, a deduction which is also supported
by data on the rate of deposition of sediments and by limited seismic measurements.

Most of the basins have rectangular outlines, although some (Santa Cruz, San Nicolas) have one or more curving sides and
several (San Clemente, West Cortes, Tanner)
are irregular with sides consisting of several
segments, each more or less straight. Long
dimensions of all except Santa Barbara Basin
trend northwest-southeast, paralleling the
structural trend of the peninsular ranges in
southern California. The long axis of Santa
Barbara Basin is east-west, paralleling the
structural trend of the Transverse Ranges
which are represented on its north side by
the Santa Ynez Mountains and on its south
side by the San Miguel–Anacapa chain of
islands. Trends of the land basins show the
same division, and in fact there is some justification for considering the Ventura Basin as
a landward extension of the still submerged
Santa Barbara Basin (Rand, 1951). These
relationships show that the submarine basins
are closely related in present form and probable origin to the land basins, and that both
are controlled by regional structure.

Filling by Sediments

The chief source of detrital sediments is
the mainland from which sediments are
contributed by streams, waves, and wind.
Streams, carrying the bulk of contribution,
obtain most of their load from the areas of
steepest slope and highest rainfall. Thus in
southern California it might be expected that
most of the sediments reaching the ocean

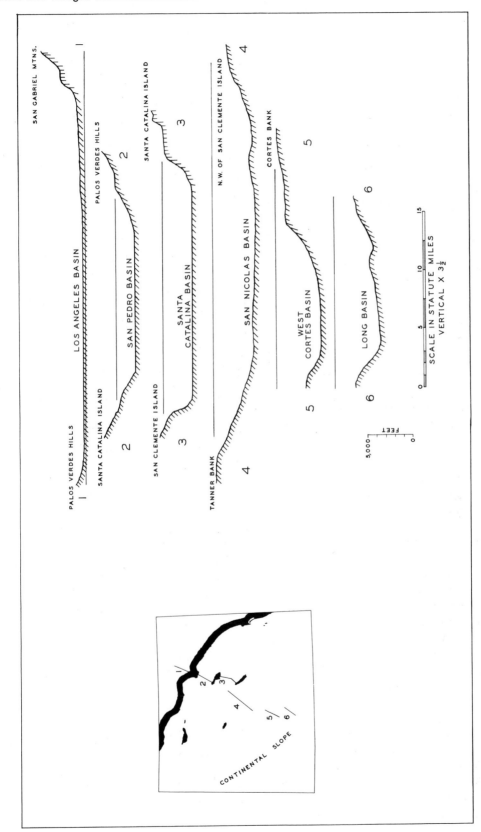

Figure 50. Cross sections showing the inverse relationship of shoaling, broadening, and flattening of basins with distance from the mainland shore.

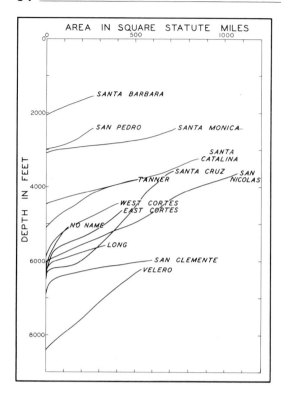

Figure 51. Hypsographic curves for basins. The slopes are gentler for the shallower (nearer shore) basins, and the deeper basins lack broad flat floors. From Emery (1954d, Fig. 2).

were derived ultimately from the high Transverse Ranges, the San Bernardino and San Gabriel Mountains, with lesser amounts from the smaller Santa Ynez, Santa Monica, and Santa Ana Mountains. Support for this belief is given by a cross section (Fig. 52), which shows that the sediment is much thicker in basins nearer the Transverse Ranges, whether on the seaward or the landward sides, than in basins farther away. So much sediment has been deposited on the seaward side that the Ventura, San Fernando, Los Angeles, and San Gabriel Basins on land and the San Diego Basin on the sea floor have been filled to overflowing. Filling of basins on the north side of the Transverse Ranges has formed the Mojave Desert, a region of numerous small and very shallow playa lake basins separated by low divides. The presence of deep closed basins farther seaward of the Transverse Ranges (such as Santa Cruz, San Nicolas, East Cortes, and

West Cortes Basins) and farther landward (such as Death Valley and other basins of the Basin and Range Province) means that these distant basins have received detrital sediments much more slowly than have closer basins, provided all basins were of about the same original size and date of origin.

A very rough estimate of the quantity of sediment that has been deposited in the basins can be obtained from the topography and from seismic measurements of the depth to basement. Evidence to be presented later indicates that the basin topography was initiated mostly during Late Miocene times, so the estimate of sediment volume will be confined to post-Miocene strata. Well records and seismic exploration show that the volume of post-Miocene sediment in the Los Angeles Basin is about 1200 cubic miles and that in Ventura Basin it is about 10,000 cubic miles. Basins and other deep fairly flat areas on the present sea floor total about 9000 square miles. If we assume that there is a fill of 7000 feet above basement (based on seismic surveys to be discussed later) and that 60 per cent of this fill is post-Miocene (the same as in Los Angeles Basin), the total volume is about 7000 cubic miles. Thus, about 18,000 cubic miles of sediment has been deposited south of the Transverse Ranges. This is nearly the same as the present volume of water in the area of Chart I, about 20,000 miles (30,000 square miles times 3500 feet, average depth). If we extend these figures throughout the entire area of the continental borderland (south to Cedros Island), the estimated total volume of sediment is about 30,000 cubic miles (125,000 cu km) and the volume of water about 50,000 cubic miles (208,000 cu km). In comparison, the present volume of the Transverse Ranges (San Bernardino, San Gabriel, Santa Monica, Santa Ynez Mountains) is only about 2400 cubic miles.

The manner of filling as well as the amount of filling can be inferred from the topography (Fig. 53). Three main modes of filling appear to be worthy of consideration. If sediment were deposited uniformly in all areas of the continental borderland, such as

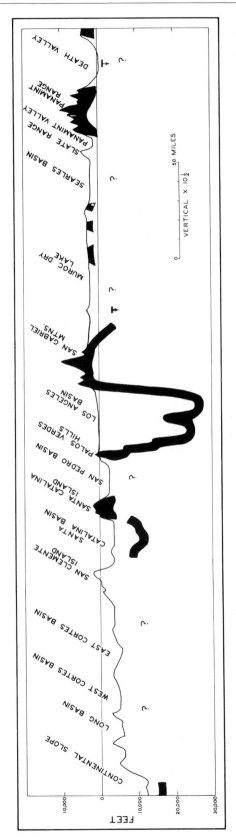

Figure 52. Profile of sea floor and land topography from the continental slope through Los Angeles Basin to Death Valley. The wide black line indicates the topography of the basement rocks, as compiled from various sources. From Emery (1954*d*, Fig. 3).

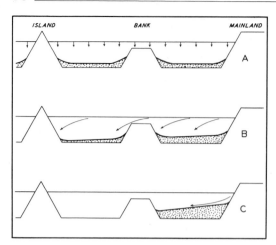

Figure 53. Cross sections of basins showing sediment fill consisting of: A, organic debris and chemical precipitates from near the water surface; B, detrital sediments diffused from mainland by volume suspension; C, detrital sediments contributed by turbidity currents from near mainland.

would be approximately true for organic debris and some chemical precipitates, we would expect the basin floors to become flat eventually, except for marginal slopes consisting of sediment that would have slid down the flanks of islands and banks. Secondly, clastic sediments may diffuse outward from the mainland shore, float outward with fresh water atop sea water, or be blown out to sea by wind. When deposited, these sediments should be progressively finer-grained and thinner with distance from shore. The cross sections of the basins would be similar to that produced by deposition of organic debris, except for a gradual slope away from shore. A third form of deposition is that of turbidity currents which may travel along the sea floor outward from the mainland, perhaps largely from the mouths of submarine canyons, depositing their sediment as extensions of the canyon mouth fans. Such sediments would form a steeper slope across the basin floors than would deposition from the surface or from suspension throughout the whole water column.

Examination of the contours of the basins shows that the floors of the outer basins have a more or less symmetrical cross section which fits either deposition of organic debris

or deposition from general suspension (the first two forms of deposition). This conclusion is supported by the known high content of planktonic tests and debris in these basins. The floors of some of the nearshore basins, however, are quite different. The flat bottoms of the Santa Monica and San Pedro Basins have a gentle seaward slope (0.3°) (not obvious from the 300-foot contours of Chart I). Sediment appears to form a southward slope into the San Diego Trough (0.4°) and westward into Santa Catalina Basin (0.4°) as though turbidity currents from the north (perhaps also partly from San Pedro Basin) divide, some flowing southward and some westward (Fig. 54). The bottom of the western end of Santa Catalina Basin is slightly steeper, as though only a small amount of sediment has been able to reach that far. The San Diego Trough also has a steep slope (2.0°) which extends southward out of the basin and into part of the bordering San Clemente Basin. It is therefore probable that sediment in these nearshore basins has an additional form of deposition to that in the offshore basins. If turbidity currents are in reality the chief source of sediments in the nearshore basins, the islands and banks form effective barriers preventing

Figure 54. Source of bulk of sediment in marine basins. Solid lines show axes of canyons, dashed lines show probable routes followed by turbidity currents, and S indicates that most of the fill is from suspension in the water column or from near the water surface.

the turbidity currents that start near the mainland from reaching the offshore basins. Turbidity currents from island and bank sources are probably too small to exert much effect on the topography of the offshore basins. The net result is that all three modes of deposition are important in nearshore basins, whereas only the first two are important in offshore basins and one of these is even less important than in nearshore basins. These relationships may easily account for the fact that the rate of deposition is faster in nearshore than in offshore basins.

Continental Slope

A length of about 200 miles of continental slope lies off southern California (Chart I) at a distance of 50 to 160 miles beyond the shoreline. The general trend is N25°W, about the same as its continuation farther north and south. Five gaps are present, none of which is related to known submarine canyons; therefore, they may be of tectonic origin. The northernmost, west of San Miguel Island, appears in fact to represent a slight landward offset of the continental slope.

Off southern California the average width of the continental slope is about 10 miles and the depth at its base is about 12,000 feet. Its profile shown by contours is nearly straight, but where more detailed soundings are available (Fig. 55) small irregularities are shown. At its base the continental slope locally descends into shallow depressions that have the appearance of remnants of a nearly filled deep-sea trench (Fig. 56). The straightness of profile and the absence of an apron at the base show that its physiographic age, according to Dietz' (1952) classification, is initial. To the south, off Cedros Island, Mexico, and farther south the depression is deeper and much longer (Heacock and Worzel, 1955; Fisher and Shor, 1956). Farther north, off San Francisco, the basal depression has been replaced by an apron, and the physiographic age is late youth. Thus the base of the continental slope off southern California is intermediate in character between that to the south and that to the north.

Trenches are much more highly developed along island arcs of the western Pacific Ocean, where the supply of sediment is extremely small. They may have been formed by downbuckling of the crust on compressional downfolding (Vening Meinesz, 1954; Hess, 1948) or by compressional faulting (Emery, 1950a). Recently, however, Worzel and Ewing (1954) have shown that the large negative gravity anomalies associated with a trench in the West Indies are due to great thickness of sediment, rather than to local thickening of the crust by downfolding or ramp faulting. This may also prove to be true off southern California when suitable measurements are made. Where the rate of deposition of sediments in the trenches is slow, as off island arcs, the trenches are very deep, but where sedimentation is rapid the trenches may become filled faster than they are formed. If the rate of trench formation is about equal off northern California, southern California, and Mexico, the presence of an apron at the base of the continental slope in northern California indicates that sediments are being deposited rapidly, whereas the presence of a trench at the base as off Mexico indicates that sediments are being deposited slowly. The presence of neither a thick apron nor a deep trench off southern California means that sediments are being deposited about as fast as the trench is being formed by folding or faulting. Fast sedimentation off northern California is promoted by the high coast and perennial streams, sedimentation off southern California is limited by trapping of most of the sediment in the offshore marine basins, and very slow sedimentation off Mexico is caused by the barrier provided by the peninsula of Baja California as pointed out by Menard (1955).

Hypotheses for the origin of the continental slope have included warped peneplain, steep normal step faults, gentle normal fault, delta-like foreset beds, and prograding of sediments over a subsiding continental margin (Shepard, 1948, p. 191; Kuenen, 1950, p. 160). The finding of bedrock at several points on and near the top of the continental

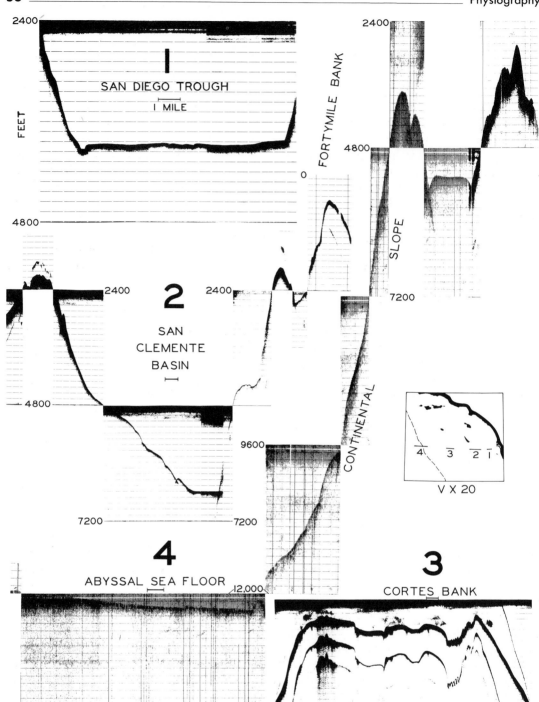

Figure 55. Topographic profiles made by compositing sections of a record drawn by the precision depth recorder (Luskin, Heezen, Ewing, and Landisman, 1954). The original, recorded on 19-inch newspaper facsimile tape, was photographed, cut into sections, and assembled as shown. The 19-inch tape width represents only 400 fathoms (2400 feet); thus, as the water deepens the scale changes from 0–2400 feet to 2400–4800 feet to 4800–7200 feet, etc. In 1, note deep sagpond at west side of San Diego Trough. In 2, the crossing of traces at east side of San Clemente Basin is result of side echoes from steep east slope. In 3, the scattered echoes above bottom of Cortes Bank represent schools of fish; two partial traces beneath bottom are double and triple echoes. Record from Chinook Expedition, Scripps Institution of Oceanography.

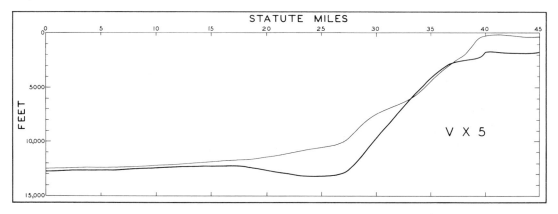

Figure 56. Profiles of continental slope: heavy line, off southern California (lat. 33°) showing shallow trench at base of slope; light line, off northern California (lat. 38°) showing apron at base of slope.

slope off southern California and the complex nature of the topography inshore of it indicates that this particular continental slope cannot be a depositional feature. Lawson (1950), mistakenly impressed by the apparent smoothness of the continental slope shown by generalized contours of that area, concluded that it is a warped peneplain; this belief may be supported by the rarity of seismic activity along the continental slope as compared to that of areas farther east of it. However, the en echelon offsets of trend off middle and northern California and the straightness and general uniformity of its profile (except for trench and apron at its base) are more suggestive of some type of faulting. In the absence of more than mere scraps of factual information, further speculation about its origin seems worthless.

Abyssal Sea Floor

Although it has been known for many years that the abyssal sea floor is not the featureless plain it once was supposed to be, the recent work of Menard (1955, 1956) has given system to the irregularities present in the northwestern Pacific. He has shown a close correlation of smoothness of the bottom with supply of clastic sediment from the mainland. Extensive smooth flat plains exist in the Gulf of Alaska (Fig. 57) where the blanket of sediment has buried the lower

flanks of many seamounts (Menard and Dietz, 1951). Off Vancouver Island, however, a trough has intercepted the flow of sediment carried presumably by turbidity currents, so that the sea floor west of the trough is irregular. An alternate but less likely explanation is that diastrophism there has been so recent that sediments have not had time to bury the irregular topography as they have farther north. Off northern California there is again a deep plain composed of sediment contributed from shore. This smoothness ceases at the Murray Fracture Zone off Point Conception. South of this zone the sediment from land is intercepted by the basins of the continental borderland and by the peninsula of Baja California so that the topography there is highly irregular.

Crossing parts of the abyssal plains of sediment are ten or more deep-sea channels which appear to be the routes followed by turbidity currents, most of which appear to have started at the mouths of submarine canyons. These channels are similar to those previously described on the floors of basins of the continental borderland.

Menard (1956) has shown the presence of four major fracture zones which extend 1400 to 3300 miles, mostly west of the shoreline (Fig. 58). One of these, the Murray Fracture Zone, appears to be a westward extension of the Transverse Ranges on land. It is separated from the Transverse Ranges by

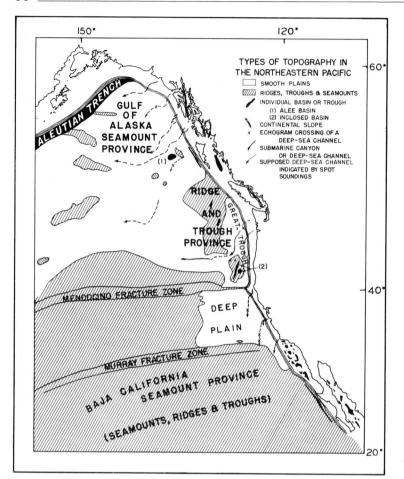

Figure 57. Regional variations in topography of the abyssal sea floor. From Menard (1955, Fig. 2).

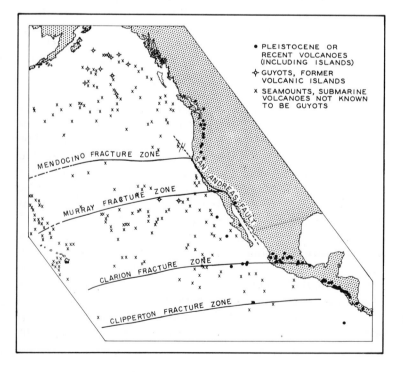

Figure 58. Fracture zones, seamounts, guyots, and known volcanoes of abyssal sea floor. From Menard (1956, Fig. 2).

the gap in the continental slope west of San Miguel Island, and it may have caused the gap. Sounding profiles across the Murray Fracture Zone show it to be irregular with several asymmetrical ridges, some of which rise as much as 6800 feet above their surroundings. The width of the zone is 30 to 60 miles, about the same as that of the Transverse Ranges.

Also present on the abyssal sea floor are numerous seamounts. One of these, San Juan Seamount, just at the border of Chart I, was surveyed in detail in 1938 (Shepard and Emery, 1941, p. 3). It has the appearance of a volcano, even to the possible presence of several craters at the top. A dredging also recovered a few chips of basalt.

Other smaller seamounts occur near the continental slope both to the south and north. Still other seamounts which are present farther seaward have been sounded and dredged (Carsola and Dietz, 1952), and basalt was recovered from two of them. Many rounded cobbles from the flattish top of one suggest that its top was planed off during a lower relative stand of the sea.

In summary, the topography of the abyssal sea floor is of diastrophic origin (volcanic, faulting, and folding) except where sediments have blanketed it. Erosion is considered virtually nonexistent. Thus, this topography is more closely allied in origin to that of the moon than to that of the continents (Dietz, 1958).

Lithology

One of the factors that control physiography in areas of marine erosion is lithology. In addition the mineral and fossil contents of the rocks provide information about the past development of the physiography—in other words, the paleogeography.

Rock Bottom

When lead-line soundings were used in past times as the only method of learning about sea floor topography, they showed the common presence of rocky bottom because rocks made scratches on the lead weight, and occasionally pebbles were found embedded in tallow that had been put into a small hole in the base of the lead. Even after sonic sounding methods were developed, periodic depth checks by lead line added to the store of information about bottom materials. Smooth sounding sheets of the U. S. Coast and Geodetic Survey for southern California, nearly all of which were made before 1937, show about 160 notations of rock bottom in areas deeper than 600 feet and several thousand more in shallower areas. Between 1936 and 1940 large samples of the sea floor were obtained by Shepard and Revelle of Scripps Institution of Oceanography, using dredges, covers, and snappers. These brought the total number of rock or gravel samples available for study to

131 for the whole region. On the basis of these samples, the earlier chart notations, the presence of kelp, and an interpretation of the topography, Revelle and Shepard (1939) compiled a map showing the general pattern of bottom materials in most of the region. Rock bottom was shown to exist on shelves, walls of submarine canyons, bank tops, and steep slopes. The actual positions of the samples and notations on which their chart was based are shown on another chart by Shepard (1941).

Since 1941 few additional data on the regional distribution of rock bottom have been secured; instead, most of the effort has been directed toward intense studies of small areas mostly as graduate theses at the University of Southern California and Scripps Institution of Oceanography. Among the most important of these are the shelf off San Nicolas Island (Norris, 1951), the shelf off San Diego (Emery, Butcher, Gould, and Shepard, 1952), Cortes and Tanner Banks (Holzman, 1952), the shelf of San Pedro Bay (Moore, 1954a), Santa Rosa-Cortes Ridge (Uchupi, 1954), the shelf of Santa Monica Bay (Terry, Keesling, and Uchupi, 1956), the shelf off Santa Catalina Island (McGlasson, 1957), the shelf off Santa Barbara Island (Grady, in preparation), the shelf off Anacapa Island (Scholl, 1959), the sides of San Pedro and Santa Monica Basins (Gorsline, 1958), and Lasuen Seamount

(Fowler, 1958). Through these detailed studies the number of rock samples available for identification has been considerably increased. About 450 samples contain rock other than phosphorite and are judged to be in place according to the following criteria:

1. Fresh fractures.
2. Large size of individual rocks.
3. Abundant rocks of similar lithology.
4. General angularity.
5. Fragile or poorly consolidated rock.
6. Catching of the dredge on rock firm enough to stop the ship's progress abruptly.
7. Strong pull on the cable as measured by an accumulator spring or other device.

In addition, about 250 other samples contain rocks that had probably been transported, as suggested by

1. Varied lithology.
2. General rounded character.
3. Small size of individual rocks.

Rock bottom has also been observed locally by divers (Shepard, 1949; Menard, et al., 1954), and more than 200 photographs of rock bottom (Fig. 59) have been made by remote-control cameras (Shepard and Emery, 1946; Emery, 1952*a*). Irregular topography shown by fathograms (Figs. 33 and 55) reveals the larger features of rocky bottom as peaks of uneven height and slopes too variable in direction and steepness to be depositional surfaces. In short, each of several methods of investigation covers a different portion of the size spectrum of bottom features, generalized approximately as follows: echo sounder, more than 100 feet; camera and diving, 100 to 1 foot; and dredging, 1 foot and less. Still other indicators of rock bottom are the presence of kelp and nearness to rocky shores.

When plotted in map form (Fig. 60), rock bottom based on samples alone is present in a variety of environments but nowhere is the sample density very great. Use of the

Figure 59. Top of Osborn Bank (lat. 33°22.0′, long. 119°′02.9′, 190 feet). Irregular masses of rock, covered by hydroids and encrusting organisms, project through a blanket of coarse foraminiferal glauconitic sand having abundant ripple marks. Bottom edge is about 10 feet wide. November 19, 1951. (AHF 2086.)

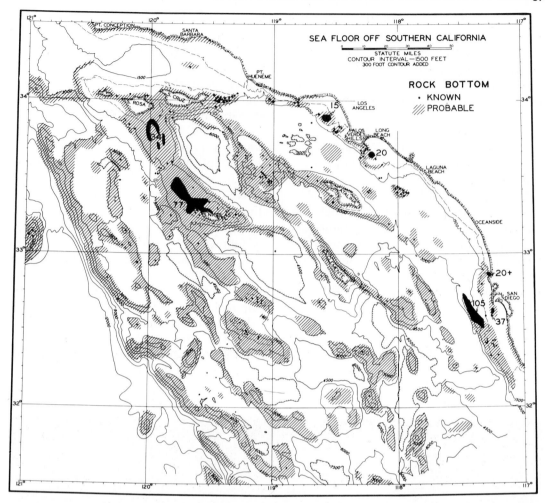

Figure 60. Distribution of rock bottom. Samples containing rock judged to be in place are shown by dots or by large black spots where many rock samples are available. Areas believed to be underlain by rock, patchily covered by sediments, are indicated by cross-hatching.

supplementary indicators of rock bottom, however, adds to the completeness of the map, showing that in an area of about 750 square miles (about 3 per cent of the region) heavy dredges and corers are more likely than not to encounter rock, whereas in the rest of the region the same equipment is more likely than not to encounter only unconsolidated sediment. In general, rock bottom is likely to be found in the following kinds of areas:

1. Adajacent to rocky shores.
2. On irregular hills which rise above the level of the mainland or island shelves or above the level of large flat bank tops.

3. At the outer edge of the mainland or island shelves or of large bank tops.
4. On the walls of submarine canyons.
5. Atop small sharp banks.
6. Atop even small deep hills which rise above the floors of basins or of the abyssal sea.
7. On the upper parts of steep basin slopes or of the continental slope.

Kinds of Rocks

Rocks judged to be in place include all three major groups: sedimentary, igneous, and metamorphic. Sedimentary rocks (Fig.

61) occur at about 90 per cent of the stations having any kind of rock in place, with igneous rocks at 7 per cent of the stations and metamorphic rocks at 3 per cent. These percentages probably serve as an indication of the nature of rock bottom in the areas of densest sampling more than they do for the region as a whole. If the three groups of rocks were considered on the basis of number of individual specimens, including transported pebbles, the percentage of igneous rocks would be approximately doubled, owing to the greater resistance to abrasion offered by igneous as compared with most sedimentary rocks.

The sedimentary rocks consist of many types, one of the most abundant of which is phosphorite. Because of its special interest and problems phosphorite will be considered in a separate section. Shale and mudstone together are even more abundant than phosphorite (Emery and Shepard, 1945). They are followed in order by limestone, sandstone, conglomerate, and chert. These sedimentary rocks are widespread throughout the entire continental borderland just as they are on the adjoining mainland. Geological ages of most of the sedimentary rocks in place have been determined on the basis of Foraminifera (mostly in mudstones and shales) or on lithological similarity to strata of known age on nearby shores. By far, the

Figure 61. (*a*) Large quantity of Chico (Cretaceous) shale broken from walls of La Jolla Canyon (FPS 23, lat. 32°51.4′, long. 117°16.3′, 210 feet). The large piece is 45 cm long. In contrast, note the small recovery from two nearby samples in right foreground. The group of kelp holdfasts, picked up on the adjacent beach, are of similar shale.

(*b*) Sample from San Clemente Rift Valley (FPS 45, lat. 32°47.1′, long. 118°15.7′, 3600 feet). The pieces on the right are Mohian (Miocene) mudstone; because of their size (45 cm), number, and fragileness it is believed to be the local bedrock. Middle-sized pieces of limestone and phosphorite are believed to have undergone little transportation, whereas small and partly rounded volcanic rocks are from more distant outcrops. From Emery and Shepard (1945, Pl. 2, 3).

bulk of the rocks are of Miocene age, but Jurassic, Cretaceous, Eocene, Oligocene, Pliocene, and Pleistocene are also locally present. One of the most interesting of the sedimentary rocks from the point of view of origin is the San Onofre breccia, originally described by Woodford (1925). Characteristically, it consists of small-to-large, angular-to-subround pieces of glaucophane schist and quartzite in a clayey to sandy matrix. It crops out at San Onofre (northwest of Oceanside), Palos Verdes Hills, Point Dume, Anacapa Island, and Santa Cruz Island, and it is recognized in well cuttings in other areas. In addition, occasional loose pieces of quartzite and schist occur atop San Nicolas and Santa Barbara Islands, on which there are no outcrops of the breccia or of the metamorphic source rock; possibly these scattered fragments are remnants of a former thick bed now removed by erosion. On the sea floor San Onofre breccia has been found in place in Santa Monica Bay (Terry, Keesling, and Uchupi, 1956, pp. 102, 160), on Lasuen Seamount (Fowler, 1958), and off Anacapa Island (Scholl, 1959).

Igneous rocks are represented by both extrusive and intrusive types. Andesite and basalt are about equally abundant, with andesite probably somewhat concentrated in the landward half of the borderland and basalt in the seaward half. These extrusive or fine-grained intrusive rocks are considered to be in place for only about 35 samples at Point Dume, the shelves or slopes of Santa Barbara, San Clemente, Anacapa, and Santa Cruz Islands, Cortes and Tanner Banks, San Juan Seamount, and on several small hills in the San Diego Trough. Transported specimens are much more common, probably occurring in about half of all the rock samples (Emery and Shepard, 1945; Holzman, 1952). This wide distribution is a result of both resistance to abrasion and the probable presence of many lava flows and thin sills interbedded in Miocene sedimentary strata of the sea floor, as along much of the mainland and on most of the islands (Smith, 1898; Woodring, Bramlette, and Kew, 1946; Shelton, 1954). In fact, one island, Santa Barbara, is probably the north

slope of a Miocene volcano, as indicated by lava bombs, thick coarse agglomerate, and steep dips near its southern end and on the small adjacent Sutil Island. Only San Nicolas Island has but minor amounts of igneous rock; there it is in the form of small diabase dikes (Norris, 1951). Coarse-grained intrusive rocks, such as granite and granodiorite, were found only as rounded and transported pieces. Nearly all these specimens came from samples of the mainland shelf between Hueneme and Newport, from which they had probably been carried by streams from outcrops in the Santa Monica and San Gabriel Mountains (Bailey and Jahns, 1954). They are also present as rare single pebbles associated with other rocks in a few scattered samples farther from shore; these are almost certainly examples of rafting, probably by kelp.

Metamorphic rocks, schists, gneisses, and quartzites mostly containing glaucophane were sampled in place on Sixtymile, Fortymile, and Thirtymile Banks. Transported pieces are abundant on these banks and also around Santa Catalina Island, in Coronado Canyon, in La Jolla Canyon, and at the center of Santa Monica Bay (Emery and Shepard, 1945). At Santa Catalina Island and possibly Sixtymile Bank these transported pieces have been derived from outcrops of metamorphic rocks on the island or sea floor, but in the other areas they probably represent the Miocene San Onofre breccia or reworked fragments of it. The lithology of these metamorphic rocks strongly suggests that they are part of the great Jurassic-Cretaceous Franciscan complex which in southern California is known as the Catalina facies (Woodford, 1924; Bailey, 1941; Woodford, Schoellhamer, Vedder, and Yerkes, 1954; Irwin, 1957). Schist in place on a bank about 20 miles north of Sixtymile Bank is similar to the possibly pre-Cambrian Pelona schist of the San Gabriel Mountains. Cobbles of the Triassic-Jurassic Black Mountain metaigneous series found in many dredgings near La Jolla and San Diego are doubtlessly reworked from the nearby Eocene conglomerates. A few pieces of transported slate, probably Triassic (?) Santa Monica slate, were found in Santa Monica Bay (Terry, Keesling, and Uchupi, 1956).

Geological Map

The most useful method of presenting lithological information is in the form of a geological map. Preliminary versions published in 1951 and 1954 have been brought up to date in the accompanying map (Fig. 62) which is based not only on the sea floor samples but on data from the mainland and islands. Sources for the latter are as follows: Los Coronados (Emery, Butcher, Gould, and

Shepard, 1952), San Clemente (Smith, 1898), Santa Catalina (Smith, 1897; Woodford, 1924), Santa Barbara (Kemnitzer, 1933; Grady, in preparation), San Nicolas (Kemnitzer, 1933; Norris, 1951), Anacapa (Yates, 1890; Scholl, 1959), Santa Cruz (Bremner, 1932; Rand, 1933), Santa Rosa (Kew, 1927; Bremner, 1933), San Miguel (Bremner, 1933), and general northern islands (Redwine, 1952).

Basement rock in the region is mostly schist of Mesozoic or even pre-Cambrian age. Granitic basement rocks are known only on Santa Cruz Island. Thus, the distribution of these basement rock types

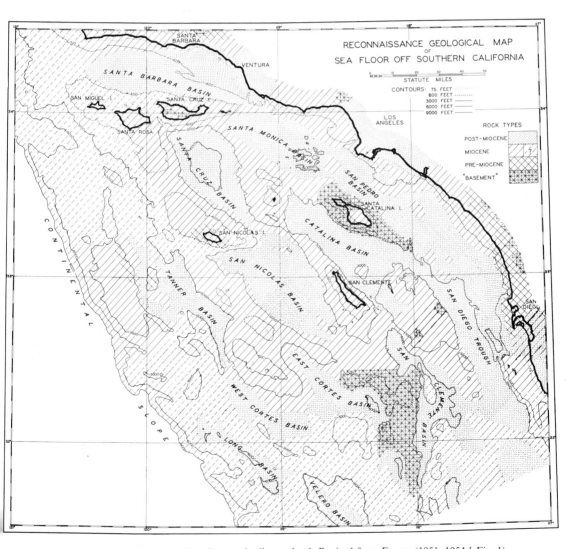

Figure 62. Geological map of sea floor and adjacent land. Revised from Emery (1951, 1954d, Fig. 1).

closely corresponds to that of Reed's (1933, p. 28) metamorphic Southern Franciscan and granitic Anacapia Provinces. For simplicity, however, both types of basement are shown on the geological map as "basement," with no distinction made between them.

Pre-Miocene rocks consist of Jurassic (?) green chert and chloritic altered sandstone on several deep banks west of Tanner Basin. Because no schist was found associated, this area should probably be considered one of sedimentary rocks—possibly the oldest of the entire continental borderland. Fossiliferous Cretaceous (Chico) shale and sandstone are present nearshore at La Jolla and Point Loma. Eocene shale, sandstone, and conglomerate also occur nearshore at La Jolla. Shale, sandstone, and limestone of Eocene age surround San Nicolas Island, which consists exclusively of rocks of that age.

Miocene rocks bulk largest by far of all the Tertiary strata, occurring on nearly all topographic highs of the region. They consist of Early, Middle, and Late Miocene shale, chert, and limestone. The enclosed fauna is dominantly Luisian and Mohnian. Volcanic rocks on the sea floor are also probably mostly of Middle Miocene age, just as they are on the islands and adjacent mainland. Because of the insufficient sample density throughout most of the borderland, no distinction is made on the geological map for different parts of the Miocene series.

Pliocene strata are represented chiefly by mudstones, some of which are so soft as to be confused with some Recent muds. On foraminiferal evidence Pliocene mudstones have been recognized in two samples on the northeast slope of San Clemente Island, in one from near the sill of San Nicolas Basin, in one from the west slope of the Santa Rosa–Cortes Ridge, and in five samples from the northeast slope of the San Pedro and Santa Monica Basins (Emery and Shepard, 1945; Moore, 1954a) and in two from Lasuen Seamount (Fowler, 1958). Eleven samples from Coronado Bank off San Diego contain Foraminifera which range from Late Pliocene to Recent. On the basis of the fauna and of lithologic and physiographic evidence,

Emery, Butcher, Gould, and Shepard (1952) considered that the bank is overlain by strata of Late Pliocene to Late Pleistocene age. Large areas of Repetto (Pliocene) shale also occur on the shelf of San Pedro Bay and along the coast between Ventura and Santa Barbara, mostly adjoining coastal outcrops. In addition, Foraminifera of Pliocene age occur in phosphorite which cements together older nodules atop several banks (Dietz, Emery, and Shepard, 1942). Unconsolidated iron-stained sands found at numerous localities on the mainland shelf are believed to be of Late Pleistocene age—they will be discussed in a later section on sediments. Finally, basins and their lower slopes are floored by thick muddy sediments which probably range in age from Pliocene at depth to Present at the surface (as in the now-filled Los Angeles Basin).

Phosphorite

Description and Composition

One of the most important kinds of rock present on the sea floor off southern California is authigenic phosphorite. Its composition and distribution provide useful information on the paleogeographic development of the region. About 330 samples containing phosphorite have been obtained from the continental borderland (Fig. 63). These samples are from bank tops, ridges, deep hills, some basin slopes, and parts of the mainland shelf that are shallower than their surroundings. All these areas are characterized by a very slow rate of deposition of modern detrital sediments. More than 95 per cent of the samples are from depths between 100 and 1000 feet. Most shallower areas border the mainland shore where either detrital sediment is deposited so rapidly as to dilute or bury all authigenic materials or where vigorous wave action is actively eroding bedrock. In many areas deeper than about 1000 feet a mantle of fine sediment also dilutes or buries authigenic materials; however, the tops of deep hills are free of such sediment, and phosphorite may be found on them, although few have

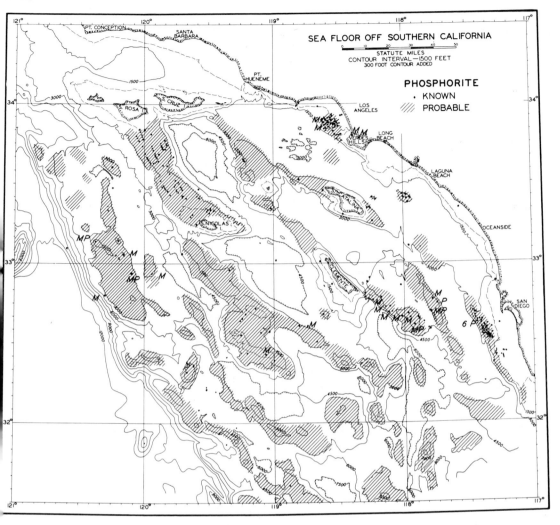

Figure 63. Distribution of phosphorite nodules. Samples are shown by dots; areas probably containing nodules are cross-hatched. The letter *M* denotes samples containing Foraminifera of Miocene age; *P* is Pliocene to Recent age.

been sampled. The rare small pieces of phosphorite that have been obtained within basin or slope muds deeper than about 3000 feet have almost certainly been transported from shallow areas by slides or turbidity currents.

The total area that is known or believed to be covered by phosphorite is about 6000 square miles. If the average thickness of phosphorite is 1 inch, the region contains approximately 1 billion tons of rock, about one-tenth of the other phosphate rock reserves of the United States according to Mansfield's (1940) estimate.

Characteristically, the phosphorite consists

of nodules and slabs commonly having flat bottoms and nodular tops (Fig. 64). The largest piece recovered to date is 2 feet long and weighs 150 pounds, but doubtlessly larger dredges could obtain larger pieces. Small grains or oölites occur in nearly every sample of coarse sediment seaward of the mainland shelf that has been examined, strongly suggesting their proximity to the larger nodules. In addition, phosphorite commonly forms a thin coating on other kinds or rock. The nodules and grains are hard and dense with a smooth glazed brown surface which in deep water is usually covered by a film of manganese oxide (Dietz,

(a)

(b)

Figure 64. Photographs of phosphorite. (*a*) Nodules (irregular masses, such as in upper center) and detrital cobbles mostly of andesite (such as smooth one in center) imbedded in foraminiferal glauconitic sand. Fortymile Bank (lat. 32°40′, long, 117°58′, 588 feet). Photograph by Dietz, Kierstad, and Shumway, April 15, 1952. Bottom edge is about 4 feet long. (*b*) Phosphorite in two dredgings from ridge west of Tanner Basin. Only five small pieces of nonphosphatic rock, shown in foreground, were included. At station FPS 159, on the left (lat. 33°04′, long. 120°10′, 1620 feet), a large number of small nodules were recovered. The large nodule on the right (2 feet in diameter) is from station FPS 162 (lat. 33°08′, long. 120°22′, 780 feet). Note the irregular bumpy surfaces of phosphorite. From Emery and Shepard (1945, Pl. 3).

1955). In shallow water the top, exposed surface is lightly to heavily encrusted with organisms such as bryozoans, worm tubes, sponges, and corals, showing that the nodules are rarely if ever rolled about the bottom.

Internally, the nodules exhibit a wide range of purity (Fig. 65). Some small ones are homogeneous and very fine-grained. Most of the large ones, however, contain some to much nonphosphatic material which ranges from cobbles to grains finer than sand and is of the same composition as the nearby bedrock or sediment mantle. Frequently, older and darker nodules are cemented together as a nodular conglomerate. Especially significant is the presence of glauconitic foraminiferal sand both within and surrounding the nodules. Very commonly small pockets of this sand lie atop internal discontinuities marked by thin layers of darker-than-ordinary phosphorite or by films of manganese oxide like those that form the outer surface of the nodules.

The bulk of the phosphorite has the optical, X-ray, and chemical properties of collophanite, a nearly isotropic microcrystalline mineral. In minor amounts is another min-

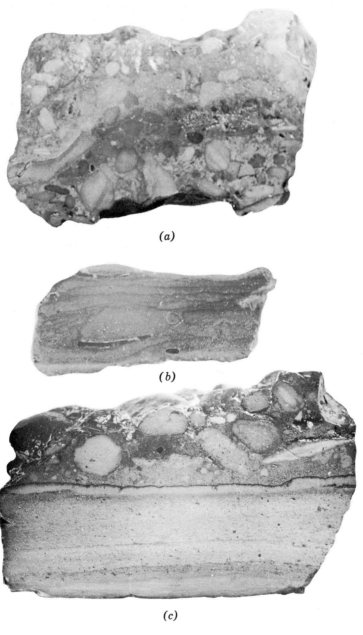

(a)

(b)

(c)

Figure 65. Polished sections of phosphorite slabs. Photographs by M. F. Karim ($\times$ 0.8). (a) Conglomeratic phosphorite dredged from Santa Monica Bay by Charles Gunnerson (lat. 33°53′, long. 118°31′, 190 feet). Near the middle is the fibrous cross section of a mammal bone. (b) Layered phosphorite from ridge north of Santa Barbara Island (AHF 3015, lat. 33°39′, long. 119°4′, 1903 feet). Note irregularity of laminations which show that growth was intermittent and characterized by a surface as irregular as that of the present top of the nodule. In contrast, the bottom is typically flat. (c) Conglomeratic phosphorite from Lomita Quarry on north flank of Palos Verdes Hills. Note the presence of a flat slab at the bottom which may have served as a nucleus for deposition of the later phosphorite.

eral that forms small disseminated grains, layers in oölites, and replacements of originally calcareous foraminiferal tests and mollusk shells. This mineral is anistropic and probably is francolite or dahlite, close relatives of collophanite. Chemical analyses show that the phosphorite from the sea floor has very nearly the same composition as reported for large deposits of phosphorite on land in the United States and elsewhere (Table 6). It has the following approximate empirical formula, neglecting sulfate, which is probably also present:

$$10Ca_3(PO_4)_2 \cdot 5CaCO_3 \cdot 4CaF_2 \cdot CaO \cdot nH_2O$$

On the assumption that phosphorite has this composition, the purity of samples ranges up to about 85 per cent.

Origin

The presence of phosphorite in a widespread surface blanket, its unique internal layering, its nodular shape, the large size, its usual purity, and the fact that the impurities that do exist are identical with the enclosing sediment strongly indicate a primary or syngenetic origin *in situ*. The microcrystalline character of the collophanite is regarded as evidence that the material accumulated as colloids rather than by the molecular attraction by which crystals grow in saturated solutions. The originally calcareous tests and shells within the nodules are the only materials that clearly have been secondarily or epigenetically phosphatized. Such phospha-

tization to francolite or dahlite is probably to be expected, owing to the large volume of collophanite that enclosed calcareous organic remains.

Catastrophic killing of many animals was suggested by Murray and Renard (1891, p. 133) and others as the origin of phosphorite. Such seems not to be true for these deposits, because the internal layering and the common inclusion of older phosphorite in nodular conglomerates indicate many periods of accumulation. Blackwelder (1916), Mansfield (1927, p. 210), and Rankama and Sahama (1950, p. 591) suggested that phosphorites accumulate in stagnant water where regeneration of phosphate from falling organic debris cannot occur. However, most of these deposits occur only in the most oxidizing environment of the entire continental borderland, the tops of banks; and in any event none of the water off the coast is stagnant. Others have tried to relate phosphorite deposition to times of cool climate or to times of volcanism with indifferent success.

An examination by Dietz, Emery, and Shepard (1942) of the solubility of tricalcium phosphate in sea water suggested that it may well be oversaturated. If so, then it is reasonable to expect that a colloidal phase may be present (Emery and Dietz, 1950) and available for deposition. Only the most sketchy chemical data were available for the computations and the situation is little better now, exeept that Rittenberg, Emery, and Orr (1955) have shown that the southern

Table 6
CHEMICAL ANALYSES OF PHOSPHORITE[1]

| | California Sea Floor Samples | | | | | | | | | |
	69	106	127	158	162	183	Idaho	Florida	Tennessee	Bone
CaO	47.35	45.43	45.52	46.58	37.19	47.41	48.0	36.4	45.4	51.0
P_2O_5	29.56	29.19	28.96	29.09	22.43	29.66	32.3	31.3	31.0	38.5
CO_2	3.91	4.01	4.30	4.54	4.63	4.87	3.1	2.2	2.2	1.5
SO_3	–	–	–	–	–	–	2.3	0.1	1.3	0.0
F	3.31	3.12	3.07	3.15	2.47	3.36	0.5	2.0	3.8	–
R_2O_3	0.43	0.30	2.03	0.70	3.93	1.40	1.2	12.7	4.6	0.1
Organic	0.10	1.90	2.25	0.44	0.35	1.50	–	6.2	3.8	8.3
Total	84.66	83.95	86.13	84.50	71.00	88.20	87.4	90.9	92.1	99.4

[1] Dietz, Emery, and Shepard (1942); Emery and Dietz (1950).

California waters contain three times as much phosphate ion as was originally assumed, and thus the degree of saturation is greater than computed. The great difference between phosphorite and simple tricalcium phosphate vitiates further refinement of the original calculations. Although not proved, it seems likely that phosphorite may owe its origin to direct precipitation as colloids from sea water in areas of strong upwelling, that is, areas where cool deep water containing much phosphate ion and other nutrients rises to the surface and undergoes an increase of pH and temperature and a decrease of pressure. This would explain much more satisfactorily than other hypotheses the presence of phosphorite in the oxidizing environments of southern California and off other coasts, at least some of which are also areas of upwelling.

Age

Fossils within the nodules include bones and teeth of fishes and bones of sea mammals. The most abundant and useful fossils, however, are the tests of Foraminifera. These appear to belong to two distinct age groups. Foraminifera in most of the dark-brown nodules, some of which are cemented together by later phosphorite, contain only Foraminifera that are characteristic of Middle to early Late Miocene (Relizian, Luisian, and Mohnian). Most are Luisian and Mohnian, the same as the age of most determinable mudstone, shale, and limestone of the continental borderland. No Early Miocene (Saucesian) or late Late Miocene (Delmontian) Foraminifera have been recognized in the phosphorite. The second age group of Foraminifera is represented by those found mostly in light-brown nodules and in the matrix of phosphorite conglomerates. These Foraminifera are Late Pliocene to Recent forms, whose age is supported on Coronado Bank by the presence of the phosphorite atop sedimentary strata of Late or post-Late Pliocene age. Where determinable, these Foraminifera are benthonic and characteristic of the same general depth of water as that in which their enclosing nodules were dredged.

When the problem of the phosphorite off southern California was first studied (Dietz, Emery, and Shepard, 1942), the Miocene age of it was recognized to be strongly opposed by the wide distribution on the sea floor of large nodules, in contrast to their scarcity on the adjacent land and by the obvious *in situ* position of many of the nodules atop banks that must have been eroded in post-Miocene times. The post-Late Pliocene age was opposed by the frequency of pure Miocene faunas in the nodules, although it was favored by the Late Pliocene to Recent and mixed faunas in other nodules. As a result, the pro and con evidence for both ages was presented, but no very strong stand on either age could be taken.

The age question was reviewed in 1950 by Emery and Dietz in the light of some new evidence. This new evidence was the presence of large nodules similar to those of the sea floor on an unconformity between the Valmonte diatomite and the Malaga mudstone in Malaga Cove of the Palos Verdes Hills, as described by Woodring, Bramlette, and Kew (1946). This phosphorite is only slightly younger (Mohnian-Delmontian) than the sea floor material, and it shows conclusively that large nodules did form during the Miocene Epoch. The conclusion was reached that most of the sea floor phosphorite was deposited during Miocene time but that the nodules during their subsequent exposure on the sea floor served as nuclei for renewed Quaternary deposition of phosphorite.

Later, a study of Coronado Bank by Emery, Butcher, Gould, and Shepard (1952) showed an abundance of phosphorite atop strata that is no older than Late Pliocene. This phosphorite is quite obviously of Late or post-Late Pliocene age. It is now evident that the original uncertainty about whether the phosphorite is Miocene or post-Late Pliocene age must be resolved in favor of both ages. It is believed that much of the phosphorite, especially the dark-brown nodules containing only Miocene Foraminifera, was deposited during the Middle or early Late Miocene Epoch. Perhaps a slowing of the rate of deposition of detrital sediments allowed the accumulation of large nodules at that time in place of the thin laminar beds of phosphorite that occur within many Middle Miocene shales. Deposition probably ceased or was negligible during latest Miocene and early Pliocene time, and then it was renewed in latest Pliocene time and continued through part of the Pleistocene. The scarcity of phosphorite on the walls of submarine canyons and at the topmost peak of Fortymile Bank suggests that deposition again ceased in Late Pleistocene to Recent time.

Paleogeography

When stratigraphic information for a region is fairly complete, one of the best methods of summing and testing it is the construction of paleogeographic maps, provided we keep in mind the large number of uncertainties inherent in such maps. Because of the rarity of shoreline deposits, the ancient shorelines can almost never be traced with exactness; locally, however, nearness to an ancient shoreline may be shown by the presence of thick and very coarse marine detrital sediments, especially if supplemented by the inclusion of remains of shallow-water animals. For any given time unit the general distribution of marine and continental deposits may be the chief criteria used for paleogeography. Because continental deposits are usually thin or not preserved at all, to a large extent paleogeographic maps depend on the negative evidence of absence of marine strata. The first paleogeographic map of California was drawn by Clark (1921), largely on the basis of presence or absence of strata. It is obvious that the absence may also result from deep erosion at some time after marine deposits have been formed. In addition, it cannot be assumed that all marine areas are characterized by deposition, for some, such as the tops of banks, receive very minor quantities of detrital sediment.

In some circumstances the presence of a former land area may be assumed to account for the presence of detrital sediments having a lithology or texture such that no other known land area could have been the source; such is the chief basis for Woodford's (1925) Catalinia. Among the remaining uncertainties of paleogeographic maps resulting from incomplete information are the questions of changes in land and sea areas within the particular time interval of the map and the known distortion of land and sea areas during postdepositional times of folding and faulting (Reed, 1933, p. 296).

Following Clark's and Woodford's lead, Loel and Corey (1932) constructed a paleogeographic map of Vaqueros time, and then Reed (1933) made maps for many intervals between Cretaceous and Pliocene times. Of necessity these maps were based entirely on data from outcrops on the mainland and islands. When stratigraphic data from samples of the sea floor were presented by Dietz, Emery, and Shepard (1942) and Emery and Shepard (1945), some modification of the maps was needed. In succeeding years additional changes have been required by new lithologic, paleontologic, and structural data from land and sea floor areas. Many of those new data have been incorporated by Corey (1954) in maps that also considered facies distribution of sediments for seven units of the Tertiary Period. These maps were supplemented by Clements (1955) for the Early and Late Pleistocene Epochs on the basis of topography alone. Still more data have become available from the sea floor since these maps were published, requiring additional changes. The present maps (Fig. 66) are shown as highly generalized and are subject to further corrections, especially when more consideration is given to faunal facies. Their main value is perhaps in showing that the sea floor off southern California has undergone great changes during the distant as well as the recent past.

Eocene and Oligocene seas appear to have been restricted by the presence of broad and probably low land areas. Beginning in Early Miocene time the seas advanced until by Middle and Late Miocene they extended far inland of the present shoreline. Extensive block faulting began in the Oligocene, probably reached a maximum rate in Late Miocene, and continued into the Pliocene Epoch.

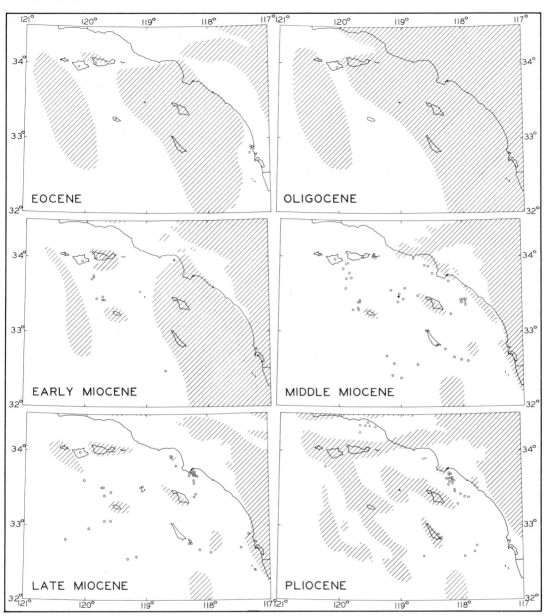

Figure 66. Paleogeography for Eocene, Oligocene (Refugian and Zemorrian), Early Miocene (Saucesian), Middle Miocene (Relizian and Luisian), Late Miocene (Mohnian and Delmontian), and Pliocene. Cross-hatching indicates probable land areas for each time unit. Circles show sample positions for underwater area and for islands. Modified from Corey (1954).

The upthrust blocks formed high island areas, erosion of which supplied sediment to surrounding seas, and banks, atop which only phosphorite, glauconite, and organic sands were deposited. During Pliocene time the blocks restricted the sea to long narrow bays that occupied the downthrown areas.

It is believed that during the Pleistocene Epoch the topography of the offshore area was essentially as at present, but that some of the blocks moved individually and that sea level fluctuated a few hundred feet. These movements connected some islands with the mainland, permitting migration of elephants to the northern islands (Stock, 1935), and separated others so that certain marine invertebrates, land animals, reptiles, insects, and plants began to develop endemic varieties (Grinnell, Dixon, and Linsdale, 1937; Cockerell, 1938, 1940; Dunkle, 1950).

Unless diastrophic activity greatly increases in the future, it seems probable that the future geography will be characterized by a general retreat of the shoreline as one after another of the basins becomes filled by sediment from shore. Because the volume of water in the continental borderland far exceeds the volume of rock above sea level in the tributary drainage area, it seems evident that the rate of filling of the basins will decrease unless large additional drainage areas are captured. Thus, the rate of seaward movement of the shoreline should also decrease in the future.

Structure

The geological structure of a region can often be inferred from its physiography, particularly when the latter is largely of tectonic origin. Information about deep structure must come from indirect geophysical measurements. Although such measurements are incomplete off southern California, those that do exist permit the drawing of some conclusions about the composition and origin of the region.

Faults Inferred from Topography

The location of faults on the sea floor presents somewhat different problems from those of locating faults on land. Detailed lithologic and stratigraphic evidence is so much harder to obtain on the sea floor than on land that it has been used only in a few nearshore areas where intensive surveys of the bottom have been made mostly by oil companies. Visibility in the ocean is so poor that fault contacts, slickensides, offsets of bedding planes, and other minor details can rarely be recognized except in shallow water. Topography, however, is a better tool for locating faults on the sea floor than on land. Recognition of fault scarps on land is often made difficult by the masking effect of erosion by streams. Locally, of course, erosion on land aids recognition by the selective removal of rocks that have been mechanically weakened by faulting or chemically altered by weathering where faulting has opened avenues for passage of ground water. On the sea floor weathering is practically nonexistent, and erosion is far less important than on land. Consequently, the topography of the sea floor is chiefly of structural origin; exceptions occur in shallow water where wave erosion has truncated the structures or locally in deeper water where submarine canyons have been cut perhaps by turbidity currents. Deposition, a greater factor than on land, eventually buries the fault scarps, but sediments are first deposited only around the lower parts of the topography, leaving the higher parts virtually unaffected.

The difference in rate of erosion of fault scarps on the land and the sea floor makes difficult any estimation of their comparative ages from physiography alone. For example, many Pleistocene fault scarps on land have been so eroded as to be practically unrecognizable, whereas some scarps on the sea floor that are believed to be of Late Miocene age appear sharp and clear from sounding data.

As discussed in the section on topography, the criteria for fault origin of the sea floor scarps is straightness, offsets, height, steepness, step-like profiles, and linear depressions at the base. Using some of these criteria, Lawson (1893b) was one of the first to point out the presence of fault topography off southern California, citing as one example the scarp bordering San Clemente Island (Fig. 67). Some additional details for Santa Catalina Basin were given by Taber (1927), and in 1941 Shepard and Emery mapped some of the more definite sea floor faults. A better-defined relationship to known faults on land was given by Corey (1954). A new map (Fig. 68) extending farther south than Corey's map contains more detail and additional faults drawn on the assumption that the topography is basically of structural origin. Interpretations by other geologists would be different in detail but probably closely similar in general. Even casual examination of the contours of Chart I shows a remarkable linear series of elongate features for which an origin other than by faulting or folding is difficult to conceive. For example, when we draw a possible fault along the west side of Santa Rosa–Cortes Ridge, it can easily be continued southward from scarp to scarp along noses, "sagponds," and saddles. Another example is the northeast side of San Clemente Island, and another is the east side of the San Diego Trough.

Seven long primary faults are believed to be present. It seems quite possible that these are the result of large strike-slip movements. A movement of 25 miles was suggested by Shepard and Emery (1941, pp. 24–25) to explain the topographic relationships of San Clemente Island to Fortymile Bank and of Santa Catalina Island to Thirtymile Bank. Alternately, the topographic relationships might have been caused by rotation of a block on a horizontal axis extending northeasterly from the southeastern end of San Clemente Island. However, large strike-slip movements are known in the region. According to W. H. Corey (personal communication), there are four lines of evidence for at least 10 miles of left lateral movement on the Santa Rosa Island fault. Even larger horizontal movements have been suggested for land faults of the region by Hill and Dibblee (1953). Data from earthquakes are also strongly suggestive of strike-slip movements, as discussed in the next section.

Between each of the seven primary faults are blocks containing other scarps which are usually shorter and less straight than those along the primary faults. Many of these scarps lie at an angle of 20 to 40° from the trend of the primary faults. Good examples exist in the block that contains Cortes and Tanner Banks and in the block bordering the continental slope. In the former, San Nicolas Island is known to be an anticline from subaerial geology and also from the finding of progressively younger rocks on either side

Figure 67. Long straight steep fault scarp along northeast side of San Clemente Island viewed from near the southeast end of the island. Photograph from elevation of 2000 feet by Navy Fleet Air Wing Fourteen.

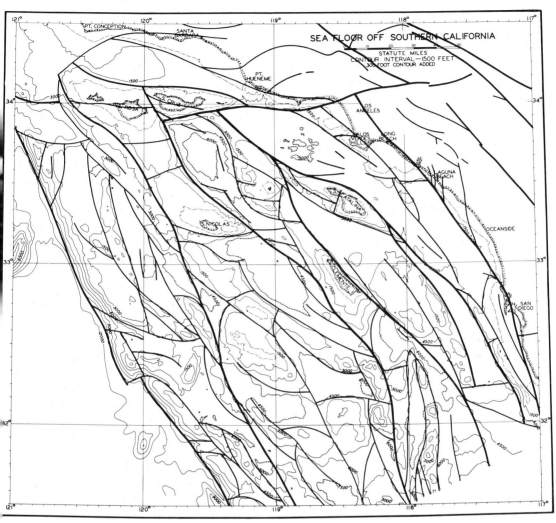

Figure 68. Fault map based chiefly on sea floor topography. Locally, positioning was aided by data on stratigraphy of the sea floor and by extension of known faults on land. Wide lines indicate long primary faults; narrow lines show shorter secondary faults, some of which may prove on future study to be the limbs of folds. Note that many of the secondary faults or folds have a more westerly trend than the primary faults.

on the sea floor (Norris, 1951; Menard et al., 1954). In the latter block several troughs and ridges are indicative of synclines and anticlines; however, they are shown on the structural map as faults because of the impossibility of distinguishing between faults and steep limbs of folds on the basis of topography alone.

The alternating hills and depressions along the primary faults may be a result of secondary dip-slip faulting or of folding with trends at an acute angle to the primary faults. Either feature may possibly be the result of large drag movements along the primary faults if the latter are strike-slip faults. As pointed out by Reed and Hollister (1936, p. 127) and by Moody and Hill (1956), many large strike-slip faults on land are bordered by drag features of similar appearance. The axes of these secondary features trend more westerly than the primary faults, indicating a right lateral, or clockwise, movement along the strike-slip primary faults. In addition to these large primary and secondary faults, there must be a network of small ones similar to those revealed on land by detailed mapping in the Santa Monica Mountains (Durrell, 1954) and elsewhere. At the present stage of information little further speculation about the kind, direction, and amount of movement based on topography alone seems warranted. As age and facies distribution data accumulate and their areas of distribution become better known, more offsets will probably become apparent.

Seismicity

Earthquakes were first noted in southern California by the Portola expedition which experienced four violent ones on July 28, 1769, near the Santa Ana River and many more the following week in the Los Angeles area (Bancroft, 1884, p. 146; Bolton, 1927). Earthquakes felt during the following 160 years are listed by Wood, Allen, and Heck (1934) and by Townley and Allen (1939). Recent destructive shocks in the area of Chart I occurred on June 29, 1925, at Santa Barbara and on March 10, 1933, at Long Beach. Because of the great seismic activity of the region a network of seismograph stations was begun in 1926 by the Carnegie Institution of Washington and California Institute of Technology. At present six stations in southern California are located between Santa Barbara and La Jolla, but three of these are concentrated east of Los Angeles.

Using data from the seismograph stations, Wood (1947) showed a good correlation of earthquake epicenters with known major faults in California, and in a similar study Clements and Emery (1947) tried to correlate offshore epicenters with inferred geological structures. During the 10 years since 1947 additional earthquake data have accumulated. Between January 1, 1934, and January 1, 1958, there occurred within the area of Chart I a total of 404 earthquakes of magnitude 3 or greater on the Richter scale (Gutenberg and Richter, 1942), having epicenters of A or B quality (geographical position known to within 5 km—3.1 statute miles). The elimination of low-magnitude

shocks, detectable chiefly only when the epicenter is near a seismograph, is intended to help show the true geographical density of epicenters through the whole continental borderland (Fig. 69). The restriction to A and B quality insures enough accuracy of position to reveal possible relationships to known topographic features. Shocks occurring within a month and at the same locality as an earlier one were arbitrarily considered aftershocks and were not counted or plotted. Because of these restrictions the epicenters chosen are considered highly reliable.

Most epicenters are concentrated in the land region near Los Angeles, doubtlessly more because of greater seismic activity in this region than simply because of nearness to seismographs. Correlation of epicenters with known faults is not obvious, perhaps because of the great number and close spacing of large faults; in addition, the average focal depth of 18 km (Gutenberg and Richter, 1949, pp. 33, 89) can result in a wide geographic separation of an epicenter and the surface trace of the fault on which movement took place. In the offshore area epicenters are too sparse to permit detailed identification with geological structures; nevertheless, it is notable that the greatest concentration occurs near San Clemente Island whose northeast scarp is one of the steepest and straightest of the continental borderland. In addition, most epicenters lie within basins, suggesting that the planes of the bounding faults dip basinward. Contrary to the situation along most parts of the continental slope of North and South America (Gutenberg and Richter, 1949, pp. 31, 35, 41), no epicenters of A or B quality and of magnitude greater than 3 have been found along the continental slope off southern California since 1934. However, on November 4, 1927, one of intensity X occurred on the continental slope at latitude 34°32′, longitude 121°24′, just beyond the boundary of Chart I off Point Conception. The scarcity of registered epicenters along the continental slope may reflect to a certain extent the great distance from seismographs, but it also appears to indicate a truly lower degree of seismic activity there than near Los Angeles.

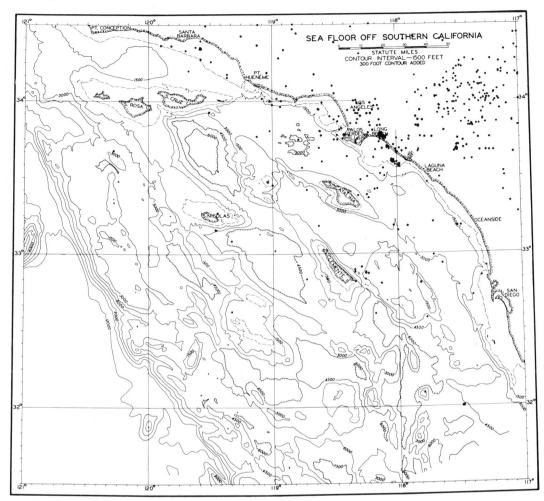

Figure 69. Positions of epicenters of earthquakes that occurred between January 1, 1934, and January 1, 1958. Only epicenters of magnitude 3 or greater and of *A* and *B* quality (position accurate to within 5 km) are shown.

Only five shocks of magnitude 5 and two of magnitude 6 occurred in the area of Chart I. Compared to these shocks all the others are of lower magnitude represent only a minor quantity of energy (Gutenberg and Richter, 1942; Wood, 1947). The energy in the earthquakes during the 22 years is roughly equal to that in about seven atomic bombs of the 1946 Bikini variety, these being rated as equivalent to earthquakes of magnitude 5.5 (Gutenberg and Richter, 1946).

Movement on a strike-slip fault is followed by earthquake waves having a first impulse that theoretically is one of compression in two quadrants and of dilatation in the other two quadrants. Thus, Gutenberg (1941*b*)

believed that an examination of the nature of the first impulse of seismograms should indicate the direction of movement on strike-slip faults of the region. His study showed that in the area south of the Transverse Ranges, west of the San Andreas Fault, and east of longitude 119° the records of almost all earthquakes indicated right lateral movements along the faults, according well with the general direction of movement known from geological data.

Surface earthquake waves also provide information about the crust. In southern California Press (1956) has shown that the phase velocity of Rayleigh waves indicates that the crust above the Mohorovicic discontinuity is about 15 km thick under the continental borderland and that it thickens to about 35 km under the Transverse Ranges and to about 50 km under the Sierra Nevada. These estimates accord reasonably well with data provided by the average depth of earthquake foci and of gravity interpretations.

Geomagnetism

For several decades the U. S. Coast and Geodetic Survey's *Coast Pilot* has reported a magnetic compass variation of 3° near San Clemente Island and another one near Sixtymile Bank. In order to investigate these irregularities and to learn something about the general magnetic trends in the region, an aeromagnetic survey was made in 1949 as a cooperative project of the U. S. Geological Survey (Bromery, Emery, and Balsley, in press). A pattern having a total flight distance of 1300 miles was flown, mostly at an elevation of 1500 feet.

After removal of the regional magnetic intensity, the measurements have a range of between plus 1365 and minus 130 gammas. The anomalies are only slightly related to topography, and they reveal only a few of the local sharp discontinuities that might be interpreted as faults (Figs. 70, 71). High magnetic anomalies were found over Santa Cruz Island, Santa Monica Mountains, and San Gabriel Mountains where outcrops of granodiorite were crossed (see also Schoellhamer and Woodford, 1951). Outcrops of volcanic and metamorphic rocks failed to produce high anomalies except near the basaltic seamounts of the deep sea floor. These anomalies are perhaps similar to ones found (Alldredge and Keller, 1949) around seamounts of the North Pacific Ocean, where the topographic projections were believed to be polarized by the magnetic field of the earth. Sedimentary rocks of the topographically high areas and unconsolidated sediments of the basins produced no definite magnetic effects, so the broad anomalies encountered in these areas are presumed to re-

flect variations in the composition of the deeply underlying basement rocks.

The greatest magnetic high anomaly is adjacent to the most conspicuous magnetic low near San Clemente Island. The area may, therfore, be one in which a considerable volume of relatively highly magnetic basement rock has been faulted much nearer to the surface than in the adjacent basin and, in fact, than in most of the continental borderland. Because the magnetic intensity here is greater than over the outcrops of granodiorite, the basement below San Clemente Island may be more magnetic than the granodiorite to be found elsewhere. Possibly the high anomaly results from a large covered diorite or gabbro intrusive. Such an interpretation would fit the known pattern of distribution of basement rock types better than would the presence of granodiorite. The belts of high and low magnetic anomaly near San Clemente Island are elongate in a northwesterly direction and are paralleled by four less intense belts of high and low anomaly located farther seaward. The northwesterly extension of these belts parallels the structural trend of the region, but the significance is admittedly unknown at present.

Gravity

Published information on gravity measurements for southern California was so sparse that up to 1955 the intensity was sufficient to be considered only as preliminary reconnaissance (Woollard, 1955). About 30 pendulum stations were established in the region by the U. S. Coast and Geodetic Survey (Duerksen, 1949), and some additional measurements were made by Woollard (1949) as portions of transcontinental or transoceanic profiles. Subsequently, a very thorough study of gravity in the region was made by Brisbin (1957) who occupied about 300 stations on land plus 17 others on islands. A very detailed study of the western part of the Los Angeles Basin was also made by McCulloh (1957) on the basis of 840 stations. Other local gravity meter studies have been

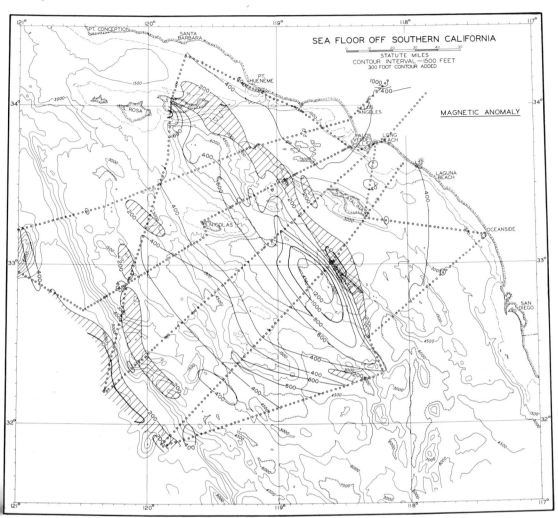

Figure 70. Preliminary aeromagnetic map made in cooperation with U. S. Geological Survey in 1949. Contour interval is 200 gammas. Circles show positions of profiles flown at 1500 feet above sea level. These preliminary values of magnetic anomaly are only slightly different from final ones of Bromery, Emery, and Balsley (in press).

made by oil companies, but results have not been released. For the offshore region there are in addition to Brisbin's data for islands 22 pendulum measurements made aboard submarines by Harrison, Brown, and Spiess (1957). Data for several other stations whose positions were reported by Worzel, Shurbet, and Ewing (1955) have not yet become available.

Bouguer anomalies for the region show slightly positive to slightly negative values near the coast, decreasing inland to values more negative than 100 milligals. This

relationship continues up the entire West coast of the United States (Daly, 1940, p. 162) and indicates that the crust is progressively thicker (Airy theory), progressively less dense (Pratt theory), or both (Heiskanen theory) inland from the coast. An analysis of Bouguer anomalies in northern and middle California by Tsuboi (1956) indicated that the crust (above the Mohorovičić discontinuity) increases in thickness from about 24 km at the shore to about 50 km at a distance inland of 350 km. Seaward from the shore in southern California Bouguer anom-

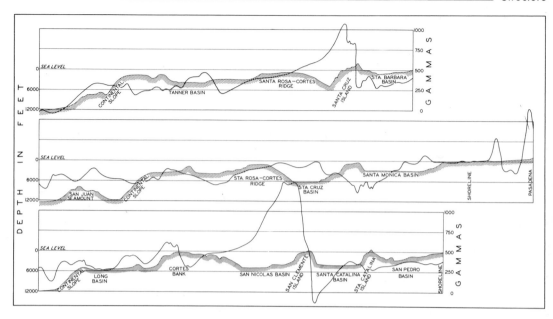

Figure 71. Profiles of magnetic anomaly from Figure 70. Note general absence of relationship to topography.

alies become progressively more positive until near the edge of the continental slope the values are about +100 and rise sharply farther seaward to about 250 milligals. (Fig. 72). These Bouguer computations are based on the assumed replacement of sea water by material of density sufficient to rule out topographic effects—for the continental borderland 2.67 (Brisbin, 1957).

Data computed by Duerksen (1949) allow the construction of an isostatic anomaly map based on the Hayford (Pratt) theory of lower density of crystalline rocks for areas of higher elevation than of rocks for lower areas. Results using depths of compensation of 56.9, 96.0, and 113.7 km, as well as the Airy or Heiskanen theories of mass distribution (Daly, 1940, p. 189), show that the region of southern California is negative, averaging −20 to −30 milligals. This, too, is characteristic of the entire Pacific coast and is difficult to interpret in terms of isostatic theory.

Prominent minor features of the general pattern are the strong negative Bouguer anomalies in the area of thick sediments of the Los Angeles Basin (McCulloh, 1957). They are the result of the low density of the thick basin sediments, as Ewing and Worzel

(1954) have shown for the Puerto Rico Trench. Measurements above the submerged basins of the continental borderland also show lower Bouguer anomalies than the nearby islands as a result of a low density of sediment fill (Brisbin, 1957). Larger deficiencies in gravity were found for Santa Catalina Basin and San Diego Trough than for San Nicolas Basin, indicating greater thickness of sediments in nearshore than offshore basins.

Near the continental slope off the Atlantic coast of the United States (Worzel and Shurbet, 1955) a sharp +10- to +70-milligal peak in Free Air anomaly may be caused by sediments deposited on the slope with incomplete isostatic downbowing. No such sharp peak exists at the continental slope of southern California because the basins of the continental borderland trap most of the sediment before it can reach the continental slope and produce an apron of sediment.

Seismic Surveys

Information about the earth's crust obtained by artificial earthquakes supplements that derived from natural ones. Detonation of many tons of explosive at Corona, about 72 km east of Long Beach, in 1949 and again in 1951 provided opportunities to measure the velocities of earth waves at various distances and thus at various depths below the surface. By these measurements Gutenberg (1952) found that the bottom of the crust (Mohorovičić discontinuity) lay at a depth of about 40 km. Velocities of the longitudinal waves were 8.2 km/sec below the crust and 6.5 km/sec at a depth of 5 km, corresponding closely to velocities obtained from earthquakes. For comparison, a similar large explosion at Beecher's Bay of Santa Rosa Island in 1950 showed that the Mohorovičić discontinuity in this part of the continental borderland is as shallow as 20 km and that velocities above and below it are similar to those at Corona (Tatel and Tuve, 1955).

Most seismic surveying utilizes much smaller detonations than those discussed above and for marine work are of two types, reflection shooting and refraction shooting. Reflection work is the simpler and consists of finding the lapsed time between shot, reflection from the bottom and layers within the bottom, and reception at the hydrophone (Figs. 73, 74). Seismic surveying by oil and service companies to locate and characterize structures in shallow water is almost exclusively reflection work. An array of hydrophones strung out from a receiving ship receives sound impulses that travel different paths from the shot point to the reflection surfaces and thence to the hydrophones. Many hundreds of reflection records have also been made in the basins by Raitt (1952) because the work can be done quickly and by a single ship. However, for proper interpretation the measurements require data on sound velocities in the different layers of the bottom. These data are supplied only in part by acoustic studies of bottom samples (Shumway, 1956); mostly, therefore, the work must be coordinated with refraction shooting.

Refraction work in the ocean requires two ships, one to be the receiver and the other to drop explosives at intervals as it moves toward and then past and away from the receiving ship. For areas as small as the basins the maximum possible distance between the ships is so short that sound waves cannot be received from great depth. However, using this method Raitt (1949) and Shor and Raitt (1956, 1958) reported that from the few points obtainable the Mohorovičić discontinuity rises from about

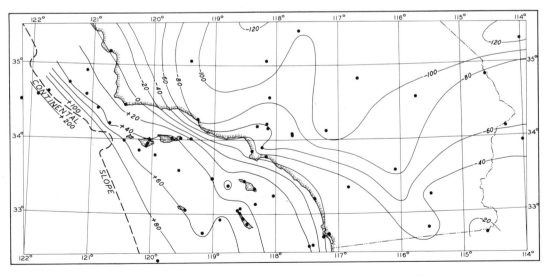

Figure 72. Generalized Bouguer gravity anomaly map of southern California region (milligals). Data for mainland are from Duerksen's (1949) pendulum stations, those for islands are from Brisbin's (1957) stations, and those for the sea floor are from submarines (Harrison, Brown, and Spiess, 1957).

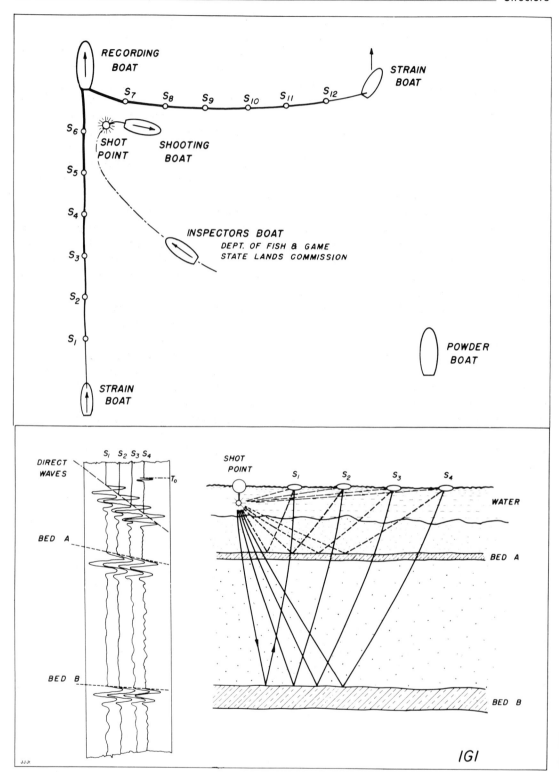

Figure 73. Top, typical geophone cable layout in an "L" spread designed to obtain data for computation of true dip and strike components. Bottom, ray paths followed by sound from shot point to reflecting horizons to geophones. Courtesy International Geophysics, Inc.

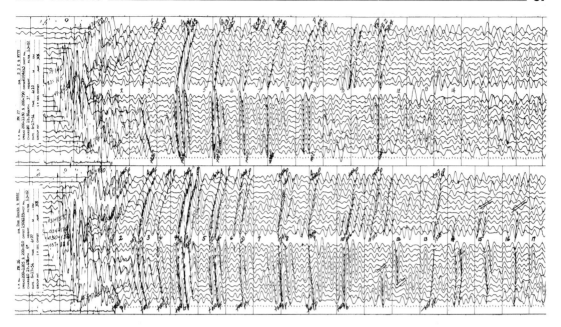

Figure 74. Character of record obtained on shelf of southern California by "L" spread of geophones. Note that beds on one side of the shot point appear to be horizontal, whereas on the other side they dip and diverge from each other. Courtesy International Geophysics, Inc.

32 km below sea level near the shore at San Diego to 18 km at the top of the continental slope to 13 km on the abyssal sea floor. This seaward decrease in depth corresponds well with gravity data. Below the discontinuity the rocks have a seismic velocity of about 8.3 km/sec and above it about 6.7 km/sec. Above the latter zone is a less widespread zone, having a velocity of 5.9 to 6.3 km/sec, that may consist of intrusive igneous or metamorphic rocks that probably form the basement series of the region. Its top is at a fairly uniform depth of about 7 km throughout the borderland and beneath the abyssal sea floor beyond. Within the basins is a zone having a seismic velocity of 4.3 to 5.1 km/sec that rises under the islands and presumably consists of sedimentary and volcanic rocks (Shor and Raitt, 1956, 1958). Lastly, the basins contain a variable thickness of material having a seismic velocity of between 1.8 and 2.8 km/sec and believed to be unconsolidated sediments. Maximum thicknesses of unconsolidated sediments were estimated as 11,000 (?) feet for the Santa Cruz Basin (Fig. 75), 9000 feet for San Nicolas Basin, and

7000 to 9000 feet for both Santa Catalina Basin and San Diego Trough. Estimated depths to basement for the same basins are 11,000 (?), 23,000 (?), 10,000 to 31,000, and 10,000 to 13,000 feet, respectively. About 4500 feet of sediment was found on the sea floor near the base of the continental slope, in contrast to typical thicknesses of 1500 feet on the abyssal sea floor farther west. Unfortunately, at present the seismic refraction tool is too coarse to yield results as precise as desired for making geological studies of the basins.

Minor Structures

Superimposed atop the major structural units of the continental borderland are many secondary structures that are minor in size, although some are important as oil traps. Truncation of some structures by wave erosion in very shallow water has resulted in a slight topographic relief of harder layers which then serve as places for attachment of kelp, so that linear patterns of kelp often reflect the underlying structure (Fig. 76).

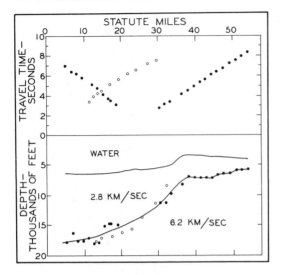

Figure 75. Seismic refraction profile from near the middle of Santa Cruz Basin (left) extending southeasterly through the basin sill. Material of 4.3 to 5.1 km/sec seismic velocity was not detected but may be present, separating the 2.8 km/sec unconsolidated sediments from the 6.2 km/sec basement rock. Redrawn from Shor and Raitt (1956).

Construction of geological maps of the continental shelf from bottom sampling operations served to locate a linear anticline or fault (Fig. 77) extending southeasterly through San Pedro Bay (Moore, 1954a), an anticline possibly penetrated by schist basement in Santa Monica Bay (Fig. 78) (Terry, Keesling, and Uchupi, 1956, Figs. 32, 37), an anticline extending southward from Point Loma at San Diego, and another probably underlying Coronado Bank also off San Diego (Emery, Butcher, Gould, and Shepard, 1952). Structural contours developed by drilling of oil fields on shore clearly show an extension of anticlines beyond the shoreline at Huntington Beach, Wilmington, Playa del Rey, Rincon, Montecito, Summerland, Elwood, and Capitan (see structural contour maps in *California Division of Mines Bulletin 118,* pp. 281–424). Many of these extensions have subsequently been verified and supplemented by marine seismic surveys of the continental shelf (Johnson and Galeski, 1949; Jakosky and Jakosky, 1956). Still other minor structures on the shelf have been detected and mapped

through use of a powerful echo sounder (Fig. 79) capable of obtaining reflections of sound from strata as deep as 200 feet below the surface of the shelf (Moore, 1957).

In the Los Angeles Basin four northwest-southeast structural trends are present (Troxel, 1954; Poland, Piper, and others, 1945). One of these in particular, the Newport-Inglewood structure, has distinct topographic expression as a series of en echelon domal hills. Because the structural relief of these domes increases with depth, folding must have begun early and continued throughout the whole period of filling of the basin with sediments, so that the domes had the form of low hills during all or most of the history of the basin. Since the present sea floor basins are similar in many respects to early stages of the Los Angeles Basin, we might also expect to find structural domes or anticlines in these basins, revealed by hills or ridges rising above the general basin floors. One of the shallowest of these possible secondary structures is the long nose that extends westerly into the Santa Barbara Basin (Fig. 80); (see also 600-foot contour of Chart I). This may be an extension of the Oak Ridge fault (Bailey and Jahns, 1954). The broad ridge that rises above the northern end of the San Diego Trough about 15 miles southwest of Dana Point may be similar. A much deeper one may be indicated by the long ridge that extends diagonally up the northeast side of San Nicolas Basin, another by the ridge on the northeast side of Tanner Basin, and lastly a very deep one by the ridge at the north end of Velero Basin. All the basins of the continental borderland contain less pronounced irregularities which might prove to be topographically similar to the Newport-Inglewood structure if they were to be very carefully surveyed.

General Structural History

Data presented in the sections on physiography, lithology, and structure provide a vague outline of the structural history of the region. Vaguest of all is the pre-Cretaceous history. Knowledge of the origin of the basement complex of metasediments and metaigneous rocks is little more complete than when Reed and Hollister (1936, p. 7) and Taliaferro (1943) wrote of it as probably made up of deposits in a Mesozoic geosyncline. The Franciscan series and its probable Catalina equivalent have such a great thickness and a distribution in a belt with a length of about 1200 miles (Cedros Island, Mexico, to Oregon) and a width of less than 100 miles as to be suggestive of eugeosynclinal or perhaps paraliageosynclinal geometry. Accumulation of thick sediments in deep trenches marginal to continents or continental-type areas is common around the Pacific Ocean. With intense compression and downfolding during Middle Cretaceous time these materials were converted into the metasediment and metaigneous series known

Figure 76. Folds in shallow water shown by kelp living atop beveled edges of alternating hard and soft Miocene strata at Rincon Point. Photograph by Fairchild Aerial Surveys, Inc.

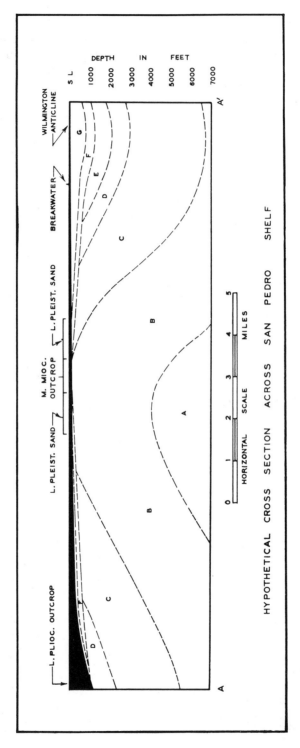

Figure 77. Geological cross section of San Pedro Bay (south 10° west from mouth of Los Angeles River), based chiefly on rock samples of bottom. G, Upper Pleistocene to Recent; F, Lower Pleistocene; E, Upper Pliocene; D, Lower Pliocene; C, Upper Miocene; B, Middle Miocene; A, Jurassic (?) basement. From Moore (1954a, Fig. 4).

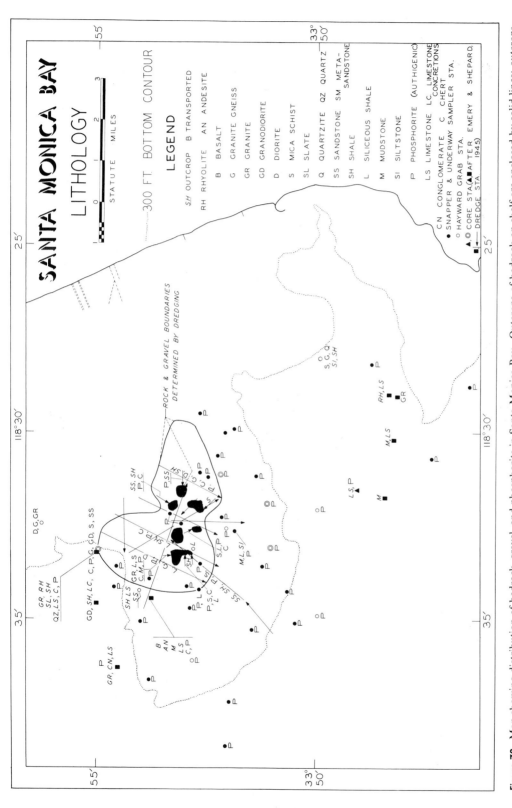

Figure 78. Map showing distribution of bedrock, gravel, and phosphorite in Santa Monica Bay. Outcrops of bedrock on shelf are enclosed by solid lines; outcrops in deeper water are shown only as positions of individual samples. The sedimentary bedrock is of Late Miocene age and the schist from outcrops is from Jurassic (?) basement or a Miocene breccia. From Terry, Keesling, and Uchupi (1956, Fig. 32).

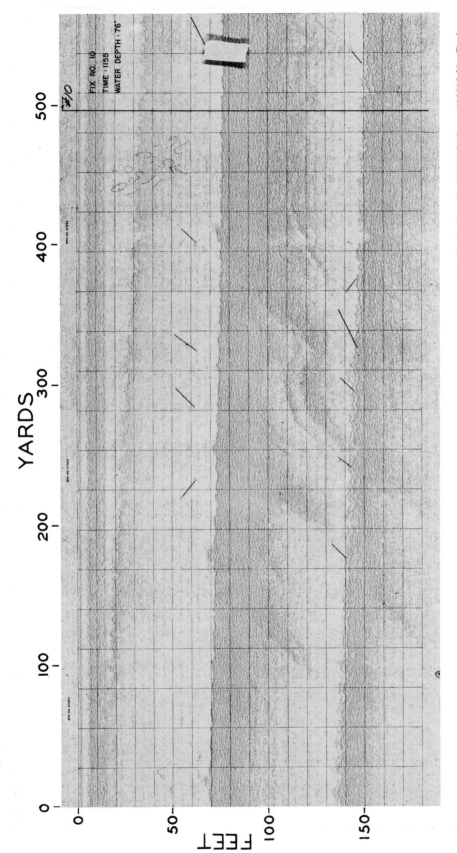

Figure 79. Marine Sonoprobe profile showing small folds associated with northwest-southeast trending fault zone in San Pedro Bay (lat. 34°00.2′, long. 118°13.2′). Dark area between 0–15 feet is outgoing signal; at 70–77 feet, bottom; at 100–140 feet, structure within bottom; at 135–150 feet, double reflection of bottom; at 15–25 feet, triple reflection of bottom. Lines indicate apparent dips of beds. Courtesy Fairchild Aerial Surveys, Inc.

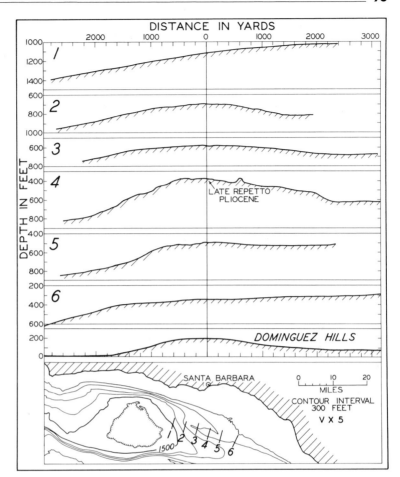

Figure 80. Profiles of probable small fold in Santa Barbara Basin as compared with one of Dominguez Hills, part of the Newport-Inglewood structure in the Los Angeles Basin.

as the Franciscan. The folding and thickening resulted in isostatic uplift which converted the former sea floor into a land area. However, the uplift is incomplete even now, as shown by an existing coastal belt of negative isostatic anomalies, and it has not been great enough to expose the base of the metamorphic series.

Traces of a nearly filled marginal trench exist at the base of the present continental slope off southern California, and well-developed trenches are present farther south off Central and South America, where still smaller supplies of sediment are available. Perhaps these trenches are modern relatives of the geosyncline in which sediments accumulated and were downfolded and altered to become the metamorphic basement rocks of coastal California; however, they may differ from the earlier geosyncline in that the latter is believed to have received much

sediment from a bordering highland to the west (Taliaferro, 1943, p. 187). The fact that the modern trenches are parallel to and seaward of the Mesozoic geosyncline indicates a seaward migration of the zone of downfolding, perhaps similar to the progressive seaward shifting of belts of geosynclinal folding in Australia, Japan, and elsewhere in the world.

Late Cretaceous Chico strata, chiefly sandstones, have been found only in a narrow coastal belt in southern California. The meager distribution of Paleocene rocks is similar. However, Eocene sedimentary rocks, mostly sandstones, are more widely distributed in the continental borderland, being found also on San Nicolas and some of the northern islands. Next, Oligocene marine sedimentary rocks are known only from the northern islands and the mainland near Point Conception. Nonmarine coarse clastic sedimentary rocks of Oligocene age are more common along the coast. The general scarcity of pre-Miocene strata suggests three explanations. (1) the strata were not deposited in the offshore region because it was then a topographically high area of incompletely base-leveled metamorphic rocks; or (2) they have been so deeply buried by later strata that they have not been exposed; or (3) a widespread later uplift caused them to be so completely eroded away that few remnants have been found. Probably each of these possible explanations holds best in one part of the region or another. The writer, however, believes that the simplest and most general explanation for this distribution of rocks is that during Cretaceous and Paleocene times the continental borderland was a topographic high which was being eroded to provide coarse sediments to its margins and fine sediments to distant areas. In Eocene time local downwarping caused some of the area to receive rather than to provide coarse sediments. Afterward, in Oligocene time, upwarping again reduced the areas of deposition. Support for this explanation for pre-Miocene strata is provided by the nature and distribution of Miocene rocks.

During most of Miocene time the region must have been downwarped to account for the unusually widespread distribution of marine sediments, predominantly shales, of this age. In several areas, Santa Catalina Island, Fortymile Bank, and Thirtymile Bank, the Miocene sedimentary rocks overlie metamorphic basement in such a way that either no earlier strata was deposited or it had been completely eroded away before deposition of the Miocene rocks; at least, none is now present. Along the present coast and on the northern islands, however, older sedimentary rocks are associated with the Miocene rocks, indicating that in these areas accumulation was more continuous. Because of the widespread distribution of the Miocene beds and their general uniformity, commonly thin-bedded cherty shales, it may be supposed that the continental borderland had for the most part reduced to a low gently sloping peneplain before the Miocene

Epoch. This suggests a long pre-Miocene period of quiessence.

During Middle Miocene time extensive volcanism, shown by sills, dikes, tuffs, and ash beds, indicates a renewal of diastrophic activity. A physiographic form of the diastrophism was the faulting that is known to have blocked out the Los Angeles and Ventura Basins. Similar basins separated by high areas which are now islands and banks began to form in the offshore area, as shown by the abundance atop the banks of phosphorite, most of which contains only Miocene Foraminifera. Since phosphorite is an authigenic rock of very slow deposition, its presence in a surface blanket deposit means that inorganic detrital sediments could not reach the bank tops to mask the phosphorite. The absence of post-Miocene strata of inorganic detrital sediments on most of the banks and all the islands supports the belief that blocking out of the continental borderland began late in the Miocene. Recurrent or additional block faulting continued, however, in some areas of the continental borderland. It is shown by the thick blanket of Pliocene and Early Pleistocene shale atop Coronado Bank off San Diego, now separated from its source; by folded and beveled Pliocene shale cropping out on the shelf in San Pedro Bay and in the Ventura–Santa Barbara region; and by Pliocene outcrops on and near the scarps that form the sides of Santa Catalina, San Pedro, and Santa Monica Basins. Mid-Pleistocene folding and uplift are well documented at Ventura and at other places of the mainland and islands where marine terraces occur 1000 feet or more above sea level, such as the Palos Verdes Hills and San Clemente Island, as well as in submerged areas where flat erosional surfaces and gravel deposits occur 2000 feet or more below sea level (Fig. 81). Local diastrophic movements are still occurring, as shown by differences between repeated geodetic surveys of the Newport-Inglewood zone of the Los Angeles Basin and of the Transverse Ranges near Cajon Pass (Gilluly, 1949). The active seismicity of the region is a result of such movements.

On a larger scale than the block faulting

Figure 81. Andesite pebbles rounded by wave action on ancient beaches. On the right are two pebbles from 1950 feet above sea level on San Clemente Island; on the left are five pebbles from AHF 5227 at 2230 feet below sea level near the top of a submerged hill at latitude 33°36.2′, longitude 120°14.4′. Weathering has removed part of the rounded surface of the large pebble from land. The large one from the sea floor was broken in order to identify the kind of rock (×0.6).

is the broad regional warping shown by the submerged terraces of the shelf; these terraces were probably formed during eustatic low sea levels of the Late Pleistocene. The lowest and presumably oldest of these is only about 250 feet deep near Los Angeles but about 480 feet deep far to the south and the west. The fact that the maximum lowering of sea level during the Pleistocene was probably about 400 feet and that the shelf-break beyond the northern and southern limits of Chart I is probably about 400 feet indicates that the continental borderland northeast of the approximate 400-foot contour of the shelf-break must have been warped upward and the one to the south and west of that contour downward. Thus, the 400-foot contour must be the approximate hinge line of

the post-Late Pleistocene warping. Warping, however, was not confined to the late history of the continental borderland.

Islands are obviously concentrated in the northern half of the continental borderland, and most of the deep basins are in the southern half. A more complete analysis was made by plotting the height above sea level or the depth below sea level of the top of each major mountain against distance south of the northern border of Chart I (lat. 34°30′). The same procedure was followed for the bottoms of the basins and for their sills (Fig. 82). It is evident that all three features systematically decrease in altitude toward the south (Emery, 1953). The steepest part of the curve for the tops of mountains is due to the presence of the

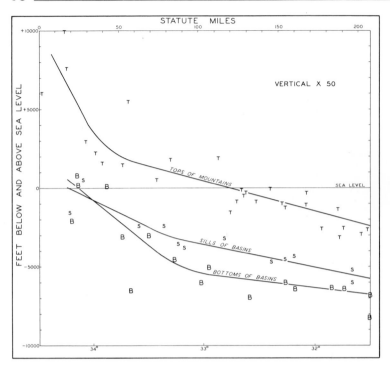

Figure 82. Plot of the variations of the height or depth of mountain tops (T), basin floors (B), and basin sills (S) with distance south of latitude 34°30′, the northern border of Chart I. Data are restricted to areas shown by Chart I. From Emery (1954d, Fig. 4).

high Transverse Ranges at the north, and the steepest portion of the curve for the bottoms of basins is, at least in part, the result of the rapid decrease in rate of deposition of basin sediments in an offshore direction.

On land the sills are lower than the basin floors because these basins are filled to overflowing. Far to the south the sills are not as high above the basin floors as at intermediate distances, possibly because the original basin-forming deformation was less intense there. Aside from the local steepening, all three curves show an average southward decrease in altitude of about 3000 feet per hundred miles, or a slope of about ⅓°. Three hundred miles southeast of the southern border of Chart I the sea floor again rises to form the spur of Baja California near Cedros Island. If the basin and island topography of the whole continental borderland was blocked out at about the same time and at a more or less uniform depth throughout the region, there must have occurred a subsequent broad downwarping between Point Conception and Cedros Island. This warping has continued into post-Pleistocene times as shown by the similar but smaller

warp of the depth of the shelf break. The latter amounts to about 160 feet per 100 miles, about one-twentieth the warp of the mountain tops and the sills and botoms of basins. This ratio is in agreement with the age of the continental shelf, which is much younger than the basin topography in southern California.

A major question concerned with the downwarping is what happened to the rocks that were displaced. The continental borderland contains about 30,000 cubic miles of post-Miocene sediment and about 50,000 cubic miles of overlying water between Point Conception and Cedros Island. Perhaps the downwarp was accompanied by a plastic flow at depth, somewhat like that discussed by Lawson (1950). Conceivably, this subflow added to the uplift of the Transverse Ranges and to the Peninsular Ranges; however, the volumes of these ranges are too small (2400 cubic miles for the Transverse Ranges) to have absorbed the entire flow. Moreover, no adequate bulge of the abyssal sea floor is present. We might conclude that any lateral flow which occurred must have continued far beyond the region.

Water

On land geological and biological processes are largely controlled by the nature of the atmosphere, but on the sea floor these processes are controlled more by the overlying water, which in turn may be influenced by the atmosphere. Clearly the degree of freedom of movement of the water must be limited by the topography of the bottom, especially in this area of basins and banks; thus, bottom topography as well as surface source of solar energy require subdivision of the water column into depth zones for ease in discussion.

Currents

Surface

The classical method of determining currents is that of computation from dynamic topography in much the same manner as winds can be computed from isobaric contours of the atmosphere. Because of some uncertainties in the basic assumptions the computed currents are checked wherever possible by current meters, drift bottles or cards, and electrical measurements. Nevertheless, the geographical variation of water characteristics remains the main indication of the existence and nature of the currents. Chief among these water characteristics are temperature, salinity, oxygen content, and nutrient concentration (usually phosphate-

phosphorus). Nearly all the available data for waters at the surface and intermediate depths in the region were obtained by ships of Scripps Institution of Oceanography during cruises in 1937 (Sverdrup and Fleming, 1941) and 1938, 1939, 1940, and 1941 (Sverdrup and Staff, 1942, 1943, 1944, and 1947), and ships of Scripps, the U. S. Fish and Wildlife Service, and the California Division of Fish and Game (the cooperative Marine Life Research Program) during cruises in 1949, 1950, 1951, and 1952 (Scripps Institution of Oceanography, 1949–1952). Two of these cruises (February and July, 1950) were selected as illustrative of general water conditions on the basis of their relatively dense pattern of stations and their completeness of data and computations, although this year was one of somewhat colder water than usual. Many of the other cruises provide relatively incomplete information about the region off southern California because their stations were set in widely spaced grids in order to provide a picture of conditions along much of the coast between Washington and the tip of Baja California.

Nearly all cruises having adequate data show the coldest water confined to an area extending roughly from Point Conception and Santa Cruz Island to San Nicolas Island (Fig. 83). Average temperatures here between 1937 and 1952 range from 12.5°C in the spring to 17.0° in the fall. In contrast,

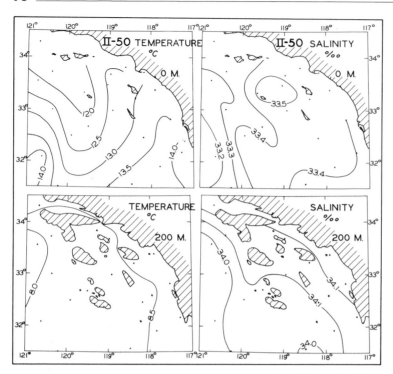

Figure 83. Regional pattern of water temperature and salinity at the surface and at a depth of 200 meters during the Marine Life Research cruise of February 1950. Note the surface area of low temperature and high salinity between Santa Cruz and San Nicolas Islands and its absence at 200 meters.

the temperature near the southwestern corner of Chart I exhibits a smaller range, from 14.5 to 18.0°, and the temperature near San Diego a greater range, from 14.0 to 19.5° (Fig. 84). Fewer than 10 per cent of the observations differ by more than 2.0° from the average curves; however, these small variations may have important effects on the fishing industry, as will be discussed in a later section. Almost identical average results for the area near San Diego were obtained by McEwen (1916) in a summary of results of cruises made between 1908 and 1915, and by Emery, Butcher, Gould, and Shepard (1952) in a summary of cruises between 1942 and 1945. In contrast to the temperatures at the water surface, those at 200 meters are nearly uniform throughout the year; at the same three stations 80 per cent of the temperature measurements at 200 meters are between 8.0 and 9.0°C.

During many of the cruises the same general area of lowest temperatures is characterized by slightly higher salinities than elsewhere, slightly lower oxygen content (Fig. 85), and much higher concentrations of phosphate-phosphorus. Because

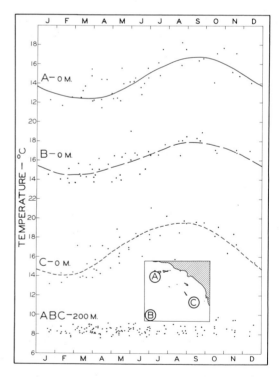

Figure 84. Annual variation of water surface temperature at three localities for 49 Scripps cruises during the years 1937–1941 and 1949–1952. Temperatures at 200 meters for all three localities are plotted together because of their similarity.

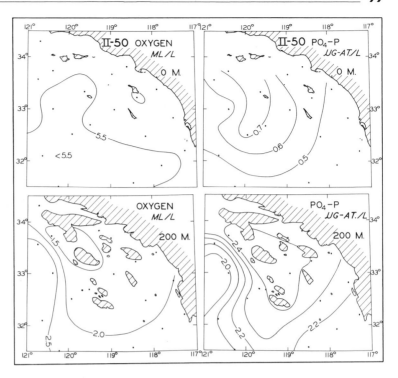

Figure 85. Regional pattern of contents of dissolved oxygen and phosphate-phosphorus at the surface and at a depth of 200 meters during the Marine Life Research cruise of February 1950. Note the presence of low oxygen and high phosphorus at the surface between Santa Cruz and San Nicolas Islands and the still lower oxygen and higher phosphorus at 200 meters.

temperature and oxygen decrease with depth below the sea surface and salinity and phosphorus increase with depth, it is evident that some mechanism is causing subsurface water to rise to the surface. When this nutrient-rich water reaches the zone of sunlight, it supports a dense crop of phytoplankton (Sverdrup and Allen, 1939; Allen, 1945; Sargent and Walker, 1947) which serves as food for many small and large animals. The plankton may become so abundant that it reduces the transparency of the sea water in this area (Fig. 86), but not so much as sediment and plankton together reduce it near the mainland shore (Emery, 1954b). In addition to reducing the transparency, high concentrations of sediment and plankton change the deep blue of the ocean to green far from shore and finally to brown close to shore. Crews of fishing boats are keenly aware of the general distribution of colors because they find and harpoon most of their swordfish and troll most of their tuna near the boundary between green and blue waters.

The classical computation of currents is based on dynamic topography computed in turn from measurement of temperature and salinity at many depths in a grid of stations occupied in as short a time as possible. For absolute currents we must have, or be able to assume, at some depth an isobaric (equal pressure) level that is horizontal and, thus, a surface of no motion. Currents can be computed above a sloping surface of equal pressure only on a basis of movement relative to that of the sloping surface. Given a selected isobaric level, the next step is to compute the total height at each oceanographic station of the water column above that level. This computation is based on the known inverse relationship of water density to temperature and direct relationship to salinity and pressure. Details of computation are given by Sverdrup, Johnson, and Fleming (1942, pp. 289–418). In addition, a complex correction for periodic variations of density caused by internal waves of tidal period must be made (Defant, 1950b).

The maps of topography of the surface relative to the 300-decibar level (1 decibar equals the pressure exerted by a column of sea water 1 meter high) show a variation of

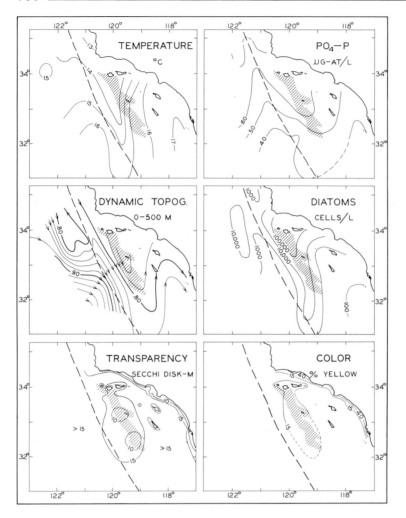

Figure 86. Comparison of temperature, phosphate, dynamic topography, and diatom concentration at the surface for the *E. W. Scripps* cruise of June 7–16, 1938. Note the similarity of all four maps and their relationship to the closely cross-hatched Santa Rosa–Cortes Ridge. Transparency of water in terms of Secchi disk readings in meters is based on about 1200 measurements, mostly in waters atop the mainland shelf; the depth is that at which a 30-cm white disk disappears from view. The color of water is the per cent of yellow solution in a mixture of basic yellow and basic blue; yellow was made by dissolving 1 gram K_2CrO_4 in 200 ml water, blue by dissolving 2 grams $CuSO_4$ and 4 grams $(NH_3)_2CO_3$ in 200 ml water. Method and much of color data by D. W. Scholl.

sea level of as much as 20 cm within the area of Chart I (Fig. 87). During most of the cruises there existed a trough extending south of Point Conception to the vicinity of San Nicolas Island. Sea level was usually highest west of the trough near the southwest corner of Chart I, the point farthest from shore. A secondary high commonly was present in a ridge east of the trough, trending southeasterly from near Santa Catalina Island about 30 miles offshore. Nearer shore a secondary low was shown by data of most cruises having stations in that area.

Water tends to flow downhill from the areas of high sea level, but owing to the deflection caused by earth rotation (Corioli's force), it is deflected to the right of this path in the Northern Hemisphere. In a frictionless medium the deflection is theoretically at a 90° angle to the slope; thus, the current is assumed to move along the contours of dynamic topography in the direction such that high topography is on the right-hand side of an observer facing the same direction that the current is moving. Arrows drawn on the contours of dynamic topography show the direction of current flow, and the spacing of the contours is inversely proportional to the velocity of the current. In the five cruises between 1950 and 1952 chosen as examples the surface current with respect to the 300-decibar level flows at velocities as great as 30 cm/sec, or 0.6 knot. Usually, the greatest velocities occur in the area farthest from shore, where the eastern side of the southeasterly flowing California Current is encountered. Like the Gulf Stream (Ford and Miller, 1952; von Arx,

Bumpus, and Richardson, 1955) and the Japanese Current (Uda, 1951), the California Current has a complex meandering and changing pattern. It is a continuation of the warm Japanese Current after the latter has become mixed with so much cold subarctic water that it is called the Aleutian Current. About 400 miles wide, the California Current has a total transport amounting to about 10,000,000 cu meters/sec, about three times the total discharge of all the rivers of the earth, but only a fifth to a tenth the transport of the Gulf Stream or of the Japanese Current.

East of the California Current the pattern of flow is dominated by a large eddy centered at the topographic trough of the sea level

and turning counterclockwise so slowly as to require 10 to 20 days for a half revolution. On the east side of the eddy most of the water turns southeastward and follows the coast to Mexico. This pattern of southeasterly flowing offshore current bordered by an eddy, or countercurrent, and by a return flow nearer the shore is characteristic of most of the 49 cruises conducted by Scripps Institution between 1937 and 1952 (Fig. 88). Only three of the cruises fail to show this pattern to some degree, and these particular cruises had only a few stations in the area because of storm conditions or because the station grid was laid out for mapping of larger current features than this one. Only minor differences exist in the pattern

Figure 87. Dynamic topography during five cruises of the Marine Life Research Program, 1950–1952. Contours show topography of sea surface with respect to the 300-meter level at 2-cm intervals. Arrows indicate the theoretical direction of current at the surface relative to that at 300 meters. The velocity scale for all maps is given in the map at the upper left corner, with high velocities where contours are close together and low velocities where they are widely spaced. Surface current vectors in the lower right map are based on geomagnetic electrokinetograph records made during two cruises of 1952.

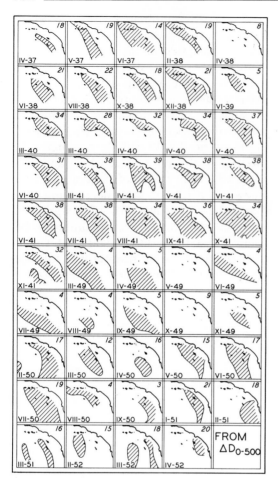

Figure 88. Generalized patterns of theoretical surface currents relative to those at a depth of 500 meters for 49 Scripps cruises between 1937 and 1952. Correction for tidal effect has been made only for the 1949 and later cruises. Cross-hatched areas indicate northward currents, and plain white areas show southward currents or areas where data are lacking, mostly near shore. Note the great similarity of most of the maps.

of surface currents based on the 300-decibar level and that based on the 500- or even the 1000-decibar level, indicating that currents at depth are relatively sluggish. Support for the general pattern of surface currents is provided by experiments with drift bottles (Tibby, 1939) and in a general fashion by limited measurements with the shipboard geomagnetic electrokinetograph (von Arx, 1950). Interesting checks can be made in the future through electropotential measurements between the mainland and offshore islands, as previously done for the Florida Current by Wertheim (1954).

The frequency of the current pattern and its important bearing on the distribution of organisms and sediments require some speculation about its origin. Sverdrup and Fleming (1941) supposed that the area of cold water and its related eddy is a product of upwelling caused by winds from the northwest near Point Conception blowing most strongly during the spring and early summer months. They recognized a sub-surface current flowing northwesterly during all times of the year but flowing at the surface only during the fall when upwelling was less intense. Their studies were based on cruises of 1937 through 1940, but inspection of current patterns for later cruises fails to show such limited areas of countercurrent as apparently occurred during the springs of 1937 and 1940. Data from later cruises show general similarities of the current pattern throughout the entire year and a lack of correspondence of average wind velocity and direction to average water temperature (Fig. 89), such as to cast doubt on the concept of seasonal upwelling due to winds, as a full explanation at least.

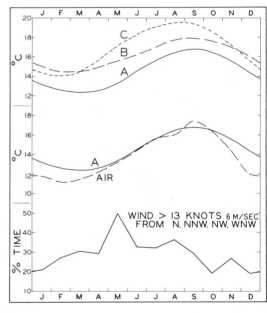

Figure 89. Comparison of annual surface temperature curves of Figure 84 with average annual air temperature and wind at San Nicolas Island for the period April 1945 through December 1945 and March 1947 through June 1953. Meteorological data from records of the U. S. Weather Bureau.

An alternate concept is that of entrainment of water by the California Current. Studies of the Gulf Stream in the Atlantic Ocean show that along its course it entrains vast quantities of water from the opensea side (Sverdrup, Johnson, and Fleming, 1942, pp. 676–677); presumably the California Current is capable of similar entrainment. During its passage southeasterly along the northern California coast the California Current is unable to entrain water on its left because little is available. However, when the California Current passes Point Conception it encounters a large body of water on its left. Because the Santa Rosa–Cortes Ridge rises to a depth of less than 200 meters along most of its length, only water shallower than its crest can be entrained. When this water is carried away, it is replaced partly by surface water from farther east and partly by colder subsurface water. The bringing up of water from depths greater than the crest of the Santa Rosa–Cortes Ridge should produce much the same changes in the surface water as ordinary upwelling induced by wind, but without requiring the presence of high wind velocities. South of Cortes Bank the ridge is continued as a series of widely separated topographic high areas between which entrainment can occur at all depths so that there is no necessity for surface water to be replaced. Because mixing of cold water with the surface of the California Current occurs only north of Cortes Bank, it must depress the dynamic topography only in that area and cause some of the water at the east side of the California Current to become deflected toward the coast and around the south end of the area of colder water near Cortes Bank. On passage of a temperature-stratified mass of water across a ridge, even a deep one, the current and its isotherms are deflected to the right in the Northern Hemisphere (Sverdrup, Johnson, and Fleming, 1942, pp. 466, 672). Such a deflection probably adds to the area of cold water around which the countercurrent must flow until the configuration of the coast causes it to turn southward again and flow out of the area. Until a more rigorous study is made, it is impossible to determine the relative roles of wind and entrainment in producing upwelling along the ridge; however, both processes may act more or less in unison to produce the characteristic surface current pattern off southern California.

Intermediate Depths

At intermediate depths off southern California there occurs water distinctly different from that at the surface. Sverdrup and Fleming (1941) showed that the water at depth has a southern origin in contrast to the northern origin of most of the water near the surface. The bottom of the intermediate water, or Southern Water, is taken as the depth of basin sills, a depth which varies between about 500 and 1900 meters in the continental borderland. Nearer the surface is a broad zone of mixing of the two water types. Pure examples of the two types have quite different salinities for given temperatures, the Southern Water being the more saline. A plot of temperature against salinity (a T–S diagram—Fig. 90) clearly defines each of the two types. The proportions of the two types present in a water of mixed origin can be determined by the position of its temperature-salinity curve with respect to those of the pure Southern and Northern Water types. At most stations the waters are mostly of northern origin at the surface and of southern origin at depth. Inspection of plots of such mixed waters in a T–S diagram readily indicates the depth at which the mixed water is 50 per cent Southern and 50 per cent Northern Water. The depth over the continental borderland at which this particular mixture occurs is variable but is mostly between 200 and 300 meters, locally as deep as 500 meters; the mixture is commonly absent or occurs deeper than 500 meters beyond the continental slope (Fig. 91). A reasonable average depth throughout the continental borderland of Chart I is 300 meters; for this reason the surface currents of Figure 87 discussed in the preceding section were based on the dynamic topography of the sea surface relative to the 300-decibar level.

The chief depths of mixing of the two water types are those immediately above

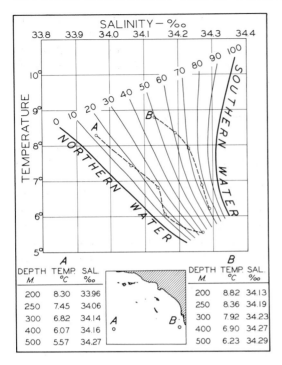

A		
DEPTH M.	TEMP. °C	SAL. ‰
200	8.30	33.96
250	7.45	34.06
300	6.82	34.14
400	6.07	34.16
500	5.57	34.27

B		
DEPTH M.	TEMP. °C	SAL. ‰
200	8.82	34.13
250	8.36	34.19
300	7.92	34.23
400	6.90	34.27
500	6.23	34.29

Figure 90. Temperature-salinity (*T-S*) diagram showing percentage mixtures of waters characteristic of northern California and those of Mexico. Two examples of mixed waters (stations occupied during February 1950) show the method of computing percentage of Southern Water (20 and 65 per cent, respectively) and depth in meters to water consisting of 50 per cent mixture of southern and northern types (more than 500 meters and 200 meters, respectively).

and below the depth of 50 per cent Southern Water, taken for simplicity as between 200 and 500 meters. Incomplete mixing of the waters is sometimes revealed by small temperature inversions measured with a 300-meter bathythermograph over San Pedro and Santa Monica Basins (Fig. 92) and with an electronic method (Snodgrass and Cawley, 1957) over San Diego Trough. The percentage of Southern Water between 200 and 500 meters at each oceanographic station of a cruise can be determined from the *T-S* diagram. Resulting maps (Fig. 91) commonly show a tongue of high percentage of Southern Water extending into the continental borderland, where most of it is trapped by the Santa Rosa–Cortes Ridge. Small amounts of Southern Water that are present seaward of the ridge reached that area by moving northward along the out-side of the ridge, by leaking through gaps in the ridge, or by passing over it.

Approximate currents at the depth of 50 per cent Southern Water can be computed by mapping the dynamic topography of the 300-decibar level with respect to the 800-decibar level. Reference to deeper levels would have provided more accurate current data, but the necessary measurements of temperature and salinity are relatively rare for depths greater than 800 meters. The resulting computed currents at 300 meters show a characteristic northwesterly movement (Fig. 91). For many of the cruises, such as the one for July 1950, much more water flowed past San Diego at velocities of as much as 12 cm/sec, 0.25 knot, than escaped from the continental borderland through the gaps at 300 meters in the Santa Rosa–Cortes Ridge. That the water is not merely temporarily trapped is shown by the frequency of this current condition. It is evident, therefore, that the water must escape, and the only avenue available to it is that of rising and crossing the top of the Santa Rosa–Cortes Ridge. This flow of intermediate water replaces part of the surface water entrained by the California Current and drawn off across the Santa Rosa–Cortes Ridge. Precise computation of transport volumes would make an interesting study.

Amounts of dissolved oxygen in the water at intermediate depths are much lower than those at the surface, probably chiefly because most of the oxygen has been used in the oxidation of organic matter that sank from the surface through the intermediate water. The same results are achieved whether the oxidation is by respiration of the phytoplankton, feeding and respiration by zooplankton or larger animals, bacterial activities, or chemical reactions. Because of the probable longer time since the Southern Water was at the surface and able to absorb oxygen, its oxygen content is lower than that of the Northern Water for any given temperature (Fig. 93) as shown by Sverdrup and Fleming (1941). If controlled only by the percentage of Northern and Southern Water, the oxygen content at intermediate depths could be computed from the temperature-salinity curves. However, observed

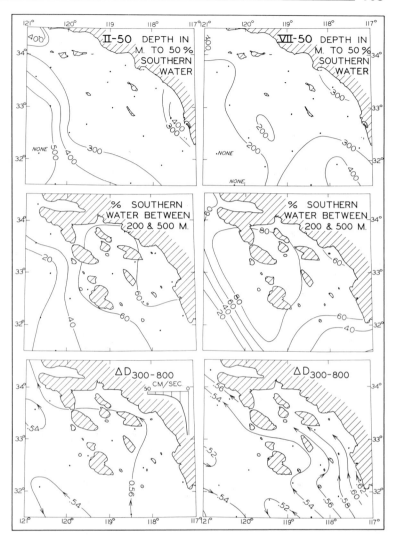

Figure 91. Top, maps showing depths to 50 per cent Southern Water during Marine Life Research cruises of February and July 1950; computed according to the method of Figure 90. *None* indicates that Southern Water is less than 50 per cent at all depths sampled. Middle, percentage of Southern Water in zone of mixing between 200 and 500 meters for same two cruises; computed according to the method of Figure 90. Bottom, dynamic topography at 2-cm contour interval for 300-meter surface with respect to 800-meter level. Arrows show direction of current, and the spacing of contours is an inverse measure of current velocity according to the velocity scale on the map at lower left.

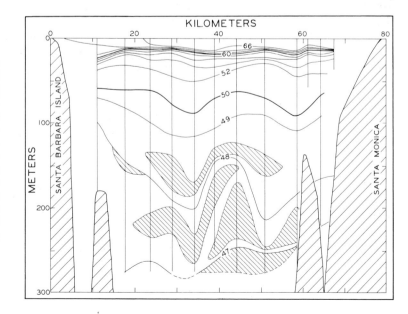

Figure 92. Temperature section between Santa Barbara Island and Santa Monica, showing mixed layer at surface, thermocline, and underlying zone of gradually decreasing temperature on June 26, 1957. Within the latter zone are several widespread temperature inversions amounting to nearly 1°F; these may correspond to incomplete mixing between Northern Water at the top and Southern Water below. From Gunnerson (1957a).

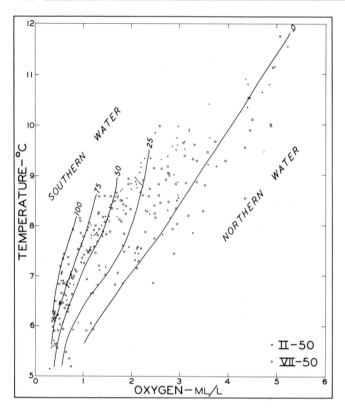

Figure 93. Relationship between dissolved oxygen and water temperature for Marine Life Research cruises of February and July 1950. Data for other cruises are similar. The plot includes only depths between 100 and 500 meters. Contours show percentage of Southern Water with only 10 per cent of points differing by more than one contour interval.

oxygen contents inshore of the continental slope were found by Sverdrup and Fleming (1941) to be less than the computed ones. They interpreted the deficiency as caused by oxidation of organic matter settling through the water from the area of high production near the surface. The greatest deficiency in oxygen content occurs in the area of Santa Barbara Basin. For the whole region the deficiency in 1938 was 40 to 80 ml in a 1 sq cm column of water between 50 and 700 meters. This corresponds to an annual production of 500 to 1000 grams of dry plankton per square meter, with the higher figure being more nearly correct, because the data omits oxygen consumption in the 0- to 50-meter depth zone and because some of the organic matter falls entirely through the top 700 meters of water without becoming completely oxidized. For comparison, Holmes (1957), using a radiocarbon method, obtained a daily production of about 0.5 grams of carbon per square meter per day; this corresponds to about 420 grams of dry plankton per square meter per year.

One result of the oxidation of organic

matter falling through the water column is the regeneration of nutrients; accordingly, the nutrient content of the water must be in approximate inverse proportion to the oxygen content. Such is true for phosphate-phosphorus, the only nutrient that has been determined routinely off southern California (Fig. 94). In addition to bearing an inverse ratio to oxygen, the phosphorus concentration appears to show a seasonal variation, being somewhat more abundant in water of a given temperature during July than February (Fig. 95). This may be a reflection of greater regeneration after the spring season of plankton blooming than occurs during the winter, but it is curious that the oxygen content is not markedly lower during July than February. This problem of regeneration of nutrients deserves more attention than has been given it in the region off southern California.

Basins

About 5 per cent of all the water atop the continental borderland in the area of Chart

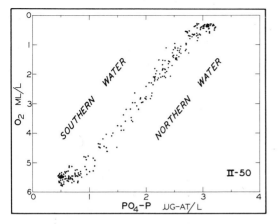

Figure 94. Relationship between dissolved oxygen and phosphate-phosphorus for all depths at stations of the Marine Life Research cruise of February 1950. Data for other cruises in the area are essentially identical. Data for waters south of latitude 31°30′ fall at the upper left of the plot and for waters north of latitude 34°30′, at the lower right. Note the inverse relationship of the two parameters.

I lies below the sill depths of the basins. The properties of the water in each basin are unique to that basin but are similar to those at some depth in the overlying intermediate and surface waters. The most characteristic properties are temperature and oxygen content; salinity and nutrients are more nearly uniform in the various basins (Table 7).

In the open sea the water temperature decreases with depth except for local minor inversions mostly near the surface. In each basin, however, the temperature is nearly uniform from near the sill depth to the bottom (Fig. 96) (Emery, 1954c). Temperature at the sill of each basin is approximately the same as that of the open sea at the depth of that sill. The water in several basins presents a decrease of temperature of not more than 0.13°C in the first hundred meters below the sill, presumably because of mixing with the overlying intermediate water. Below that depth, at least in Santa Cruz and Velero Basins, there is a slight increase

Figure 95. Relationship between phosphate-phosphorus and water temperature for same cruises and depth range as those in Figure 91. Percentage of Southern Water is shown by solid lines for February and by dashed lines for July.

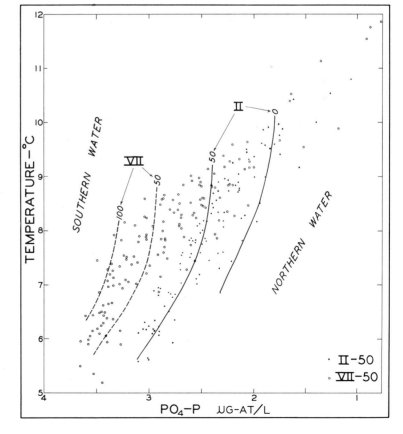

of temperature with depth of less than 0.01°C/100 meters that can be attributed to adiabatic heating. Both the mixing and the adiabatic gradients are small compared with the decrease of temperature at the same depth range in the open sea. Accordingly, the temperature depth curves of the basins depart markedly from that of the open sea, causing the basin floors to be covered by water 0.8 to 2.0°C warmer than that at the same depths in the open sea. Because of the wide variation in depth of the basin sills, the temperature in different basins ranges between 2.52 and 6.26°C, about 200 times the error of its measurement.

Salinity within the basins is about the same as that of the open sea at the same depth as that of the basin sills, and it remains nearly uniform from the sill to the bottom depth of each basin (Emery, 1954c). The salinity range of the different basins is 34.25 to 34.58‰, only about ten times the error of measurement. This small range of the basin water salinities and the fact that the salinity at the basin floors is less than 0.20‰ lower than that of the open sea at the same depths are results of the very gradual change of salinity with depth in the open sea, as compared with the change of temperature with depth.

Oxygen in the open sea is saturated near the surface at about 6 ml/liter, decreases to a minimum of about 0.5 ml/liter at 500 to 700 meters, and increases with depth below 700 meters to about 2.0 ml/liter at 2000 meters (Fig. 97). This depth variation is produced by photosynthesis and exchange with the atmosphere near the surface, rapid oxidation of easily oxidized organic matter falling through waters at intermediate depth, and slow oxidation of the more resistant organic matter that reaches greater depth. The basin waters have approximately the same oxygen content as does the water outside the basins at the same depths as the basin sills. Because the shallowest basins have sills at depths within the oxygen minimum, their waters have oxygen contents of only 0.2 or 0.3 ml/liter in contrast to about 2.0 ml/liter for waters in the deepest basins. These contents represent only 1 to 7 per cent of saturation values in water of the same temperature and salinity at the surface.

The nutrients, phosphate-phosphorus, nitrate-nitrogen, and silicon, have been measured in only three of the shallowest basins (Rittenberg, Emery, and Orr, 1955), and the values are nearly the same as those found in the open sea at the same depths. Relatively little variation in phosphate and nitrate is found from basin to basin because in the open sea the concentrations of these nutrients are nearly uniform below about 800 meters. A much greater variation

Table 7

PROPERTIES OF BASIN WATERS

Basin	Temper-ature, °C	Salinity, ‰	Oxygen, ml/liter	PO_4–Pr	NO_3–N	Si	Bottom	Sill	Effective Sill
				μg-atom/liter					Depths, meters
Santa Barbara	6.26	34.25	0.3	3.1	40	135	627	475	510
San Pedro	5.06	34.29	0.2	–	–	–	912	737	750
Santa Monica	5.05	34.31	0.3	3.2	35	160	938	737	750
Santa Catalina	4.02	34.42	0.4	3.0	35	165	1357	982	1010
Santa Cruz	4.15	34.52	0.8	–	–·	–	1966	1085	980
San Nicolas	3.71	34.52	0.5	–	–	–	1833	1106	1100
Tanner	3.85	34.56	0.6	–	–	–	1551	1165	1060
West Cortes	3.37	–	–	–	–	–	1796	1362	–
East Cortes	3.13	34.52	0.9	–	–	–	1979	1415	1370
No Name	2.9?	–	–	–	–	–	1915	1553	–
Long	2.7?	–	–	–	–	–	1938	1697	–
San Clemente	2.60	34.56	1.3	–	–	–	2107	1816	1750
Velero	2.52	34.58	2.0?	–	–	–	2571	1902	1700

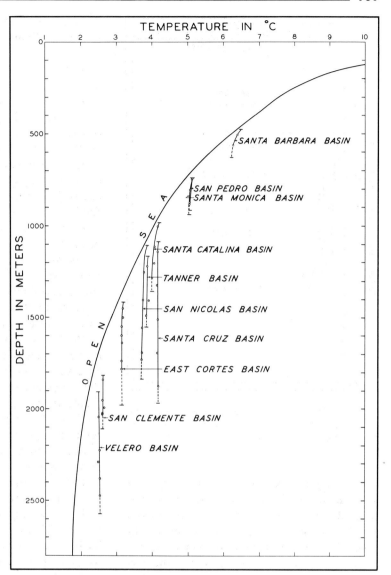

Figure 96. Temperature-depth curves for open sea and for waters below basin sills. Short horizontal lines indicate depths of sills and bottoms of basins. From Emery (1954c, Fig. 2).

would characterize basins having sills shallower than 500 meters. Silica, on the other hand, is least in the basin having the shallowest sill and greatest in the one having the deepest sill, doubtlessly because in the open sea the depth at which silica becomes uniform with depth is about 1000 meters, slightly deeper than for phosphate and nitrate.

In summary, temperature, salinity, oxygen, and silica differ from basin to basin, but within individual basins each is nearly uniform from sill depth to bottom and nearly equal to values in the open sea at the depth

of the basin sill. The range of variation from basin to basin as compared with error of measurement is greatest for temperature; moreover, temperature is least subject to change by biological activities. Thus, temperature is the best of these parameters for characterizing the basin water and indicating its source. Water at the bottom of San Nicolas Basin must have come either from the northwest or the southeast, owing to blocking of flow from other directions by the high basin side slopes, some of which are capped by islands. It is obvious, however, that the water could not have come

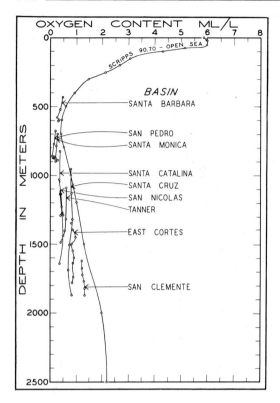

Figure 97. Oxygen-depth curves for open sea and for waters below basin sills. Arrows indicate sill depths. From Rittenberg, Emery, and Orr (1955, Fig. 2).

from the northwest because the adjacent Santa Cruz Basin contains no water that cold. Clearly, the water had to come from San Clemente Basin, adjacent to the southeast, where water at the approximate depth of the sill of San Nicolas Basin is of the correct temperature (Fig. 98). Colder and denser water at greater depth was blocked off by the sill. By making similar comparisons for all basins, the route of the basin water can easily be traced. Comparisons of the less definite salinity, oxygen, and silica concentrations provide confirming evidence of the direction of flow. The exact depth in the San Clemente Basin having water of the same temperature as that at the bottom of the San Nicolas Basin is a measure of the effective sill depth of the San Nicolas Basin. For basins having charted, or sounded, sills shallower than 1000 meters, the effective sill depth is less than 50 meters shallower than the charted sill depth; for basins having

deeper sills, the effective sill depth is as much as 200 meters deeper than the charted one.

Water present in most of the basins in the area of Chart I funneled northwestward through an unnamed and unexplored basin east of Velero Basin (Fig. 99). Since the sill of each basin along the path of the water is shallower than that of the basin immediately to the south, each sill acts as a submerged dam preventing the northward flow of successively shallower layers of bottom water. Dividing, and in some places rejoining, the bottom water flows northwestward from basin to basin. It is confined to definite paths by high basin slopes except for the San Pedro and Santa Catalina Basins, whose sills are so shallow compared to surrounding topography that water can enter these basins from a variety of directions. All the water in the Santa Barbara Basin and some of it in the Tanner, West Cortes, and Long Basins enters from the open sea to the west because these basins have their lowest or low sills facing in that direction. In view of the directions of flow and the temperature-salinity relationships (*T-S* curves) of the basin waters, it is evident that most of the basins contain a high percentage of Southern Water.

The fact that there is a slight mixing gradient just below the basin sills suggests a slow loss and replenishment of the basin water. This is verified by the fact that the basin water is not stagnant and devoid of oxygen. In fact, Rittenberg, Emery, and Orr (1955) showed that about 3.0 ml of oxygen is required annually for oxidation of organic matter in the top 30 cm of a 1 sq cm column of sediment at the bottom of Santa Catalina Basin and about 1.5 ml is needed for that of the Santa Barbara Basin. At these rates of use, all the oxygen in the basin waters would be used in only about 2 years; thus, there must be complete replenishment in less than 2 years to account for the absence of appreciable depletion of oxygen in the basin waters as compared with those of the open sea at the same depths as the basin sills. Confirmation for this rapid rate of replacement of the water was found in the fact that ammonia regenerated from the sedi-

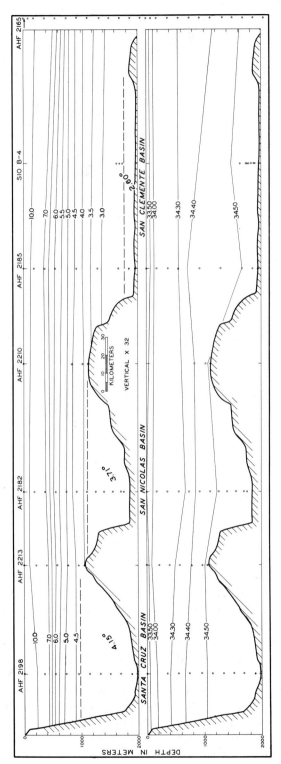

Figure 98. Longitudinal section through San Clemente, San Nicolas, and Santa Cruz Basins. Isotherms in °C at top, isohalines in ‰ at bottom. Horizontal dashed lines indicate effective sill depths. Water at extreme right is assumed to be like that of Velero Basin. From Emery (1954c, Fig. 4).

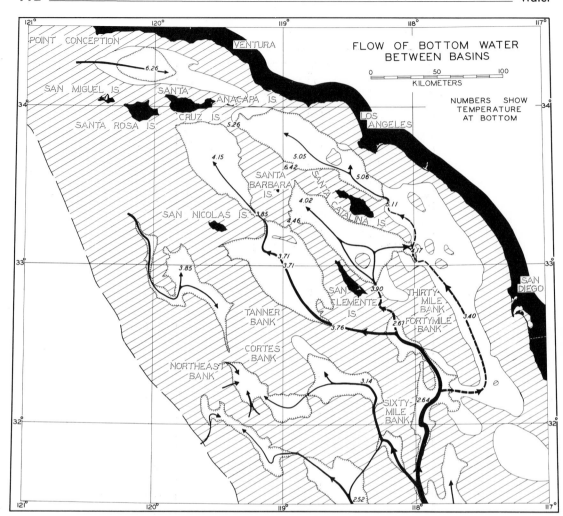

Figure 99. Paths followed by waters in flow from basin to basin. Width of lines serves as rough indicator of transport volume. From Emery (1954c, Fig. 6).

ment of Santa Barbara Basin would lead in 20 years to an increase of nitrate-nitrogen concentration in the basin water to values more than 5 µg-atoms/liter in excess of those of the open sea at the depth of the basin sill. The lack of a measurable difference in the nitrate-nitrogen concentration indicates that the water is replenished in less than 20 years. As is discussed in a following section on standing internal waves of the basins, it is believed that more or less continuous mixing of basin waters with the overlying intermediate water is the chief method of replenishment of the basin waters.

It is clear that the characteristics of the waters below the sills of basins off southern California are completely independent of processes operating at the sea surface in the region. In this respect the waters are similar in origin to those of basins in the East Indies (van Riel, 1934; van Riel, Hamaker, and van Eyck, 1950), the southern basins of the Gulf of California (Sverdrup and Staff, 1943), the West Indies (Parr, 1937; Dietrich, 1939), and the floor of the Atlantic Ocean (Schott, 1902). Oxygen content may be high or low, depending on the depth of the sill relative to the zone of oxygen minimum in the open sea. A second, third, and fourth kind of basin exists, each of which contains water having properties that are controlled by sea surface processes (Fig. 100). Basins of the second group are in areas where the surface waters are characterized by an excess of evaporation over runoff plus direct precipitation, whereby the surface sea water is made so salty and dense that it sinks below the basin sill. Examples are the Mediterranean Sea (Maury, 1855, p. 136; Schott, 1928; Pollack, 1951), the Red Sea (Thompson, 1939a, 1939b), and the Persian Gulf (Emery, 1956a). Surface sea water flows inward and forms the surface layer. Beneath it the denser basin water, which is of abnormally high salinity and temperature, flows outward when the interface is above the sill depth. Oxygen content of the basin water is generally high. The third kind of basin occurs in areas where freezing forms sea ice from surface sea water, rejecting much of the salt in the process. The resulting cold brine is denser than the original surface sea water, so it sinks to form basin water. Examples are the Japan Sea (Suda, 1932), Baffin Bay (Smith, Soule, and Mosby, 1937), and the Norwegian Sea (Helland-Hansen and Nansen, 1909). In such basins the surface sea water flows inward and the denser basin water flows outward, just as in basins of the second type. Oxygen content is generally high in the basin water. In basins of the fourth group the density-depth relationships are controlled by the influx of large quantities of fresh water from runoff. The fiords

of Norway (Ström, 1936), the Arctic Sea (Shirshov, 1940; Sverdrup, Johnson, and Fleming, 1942, p. 658), and the Black Sea (Pora, 1946) are examples. The surface water is of low salinity and of either higher or slightly lower temperature than the underlying trapped basin water. Water of the open sea flows inward at depth to make up for losses of basin water through mixing with the overlying fresher water. Oxygen in many basins is low or absent, but in others it may be high.

Shelves

Currents on the shelves cannot be computed from dynamic topography as can currents in areas of deep water, for on the shelves there is not a depth of no movement (a horizontal pressure surface—see p. 99) above the bottom. As a result, measurements of temperature and salinity can be used for indicating only the approximate direction of flow and not at all for the velocity. Checks on direction can be made using drift cards, drogues, and current meters.

Water atop the shelves, like that in deeper areas, has a mixed layer (often isothermal) at the surface, a thermocline below it, and colder denser water at greater depth. Close to shore where the depth is only a few tens of feet and where wind mixing is great, especially during storms, the mixed layer may occupy the entire column of water. The

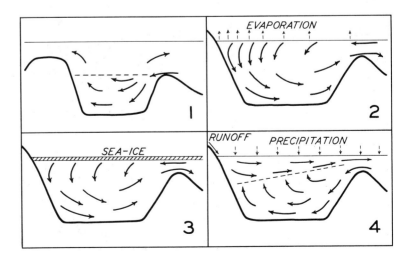

Figure 100. Types of basins and generalized cross-sectional direction of flow of their waters: 1, Submerged dam, as for southern California basins; 2, evaporation greater than runoff plus precipitation, as for Mediterranean Sea; 3, freezing and rejection of cold brine, as for Baffin Bay; and 4, evaporation less than runoff plus precipitation, as for Black Sea.

mixed layer may also be thick where winds have caused it to pile up against coastal points (Fig. 101), and it may be thin or absent where winds have swept it away from the leeward side of the same points. As a result, the difference in temperature on opposite sides of points may be as much as 10°C, as pointed out long ago by McEwen

(1916) and confirmed in many unpublished measurements by C. L. Hubbs. This difference is sufficient to produce differences in species and abundance of fishes, mollusks, crabs, algae, and probably many other organisms, which in turn may be reflected in the types of sediment present on opposite sides of points, as shown for a bay of Baja

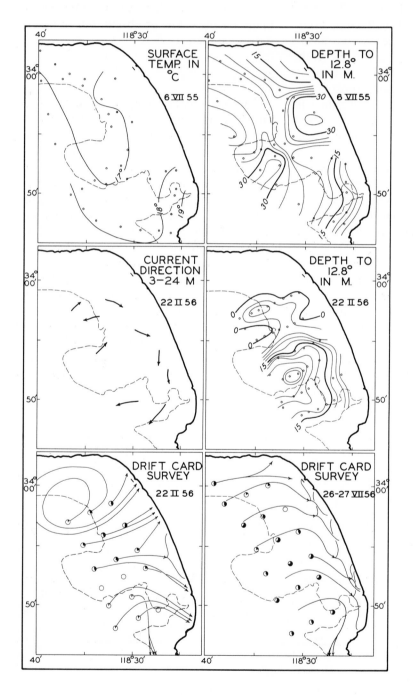

Figure 101. Typical surface temperatures, depths to 12.8°C surface, and probable paths of drift cards for summer and winter in Santa Monica Bay. Surface temperature during the July 6, 1955, cruise was highest at the windward side of the point that forms the southern limit of the bay; surface temperatures during the February 22, 1956, cruise were nearly uniform at about 13°C. Depth to the 12.8°C isothermal surface is given for both cruises, with an interpretation of current direction for the winter one. Estimated trajectories of drift cards for winter and summer are given at the bottom, with the shaded part of the circles showing the percentage recovery of the 14 to 50 drift cards released at each station. Compiled from charts and data of Stevenson, Tibby, and Gorsline (1956).

California by Emery, Gorsline, Uchupi, and Terry (1957) and by Valentine (1955).

Variations in thickness of the mixed layer produce variations in the depth to a given isotherm in the thermocline. Parts of the shelf having a much greater depth to the isothermal surface than elsewhere must usually also be characterized by having a higher sea level. Just as in deep water, the current tends to parallel the contours of depth to the isothermal surface, flowing in a direction such that this surface is deeper on the right-hand side of the current. Precise directions of the current cannot be obtained because the isothermal surface itself is not stationary and because of frictional effects of the bottom. Maps showing the topography of isothermal surfaces in Santa Monica Bay were prepared for about twenty cruises during 1955–1956 by Stevenson, Tibby, and Gorsline (1956). Most of the maps (Fig. 101) indicate a general flow into the center of the bay and outward flow at both ends. The circulation pattern was not constant, however, and different circulations exist in other bays and shelf areas having different shapes and relationships to winds and offshore currents. Currents in shallow water cannot usually be predicted accurately but must be measured for each individual area.

Current meters can be used as effective indicators of current direction and velocity in some areas of the shelf, particularly off exposed open coasts (Shepard, Revelle, and Dietz, 1939). Within bays such as Santa Monica, however, the currents are so slow (averaging 10 cm/sec) and changeable as to be below the accurate range of the meters which is set by friction and inertia of their propellors and vanes. For some purposes drift cards or drift bottles are more suitable instruments. These devices are serially numbered and distributed in quantity at many stations at sea. When they wash ashore their bright markings attract the attention of people who find within them a note asking that the time and place of finding be indicated on an enclosed form to be mailed to the agency making the study. About 5200 plastic drift cards were set afloat in 14 cruises in Santa Monica Bay during 1955–1956 with a recovery of 38 per cent. Commonly, cards released within the bay came directly ashore or moved laterally away from the center, paralleling the flow inferred from the distribution of temperature (Fig. 101). Many cards dropped just outside the bay floated southward and westward to points as distant as San Diego and Hueneme. Others may have reached the California Current to be carried across the Pacific Ocean unless they sank en route.

Drogues are more elaborate versions of drift cards designed to measure the currents at depth. They consist of a weighted vane-like structure or a weighted parachute (Volkmann, Knauss, and Vine, 1956) suspended from a buoy. By tracking several of these buoys with a boat, we can obtain the general patterns of currents at various depths more or less simultaneously. At Santa Monica Bay the drogues followed the same paths as the computed currents, that is, parallel to contours of depth of an isothermal surface; these paths were approximately the same as those followed by drift cards. They showed that the surface and subsurface currents moved in approximately the same direction, but this is not necessarily true of all shelf areas. The most complete study of shelf water based on drogues was made by Stewart (1957) for parts of the shelf off San Diego mostly shallower than Santa Monica Bay. A total of 406 observations on drogues were made between June 1955 and March 1957. Comparison with wind direction showed that surface currents moved at the greatest angle (often more than 45°) to the right of the wind when the winds were perpendicular to the shore and at a smaller angle when the winds were parallel to shore. This is doubtlessly a result of the boundary effect of the shore. The largest ratio of water current to wind speed was about 1.8 per cent, obtained when the wind was perpendicular to the shore. Subsurface currents moved to the right of the surface current, except in shallow water where they tended to follow the contours of the bottom rather than move strictly to the right of the surface current, again an effect of boundary conditions. Speeds of subsurface currents were half or more of those of surface currents (which average about 10 cm/sec), with the greatest difference present when the winds followed and added to the surface currents and the two currents were separated by a thermocline.

An effect of currents near shore commonly encountered by swimmers is the presence of warm spots. These may be as much as 3°C warmer than the surrounding water, and commonly they are conical to lens-shaped, as though in response to their relatively low density. Diameters range up to 16 meters and depths are rarely as much as 4 meters (Smitter, 1955). They originate from several kinds of traps in which water is held until it becomes abnormally warmed by insulation before it escapes to the sea. Among the traps are kelp barriers, tide pools, small bays or estuaries, points projecting into longshore current, oil slicks, and perhaps pinched-off slicks.

Waves

Wind Waves and Swell

Near Point Arguello wind stream lines show a flow of air from the northwest, but south of that point the stream lines fan out into the broad embayment off southern California. This pattern results in an area of high wind velocity in the northwestern corner of Chart I bordered by concentric zones of progressively lower wind velocity to the east and southeast (Anonymous, 1956b). Although daily winds may depart from the annual average, the pattern is fairly constant (Fig. 102). During the night and early morning a land breeze occasionally reaches as far as 10 miles out to sea, but during the late morning and afternoon the westerly pattern of stronger winds becomes re-established. On a smaller scale land breezes occur on each of the islands. During all seasons, but chiefly in summer, there may be superimposed on the general pattern a counterclockwise eddy centering north of Santa Catalina Island and named the Catalina Eddy (Graham, 1950). A smaller one farther northwest is known as the Point Arguello Eddy. The general pattern is also sometimes interrupted

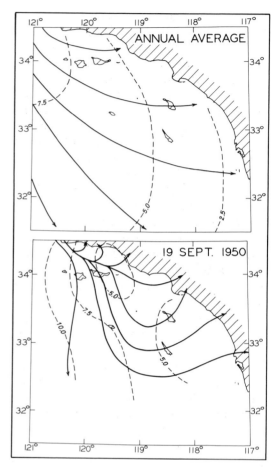

Figure 102. Prevailing winds. Average annual stream lines and wind velocities (meters/sec) and those for a typical day having well-developed examples of the Catalina Eddy and the smaller Point Arguello Eddy. Adapted from Graham (1950).

for periods of several days in all seasons except summer by strong dry winds named Santa Anas which blow seaward down slopes and valleys from the desert area (Bailey, 1954). Once in a while the region is also reached by largely spent hurricanes from off Mexico; the latest such storm occurred in September, 1939. Most storms, however, are part of winter systems which move into the region from the northwest, west, or southwest (Todd and Wiegel, 1952). Except during these storms, the winds in the offshore area south of Point Arguello are of low velocity during the winter, giving rise to lower average wind velocities in winter than in summer.

When the wind exceeds a certain critical velocity (6 to 7.5 meters/sec according to Munk, 1947a, and Mandelbaum, 1956), its influence on the ocean surface is markedly greater than at low velocities. Such winds are the chief cause of the main oceanic currents, but they also produce the sea or wind waves that are responsible for many near-shore processes of erosion and deposition and for some of the depth zonation of shore-living organisms. In the area off southern California several sets of waves are usually present, one or more of which consist of short-period (5 to 10 seconds) waves from strong local winds such as those between Point Arguello and San Nicolas Island. The strong northeasterly Santa Anas also produce waves, but these reach only a short distance seaward. Diurnal land breezes are so weak and short in duration that they rarely produce even small local waves; their main effect is that of partly counteracting the westerly winds and smoothing the sea during early morning hours. The highest waves of the region ordinarily occur in the area between Point Arguello and San Nicolas Island; these are commonly 1 to 2 meters high, but by the time they have traveled to the lee side of Santa Catalina Island they are only one-third as high (Fig. 103). Storms, such as the one in September 1939, create larger waves of up to 6 meters which are capable of considerable erosion of shores and damage to shore structures (McEwen, 1935). Waves 8 meters high produced by a storm of November 14 and 15, 1958, capsized several fishing boats as well as damaging shores.

Particularly well developed during the summer are the long-period (13 to 20 seconds) waves originated by storms in the Southern Hemisphere, but now far beyond the influence of the causative winds and therefore known as swell, in contrast to sea. Occasional large waves of this origin wash high on beaches during summer, spreading consternation, sunbathers, and blankets. As shown by Sverdrup (1947) and Munk (1947b), the period and length of the waves are a function of the distance from the storm center; thus, the period and approach direction of swells serve as criteria for determining the paths followed by storms far at sea. Even more useful for storm tracking are longer period (up to 30 seconds) and faster forerunners of swell (Munk, 1947c) which have such a low amplitude that they cannot be detected except by wave meters having suitable frequency filters.

More common are swells that enter the region from several different small storm centers. Nearly always present are the waves from the North Pacific, from one or more centers west of California, and from local winds. These different sets of waves spread throughout the continental borderland, and

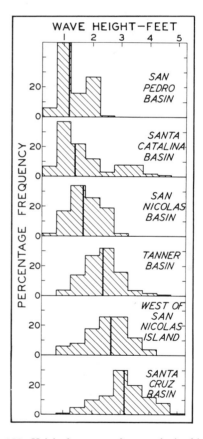

Figure 103. Height frequency of waves obtained by estimating from shipboard the heights of 75 to 100 successive waves at points near the middles of various basins having different degrees of exposure. The top three diagrams were measured on June 17, 1957, and the next two on June 18, both days having light winds. Bottom measurement was on June 19 after the wind had increased to about 40 knots. Wide vertical lines indicate mean heights of waves in each diagram. Mean periods of waves were 5 to 7 seconds.

their movements may easily be studied by visual observation from the air (Fig. 104).

In addition to being caused by two or more different storm centers, crossing sets of waves are also produced by refraction around both sides of islands and banks. In fact, the Polynesians used crossing wave sets on the lee side of islands as a navigational aid, incorporating the information on their famous stick maps (Emery, Tracey, and Ladd, 1954, p. 45, Pl. 1). Still other, but smaller, waves are reflections from shores of the mainland and islands. The many islands off southern California give rise to complicated patterns of crossing sea and swell which can be observed visually (Pierson, 1951) or recorded by wave meters.

Commonly, the records show very complex patterns which have been produced by interference between many different sets of waves coming from various directions and with different periods (Shepard and LaFond, 1940; Sverdrup, Johnson, and Fleming, 1942, p. 530). Some records, however, show relatively simple envelopes of alternating sequences of small and large resultant waves produced by only two main sets of interfering waves (Fig. 105). Usually each record is dominated by one set of high waves which may be of either long or short period.

The velocity of waves depends on wave length and depth of water,

$$V = \sqrt{(gL/2\pi) \tanh (2\pi D/L)},$$

where V = velocity, L = wave length, and D = water depth. In water deeper than $L/2$ this equation is approximated by $V = \sqrt{gL/2\pi}$, showing that the velocity is con-

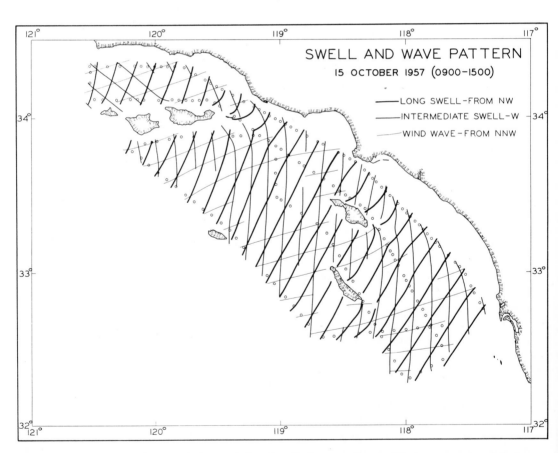

Figure 104. Pattern of crossing wave trains consisting of swells from two distant offshore storm centers and of waves from local winds. Production of crossed waves in the lee of islands is suggested but is not clearly shown because of the wide spacing of lines of observation. Data from visual examination aboard Marlin seaplane of Fleet Air Wind Fourteen, San Diego, at altitudes of 300 to 600 meters on October 15, 1957.

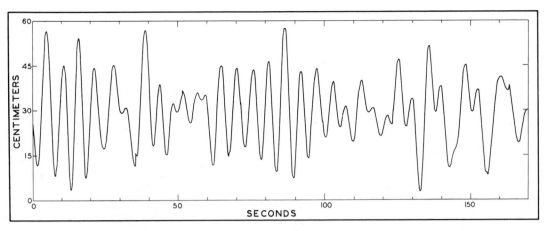

Figure 105. Wave record made with Vibraton wave recorder in 35 feet of water near the end of Scripps Pier, La Jolla. Taken during a period of low waves, it shows characteristic envelopes developed by superposition of 12.5-second swell and local 5-second wind waves. Courtesy of Walter H. Munk.

trolled only by the wave length. In water shallower than $L/20$, the equation is approximated by $V = \sqrt{gD}$. Since the velocity is progressively less in shallower and shallower water, a wave approaching shore diagonally becomes refracted, bending more or less parallel to shore. A spectacular example of wave refraction is exhibited at the east end of San Nicolas Island where waves moving southeasterly have been refracted by both the north and south coasts of the island and crash together at the end of a wave- and current-shaped spit (Norris, 1952). Waves from each side pass around the end of the spit and are further refracted and diffracted so that they move northwesterly, 180° from their original path (Fig. 106).

Variations in depth of water near the shore produce curvatures of the wave crests because of slowing of the part of the wave in shallow areas as compared to the part in deeper waters. The spacings of wave crests as measured on aerial photographs served as a wartime method of estimating water depth at prospective sites for amphibious landings; similarly, the relative wave heights along a coast can be predicted from a knowledge of the offshore bottom topography (Anonymous, 1944; Munk and Traylor, 1947; Dunham, 1951). As a result of refraction, wave energy is concentrated at seaward projecting points and is diffused within bays (Fig. 107). Thus, waves tend to develop a straight coast

by erosion of points and deposition in indentations, but straightening is opposed by variations in resistance to erosion of coastal strata. For example, the projecting points of the Palos Verdes Hills (Fig. 37) owe their origin to thick sections of basalt sills which are much more resistant than the Miocene shales that form the cliffs within the small bays.

This refraction of waves is the first indication of transfer of wave energy to the bottom and the beginning of appreciable geological work by the waves. Since refraction occurs only where the water depth is considerably less than half the wave length, Dietz and Menard (1951) have pointed out that effective wave base must be less than about 10 meters off most coasts such as that of southern California. Between this depth and the highest shore level reached by waves, nearly all wave erosion and most transportation and deposition take place. The turbulence and orbital motion of the water before and after the waves break causes much of the erosion. The orbital motion is such that a water particle on the forward slope of an advancing wave crest is lifted when the crest overtakes it, is carried forward with the crest, drops as it is left behind, and is finally carried back seaward in the trough between crests to begin the cycle anew (Fig. 108). Before the wave breaks, the orbit is more or less circular; afterward it is a very

Figure 106. Wave refraction at San Nicolas Island. Swell from northwest is refracted around the island, meeting at a spit on the east side of the island and producing crossed wave crests beyond the end of the spit. Photograph by U. S. Geological Survey, courtesy of J. B. Schoellhamer.

elongate ellipse. Breaking (Fig 109) occurs where the waves drive into water too shallow to fill the circular orbit, usually about four-thirds the breaker height (Munk, 1949a). Breakers can occur at somewhat greater depths (to twice the breaker height) when the onshore wind velocity is great or where the bottom has a sharp break in slope. At that point the wave rises to as much as 20 per cent higher than before breaking, and the crest curls over and collapses on the hollow orbit. When the wave fails to become steep enough to break, the crest merely spills down the steepened front of the wave. After either breaking or spilling the wave changes to one of translation, in which the water drives to-ward the shore, more nearly keeping pace with the crest.

Breakers and Associated Currents

The orbits of water particles in waves are larger near the surface than at depth, giving rise to a shoreward mass transport of water in the direction of wave propagation. After the waves break, their onshore momentum greatly increases the transport so that more water is brought into the breaker zone than can escape between wave crests. This wave pressure can result in water piling up as much as a meter above the level outside the breaker zone. Most of this water escapes in rip currents (Shepard, Emery, and LaFond, 1941) which flow seaward more or less perpendicular to sandy shores (Fig. 110). At their landward end these rip currents are supplied by lateral feeder channels which gather water from one or both sides. Where the rip current passes through the breaker zone it is narrow and reaches its greatest speed, as much as 1 meter/sec. Speeds within and landward of the breaker zone are more or less uniform from surface to the bottom, excepting for minor reduction by bottom friction, so that channels are commonly cut several feet deep in the sand along the route of the rip currents (Fig. 31). Fairly high speeds may continue as far as 1000 feet beyond the breakers where the water forms a large bulbous head which may be sheared away by the general coastal current and moved parallel to the shore.

The rest of the water piled up landward of the breakers escapes by a seaward movement at the bottom, but the velocity is low, mostly less than about 1 per cent of the orbital velocity under the wave crest (Munk, 1949*a;* Shepard and Inman, 1951*b*). Where rip cur-

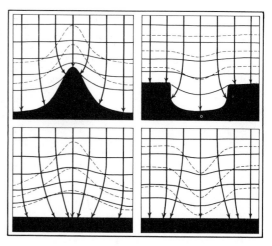

Figure 107. Effects of refraction of waves on various kinds of shores. Dash lines indicate bottom contours; narrow lines, wave crests; wide lines, orthogonals; black areas, land. Note that orthogonals converge on a projecting point inshore of a submarine ridge, leading to concentration of wave energy and maximum erosive force. Orthogonals diverge within a bay inshore of a submarine canyon, leading to diffusion of wave energy and minimum erosion or even deposition of sediments.

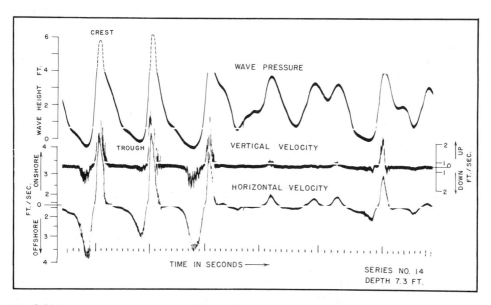

Figure 108. Orbital current meter record made 0.8 foot above sand bottom at a depth of 8.5 feet just seaward of breaker zone at Scripps Pier. Note that the maximum horizontal water velocity is onshore under the wave crest. In this particular zone the maximum vertical water velocity is upward and is also nearly under the wave crest owing to steepness of the wave fronts. From Inman and Nasu (1956).

Figure 109. Development of a breaker—curling over of crest followed by collapse. Height is about 1.5 meter. July 22, 1957, at Newport Beach.

rents return seaward most of the water trapped within the breaker zone by mass transport, there may be no seaward return at the bottom. In any event neither the high-speed rip currents nor the slow bottom return of water fits in any way the popular concept of undertow capable of sucking a swimmer down and drowning him. Perhaps the undertow myth is a result of faulty observation in the breaker zone where a bather can be bowled over by the crest of a wave which strikes him head to foot, and then, by the time he regains his feet, the longer slower backwash between crests pulls his feet from beneath him again. The combination of landward push from head to foot and seaward pull about the legs, even though not simultaneous, may give the illusion of undertow, particularly to a frightened bather. In fact, the stories in southern California newspapers of drowning by undertow refer mostly to victims carried beyond their depth by rip currents. According to Captain J. F. Stevenson, Chief Life Guard, Los Angeles County, about 95 per cent of the 1500 annual rescues made by county life guards are of bathers

caught in rip currents. Since the currents are strongest in the spring when waves are highest (April 1 to June 15), about 75 per cent of the rescues are made in this period,

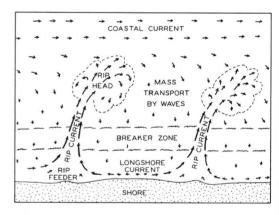

Figure 110. Superimposition of nearshore current system on general coastal current. Shoreward mass transport of water by waves is accelerated in breaker zone, longshore current forms in surf zone, rip currents develop and return most of water seaward through the zone of mass transport by waves, and the head of the rip current is moved parallel to shore by the coastal current. Adapted from Shepard and Inman (1951b).

even though the number of bathers is smaller than during the late summer when the water is warmer. These rescues and the occasional drownings are usually needless because rip currents can easily be recognized and avoided by noting the yellow-greenish color of the water produced by suspended sand, the presence of a peripheral line of foam or debris, a gap in the line of breakers, and a peculiar peaked and splashy character of the water surface.

Generally, the rip currents are active in spurts of several minutes duration. After a sequence of especially large waves, the water level shoreward of the breaker zone rises and the resulting hydraulic head is great enough to force a passage through the crests of advancing breakers, especially when the next waves are smaller ones. When most of the trapped water has drained away, the rip current ceases; a few minutes later the cycle is renewed when large waves build up the water level again (Shepard and Inman, 1950). This

intermittent rise and fall of water near the beach produces a low wave of long period (2 to 4 minutes) which has been termed surf beat by Munk (1949b), who recognized it on tsunami recorders. The variations in water level inshore of the breaker zone are also shown by transgressions and regressions of the swash zone (area alternately exposed and covered by thin sheets of water) on sandy beaches. Smaller transgressions and regressions of the water-saturated part of the beach result from advance of large waves far up the beach and the breakdown of subsequent smaller waves by backwash from the first one (Fig. 111) (Emery and Gale, 1951). This has given rise to another misconception of the sea, that every seventh wave is a large one.

Where the waves strike the beach at an angle, the wave pressure develops longshore currents inshore of the breaker zone. Other things being equal, the fastest currents are produced by waves having crests that make

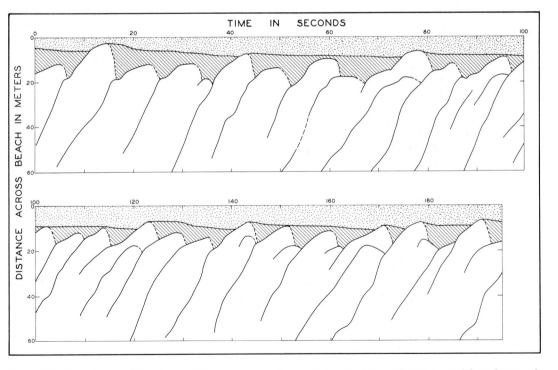

Figure 111. The advance of breakers and their run-up on the sandy beach at Point Dume as read from frames of slow-speed motion pictures. Lined area is fully saturated sand; dotted area is partly drained or dry sand. Note that only occasional waves run far up the beach and saturate the sand, which then slowly drains until covered by the next large wave. From Emery and Gale (1951, Fig. 2).

the largest angles with the shoreline (Putnam, Munk, and Traylor, 1949). However, as pointed out by Shepard and Inman (1950), so much water may be piled up at local shore areas of wave convergence owing to submarine ridges that it can flow as a longshore current against approaching breakers. The most complete study of longshore currents in the region was made by Shepard (1950*a*) from the Mexican border to Newport. Currents were found to be dominantly southward, in response to the regional pattern of waves. This agrees with the net direction of transport of sand into breakwaters and against groins as reported by Johnson (1956) and others. During summer, however, when swell from the Southern Hemisphere is important, part of the area has northerly longshore currents. Only slight relationship of current direction and speed to tide is evident. Speeds range up to 1 meter/sec but average about 0.25 meter/sec.

Nearly all the foregoing discussion refers only to shores having sandy beaches, but this is the most common kind of shore of the southern California mainland. Rocky shores of the mainland and particularly of the islands are so irregular that they break up advancing wave crests into sections, most of which crash directly against the rocks instead of forming offshore breaker zones. As a result, there is little or no trapping of water, and rip currents form only where there is a seaward deflection of general coastal currents by projecting rocky points. Reflection of individual waves by the rocks is common, but the reflected waves are small and usually lose their identity within a fraction of a mile from the shore.

Tsunamis

At sea, earthquakes have commonly been felt aboard ships, reportedly as a sudden jar which frequently led to the belief that the ship had run aground. During the Long Beach earthquake in 1933 many of the shocks were felt aboard naval vessels anchored in the harbor (Bittinger, 1933). No tsunami was produced by this quake; a tide gauge record merely showed the earth movement

(Fig. 112). Eight local offshore earthquakes between 1934 and 1946 also failed to produce recognizable tsunamis on tide gauge records (Clements and Emery, 1947), but the November 4, 1927, shock off Point Conception was followed by a 2-meter wave on the nearby but uninhabited shore. Other small tsunamis, probably all from distant sources, were noted along various shores or on tide gauges of southern California in 1812, 1854, 1855, 1872, 1885, 1946, and 1957 (Bache, 1856; Davidson, 1872; Green, 1946; Heck, 1947; O'Brien and Kuchenreuther, 1958). New types of recorders devised especially for wave periods of 10 minutes to 3 hours have shown the presence of other possible tsunamis (mostly of about 20-minute period) too small to be recorded by tide gauges (Munk, 1953). Although only small tsunamis have been reported along the coast of southern California, the occurrence of infrequent large ones off South America (Gutenberg and Richter, 1949, pp. 94–97) suggests that southern California may not be immune. Certainly, one as great as those that struck the Hawaiian Islands on April 1, 1946 (Shepard, Macdonald, and Cox, 1950), and on March 9, 1957, would cause enormous damage and some loss of life in the low and densely populated areas of Malibu Beach and Newport Beach.

Seiches

In each of the larger bays of the Pacific coast periodic surging of the water has been noted. The surges are usually less than 15 cm high and have periods intermediate between those of wind waves and tides (Fig. 112). These are known as seiches (Sverdrup, Johnson, and Fleming, 1942, pp. 538–542), free oscillations of periods controlled by the depth and length of the bays: $T = 4L/\sqrt{gD}$, where T is the period, L is the length of an open-mouthed bay, and D is the average depth. Although it is generally believed that any disturbance of water level can start them, such as tides, strong gusty winds, barometric pressure changes, and perhaps earthquakes, tsunamis, and surf beats, no case history of a seiche in southern California has been re-

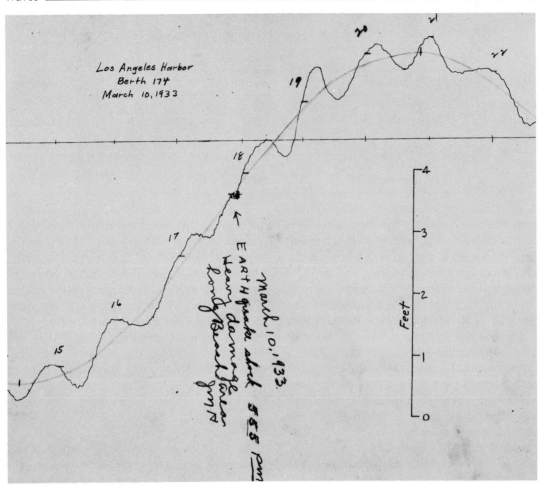

Figure 112. Part of tide curve for March 10, 1933, at San Pedro. Note small (approximately 6-inch) seiche having a period of about 1 hour. The Long Beach earthquake failed to produce a tsunami or to materially disturb the seiche, although it shook the gauge. Courtesy C. K. Green, U. S. Coast and Geodetic Survey.

ported. If the disturbance happens to have the same period as the seiche, resonance builds up the amplitude so that waves in a bay may be higher than those outside it, even though wind waves cannot enter the bay. An outstanding example is the Bay of Fundy at Nova Scotia with its 16-meter seiche of tidal period (Marmer, 1926, pp. 217–226).

As an experiment for a class in oceanography, Rich (1956) measured the water level at two stations in Los Angeles Harbor (A-1 and A-2) at 2- and 3-minute intervals for 6 hours during high tide on December 22, 1955. Additional data from three tide gauge records were made available by the U. S.

Coast and Geodetic Survey and the Los Angeles Harbor Department. Comparison of all records shows that the maximum seiche amplitude of 11 cm occurred at the two stations farthest from the harbor entrance, Station A-2 and Berth 174. The mean amplitudes present a regular decrease from 8 cm at Station A-2 to zero at the lighthouse (Table 8). Irregularities in the record from the lighthouse and in some of those at Berth 60 are ascribed to wakes of passing ships. The mean period for the three stations where it could be measured reliably was 49.9 minutes, in good agreement with the theoretical value of 53 minutes, based on an average depth of 10 meters and basin length of 8200 meters

Table 8
SEICHE DATA IN LOS ANGELES HARBOR, DECEMBER 22, 1955

Station	Location	Distance from Lighthouse, meters	Mean Amplitude, cm	Mean Period, minutes
USC&GS	Lighthouse	0	0	–
LAHD	Berth 60	2200	1.3	indefinite
A-1	Berth 74	3200	4.8	50.8
LAHD	Berth 174	6500	5.8	51.5
A-2	R/V Velero IV			47.4
	near Berth 202	8100	8.1	

from the lighthouse to the beginning of a narrow channel near Station A-2. Leypoldt (1937) suggested that this harbor seiche, which had been noted as long ago as 1853, owes its origin to the natural period of oscillation of the water between the shore and the east side of the Santa Rosa–Cortes Ridge, but the dimensions of this body of water are such that its seiche should have a period of only 14 minutes, far different from the observed period in the habor. Very possibly, however, such oscillating bodies of water contribute to the irregularity of wave and tide gauge records.

Although the seiche in Los Angeles Harbor has a much smaller amplitude than the one in the Bay of Fundy, the associated horizontal movements of water can be great enough to drive ships sideways, damaging both ships and docks and thus requiring remedial measures to reduce the movements (Vanoni and Carr, 1951). Measurements made in the spring of 1944 by Knapp (1952) showed the presence of two wave periods in the outer harbor, 15 seconds and 3 minutes. The vertical motion of ships in that area corresponded to the 15-second wave period, but the longitudinal and transverse motions had intermediate periods of between 100 and 150 seconds. Longitudinal movements as great as 4 meters were noted. Subsequent construction of harbor works has reportedly decreased the amplitude of ship surge in the outer harbor. A brief examination of ship surge at Berth 60 near the entrance to the inner harbor was made on September 2, 1957, by measuring the fore and aft movement of a 10,000-ton freighter. Movements

as great as 35 cm occurred, but the average period was only 23 seconds, closer to the period of the swell (at that time 14 seconds) than to that of the seiche. Since surge encountered during loading operations is reported to be greater at Berth 60 and other berths near the harbor entrance than at berths farther within the harbor, it appears likely that at least this ship surge is due more to swells entering the harbor than to seiches.

Internal Waves

Internal waves are periodic oscillations of a density interface beneath the water surface. They are easiest to recognize by cyclical changes of temperature at some fixed depth. Waves of this type have been found in several environments in the region, but they have not been studied extensively. The first serious attempt to study internal waves atop the mainland shelf of southern California was made off San Diego by Ufford (1947a, 1947b, 1947c). In order to learn the wave length, speed, and direction of approach, he measured temperatures with bathythermographs at intervals as short as 2 minutes for several hours at each of three or more stations, sometimes using as platforms three ships anchored in depths of 36 meters. The results of seven such sets of measurements were interpreted as showing the presence of internal waves having periods of 9–136 minutes, lengths of 97–343 meters, speeds of 3–16 cm/sec, and average heights of 1.5–5 meters. Ufford concluded that the waves were progressive and moving chiefly on courses toward land. Most of the records, however, show a complex form similar to that of surface waves and strongly suggestive of interference between two or more sets of internal waves.

In a study of slicks off the La Jolla region Ewing (1950) found that these thin films of oily organic matter are associated with the troughs of internal waves (Fig. 113). Lateral movement of the slicks toward shore indicated that the internal waves were of the progressive type with dimensions similar to those of Ufford. Bending of the slicks to conform with the shore showed that the internal waves became refracted in the same manner as surface waves. Further analogy with surface waves is shown by breaking internal waves, or internal surf, reported by Defant (1950a) in the Mediterranean and observed by R. E. Stevenson (personal communication) in a line of bathythermograph lowerings in San Pedro Bay in 1954. During 1950 a 6-day series of measurements were made by three ships of the California Cooperative Oceanic Fisheries Investigation to test the suggestion by Defant (1950a, 1950b) that internal waves of tidal period exist and are capable of causing erroneous interpretations of currents from dynamic topography. The three ships were stationed in a line 40, 160, and 320 nautical miles off

Point Sur (about 50 miles north of Chart I). At the innermost ship internal tides of amplitude 10 to 15 meters were detected at depths between 12 and 110 meters (Reid, 1956). Although the period was tidal and the wave in phase with the tide at the coast, the asymmetry of highs and lows typical of the tide curve was lacking. At the two outer ships nonperiodic fluctuations of similar amplitude were measured. Since bathythermograph lowerings were made only at 1-hour intervals, the measurements could not show the short-period internal waves measured by Ufford.

An internal tide was also found at a depth of 61 meters (200 feet) at a station near the northwest end of Santa Catalina Basin, where temperature measurements were made at 1 to 2 hour intervals for 25 hours (Emery, 1956b). Unlike the one off Point Sur, this wave lagged about 2.5 hours behind the tide ashore (Fig. 114). More interesting, however, are waves measured below the sill of the basin; these exhibit an intermediate period of 2 hours and possibly another of 18 hours. The amplitude was as much as 200 meters (650 feet). It is suggested that these deep oscillations of temperature indicate the presence of one or more standing internal waves having a node near the center of the basin (Fig. 115). Such waves also

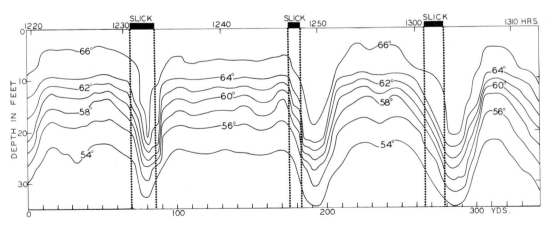

Figure 113. Temperature (°F) structure under a series of sea surface slicks measured with a fixed series of thermister beads at an anchor station off Mission Beach June 12, 1958. The position of each slick corresponds to the trough of an internal wave where the isotherms are sharply depressed. The slicks and associated internal waves move shoreward in this area at speeds as great as 0.25 meter/sec. Courtesy of E. C. LaFond, U. S. Navy Electronics Laboratory, San Diego.

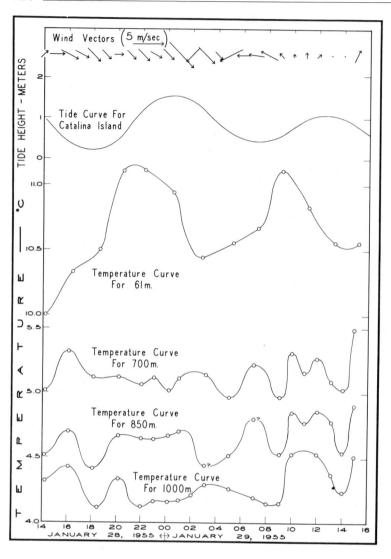

Figure 114. Variation of temperature at depths of 61, 700, 850, and 1000 meters at Station 2988 near the northwest end of Santa Catalina Basin during a 25-hour period. Note that temperature at 1000 meters is sometimes higher than that measured at other times at 850 meters. From Emery (1956*b*, Fig. 3).

help to explain the prior find of currents as great as 15 cm/sec at the floor and near the centers of Santa Cruz and San Pedro Basins and of 5 cm/sec in Santa Monica Basin. They should also contribute greatly to the mixing of basin and overlying waters, which may help to explain the known complete replacement of basin waters in periods of 2 to 20 years.

Tides

Tidal Cycles

Nearly everyone has noted the alternate exposing and covering of the shore by ebbing and flooding tide, but the chief means of obtaining precise information on the tidal cycles is by the use of recording tide gauges. Data from these records serve as a basis for the prediction of future tides (Marmer, 1926, 1932; Anonymous, 1955) which correspond very closely with those actually occurring. The small differences that do exist are mostly the result of variations in water density and local winds.

Diurnal tide curves of southern California are characterized by asymmetry such that there is usually one cycle of greater range and one of lesser range, unlike the more symmetrical tide curves of the Atlantic coast. This asymmetry is produced by interference mainly between diurnal and semi-

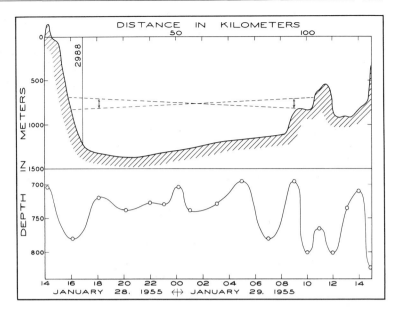

Figure 115. Oscillations of 5°C isothermal surface in Santa Catalina Basin as inferred from temperature variations measured during a 25-hour period at Station 2988. From Emery (1956*b*, Fig. 5).

diurnal tidal components, which in turn are results of the shape of the ocean basin (Marmer, 1932) or of other causes (Sverdrup, Johnson, and Fleming, 1942, pp. 545–564). The greatest diurnal asymmetry in spring tides occurs near the summer and winter solstices (June 22 and December 22) and the least near the equinoxes (March 21 and September 23).

For the region the mean range is 3.7 feet, but the extreme is 8.7 feet, reached during the spring tides of the solstices (Fig. 116). The annual mean of the lower of the two low tides which occur each day is the datum plane for hydrographic charts of the area— mean lower low water. Some topographic maps of the land, however, are based on mean sea level, 2.8 feet above mean lower low water. The lowest of the low low tides occur at the same time of the year as the maximum daily range and are used to advantage by collectors of marine life along the shore. These very low tides (called minus tides when below the level of mean lower low water) occur during winter in the afternoon and during summer in the early morning hours before sunrise. The timing during the summer is fortunate because, if the lower shore were laid bare in the afternoon, it would become heated and dried out so much that many small animals restricted to that zone would be killed.

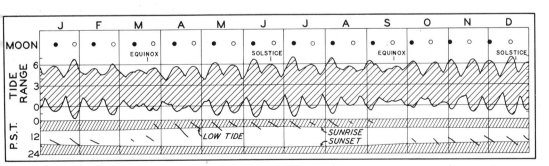

Figure 116. Range between highest and lowest tide of each day during 1956 at San Pedro. Note close relationship of dates of spring tides to times of new moon (black) and full moon (white). At the bottom is shown the time of day at which minus (below mean lower low water) tides occur; note that extreme low tides occur in the afternoon during winter and before sunrise during summer.

Just as important as the diurnal and annual cycles is the biweekly cycle of tides: spring (when the earth, moon, and sun are in line, moon either new or full) and neap (when the moon is at first or last quarter). One of the biological effects of the biweekly cycle was pointed out in connection with the egg-laying habits of grunion. A geological effect is that of erosion of the upper part of the beaches during spring tides and deposition during neap tides. During spring tides the sea reaches higher on the beach than at other times (Fig. 117), permitting erosion of that zone; when the tide falls or rises, sea level moves through the midtide zone so quickly that little erosion is accomplished. In contrast, during neap tides the tide range is small and sea level remains most of the time near midtide. As a result, during spring tides the wave energy is carried at high tide across most of the beach, per-

mitting concentrated erosion high on the beach. Some of the eroded sand may be deposited atop the berm, but most of it is usually carried seaward to be deposited at or below mean tide (LaFond and Rao, 1954). During neap tides the situation is reversed with most of the erosion near or below midtide and most of the sand carried landward to build up the upper foreshore. For a whole year, of course, the histogram of sea level position approaches a normal frequency curve with the mode near mean sea level.

Other effects on the beach are produced by seepage of water into and out of the sand. As the tide rises, water enters the sand and flows landward; however, before it can saturate the beach and form a horizontal water table the tide falls and the water on the seaward side of the beach escapes from the sand, lowering the water table there. Thus the rise and fall of the tide against the beach produces a wave of tidal period that moves landward through the sand (Fig. 118) but lags in phase behind the tide and diminishes in amplitude in a landward direction (Emery and Foster, 1948). The escape of water from the beach during low tide parallels the lesser inward and outward movement produced as a continuation at depth of the orbital movement of water particles under passing waves (Putnam, 1949). Both kinds of water movement lead to some elutriation and removal of fine silt and clay from the sand, thus tending to preserve the well-sorted character of beach sands. In some areas where heavy pumping of water wells has greatly lowered the water table (Poland, Piper, and others, 1956), some of the sea water in the beach probably drains away landward. In other areas a landward decrease in salinity of interstitial water indicates a seaward loss of fresh water at low tides.

Tidal Currents

In the southern California region the tide wave moves from southeast to northwest at such a rate that high tide reaches Point Conception about a half-hour after passing San Diego. Associated with the tide are

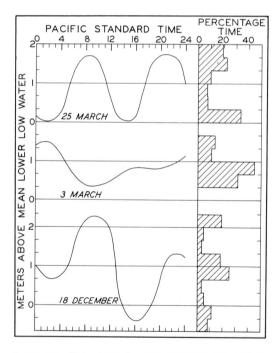

Figure 117. Tide curves for days of typical symmetrical spring tide near equinox, of an asymmetrical neap tide, and of an asymmetrical spring tide near solstice. Histograms show percentage of day that sea level stayed within each 1-foot (one-third meter) interval above or below mean lower low water; the difference in modal positions of sea level during spring and neap tides produces erosion at different parts of the beach.

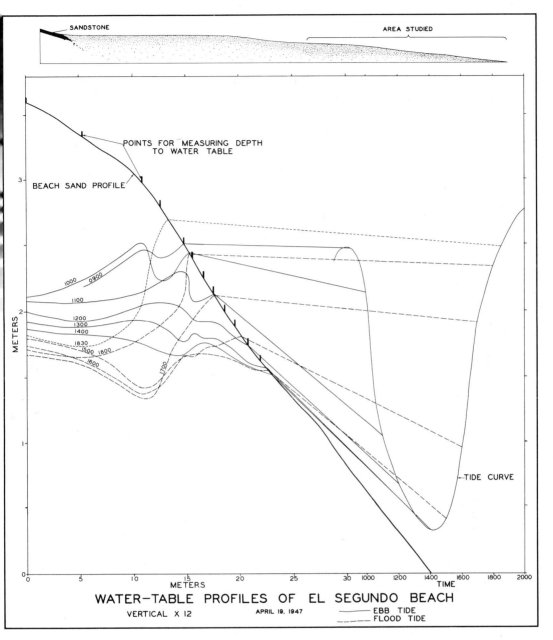

Figure 118. Positions of water table in sand beach at El Segundo. Note phase lag of water table behind that of tide curve of open sea. From Emery and Foster (1948, Fig. 1).

currents that on the open shelf theoretically reach their maximum between high and low tide, that is, at ebb and flood stages. In this region the tidal currents rarely exceed 20 cm/sec and, owing to earth rotation, the tidal current of the open shelf should change direction clockwise so that it makes a complete sweep around the compass in about 12.4 hours. Boundary conditions near the shore and at the bottom confine the tidal current largely to directions parallel to the shore and bottom contours. In addition, currents induced by winds commonly are great enough to mask those produced by tides (Fig. 119).

A quite different effect is believed by

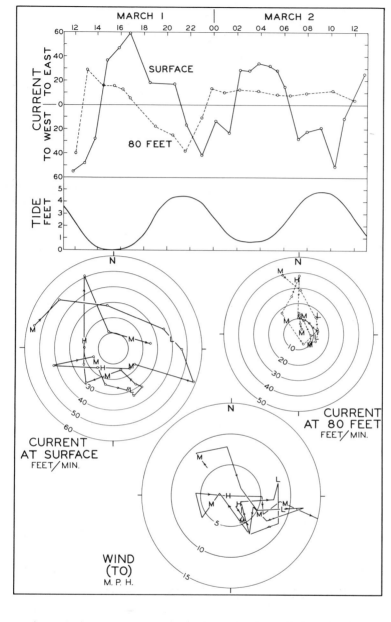

Figure 119. Currents relative to tide height in an area 120 feet deep off Point Loma, San Diego, on March 1 and 2, 1957. Upper lines (solid for surface measurements, dashed for 80-foot measurements) show tidal current in terms of flood and ebb (to east and west, respectively); note that maximum current was usually earlier than midtide and that currents at surface and 80 feet were out of phase. Lower diagrams show current ellipses having clockwise rotation with time, except when currents were slow and erratic. Times of high, middle, and low tides are indicated by H, M, and L. Note the rotation to right of currents at depth with respect to those at surface. Variation in wind direction shown in bottom polar diagram; note that the wind happens to be nearly in phase with tide so that current ellipses may be products of both wind and tide. Based on drogue measurements by Geological Diving Consultants, Inc., for city of San Diego.

Leipper (1955) and Stevenson and Gorsline (1956) to be produced by tidal action. During the week between neap and spring tides the increase of tide range and its associated net rise of sea level lead to more intense mixing of the water atop the shelf. When the water is highly stratified, as in summer, the stirring produces a cooling that may reach the water surface and form a dome-like cool spot of diameter as great as 3 miles. Movement of cool spots by tidal currents may lead to temperature variations that are of approximate tidal period (Arthur, 1954) as measured at piers. Such a development of cool spots by tidal origin may take place independently of winds, showing that care must be exerted in ascribing areas of cool water only to upwelling by wind stress.

Sea Level

The mean sea level for any period can be computed from the record of hourly tide heights. Such computations show that sea level is not constant for any given locality, but that instead it has seasonal and longer-term variations. In southern California an annual cycle of about 21 cm was observed in 1937–1938 with low sea level in the spring and high in the late summer and fall (Lafond, 1939*a*). The same cycle characterizes later years also (Stewart, Zetler, and Taylor, 1958), and it has been found to be typical of most other areas of the ocean where adequate data are available (Pattullo, Munk, Revelle, and Strong, 1955). The chief cause of variation appears to be that of density of sea water, a function mostly of temperature but partly also of salinity, which in turn is controlled by relative amounts of rainfall and evaporation. Winds exert only a minor and irregular effect on sea level in this region. It is possible, of course, that parallel variations of sea level, temperature, salinity, and barometric pressure may all be results of a more general cause not yet known.

A smooth curve drawn through a plot of yearly average sea level for California tide gauge stations (Fig. 120) appears to show a general rise relative to land since good records were begun about 1900, although the year-to-year variations are nearly as great as the long-term rise. For San Diego the rise averages about 23 cm per century, similar to but a little greater than rates observed at San Francisco and Seattle (Marmer, 1949). A rise of about 12 cm per century was obtained by Gutenberg (1941*a*) and Kuenen (1950, p. 534) based on tide gauges of the world. This rate of rise is about the same as might be expected from the return of water to the ocean by melting glaciers of the world during recent years, and it suggests that the relative rise of

sea level at San Diego is probably real. In contrast, the relative rise at stations on the United States coasts of the Atlantic and Gulf of Mexico is three times as great as at San Diego, suggesting that land subsidence and compaction in these areas may have been twice as great as the rise of sea level. A much lower rate found in Scandanavia indicates continuing emergence of the land by rebound after melting away of its former ice cap.

It has been suggested that the rate of melting of glaciers and the corresponding rise of sea level have been accelerated by a small increase of temperature of the atmosphere resulting from the greenhouse effect of carbon dioxide liberated by the burning of fossil fuels since the beginning of the industrial revolution (Plass, 1956; Revelle and Suess, 1957). If the rise of sea level continues and increases in rate, a rather damp future awaits some of southern California's resort cities which are built upon low sand spits and beaches. Another result of rise of sea level was pointed out by Munk and Revelle (1952), who showed that a 10-cm (0.3 foot) rise can lead to a 0.6-millisecond lengthening of the day and a 3-meter shift of the pole of rotation of the earth.

Paleoceanography

The chief remaining evidence of the nature of ancient seas is that preserved in their sediments. Distribution and composition of these sediments provide a more or less complete record of the outline of the seas, or the

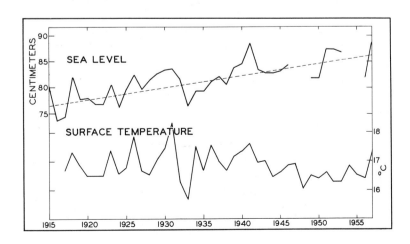

Figure 120. Yearly average sea level at San Diego (1915–1924) and La Jolla (1925–1957). Fluctuations are to some degree related to annual water surface temperature (La Jolla) which, in turn, is inversely proportional to water density. The long-term rise of sea level is ascribed to the return of water to the ocean by melting ice caps. Data from UGGI and USC&GS (Anonymous, 1940, 1950, 1956*a*).

paleogeography, of a particular time interval. Information about the depth, temperature, salinity, oxygen content, and movements of the water is more difficult to obtain, especially where the water was fairly deep, but some clues can be extracted, particularly from the organic remains in the sediment.

Before shells and other organic remains can be used as effective indicators of water characteristics in ancient seas, it is necessary to learn something of their ecology in the present ocean. Unsystematic dredgings to find new species or to establish general faunal relationships to other parts of the ocean are of little aid for making interpretations of paleoecology. The first important systematic work in the deep waters of southern California was done by Natland (1933), who collected snapper bottom samples and measured temperatures between San Pedro and Santa Catalina Island. Study of the benthonic foraminiferans in these and a few deeper samples permitted him to establish five biozones between the surface and a depth of 8340 feet (2540 meters). This work was extended into most of the other basins by Crouch (1952), who studied the foraminiferans in cores collected and analyzed for organic matter and other sedimentary characteristics by Emery and Rittenberg (1952). Crouch's results supported Natland's depth zonation and, since most of the cores were from basins deeper than Natland's San Pedro Basin, they permitted subdivision of Natland's two deepest biozones into four. In addition, the use of cores showed something of the recent history of the ocean not obtainable by the use of only snapper samples. Core lengths ranged from 1.2 to 2.75 meters (depths of penetration from about 2.4 to 5.5 meters), but no systematic change of fauna indicative of marked changes in water characteristics was found.

Most of the cores studied by Crouch contained sandy layers which included Foraminifera reworked from shallower depths and from Pliocene and Miocene strata. Reworking of foraminiferans has been noted in other deep areas and in shelf sediments by Phleger (1951), Crouch (1954), and others. Because of the difficulty in recognition of reworked foraminiferans, Resig (1958) used a stain that colored those foraminiferans that contained protoplasm and therefore presumably were alive at the time of sampling. Enough differences in the depth distribution of the living and of the dead populations were detected to justify the making of more exhaustive studies which are now in progress. Another technique for improving the quality of ecological information is that of making statistical counts, rather than mere estimates, of the abundance of different species of foraminiferans. A counting technique applied by Bandy (1953a) to short cores and snapper samples from off San Diego, Point Conception, and San Francisco verified the change of population with water depth and served for setting up eight biozones which are somewhat different from those of Natland and Crouch.

Although a depth variation of foraminiferal populations has been established, its cause is still unknown although of paramount importance for gaining a knowledge of paleoceanography. The great difference between species of marine foraminiferans, ostracodes, and other animals and those from the brackish water of lagoons (Arnal, 1955; Ladd, Hedgpeth, and Post, 1957) permits a gross estimate of salinity but is incapable of distinguishing between the small variations of salinity normally present in the offshore environment. Small but mature tests of benthonic marine forms may indicate a deficiency of oxygen (Crouch, 1952), but it is not yet known whether the critical deficiency is in the water above the bottom or merely in the interstitial water. Many have considered temperature the prime ecological factor, mainly because it exhibits a large variation with depth; others have preferred to consider the control only as one of depth, attaching no particular physical or chemical control to depth. Several attempts have been made to separate the effects of temperature and of simple depth. One, by Crouch (1952), tried to determine whether the populations are uniform between the sill and bottom depth of basins where the water is isothermal over a considerable depth range. He found that his biozones present a distinct depth zonation from basin to basin when plotted according to temperature (or to depth of basin sills) but a poor zonation when plotted by depth samples. In contrast, Bandy (1953a) discovered that some of the shallow-water species off San Diego occur in deeper and colder water off San Francisco and that there is a marked difference in the Foraminifera at equivalent depths off northern and southern California, even though temperatures are similar. A related discrepancy exists in the faunas off Alaska and Panama. In addition, Resig (1958) detected differences in living faunas at various depths in the isothermal water below the sill of Santa Cruz Basin. Depth zonation of foraminiferal populations also exists in the isothermal waters in lagoons of the Marshall Islands (Cushman, Todd, and Post, 1954).

It is possible that the depth variation of foraminiferans is such a complex function of temperature, oxygen content, food supply, nature of substrate, and other factors that a precise evaluation of oceanographic characteristics from faunas alone is almost hopeless. However, empirical extrapolation of biozones from the present southern California basins to ancient ones can still be made more or less safely. This was first accomplished for the now-filled Ventura Basin by Natland (1933) and was later somewhat extended and modified to include effects of turbidity currents (Natland and Kuenen, 1951) and rate of sedimentation and subsidence (Bandy, 1953b). Later, Natland and Rothwell (1954) and Natland (1957) applied the same technique to the Los Angeles Basin. Durham (1950, 1954) extended the general method back in time to the beginning of the Tertiary Period, using as criteria the horizontal distribution of living corals and shallow-water mollusks, instead of the vertical distribution of foraminiferans. The results of all studies suggest that the temperature of accumulation of the predominantly shallow-water strata of Paleocene and Eocene Epochs can be generalized at about 25°C, and of the Oligocene Epoch at about 23°, both higher than present water temperatures (Fig. 84).

The depths of the Miocene Epoch and particularly those of the Pliocene Epoch,

when sediments accumulated in deep water of the now-filled Los Angeles and Ventura Basins, may be identified by use of modern foraminiferal biozones (Fig. 121). Some support for estimates of ancient depths is provided by comparison of fish remains with the modern depth distribution of closely related fishes (David, 1943; Pierce, 1956). If the temperature variation with depth was the same during the past as now, the biozones may also indicate the paleotemperatures.

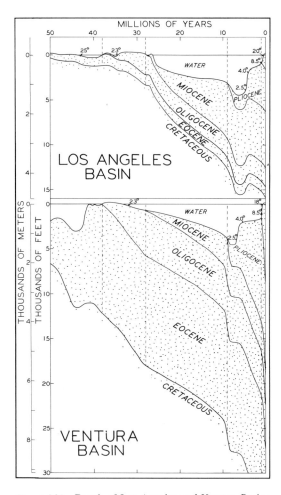

Figure 121. Depth of Los Angeles and Ventura Basins during past 50,000,000 years with possible temperature of bottom waters. Areas beneath bottom show thickness of various strata before and after physiographic basins were formed during the Miocene Epoch. Present state of compaction is assumed at all stages of accumulation because of lack of data on grain size for the strata. Time scale from Simpson (1947), depth and thickness data from Natland (1957), adaption of plot by Bandy (1953b).

Since correlation within and between basins is based on biozones, the correlations follow ecological lines rather than time lines, making uncertain the contemporaneity of events in the two basins. Even within a single basin the differential movements of separate blocks provided differences in nature of sediment, depth, and conditions of deposition. Nevertheless, along very general lines both the Ventura and the Los Angeles basins appear to have begun to subside during the Miocene from the largely shallow water and nonmarine environment of Oligocene and earlier times. The water depth appears to have reached its maximum of more than 4000 feet (1200 meters) in each basin during the Early or Middle Pliocene and, although subsidence continued, the rate of sedimentation increased so that both basins shoaled until the surface of both rose above sea level in about the Middle Pleistocene Epoch, thereafter receiving nonmarine sediments. During the times of greatest depth, analogy with modern basin biozones suggests that the temperature was lower than about 2.5°C. Afterward, as the water depth decreased, the temperature of accumulation increased to the present temperature or even higher for some Late Pleistocene and Recent sediments deposited in shallow lagoons.

The sediments deposited when the Ventura and Los Angeles Basins were physiographic depressions between Middle Miocene and Middle Pleistocene times (White, 1952) yield a partial confirmation of the conclusions reached from faunal studies. Neither evaporites nor fresh-water sedimentary rocks have been reported for this time span from the central areas of these basins, but of course such sediments could have been deposited along the shores and subsequently removed by erosion.

Inferences about paleoceanography can also be reached on the basis of paleogeography. As discussed in the section on lithology, the distribution and nature of Tertiary sedimentary rocks are such that the seas of the Eocene, Oligocene, and Early to Middle Miocene Epochs are believed to have been broad and quite shallow. Existing areas of broad shallow water are generally characterized by seasonal extremes of temperature resulting from the facts that the currents are sluggish and that the losses and gains of heat through the surface must be absorbed in only a short column of water with no opportunity for mixing with underlying water as in the deep ocean. As a result the sea off southern California during the early Tertiary Epochs must have been warmer during the summer and colder during the winter than the surface of the deep ocean at the same times. During Late Miocene and Pliocene Epochs the sea floor became broken into blocks, many of which sank to become areas of deep water. Owing to the increased depth, the water temperatures should have been more uniform, with less difference between summer and winter. Summer temperatures are probably more important than winter ones for organisms because this is usually the time of maximum growth and reproduction. If the surface temperatures of the deep ocean during the entire Tertiary were similar to those at present, the area of the continental borderland should have been populated during early Tertiary by mollusks and other fossil-forming animals which now live only in water warmer than that presently in the area, whereas during later Tertiary the animals should have been similar in their temperature requirements to those now living there. These inferences on topographic control of water temperature during the Tertiary appear to support conclusions reached from the fossil record by Durham (1950, 1954) and others.

During the Pleistocene stages of glacially lowered sea level, nearly the entire length of the Santa Rosa–Cortes Ridge must have been exposed, as shown by the distribution atop it of basalt cobbles from Santa Rosa Island and by the presence of a series of submerged marine terraces. When exposed, the ridge prevented the westward flow of surface water that now is entrained by the California Current. In the absence of such flow, upwelling due to entrainment was not possible, although some upwelling due to wind may have existed. With the consequent almost certain reduction in upwelling during stages of lowered sea level, the water temperature must have been higher relative to that of the deep ocean than at stages of high sea level such as at present. Accordingly, we might infer that the area contained many animals that now live only farther south off Mexico. Carter (1957a), Hubbs (personal communication), and others have given evidence that mollusks requiring relatively warm water have been present in the region during the past 10,000 years, but this evidence is still far from complete.

Recently, new methods of paleotemperature determination based on the ratio of oxygen isotopes 18 and 16 have been applied to stratigraphy (Urey, Lowenstam, Epstein, and McKinney, 1951). Emiliani (1955) found that cores of the deep sea (about 3000 km southsouthwest of Chart I) contain pelagic foraminiferans whose O^{18}/O^{16} ratio indicates many periodic variations between about 17 and 20°C at the depth of growth, 110 meters, which may correlate with glacial and interglacial ages of the Pleistocene Epoch. Smaller temperature variations were indicated by O^{18}/O^{16} ratios for benthonic foraminiferans that grew in the more uniform bottom water. This technique, when applied to the more rapidly deposited sediments of the California basins, may provide a more detailed record of the Pleistocene temperatures than is possible from deep-sea cores of the equatorial regions. If the temperature of growth of benthonic foraminiferans on the floor of each of the basins is determined by O^{18}/O^{16} ratios at core depths equivalent to, for example, 10,000 years based on radiocarbon dates, it can be assumed that the same temperature would have existed at the basin sill depth. If the temperature for each basin is plotted at the corresponding sill depth, a temperature-depth curve for this part of the Pacific can be constructed for the period 10,000 years ago, or for many other desired times.

The oxygen isotope method has also been applied to the Lomita marl (Lower Pleistocene) of the Los Angeles Basin by Emiliani and Epstein (1953), who found a general upward increase of temperature throughout the part of the formation that was sampled, perhaps indicating a change from glacial to interglacial conditions. The average temperature indicated by Miliolidae increased

from about 16 to 26°C, by *Elphidium* 14 to 18°, and by *Cassidulina* 12 to 14°. The differences are probably ascribable to differences in habitat of the various forms. Further application of the method to Tertiary strata should do much to remove the uncertainties inherent in the biozone method of determining paleotemperatures.

Important aspects of paleoceanography such as current direction, wave height and direction, and tide range await the development and use of proper criteria. A beginning has been made in the use of flow markings and ripple marks (Natland and Kuenen, 1951; Crowell, 1955), but until placed on a regional scale such indicators yield only information related to local slopes and areas of exposure. It is evident that the uncovering of knowledge about the ancient seas will be the subject of many future studies, particularly so because the more easily observed characteristics of the present ocean are now beginning to be understood.

Man-Made Oceanography

It is a well-known fact that shoreline engineering works of man alter local water movements by intercepting longshore currents and by providing lee-side areas of quiet water. Many structures exhibit both effects, but groins at right angles to the shore function better as current deflectors than as protectors for quiet water. The breakwater at Los Angeles Harbor probably intercepts little current because it lies in the lee of the Palos Verdes Hills and within a coastal indentation; however, the protection that it offers from waves and some current action has resulted in the accumulation of finer-than-normal sediment in the enclosed area. The Santa Monica breakwater appears to perform both functions because the longshore current is intercepted and its load of sand is caused to be deposited on the landward side, requiring removal at intervals of a few years. Many other examples could be cited including harbor works at Santa Barbara and Redondo Beach.

Although little known, other works of man are capable of producing currents or of superimposing local ones on the general coastal current. This occurs because large local discharges of warm water of low salinity form lenses that float atop the sea water of the shelf or mix with sea water to form lenses of mixed water. The light water tends, of course, to drain radially outward down the sides of the lenses, but owing to Coriole's force the water follows an outward spiral in a clockwise direction. Chief of these sources of warm dilute water are large sewage outfalls. For example, when at capacity the planned Hyperion outfall will discharge 420,000,000 gallons of Los Angeles sewage per day. If the discharge were to reach steady-state conditions such that one day's discharge remained in a conical lense of 5-km radius, its thickness at the middle would be 6 cm. At isostatic equilibrium the center of the cone would then reach about 0.15 cm above normal water level. Such a slope of 0.03 cm/km is large enough to produce a current of about 0.1 knot. Where the lens is close to shore, the clockwise movement of water probably tends to pile water against the shore. Such an explanation may well account for observed higher bacterial counts on the beach north of the old Hyperion outfall than south of it.

The amount of heat contributed to the ocean from sewage and cooling systems of steam plants designed for generating electricity is also large, as shown by Gunnerson (1956, 1958b). The temperature of the sewage is higher than that of the ocean, usually by about 9°C during both winter and summer. This high temperature means a contribution of about 3.4×10^7 kg-cal of heat per million gallons of sewage. Additional heat is liberated on further oxidation of the organic matter after it is discharged from the outfall, amounting to about 6 kg-cal per gram of sewage solids. For the concentration of suspended solids at Hyperion outfall, the heat of oxidation is equal to about 0.6×10^7 kg-cal per million gallons. When at its capacity discharge of about 420,000,000 gallons per day, the heat contributed will be $(3.4 + 0.6) \ 10^7 \times 420 = 1.7 \times 10^{10}$ kg-cal/day. To this must be added 2.8×10^{10} kg-cal/day from the cooling systems of the Redondo, El Segundo, and Scattergood steam plants, assuming that average output is 65 per cent of the rated total capacity of about 2800 megawatts/day (contemplated for about 1960) and that cooling losses are 0.83×10^6 kg-cal/hr/Mw. The combined heating from sewage and cooling systems is then 4.5×10^{10} kg-cal/day in Santa Monica Bay alone. This corresponds to the amount of solar energy falling on an area of 8 sq km in a summer day. Other sewage outfalls and steam plants along the coast perform similar but smaller contributions of heat to the ocean.

Sewage also contains about 1000 times the concentration of inorganic nitrogen and phosphate present in surface sea water, leading to considerable local enrichment of the water. If phytoplankton could grow before the nutrient-rich water became diffused, there would be great blooms near the outfalls. Since experience in southern California shows that this does not occur (Stevenson and Grady, 1956), evidently the growth rate of phytoplankton is too slow at least under most conditions. Nearly all the inorganic nitrogen in sewage is in the form of ammonia, which slowly becomes oxidized to nitrate after it is discharged from outfalls. Oxidation of the ammonia and of suspended organic matter tends to deplete the oxygen content of the sea water receiving the sewage; however, in the open sea diffusion and currents are sufficiently great to renew the water before oxygen becomes exhausted. Only in narrow restricted bays where waste discharge is great and circulation is slow, such as the inner Los Angeles Harbor, is the oxygen content of the water sometimes brought to zero with consequent formation of hydrogen sulfide (Los Angeles–Long Beach Harbor Pollution Control Committee, 1956). In larger bays or in areas receiving relatively small amounts of wastes the oxygen content is reduced but not brought to zero; examples are San Diego Bay (Miller and Nusbaum, 1952), Newport Bay (Department of Fish and Game, 1953), Alamitos Bay (Reish and Winter, 1954), and the lower San Gabriel River (Reish, 1956).

Life

The plants and animals in the ocean are obviously controlled by the nature of their water media, but less obviously the composition of the water itself is a function of withdrawal and return of elements by organisms. Plants and animals are interrelated to a certain extent with topography but far more with sediments to which they contribute waste and skeketal materials and on which, in many instances, they draw for food and shelter. Since the sediments are closely related to physiography, the plants and animals are best considered in groupings according to physiographic environment.

General

Plants and animals that live in the ocean are too numerous and varied and have too complex a relationship with each other to be well described in only a single chapter. Even an entire book on the plants and animals would be inadequate. General works on organisms living in deep water are sketchy in coverage of kinds of organisms (Sverdrup, Johnson, and Fleming, 1942, chapters 9, 16, 18, and 19; Allee, Emerson, Park, Park, and Schmidt, 1949) or are based on other oceanic areas with little information pertinent to local waters (Zenkevich, 1947; Ekman, 1953). General books on plants and animals of the intertidal areas are more numerous. Applying largely to southern California are three books that are concerned for the most part with general taxonomy and physiology of seashore animals (Johnson and Snook, 1935; MacGinitie and MacGinitie, 1949; Fitch, 1953). Another by Light, Smith, Pitelka, Abbot, and Weesner (1954) covers much the same field for the San Francisco region. The most useful book on intertidal ecology is one by Ricketts and Calvin, recently revised by Hedgpeth (1952), which is based on Monterey Bay. For algae, mostly intertidal, the only general book (Smith, 1944) is also for the Monterey Bay region, although Dawson (1945, 1946, 1956) prepared a check list booklet for algae of San Diego County and other summary descriptions. These various books represent a very incomplete treatment of plants and animals for southern California, and they are particularly incomplete from an ecological point of view. Even for precise taxonomic purposes it is necessary to refer to the hundreds of published technical papers on particular groups of animals and plants; some of these papers also contain a little information on ecology.

For these reasons it is probably worthwhile to point out here some of the relationships of organisms to the known water and bottom characteristics off southern California, to indicate geological relationships, and to list some of the more detailed appropriate references for the interested reader. Since it is believed to be more useful to start with the euphotic zone, which is the site of primary food production for all life in the ocean, the description will proceed from shallow to deep water, interposing the pelagic life between the intertidal and the benthonic life of deeper water. In this discussion the terminology proposed by the National Research Council Committee on Paleoecology (Hedgpeth, 1957) will generally be followed (Fig. 122).

Intertidal Environment (Littoral)

The intertidal environment, also known as the littoral, consists of three main types of substrate, muddy marshes, sandy beaches, and rocky shores. Each has its own unique flora and fauna. Because of the ease of collection from this zone, its plants and animals have been described far more completely than have those from greater depths.

Marshes

Marshes are dominated by land plants that have become adapted to varying degrees of submergence in tidal waters and to rapid changes of salinity. Because of their different tolerances, these plants live in distinct belts having contour-like boundaries. Zonation is well known for marshes in New England (Johnson and York, 1915; Johnson, 1925), and in Britain (Chapman, 1938–1941) and has been studied in southern California at San Diego (Purer, 1942), at Newport Bay

CLASSIFICATION OF MARINE ENVIRONMENTS

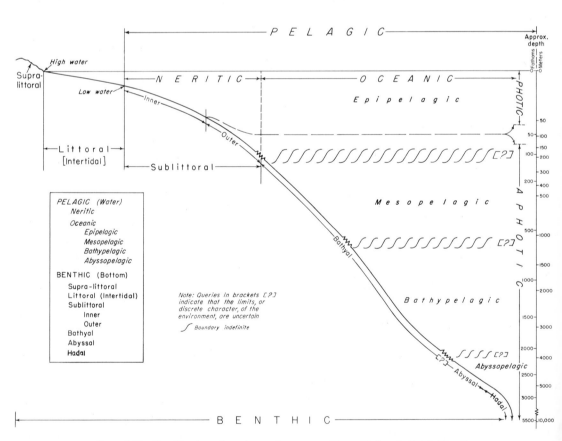

Figure 122. Classification of marine environments. From Hedgpeth (1957, Fig. 1).

(Stevenson, 1954; Stevenson and Emery, 1958), and in Baja California (Stewart, 1956). Lowest on the marshes of Newport Bay is a belt of *Zostera marina,* the thin flexible bright-green eel grass, which is rarely exposed even at low tide (Fig. 123). Above this plant is a belt that is usually devoid of attached plants and consists of bare sand or mud. At Mission Bay near San Diego the barren area is hundreds of meters wide locally. Next, in the region of midtide, is a belt thickly covered by a grass, *Spartina leiantha,* which reaches a height of 30 to 60 cm but has its base nearly always underwater. The next belt, which is just above midtide, is dominated by a low succulent, *Salicornia herbacea* (Fig. 124), although other plants are present. Still higher, but reached by most high tides, is a belt dominated by *Suaeda californica* var. *pubescens,* but again containing several other plants. Lastly, and reached only by the very highest tides, is a belt of *Distichlis spicata,* a thin-bladed branched grass usually less than 15 cm high. At greater elevations only freshwater plants are present. The salt-water marsh plants contribute much organic matter to the marsh by growth of roots into the mud as well as by burial of the leaves through undermining by waves and animals and through plastering by mud. Partial oxidation of the organic matter leads to formation of hydrogen sulfide and methane and such low *p*H values, particularly high

on the marsh, that almost all the calcium carbonate of shells is dissolved away. In addition, the living plants serve to trap mud carried by the water at high tide, so that low natural levees are commonly built at the outer margins of the marshes. Accompanying the grasses are relatively minor amounts of algae, most conspicuous of which are loose blanket-like areas of the black *Nostoc commune* which occurs mostly in the belts of abundant *Salicornia* and *Sueada.*

The commonest animals in the upper marshes other than polychaete worms are the long tapered snail *Cerithidea californica* in the belt of *Salicornia* and several species of clams and crabs in the barren belt. The snail, lying unattached atop the mud, is commonly host to many parasitic trematodes (Martin, 1955) which affect the snail's growth in such a way as to produce a shell more tapering than for unaffected snails. The clams and crabs live in burrows (Fig. 125) from which the latter emerge mostly just at night. A wide variety of other animals including sponges, oysters, echinoids, sea pens, isopods, and amphipods occur locally on the marshes and in its channels. Most of these animals are restricted to the marshes and adjoining waters because of the small size of waves, abundance of food, and ease of burrowing, and they have become tolerant of changing salinity, temperature, and tide level. Indeed, it is believed

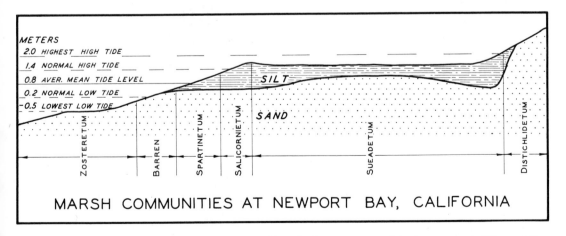

Figure 123. Plant communities and their relationship to tide and substrate on a marsh in the upper part of Newport Bay.

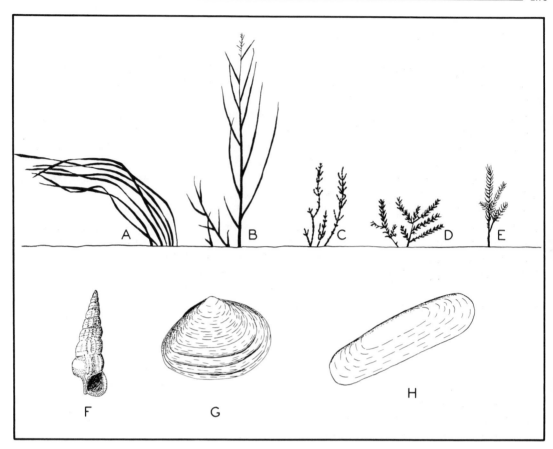

Figure 124. Some important inhabitants of marshes in southern California: A, *Zostera marina* L., eel grass (×0.05); B, *Spartina leiantha* Benth. (×0.05); C, *Salicornia pacifica* Standl. (×0.05); D, *Suaeda californica* Wats. (×0.05); E, *Distichlis spicata* (Torr.) (×0.05); F, *Cerithidea californica* (Haldeman), horn shell (×0.5); G, *Macoma nasuta* (Conrad), bent-nose clam (×0.8); H, *Tagelus californianus* (Conrad), jackknife clam (×0.5).

by some workers that bays and marshes formed the route by which animals left the sea to populate the land during the geological past (Pearse, 1936).

Marsh deposits are probably present in the geological column but cannot often be recognized through fauna alone because of nearly complete solution of shells composed of calcium carbonate. Some black shales that have chitinous fossils (graptolites and crab carapaces and claws) but few calcareous fossils may well have been ancient marshes. In some of them minor sedimentary structures (thin interrupted bedding and some ripple marks) and organic structures (trails, burrows, and faecal pellets—Häntzschel, 1955) support the interpretation of marsh or mud flat deposits. Among the best-known

black shales of this general type are those of Paleozoic age in the eastern United States and Europe (Twenhofel, 1932, p. 395).

Sand Beaches

Sand beaches form a more rigorous environment than the marshes owing to impact and continuous reworking by wave action. Because of the shifting substrate large plants cannot become established except high above the reach of waves. Microscopic blue-green algae, however, sometimes form a film covering the sand grains between high tides and serving as food for grazing Foraminifera (Reiter, 1957) and probably for other small animals. The main food supply for beaches is that of kelp and other

Figure 125. Bank of tidal channel in marsh at Mission Bay near San Diego showing mud deposited around rhizomes of *Salicornia* and bored by a crab [probably *Uca crenulata* (Lockington)] so thoroughly that slumping occurred. Photographed in February 1944.

algae and plankton washed ashore and buried in the sand. Animals of the beach are almost exclusively those that are able to bore into sand rapidly.

Among the few species living on beaches are the sand hopper, an amphipod *Orchestoidea californiana,* which expels sand from its burrow with such force that colonies are marked by a criss-crossing pattern of stripes of fresh sand a foot or so long (Emery, 1944). The sand crab, *Emerita analoga,* oval and about 2 cm long (Fig. 126), may be seen in large numbers washing up on the beach on the swash ahead of the tide and busily digging into the sand until only eyes

and antennae are left projecting to catch fine organic debris washed across the sand by the swash. Usually present on sand beaches are the separate valves of a flat 2.5-cm-long clam, *Donax gouldii.* Living specimens are usually extremely rare because the clam flourishes only at intervals of several years, there having been seven major resurgences between 1895 and 1950 (Coe, 1955). Another, the Pismo clam, *Tivela stultorum,* is heavy-shelled and prefers the surf zone. Because of its food value this clam is in danger of extermination in southern California, although formerly it was very abundant according to Ricketts and

Figure 126. Some important inhabitants of sand beaches in southern California: A, *Tivela stultorum* (Mawe), Pismo clam (×0.25); B, *Donax gouldii* Dall, bean clam (×0.7); C, *Orchestoidea californiana* (Brandt), sand hopper (×1.2); D, *Emerita analoga* (Stimpson), sand crab (×0.7).

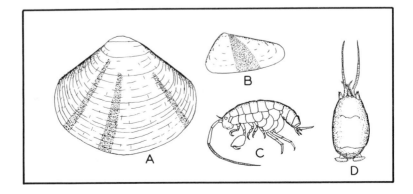

Calvin (1952, p. 196). Where not so intensively hunted in Baja California, it is still common, some older specimens being 15 cm long. Another common inhabitant of sandy beaches is a small, 2-mm-diameter, red worm, *Thoracophelia mucronata,* whose activities leave a telltale rough surface on the sand, and which along with the sand crabs and sand hoppers is of considerable interest to shore birds.

Perhaps most interesting is the occasional visitor, the grunion *Leuresthes tenuis,* a fish that flops up on the beach at night-time spring tides between March and August (Fig. 127). The female digs a hole and lays her eggs, which are immediately fertilized by the male and left to incubate in the warm sand for two weeks and be re-exposed and hatched at the next spring tide (Walker, 1947, 1952). These fishes are known only in southern California and the adjacent part of Mexico (Roedel, 1953). A reference in Vizcaíno's log (Bolton, 1916, p. 56) to "sardines" washed ashore at Cape San Lucas during the night of June 8, 1602, probably refers to grunion, since this date would be 4 days after a spring tide. Sea lions also are temporary visitors to beaches, especially beaches of islands where they are not likely to be disturbed by man or beast. On several islands they form large colonies whose incessant barking may be heard for a mile or more away.

Sand beaches are rare in the geological column because of the ease by which they are eroded when exposed; nevertheless, several ancient sand beaches are exposed in southern California. One example of Pleistocene age forms part of a sea cliff beside Highway 101 at Newport Beach. In it are many valves of *Donax* and Pismo clam (Bruff, 1946), and below it are fine-grained sediments that probably represent a marsh buried by migrating beach sands (Emery, 1950c).

Rocky Shores

The favorite collecting grounds of biologists are along rocky shores because of the abundance and wide variety of both plants and animals. Vertical variations in flora and fauna are produced within the intertidal area and the wave and spray zone above it by vertical differences in exposure, drying, light intensity, temperature change, and probably other factors. Similarly, horizontal variations are produced by differences in water temperature, exposure to waves, hours of shade, kind of rock, and other factors. Thus wide differences of organisms may be noted between rocky intertidal areas of caves, cliffs facing the open sea, rocks in the lee of projecting shore points, and boulders surrounded by sand. These horizontal and vertical variations of flora and fauna have given rise to many schemes of zonation that are largely related to a particular worker's chief site of work or to the kinds of organisms in which he is most interested. Some

Figure 127. Grunion [*Leuresthes tenuis* (Ayres)] on beach at La Jolla in 1937. At lower right note females dug into sand to lay eggs. Photograph by E. C. LaFond.

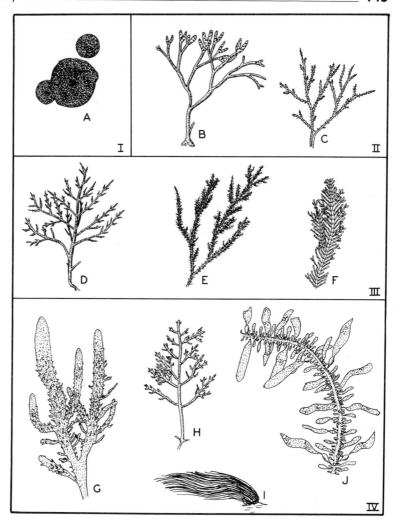

Figure 128. Some common plants of rocky shores in southern California. I, wave and spray zone: A, *Ralfsia* sp. (×0.04).

II, high-tide zone: B, *Pelvetia fastigiata* (J. Ag.) De Toni (×0.09); C, *Endocladia muricata* (P. & R.) J. Ag. (×0.5).

III, midtide zone: D, *Gigartina canaliculata* Harv. (×0.15); E, *Gigartina leptorhynchos* J. Ag. (×0.15); F, *Corallina vancouverensis* Yendo (×1.5).

IV, low-tide zone: G, *Gigartina spinosa* (Kutz) Harv. (×0.04); H, *Gelidium cartilagineum* var. *robustum* Gardn. (×0.15); I, *Phyllospadix torryi* S. Wat. (×0.02) (habit); J, *Egregia laevigata* Setch. (×0.1).

zonations have been based on both plants and animals, and some are on either one or the other. A good discussion and comparison of several classifications used in California are given by Ricketts and Calvin (1952, pp. 375–401). They concluded that a zonation into four units is most practical, with the top zone being above the 5.0-foot tide level (spray and wave zone mostly above high tide), the next between 5.0 and 2.5 feet (high-tide zone), the next between 2.5 and 0.0 feet (midtide zone), and the lowest below 0.0 tide, or mean lower low water (low-tide zone exposed only during minus tides).

In the top zone, rarely covered by high tides, the most obvious plant is the brown alga, *Ralfsia*, which forms thin circular patches on the rocks (Fig. 128); however,

the microscopic blue-green algae are more abundant although difficult to see. The animals of the zone are ones that can close their shells or otherwise protect themselves from drying out between high tides or between visits to the water. Commonest is a periwinkle, *Littorina planaxis*, which has a tightly fitting operculum or door (Fig. 129). This snail wanders about grazing on blue-green algae and other organic material present in a thin film on the rocks; in the process of feeding the snail is an active erosional agent, rasping away the rock with its sharp radula (Emery, 1946; North, 1954). Also common a little lower in this zone is a limpet, *Acmaea digitalis*, which can draw its cup-shaped shell so tightly against the rock surface that it can be pried off only with difficulty. Commonly,

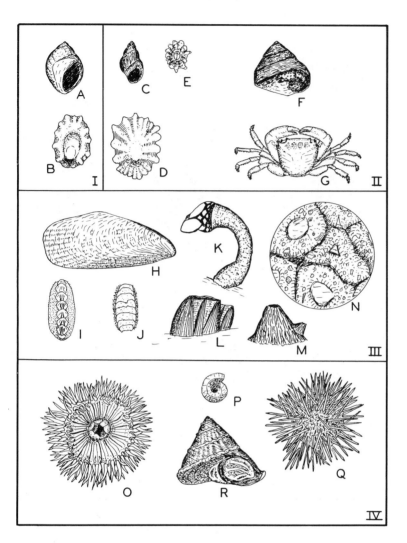

this and other limpets occupy depressions of the same shape as their shells and as much as 5 mm deep, evidently eroded by the animals.

The high-tide zone has more species of plants than the top zone, one of which, *Pelvetia fastigiata,* a fleshy brown alga, forms large clumps and blankets. Also present is a small bushy red alga *Endocladia muricata.* A wide variety of other more fragile algae inhabit tide pools of the zone, particularly during the winter when the water is cool and sunlight is not too intense. Common animals are the snails *Littorina scutulata* and *Tegula funebralis.* Grazing of these snails on shales frequently produces an intricate pattern where the surface has been scraped away; although fragile, such grazing trails have been preserved in the geological column (Seilacher, 1953). Broad flat or gently sloping rocks of the zone are covered by such enormous numbers of small acorn barnacles, *Balanus glandula,* that in some areas it is impossible to walk without crushing many of them. Locally and mosty on sloping rocks in this zone are several species of limpets, many in their small holes in the rock. Under loose boulders and in cracks live several crabs, chief of which is *Pachygrapsus crassipes* which rattles noisily as it scurries away to hide from visitors walking over the rocks. Even more common but less obvious are hermit crabs, mostly species of *Pagurus,* which occupy the shells usually of *Littorina* and *Tegula* but may sometimes be found in other discarded shells, tubes, or miscellaneous containers (MacGinitie and MacGinitie, 1949, pp. 293–299).

In the next, the midtide zone, are increased numbers of species and individuals of algae. Among the more common are the small calcareous red *Corallina vancouverensis,* the larger species of the green *Ulva,* and several red algae including *Gigartina canaliculata* and *G. leptorhynchos.* These plants are large enough that they provide protection as well as food for animals of the zone. In shady areas a crustose red alga, *Lithothamnium,* commonly forms a relatively smooth pink belt, 30 to 60 cm wide, under which many small animals may hide. The animals as well as the plants of this zone are more highly varied than in the two higher zones. One of the most typical is the black mussel, *Mytilus californianus,* which lives in dense clusters in areas of strong surf and on pilings of piers fronting the open sea. Measurements by Fox and Coe (1943) show that individuals filter as much as 22,000 liters of water per year, separating large quantities of suspended sand in the process. Associated with the mussel are large barnacles, *Balanus tintinnabulum,* and the gooseneck *Mitella polymerus.* Living on the rocks are many chitons, of which *Nuttallina californica* is the most common. Like the limpet, this chiton erodes a hole in the rock, locally as deep as 2 cm. During the night when the rock surface is cool and moist the chiton wanders about grazing, and then it returns by dawn, usually to its home depression in the rock (Lane, 1956). A sea anemone, *Bunodactis elegantissima,* is also common, living in closely packed colonies poorly disguised by attached shells and sand grains.

The lowest zone, exposed only at minus tides, grades seaward into the sublittoral area of the inner continental shelf. Because of the extremely wide variety of plants and animals as compared to the rest of the intertidal area, collection from this zone is so highly prized by biologists that they are willing to go to great lengths to be present at minus tides. Collecting from it at higher tides by swimming is difficult, largely because of surf action. Plants are dominated by the large brown alga, *Egregia laevigata,* although red algae are represented by the large *Gigartina spinosa,* by *Gelidium cartil[i]gineum* which is sometimes picked for agar, and by a wide variety of smaller forms. In this zone also is the grass-like *Phyllospadix torryi,* a marine seed plant closely related to *Zostera* which lives in the minus-tide region of marshes and bays as well as the open sea. A calcareous red alga, *Melobesia mediocris,* is commonly present as an encrustation on the blades of *Phyllospadix.* Prominent among the animals is the large green solitary sea anemone, *Anthopleura xanthogrammica.* Starfishes are also common; chief among them is the large *Pisaster ochraceus* which may be seen clinging to rocks or pilings just below the horizon of abundant mussels which also serve as part of its food supply. An animal closely related to the starfish, although outwardly different in appearance, is the spiny and purple sea urchin. *Strongylocentrotus franciscanus* and *S. purpuratus* are the most common species, and they, like many of the other urchins, are capable of drilling hemispherical holes in rock and concrete and reportedly even in steel pilings. The best rock borers, however, are several species of *Pholadidea* whose habitat ranges downward from this zone. Another animal, likely to be overlooked or mistaken for a plant, is the hydroid, a small attached linear colony of individuals which forms a life phase of medusae. Among other animals occasionally seen in this zone are solitary corals, sponges, abalones (Fig. 130), tunicates, bryozoans, worms, crabs, and others too numerous even to mention here.

A special environment more closely related to rocky shores than to sandy beaches or marshes is provided by wooden pilings of piers. Here lives a group of wood-boring animals, prominent among which are the

Figure 130. Abundant black abalones *Haliotis cracherodii* Leach in lower intertidal area of southwest San Nicolas Island. Photograph by R. M. Norris.

isopod *Limnoria* spp., the amphipod *Chelura terebrans,* and the mollusk *Teredo diegensis,* each of which can bore the wood so thoroughly that pilings break and piers may fall down (Hill and Kofoid, 1927; Menzies, 1951; Barnard, 1955).

Many examples of Pleistocene faunas from rocky shores are known on raised marine terraces of southern California. A good one is exhibited in a 2-meter section of the twelfth terrace of the Palos Verdes Hills now at an elevation of 1215 feet (371 meters) above sea level. Collections and identifications by Woodring, Bramlette, and Kew (1946, p. 94) show the presence of a fauna that is characteristic of the full height of the intertidal belt and includes *Acmaea, Haliotis, Tegula, Crepidula, Pamaulax* (similar to *Astraea*), and many others familiar to biologists who have studied the present intertidal zone of rocky shores. Foraminifera in the deposit have been identified by O. L. Bandy (personal communication) as typical of warm shallow water and of pre-Wisconsin age.

Pelagic Environment

General

The pelagic environment consists of several zones separated according to depth of water. Over the continental shelf it is termed the neritic zone and over deep water from the surface down to perhaps 100 meters it is the epipelagic zone. For southern California there may be little need for separate use of these two terms because their organisms are similar, owing to the uniformity of the waters which is produced by the small amount of runoff from the land except during infrequent storms. Some differences in pelagic organisms exist in the two areas because of interrelationships with benthos on the shelf (the sublittoral) zone, but present information indicates that these differences are minor, except for fishes. In both the neritic and epipelagic zones plankton (floaters and drifters) are far more abundant than nekton (swimmers), and phytoplankton far exceed zooplankton. In the deeper zones, mesopelagic and bathypelagic, the ratio of plankton to nekton is probably smaller, and of course neither zone contains much phytoplankton except in the form of debris raining down from the epipelagic zone above. The deepest zone of the ocean, the abyssopelagic, is absent in the continental borderland.

Epipelagic Zone

Phytoplankton is restricted to the epipelagic zone and the adjoining neritic zone because plants need sunlight for photosynthesis. These plants, although microscopic in size, form a much greater total bulk than the larger bottom-living algae of shallow water; thus they are the chief organisms capable of converting into tissue the inorganic materials present in solution in sea water. As a result, they serve as the ultimate food base of most marine life. Some animals graze directly on phytoplankton as on a pasture of grass. Others, carnivores and scavengers, are one of two steps removed but are still dependent on these plants.

Two recent books have brought together much information about both phytoplankton and zooplankton, but not specifically for southern California. One of these by Davis (1955) contains a useful set of keys and drawings to aid general identifications. The other by Hardy (1956) has excellent photographs of living plankton, made with the aid of an electronic flash, and also many color sketches and interesting bits of information about plankton collected during the author's many years of work.

Most of the information about plankton gained during the past has come from collections made with plankton nets (conical cloth parachutes) dragged through the water. However, the openings between the meshes are large enough, particularly in a new net, to permit the escape of large numbers of small forms of phytoplankton. A better method of obtaining a representative, although smaller, sample is by use of a closing type of bottle which collects all forms except some zooplankton that is capable of escaping. After the organisms have settled to the bottom the top water is decanted and the bottom portion further concentrated by centrifuging (Allen, 1939).

Phytoplankton, classed as yellow-green algae by Sverdrup, Johnson, and Fleming (1942, p. 295), is dominated by diatoms that occur locally off southern California in numbers of more than a million cells per liter of sea water. Diatom cells were counted by W. E. Allen for 690 deep-water stations occupied during 23 cruises in the years 1938, 1939, 1940, and 1941 (Sverdrup and Staff, 1942, 1943, 1944, 1947). The

maximum and average concentrations at several selected depths beyond the shelf are given in Table 9. These yield an overall average of 39,600 cells per liter in the top 60 meters, with greatest concentrations during spring (Fig. 131). In contrast, the average number of cells in the top 50 meters at 475 stations on the mainland shelf between Point Conception and Mexico between March 1957 and April 1958 was found to be only 1850 cells per liter by Johanna Resig of Hancock Foundation, who used methods similar to those of Allen. The difference in the two studies appears to be a result of shelf versus deep-water environment, because Allen's nearshore stations have lower populations than his offshore stations. In both studies the maximum concentration of diatoms was commonly encountered at depths of 20 or 30 meters, and this maximum corresponds to a depth of minimum transparency of the water to light (Young, 1939).

Table 9

Concentration of Diatoms of Open Sea Compiled from Data of W. E. Allen

Depth, meters	Number of Cells per liter	
	Maximum	Average
0	2,864,000	57,400
20	3,284,000	55,100
40	2,270,000	34,400
60	1,080,000	11,600

Diatoms consist of unicellular individuals having a thin-walled shell or frustule composed of a type of opal and are commonly linked together into chains or groups. The wide variety of shapes has given rise to perhaps 12,000 named species (Cupp, 1943). Since they have no means of locomotion and yet must stay in the euphotic zone to live, diatoms have developed several methods of delaying their sinking time. Some, such as *Coscinosira, Leptocylindrus, Rhizosolenia,* and *Nitzschia,* form long hair-like chains (Fig. 132) which must sink sideways. This tendency toward increasing the water resistance is carried much further by other types like *Chaetoceras* which have many

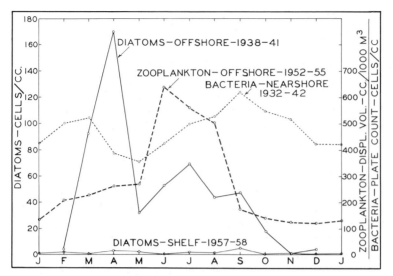

Figure 131. Average monthly abundance of diatoms and zooplankton. Diatom counts (cells per cubic centimeter) for the offshore area are averages of concentrations measured by Allen during 1938–1941 at 0, 20, 40, and 60 meters (Sverdrup and Staff, 1942, 1943, 1944, and 1947). Those for the shelf area were measured by Resig during 1947 and early 1958. Zooplankton concentrations (displacement volumes in cubic centimeters per 1000 cubic meters) were measured during 1952–1955 by the Staff, South Pacific Fisheries Investigations (1953, 1954, 1955, and 1956), from oblique tow net hauls between 140 meters and the surface. Bacterial concentrations (cells per cubic centimeter) are from plate counts reported by ZoBell (1946c, p. 75) for collections at the pier end at Scripps Institution of Oceanography during 1932–1942. Note the lag of greatest concentration of zooplankton and bacteria after the peak concentration of diatoms. Because the bacteria were collected over quite shallow water (about 6 meters), their abundance may be controlled more by the presence of bottom sediment stirred up by seasonal waves than by the presence of organic debris.

projecting spines to enlarge their surface area compared with their volume. These and other diatoms also increase their buoyancy by secreting tiny droplets of oil. On the death of the plant some of its oil may be released to form surface slicks; the rest, if not used as food, is carried inside the frustule to the bottom, where it probably serves as one of the source materials of petroleum. The siliceous frustules themselves may become so concentrated on the bottom, where not too much diluted by inorganic or calcareous sediments, that they form diatomaceous muds like those of the Gulf of California, or the much purer diatomites of the Middle Miocene strata at the Palos Verdes Hills and near Santa Maria.

Most of the other important components of phytoplankton have attributes of animals, such as flagella and ability to catch and digest solid particles, but they are generally placed in the plant kingdom because of their photosynthetic activity and the cellulose body covering on some. Most abundant of these animal-plants are dinoflagellates (peridineans), unicellular organisms having two flagella that permit a limited degree of locomotion. Although, there are many species of dinoflagellates (Butschli, 1883–1887), the bulk of those off southern California consist of only four species belonging to three genera (Allen, 1941), *Procentrum, Ceratium,* and *Goniaulax,* in order of decreasing abundance. During the summer *Procentrum* and *Goniaulax* sometimes form blooms that are so intense that the water becomes red and soupy in texture (Allen, 1946). Such blooms during July 1958 contained up to 25 million *Goniaulax* per liter. This same red color was observed during the early explorations of the Gulf of California, causing Alarcón to give it the name Vermilion Sea. Concurrently with the reddening, the water becomes phosphorescent at night, especially where agitated by the surf or by passage of a moving body such as a fish. Indicative of phosphorescent ability is a genus named *Noctiluca,* but this is rare in southern California. Summertime blooms of one species of *Goniaulax* are considered the cause of mussel poisoning when mussels and other filter feeders ingest it in large quantities (Sommer, Whedon, Kofoid, and Stohler, 1937). The poison causes paralysis and even death to people who eat the mussels, whether or not the flesh has been cooked.

Catastrophic death of fishes off Florida has also been attributed to blooms of dinoflagellates (Gunter, William, Davis, and Smith, 1948) by either poisoning or suffocation.

Two other kinds of phytoplankton that have flagella are coccoliths and silicoflagellates. Although rare, the chief genera of the first are *Coccosphaera* and *Rhabdosphaera.* Both are calcareous and so small that they generally pass between the meshes of plankton nets, yet they are reported to comprise as much as 13 per cent of some deep-sea sediments (Correns, 1939). Recent studies by M. N. Bramlette (1958) have shown that coccoliths can be useful guide fossils in the geological column. Silicoflagellates also are rare off southern California,

only *Dictocha fibula* having been recognized in studies at University of Southern California during 1955–1956, although Butschli (1880–1882) reported many others elsewhere. Their siliceous skeletal remains are preserved in the sediments, but their small size makes for difficulty in finding them.

Other planktonic organisms are definitely animal in origin. Some are protozoans, radiolarians, foraminiferans, and tintinnids. The tiny radiolarians with their siliceous skeletons contribute appreciably to some deep-sea sediments but are unimportant off southern California. Tintinnids are fairly common in the region (Kofoid and Grinnell, 1929) but have few or no hard parts. Most abundant of the three are forami-

Figure 132. Common net plankton off southern California. Diatoms ($\times$100 to $\times$250), from Cupp (1943): A, *Coscinosira polychorda* Gran.; B, *Leptocylindrus danicus* Cl.; C, *Rhizosolenia alata* Brightw.; D, *Nitzschia pungens* var. *atlantica* Cl.; E, *Chaetoceros decipiens* Cl.; F, *Ditylum brightwellii* (West) Grun.

Coccolithophorid ($\times$300): G, *Coccosphaera pelagica* Wall., silicoflagellate ($\times$50); H, *Dictyocha fibula* Ehrbg.

Dinoflagellates ($\times$100 to $\times$200), from Butschli (1883–1887): I, *Goniaulax polyhedra* Stein; J, *Porocentrum micans* Ehrbg.; K, *Ceratium fusus* Ehrbg.

Tintinnids ($\times$60), from Kofoid and Grinnell (1929): L, *Favella franciscana* K & G.; M, *Heliocostomella subulata* (Ehrbg.).

Radiolarian (rare) ($\times$170), from Sverdrup, Johnson, and Fleming (1942): N, unknown species.

Foraminifer ($\times$25); O, *Globigerina bulloides* d'Orbigny.

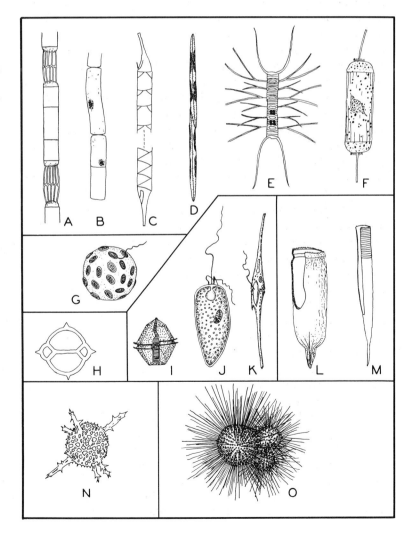

niferans, of which the genera *Globigerina, Globigerinoides, Globigerinella, Globorotalia, Globotruncana, Orbulina,* and six others are pelagic (Cushman, 1940, p. 45). Many samples of sediments from basins and banktops consist of 20 per cent or more foraminiferal tests, of which the majority are commonly of pelagic forms. More complex than the protozoans are copepods, tiny planktonic crustaceans having elaborate appendages to aid their flotation and permit a limited amount of swimming. Their most interesting movement is a diurnal vertical one in response to intensity of light (Esterly, 1912, 1928). Because of their large numbers, they probably complement the diatoms in forming a balanced oxygen–carbon dioxide system in the water. Copopods are the primary grazers on phytoplankton; their importance in the food chain of the ocean is illustrated by the parallelism in abundance of copepods, notably *Calanus,* with fish caught (Sverdrup, Johnson, and Fleming, 1942, pp. 906–907). Also grazing on the phytoplankton are larval stages of *Emerita,* the sand crab whose adult life is spent on beaches. Johnson and Lewis (1942) showed that the area of greatest abundance of the larvae in plankton catches corresponds closely to the offshore belt of cold water that is rich in nutrients and diatoms.

In addition to minute forms, zooplankton also includes large ones. Perhaps most common of these in southern California is *Velella lata,* a 8-cm siphonophore carrying a triangular sail and trailing short tentacles. It is related to the larger Portuguese man-of-war which occurs in tropical waters. Jellyfish are also fairly common and are frequently seen at or just beneath the water surface or stranded on sandy beaches. Pulsations of their mantles give them a high degree of mobility for plankton. Perhaps most common is the white and purple radially striped *Pelagia.* Another coelenterate, the transparent ctenophore *Pleurobrachia,* is less often seen. It consists of a 1- to 2-cm sphere, or cat's eye, trailing tentacles and swimming slowly through the water by rhythmic movements of combs of cilia. Tunicates, belonging to the phylum Chordata,

are also common members of the larger zooplankton. One, the salp *Pyrosoma giganteum,* sometimes occurs at the surface in a density as great as one per square meter. It is a tubular colony, commonly of 4-cm diameter and 15-cm length, which has orange transluscent walls and a cavity along the whole length, except that one end is closed. Slow jet propulsion is provided by contractions of the cavity walls. Its exceptionally high bioluminescence is recognized by the name *Pyrosoma,* which means fire body.

A discussion of the composition of plankton must include mention of bacteria. These organisms, usually referred to the plant kingdom, are not abundant in a truly planktonic form but instead become established chiefly on the surfaces of plankton that has died and is sinking down through the water. As a result, bacteria of many kinds are most abundant in areas of greatest abundance of plankton and at depths slightly greater than the depth of maximum plankton concentration (ZoBell, 1946c, pp. 67, 77). Bacteria thus begin the regeneration of organic materials soon after death of the plankton (Fig. 131) and continue their activities after the debris reaches the bottom and is buried under later sediments.

The nekton, or swimmers, consists only of animals. Some of the zooplankton, such as prawns, have some swimming ability, and so they lie astride the boundary between plankton and nekton. Aside from these doubtful members, the nekton consists of cephalopods, fishes, and mammals—all characterized by fairly high intelligence. The only invertebrates, the cephalopods, are represented off southern California by squids. The chief past source of information about them is a volume by Berry (1912), but a new book by Lane (1958) contains much new general data. As pointed out by Hardy, (1956, pp. 278–291), squids are so mobile that they are rarely caught in nets, but yet they must be present in the ocean in large numbers because they appear to be a chief food component of mammals, particularly in the Antarctic. They are able to move so fast that they frequently fly out of the water onto the decks of ships. When *R/V Velero IV* is anchored at islands off the coast, squids may sometimes be dip-netted under a bright light hung overside at night. Once, on the night of July 27, 1951, at Santa Catalina Island a swarm of thousands or tens of thousands of individuals collected for mating (Fig. 133). As observed by John S. Garth, mating was accompanied by rapid color changes and followed by deposition in the sand of the fertilized eggs.

The most varied and yet perhaps the best-known members of the nekton are the fishes. Keys, sketches, and photographs for identification of common fishes of the region are given by Barnhart (1936) and Roedel (1953). Many of the fishes are dependent on the bottom and are thus not truly pelagic, al-

though they are part of the nekton. For example, Garibaldi perch, sheepshead, calico bass, and moray eel inhabit areas of rock and kelp. In areas of sand bottom are halibut, sand dab, sole, flounder, and skates. Estuarine areas of mud or sandy mud have mullet and mudsucker. Among the fishes that live all or most of their lives far from shore and over deep water are ones such as sardine, herring, anchovy, salmon, flying fish (Fig. 134), mackerel, barracuda, tuna, bonito, marlin, swordfish, and large sharks. These pelagic fishes, in contrast to those living on or near the bottom, are capable of very fast swimming. Laboratory experiments reported by Gray (1957) indicate that they can swim at speeds such that for short bursts they can cover a distance in 1 second

Figure 133. Swarm of mating squids, *Loligo opalescens* Berry, at the water surface. Photographed by electronic flash under a light hung overside from *R/V Velero IV* at anchor in 30 meters of water at Emerald Cove, Santa Catalina Island on July 27, 1951. Station 2047.

Figure 134. Flying fish, *Cypselurus californicus* (Cooper).

about equal to ten times the length of their bodies, although cruising speeds are much less. A 4-foot 20-pound barracuda was clocked at 27 miles per hour in the ocean, establishing it as the fastest known fish. Because of their size, speed, and sharp teeth sharks are much feared here as elsewhere, but there have been few authenticated instances of attacks. One instance was on October 10, 1950, when a shark seriously injured a swimmer at Imperial Beach near San Diego; another, on December 7, 1952, killed a swimmer at Monterey in central California by repeated biting attacks while ignoring five would-be rescuers carrying the victim to shore (Bolin, 1954); on February 6, 1955, near the same site in Monterey a swimmer was attacked but only scratched by a shark which bit into the swim-fins and tore one away (Fast, 1955). More recently, on October 12, 1958, a swimmer at Coronado (near San Diego) was seriously bitten by a shark, in May 1959 another was mangled and killed 50 yards from shore near the Golden Gate at San Francisco, and on June 14, 1959, another was gripped around the chest and killed by a 20-foot shark only 40 yards from a big Sunday afternoon crowd at La Jolla Cove (press releases). In the two attacks at Monterey the shark was the notorious tropical man-eater, *Carcharodon carcharias*. According to Captain J. F. Stevenson, Chief Life Guard, Los Angeles County, no instances of shark attacks in the Los Angeles region are known. Although attacks are very rare in southern California as

compared to Australia and the West Indies (Llano, 1957), they are of considerable concern to the swimmers in the area.

In addition to the occasional presence of tropical fishes off California, distant migration of pelagic fishes is shown by tagging experiments conducted by the California Department of Fish and Game. For example, one of 215 albacore tagged near Los Angeles during August 1952 was caught less than a year later off Japan, having traveled a net distance of more than 23 km day (Ganssle and Clemens, 1953).

As a result of the differences in habitats and behavior of the various kinds of commercial fishes, several different types of fishing gear are used. Bottom fishes in flat sandy areas are caught mostly by trammel nets (a coarse-mesh net sandwiched between two fine-mesh nets), but near Santa Barbara they are taken by trawls (nets dragged over the bottom). Such nets cannot be used over very rough rocky areas, and there the chief method is by baited hooks and set lines, although since about 1948 spearfishing by sportsmen using self-contained underwater breathing apparatus has resulted in a great increase of catch. The pelagic fishes, bluefin tuna, sardine, and mackerel, are mostly caught by purse seines. Yellowfin tuna and skipjack are generally concentrated by chumming the water with live bait and then fished with a barbless hook and a short pole. Salmon and albacore are taken mostly by trolling behind a slowly moving boat, and swordfish are taken by harpooning. Among the additional fishing equipment are gill nets used chiefly for barracuda and white sea bass.

Occasional fish scales, otoliths, and bones are found in dredgings of the basin floors. According to David (1944, 1947), these materials are from several kinds of fishes which are related to ones found in fossil form in Pliocene and Late Miocene strata of California (Fig. 135), supporting the conclusion from foraminiferans and mollusks that the climate of those times was warmer but not greatly different from the present one (Jordan and Gilbert, 1919; David, 1943). However, comparison of present fish faunas with collections made as long ago as a century shows some variations which Hubbs (1948) ascribed to fluctuations of water temperature. Supporting evidence is provided by the patchy geographical distribution of cold-water fishes in areas of upwelling located south of coastal points and of warm-water fishes north of the same points. Access could have been provided these isolated and widely scattered areas only during past period of generally colder and warmer waters. Temperature control is well illustrated by the presence in abundance of albacore in the region only during summers of unusually warm water such as that of 1958.

Several kinds of sea mammals occur off southern California. Some are dependent on shore—the seals, sea lions, sea otters, and sea elephants. Because they form a resource of the state, many studies and counts have been made of them (Bonnot, 1951). Seals (no external ears) live mostly in quiet waters of bays, whereas the others mostly inhabit the rougher waters around islands. Large colonies of sea lions (external ears) live at San Miguel, Santa Barbara, San Clemente, San Nicolas, and Los Coronados Islands. Having a high degree of intelligence, some are caught and trained to do tricks as the common circus "seal." During the nineteenth century their numbers were greatly reduced by the hunt for oil and hides as graphically described by Scammon (1874). In the 1920s the remainder were nearly eliminated by slaughter for dog food and for state bounties, but now their population is again increasing (Bonnot and Ripley, 1948; Bartholomew, Collyer, and Dawson, 1951). Occasional sea elephants may be observed on the sea lion hauling-out grounds; however, most of them live on Guadalupe

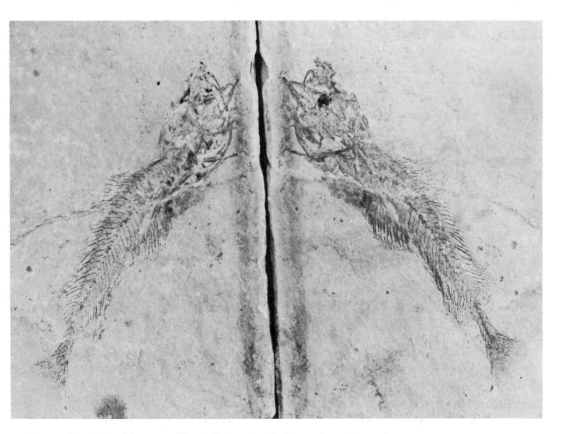

Figure 135. Fossil fish (*Eclipes* or codling fish) found on the Hancock ranch near Santa Maria in Late Miocene diatomaceous shales. Identified by Dr. Howard R. Hill, Los Angeles State and County Museum (×0.4).

Island about 300 miles south of Los Angeles (Bartholomew and Hubbs, 1952). Formerly the sea elephants were far more abundant than now, but organized killing of them for their oil brought them nearly to extinction by the end of the nineteenth century. The northern fur seals (really sea lions) which once were present off southern California were brought even closer to extinction until given international protection in the Pribilof Islands, and the Guadalupe fur seal was thought to have been exterminated until a few survivors were found recently. The fur hunt also brought the sea otter almost to extinction a half-century ago. All these mammals are now protected by law and all are increasing in number, but they have not yet reached their former numbers, as is indicated by the still abandoned hauling-out grounds where rocks have been highly polished by the sliding of generations of animals. A point of geological interest is the service of all as minor geological agents in transporting pebbles that are picked up, probably to aid in the trituration of fish bones, performing much the same function as sand in a chicken's crop (Emery, 1941b).

Dolphins, porpoises, and whales are mammals that live a wholly pelagic life. They bear and nourish their young at sea and never come ashore. In fact, whales can exist only where water aids in supporting their bulk, for they cannot lift their unsupported weight sufficiently to breath. Dolphins in the region are seen most frequently at the bows of ships, whose speed they generally can exceed. Gray (1957) reported that the closely related Atlantic dolphin has been clocked at 22 miles per hour, and there are many unconfirmed local reports of greater speeds for dolphins off southern California. Ordinarily, the dolphins and porpoises race up to the bow of a ship where they maintain position a few feet to one side or the other, seemingly with little effort and possibly by riding a form of bow wave. During their stay at the bow they signal to each other or use squeaking noises as a sort of radar; these noises are readily detected as whistles and grunts on the ship's echo sounder. After tiring of the ride, per-haps because of its slowness or wrong direction, the dolphins and porpoises break away at an angle and rapidly disappear in the distance. Following each other in single file and arcing up to breath, they look like a monstrous sea serpent and may well have inspired some of the tales of sea serpents. The total number of dolphins and porpoises is very uncertain, but Norris and Brown (in press) have counted an average of about 8000 sightings per year, mostly in the Catalina Channel. Several sightings of the same individuals may have occurred, but in compensation the area of observation is a small fraction of the whole region.

Whales are common in the region (Fig. 136), and during the past century they were beached and rendered into oil at Gaviota, Ballona Greek, Portuguese Bend near Los Angeles, and San Diego (Scammon, 1874). According to Gilmore and Ewing (1954), the gray whales also used San Diego and probably Mission Bay as calving grounds, although bays farther south were used more, and some are still being used. For several years Gilmore (1956a) has made an annual census by counting the gray whales in their fall procession southward past Point Loma. Apparently they move from point to point during their migration and mostly do not follow the curving shores between points. A few humpback, finback, sperm, and blue whales visit the region and some remain during the summer. Visits of right whales are very rare (Gilmore, 1956b).

Bones of sea mammals are common constituents of phosphorite dredged from bank tops, with the dense whale earbones nearly as abundant as shark teeth. In this respect the slowly deposited sediments of bank tops are similar to the red clays of the deep sea where many elasmobranch denta and cetacean otoliths are found (Eastman, 1903). Fossil sea mammals are also known from Tertiary strata of California, and some of them are now extinct according to descriptions by Kellogg (1931) and Downs (1956).

Although not nektonic in the sense of fishes, the sea birds have much the same relationship to plankton as fishes. This is much more true of albatrosses, petrels, and

Figure 136. Pacific pilot whale, *Globicephala scammoni* Cope, about 4 meters long. This one was captured and placed on exhibit in a large tank (Norris, 1958). Courtesy Marineland of the Pacific.

shearwaters than of the shore-based cormorants, pelicans, and gulls. The albatrosses, mostly *Diomedea nigripes*, live far from shore, spending nearly all their lives on the water or wheeling gracefully just above it. Since they feed on zooplankton and whatever nekton comes their way, they are far more abundant in the belt of cold water near the Santa Rosa–Cortes Ridge than farther seaward or landward where plankton is less abundant (Miller, 1940).

Mesopelagic Zone

Much less is known about the organisms that live deeper than a few hundred feet, owing to the difficulty of observing and collecting them. Observations at these depths must be made by instruments or men housed in pressure-tight containers (Piccard and Dietz, 1957; Pérès, 1958) and collections made mostly by nets dragged through the water. Because many of the animals that can be observed are too small or too fragile to be caught in nets, and because many of those that can be recovered in nets are too

mobile or too widely dispersed to be readily observed, there are some discrepancies in results obtained by the two methods.

Photographs made by the benthograph (Emery, 1952a) showed large numbers of tiny light-scattering objects mostly between depths of about 100 and 1000 feet (Fig. 137). Most were too small to have any character. Very likely they are the same as the "snow" that has repeatedly been observed during dives of the bathyscaphes *F.N.R.S. III* and *Trieste* in the Mediterranean Sea and the nearby Atlantic Ocean. Pérès and Piccard (1956) reported that the "snow" consists of inactive particles ranging from the size of peas to an amorphous mist, plus filamentous material as long as 16 inches. The depth range is the same as observed by photography off southern California. Hardy (1956, p. 240) added the interesting suggestion that the "snow" may consist largely of the cast skins of the tiny crustaceans of zooplankton. Unfortunately, no worthwhile observations from manned devices have yet been reported from this region.

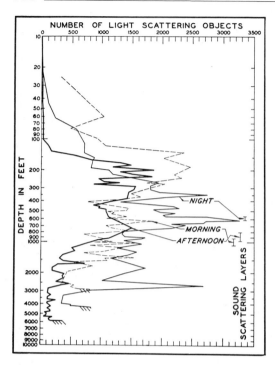

Figure 137. Vertical distribution of light-scattering objects as counted on photographic negatives exposed in benthograph. Concentrations indicated as more than 2000 are probably even greater than shown because soupy texture makes counts difficult. Night series above Santa Catalina Basin between 0330 and 0500 on March 30, 1952; morning series above San Nicolas Basin between 0830 and 0930 on November 18, 1951; and afternoon series above San Pedro Basin between 1300 and 1400 on March 29, 1952. The top of the deep sound-scattering layer is shown at the right for same times. From Emery (1952*a*, Fig. 8).

A well-publicized but as yet poorly understood phenomenon of the mesopelagic zone is the deep sound-scattering layer, D.S.L., or phantom bottom. These terms were given to describe the reflection of sound by a layer or stratum of objects at one or more depths between the surface and about 1500 feet. It was first noted during the war from the records of both echo sounders and sonar detection gear, and, because of possible military importance, some investigations were made of it at the University of California Division of War Research at San Diego. The results of some of these studies plus later fathograms made in the Pacific and Antarctic Oceans were summarized by Dietz (1948) and Johnson (1948). The layer is now known to be of world-wide distribution. Fathograms show not only the depth of the reflecting objects but permit the drawing of several deductions about their nature. It was early shown that the layer rises at dusk and sinks at dawn. Such a cycle strongly suggests that it is due to organisms rather than to some physical discontinuity in the water, especially because many kinds of zooplankton are known to undergo diurnal movements in an apparent attempt to stay in water of the same light intensity or to feed on the abundant phytoplankton at the surface during the night and to retreat from predators into darkness during the day. The vertical velocities of the layer are not incompatible with the swimming speeds of some zooplankton. Recent use of the precision depth recorder (Luskin, Heezin, Ewing, and Landisman, 1954) in the Pacific Ocean has revealed that fact that the D.S.L. here sometimes consists of more than ten separate layers. Even casual examination of the records shows that the layers do not rise and sink together but that they sometimes cut across each other, supporting the view that each layer consists of a different kind of animal which responds to light of a different intensity.

Early efforts at sampling the deep sound-scattering layer were not very fruitful of zooplankton, but a later and more intensive study by net hauls at various depths above, in, and below the layer (Boden, 1950) showed that it has a definite concentration of zooplankton consisting mostly of large copepods, euphausids, sagittae, amphipods, pteropods, ctenophores, and other animals. The numbers of large individuals ranged up to about 100 per 100 cu meters of water, and the number of small pteropods and copepods was sometimes greater. It was believed that many of the euphausids in the path of small nets may have avoided them or escaped and that a higher concentration probably exists than was indicated in the sampling, even with large nets.

Lyman (1948) suggested that zooplankton are too small to be effective sound reflectors and that instead the objects may be squids. Net hauls described by Tucker (1951) showed the presence of some squids, but perhaps more important they contained fishes which had air bladders and thus were good sound reflectors. Although neither squids nor fishes were abundant in net hauls, others may have been able to avoid capture. When the benthograph was placed in operation, it was hoped that the sound scatterers might be identified from photographs and the question resolved, but few large organisms were photographed in the correct depth range (Fig. 137). The small objects that scatter light were found from counts on the photograph negatives to be abundant in a broad zone which included, but was much wider than, the deep scattering layer. Even the depth of maximum concentration of light-scattering objects was different from the depth of maximum concentration of sound-scattering objects. More certain relationships between echoes and photographed objects might be expected of an echo sounder attached to a camera and suspended in the deep scattering layer. Such a device described by Johnson, Backus, Hersey, and Owen (1956) has shown a good correlation between echoes and the presence of small fishes.

Recently, precise measurements of light generation at depth by Kampa and Boden (1956) show the existence of flashes having a wavelength of about 489 mμ, blue-green. The maximum frequency and intensity of the flashes are greatest within the deep sound-scattering layer (Fig. 138), and the color and intensity match that of individual specimens of the euphausids that are known to be present in the layer. Curiously, the intensity of the flashes is 10 to 100 times the intensity of general illumination with which the euphausid is associated during its diurnal cycle of movement.

In summary, it seems likely that euphausids and small fishes are major causes of the layer, even though they and other organisms are present in concentrations commonly less than one per cubic meter of water.

Bathypelagic Zone

A small amount of work has been done within the bathypelagic zone of the basins off the coast through deep hauls of nets,

dredging of basin floors, and photography. In addition to collections by the Albatross and Scripps Institution of Oceanography prior to 1915 and some later unpublished work, about 33 net hauls between 270 and 1300 meters have been made aboard *R/V Velero IV* since 1949 with nonclosing hoop nets 2 meters in diameter and 8 meters long. These depths span the bottom of the mesopelagic and the top of the bathypelagic zones (Hedgpeth, 1957). Crustaceans that were recovered include mysid, euphausid, and decapod shrimps, hyperiid and gammaridean amphipods, and copepods. Of the 31 species of shrimps identified up to 1952, 13 were found only in hauls that reached depths greater than 800 meters (J. S. Garth, personal communication). They include cosmopolitan, temperate northern Pacific, tropical eastern Pacific, and weak endemic elements. A summer peak of abundance was indicated for some species. As elsewhere, these crustaceans are bright red, but because of high absorption of red by sea water they appear at depth to be black.

Many deep-sea fishes (Fig. 139) were obtained along with the crustaceans, perhaps because the fishes feed on them. Most common are *Cyclothone* spp. of the family Gonostomatidae, six species of which are known to occur in the region. At least 60 per cent of all specimens taken are of this genus, and they were found at all depths sampled (to 1300 meters). They are black, slender, range from 2 to 8 cm in length, and have small eyes. Next most abundant in the bathypelagic zone is *Lampanyctus leucopsarus,* a lantern fish of the family Myctophidae. Representatives of this family were found by Tucker (1951) to be the most common fish in the deep sound-scattering layer of the mesopelagic zone. Having phosphorescent organs, their black slender bodies range up to 12 cm long. Third most common is *Leuroglossus stilbius,* a black and silver herring-like fish of the family Argentinidae which also reaches lengths as great as 12 cm. Many other curious and bizarre fishes have been found, but only in small numbers. Few collections and studies have been made of fishes living close to the bot-

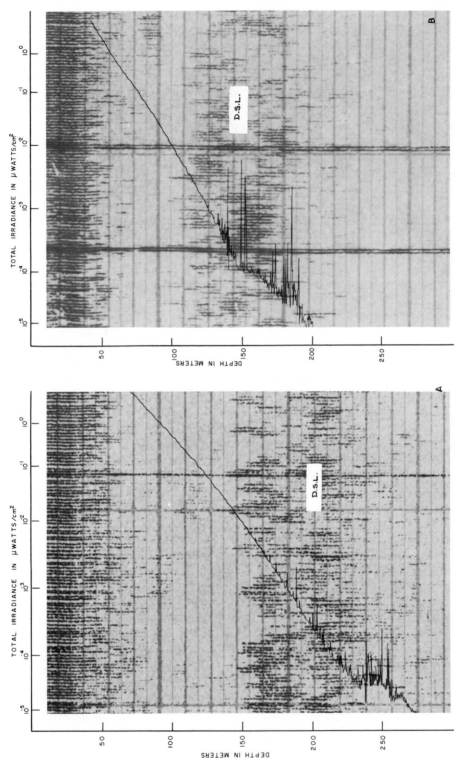

Figure 138. Fathogram of deep sound-scattering layer with superimposed tracing of total irradiance recorded at 1645 (on left) and at 1725 (on right) on January 17, 1956, above the San Diego Trough off San Diego. Sunset was at 1707. High irradiance near water surface is due to incident sunlight; peaks within deep sound-scattering layer are the result of luminescent flashing, probably by euphausiids. From Boden and Kampa (1957).

Figure 139. Example of bathyal fish—*Caulolepis longidens* Gill. This was obtained in a net haul from a depth of 830 meters at latitude 27°34′, longitude 115°06′. Note that the teeth and mouth are typically large compared to the body (×1).

tom, but twice when tow nets accidently struck bottom they recovered specimens of *Nezumia liolepis,* a fish belonging to the family Macruridae which has been widely collected elsewhere as bottom-living fishes. It has a large head, huge eyes, tapering body, and lengths as great as 20 cm. None of the fishes is unique to the region; in general, bathypelagic fishes are cosmopolitan, owing to the world-wide uniformity of this environment. Good descriptions applicable to deep-sea fishes of this region are given by Murray and Hjort (1912) for collections made in the North Atlantic Ocean and by Clemens and Wilby (1946) for collections off western Canada.

Generalizations about the characteristics and habits of deep-sea fishes are subject to uncertainty, particularly because relatively little more is known now than in the time of Murray and Hjort (1912). However, in a very general way we can state that the bright coloration of epipelagic fishes is absent at depth, replaced perhaps by patterns of phosphorescent organs in fishes of the mesopelagic zone. In general, the mesopelagic fishes are silvery, whereas the bathypelagic ones are black. In place of the large eyes of the mesopelagic fishes, the bathypelagic ones have small eyes and some are blind, and the deep bottom-living fishes such as those of the family Macruridae again have large eyes, some exceptionally large. Other characteristics of deep-sea fishes are their large mouths and teeth, their usual ability to swallow and digest animals larger than themselves, tactile structures such as barbels and long thread-like fin rays, and hook-and-line and other lures for capturing prey. How much the color, presence of photophores, size of eyes, and development of unusual structures depend on environment rather than merely on the family represented is not clear.

Fossil bathypelagic fishes have been found abundantly in Late Miocene shales at Lompoc (north of Point Conception) and the Santa Monica Mountains. According to David (1943), 82 per cent of the specimens from the Upper Mohnian (Late Miocene) of Santa Monica Mountains are bathypelagic, including *Cyclothone* as the most abundant genus, *Lampanyctus,* and several other genera. The abundance of bathypelagic fishes at this part of the Miocene Epoch accords well with the deepening water inferred from the foraminiferal faunas (Pierce, 1956).

Samples of basin floor sediment provide some information on the kinds of pelagic organisms living in the waters above, but of course they do not in themselves show the depth zone in which the pelagic forms live. In the central Santa Barbara Basin, where there are few benthonic forms, samples show the presence of many shells of the pteropods *Clio* and *Cavolina* and of the heteropod *Spiratella* (Hartman and Barnard, 1958). Many thin transparent shells of *Cyclopecten* have been found in at least 25 samples from the floors of San Pedro and Santa Monica Basins, and a few living specimens have also been recovered. Since the sediments of these particular basins support very little to no benthonic life, it seems probable that the *Cyclopecten* does not live on or in the bottom, but that it spends much of the time just above the bottom. Like some other pectens, this one doubtlessly has the ability to swim or make long leaps by a jet action produced by clapping its two shells together. Thus, *Cyclopecten* is at least a semipelagic animal.

Photographs taken with the benthograph between the sea surface and the bottom show many trachyline medusae, siphonophores, and scyphozoans (Hartman and Emery, 1956). Four different kinds of trachyline medusae (Fig. 140) have estimated diameters as great as 15 cm with 23 to 32 tentacles extending outward another 15 cm. These are closely related to others seen from the bathyscaphe *F.N.R.S. III* in the Mediterranean by Pérès, Picard, and Ruivo (1957). At least four kinds of siphonophores were recognized, some so long as to pass beyond both sides of the field of view of the camera; they may easily be more than 3 meters long. There were two kinds of scyphozoans, one about 30 cm in diameter. Of 138 coelenterates, 112 were photographed within 90 meters of the bottom. All except 2 of 82 trachyline medusae were near the bottom of the San Nicolas and Santa Catalina Basins (3.7 and 4.0°C, respectively). In contrast, nearly all the siphonophores were near the bottom of the San Pedro Basin (5.1°C) or near the side slopes of the San Pedro and Santa Catalina Basins where the water is even warmer (Fig. 141). Restriction of forms to particular basins suggests the presence of environmental controls, perhaps limited tolerances to temperatures, and their restriction to bottom waters suggests that they may feed on smaller mud-eating animals which live on or just above the sediments. All these bathypelagic coelenterates, and especially the trachyline medusae and siphonophores, are obviously so fragile that they would be destroyed if caught in ordinary nets, and so far as known no specimens of them have been recovered in this region.

Shelf Environment (Sublittoral)

Plants of the sublittoral are dominated by the giant kelps. Most abundant and largest of these brown algae is *Macrocystis pyrifera,* which with exceptional growth reaches a length of 200 meters and a weight of 140 kg (Frye, Rigg, and Crandall, 1915). It consists of blades about 30 cm long attached through a 5-cm teardrop-shaped float to a stipe or stem. One or more stipes extend down to a holdfast, or root-like structure (Fig. 142), which anchors the kelp to the bottom, ordinarily to bedrock, but sometimes to loose cobbles and even rarely to the shell of a living abalone. According to Warren Thompson (personal communication), massive holdfasts may also allow growth of the kelp over sand bottom. To a diver the kelp beds look like towering forest trees reaching to the surface and then spreading out as a thin flat canopy. The elkhorn

Figure 140. Photographs of bathypelagic coelenterates. Mostly from Hartman and Emery (1956). A, scyphozoan medusa, Santa Catalina Basin —1329 meters, 4 meters above bottom, Station 2111, April 29, 1952; B, abylid siphonophore, San Pedro Basin—889 meters, 2 meters above bottom, Station 2096, March 29, 1952; C, trachyline medusa, Santa Catalina Basin—374 meters, 947 meters above bottom, Station 2099, March 30, 1952; D, bathyphysid siphonophore, slope of Santa Catalina Basin —634 meters, about 3 meters above bottom, Station 2100, March 30, 1952; E, abylid siphonophore, slope of San Pedro Basin—472 meters, 35 meters above bottom, Station 2097, March 29, 1952; F, trachyline medusae, part of a swarm of at least fourteen, San Nicolas Basin—1703 meters, 76 meters above bottom, Station 2083, November 18, 1951; G, bathyphysid siphonophore, slope of Santa Catalina Basin—628 meters, about 9 meters above bottom, Station 2100, March 30, 1952.

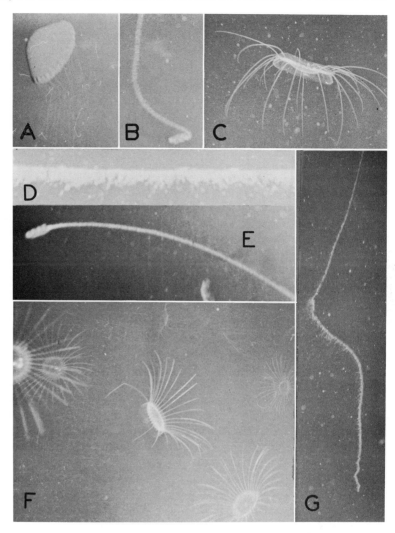

kelp, *Pelagophycus porra,* has a single stipe leading from a holdfast to a double float which is about 15 cm in diameter and above which two branches carry a half-dozen blades each. The blades are as much as 3 meters long and 30 cm wide.

Both *Macrocystic* and *Pelagophycus* live in depths as great as 30 meters. During storms the lifting effect of waves on the kelps frequently causes the anchor rock to break away and drag mostly toward shore but sometimes toward the sea. If toward the sea the floats may buoy up the anchor (Fig. 142) and allow the plant to perform a minor geological role—long-distance transportation of rocks (Emery and Tschudy, 1941). When the anchor drags shoreward or the stipe breaks and the loose kelp washes ashore, windrows of kelp about a meter thick may pile up on beaches to feed the sand flies and hoppers and discomfit the bathers. Near shore the smaller *Pterygophora californica* occurs in depths of 3 to 10 meters where the surf is strong. Its stipe is a stiff wand having no floats but several long blades branching from its top. Since all three plants require strong attachment to the bottom, they usually are good indicators of rock bottom. The same restriction limits its occurrence largely to waters near the rocky islands and adjacent to the rocky projecting points of the mainland. Because of the value of kelp as a source of algin and formerly of iodine and potassium, it has been harvested

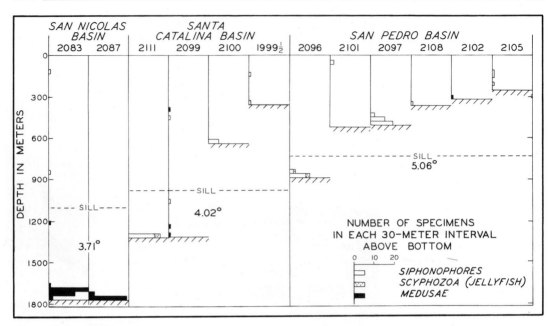

Figure 141. Distribution by basin and depth of bathypelagic coelenterates in photographs. Bars show numbers of individuals at 30-meter depth intervals above the bottom.

as an annual crop for many years (Wohnus, 1942). In spite of their fragileness, pieces of kelp are occasionally found as fossils (Fig. 143).

In addition to the large kelps, many smaller algae occur mostly on the inner halves of the shelves. Some are collected for agar by diving (Tseng, 1944, 1946), and all serve as a food source and protective cover to many kinds of animals which live on and among them. On bank tops and on some island shelves, such as part of that around Santa Barbara Island, calcareous algae in the form of balls or granules of calcium carbonate may be the chief constituent of the local sediment.

The animals of the shelves, unlike those of the intertidal area, exhibit little zonation by simple depth except in depths of only a few tens of meters. Instead, the chief control appears to be that of bottom material, important factors being grain size and content of organic matter. As discussed in the later section on sediments, these and other characteristics of sediment on shelves usually vary sharply, giving rise to a patchy distribution of sediments on such youthful shelves

as those of southern California. As a result, the animals living on them are variable and patchy in both numbers and kinds. To give a fully detailed description of the animals is impossible at present; however, work completed to date by Hartman (1955b, 1956) and Hartman and Barnard (1957) plus much unpublished material permit the making of some general statements about the faunas of the shelves.

The biomass of the mainland shelf is highly variable, 40 to 4000 grams of living organisms (with shells) per square meter of area, but it averages about 300, a figure that represents a high concentration of life. Greatest biomasses occur in areas of fine sediment and also near sources of sewage pollution. For individual orange peel bucket samples having effective sampling areas between 0.10 and 0.25 sq meters, the number of species averages about 70 and the number of individual specimens about 420. Thus the bioindex, or number of individuals per species, averages 6.0, although it ranges between 3.5 and 22.9. West of Santa Barbara the fauna has a northern aspect owing to the cold water of this area as well as to proximity to Point Conception, which has served for a long time as a supposed southern limit for many intertidal species. In contrast, the shelf south of Oceanside has a fauna of southern origin, many animals continuing southward to their areas of main concentration off Baja California. They therefore ignore the United States–Mexican boundary line which is frequently mentioned in the literature as the southern limit of many intertidal species.

Throughout the mainland shelf most of the species are of polychaete worms and amphipod crustaceans, averaging 42 and 36 per cent, respectively (Fig. 144). Similarly, most of the individuals are polychaetes and small crustaceans, averaging 42 and 38 per cent, respectively. Echinoderms and small

Figure 142. Forest of kelps (*Macrocystis pyrifera*) off Los Coronados Islands rising from the ocean floor about 25 meters upward to the water surface. Blades are about 30 cm long. Note the holdfast that has become dislodged from the bottom and is being floated away. U. S. Navy photograph by R. F. Dill.

Figure 143. Fossil brown alga collected by C. L. Hubbs and E. Y. Dawson from Late Miocene Capistrano formation 1 km south of Capistrano Beach Pier. The slight discoloration around the algal blades is from coating of collodion preservative (×0.7).

mollusks comprise most of the rest of the numbers of species and individuals. Because of their small size, the numerous crustaceans form only a small percentage of the total biomass, in contrast to the larger but less numerous echinoderms. In a general way the fauna of soft muddy areas of the shelf where unaltered by pollution consists of many species of polychaetes with no dominant one, of *Paraphoxus* sp. and several other amphipods, of urchins including *Lytechinus anamesus,* and of few species living atop the sediments. At the outer edge of the shelf and in other areas of sandy bottom, the biomass is low, and there are few animals other than smooth red ophiuroids, which may be abundant (Fig. 145). The ophiuroids and most other animals here

live at the surface of the sediment. Where the bottom is rocky, the fauna is dominated by sessile organisms such as sponges, bryozoans, hydroids, alcyonarians, tunicates, and barnacles. Areas of high sewage pollution such as the shelf off Palos Verdes Hills have an abundance of the tube worm, *Chaetopterus variopedatus,* living atop the sediment and frequently in association with the pelecypod *Lima dehiscens.* The increased biomass in polluted areas results from an increase in number of deposit feeders at the expense of filter feeders.

Little study has been made of the animals on the island shelves, but a single large sample from off Santa Catalina Island was reported by Mattox (1955) to contain at least 115 species and nearly 500 individuals. Its bioindex of 4.3 is a little lower than the average value of those on the mainland shelves but is within their range of variation. Ten large samples from the shelf off the northwest end of Santa Catalina Island (Figs. 146, 147) had an average biomass of about 100 grams/sq meter. Four species of three genera of brachiopods are common off this island, and repeated sampling over many years appears to indicate fluctuations in their numbers.

Benthonic foraminiferans from the shelves have been the subject of several studies by geologists who wished to apply a knowledge of modern ecology to problems of ancient sedimentary rocks. One of these problems, the question of degree of reworking of fossils from older rocks into later sediments, was investigated by Crouch (1954), who found that about half the total number of foraminiferal tests in modern sediments of San Pedro Bay consist of reworked fossils of Miocene to Pleistocene age. This serves as an obvious warning against too easy an acceptance of foraminiferal tests as indicative of the environmental conditions at any site of sampling. Zalesny (1956), studying foraminiferans in Santa Monica Bay, also found considerable reworking of fossil forms into modern sediments. Modern foraminiferans, both dead and living tests, show a systematic variation with depth so that different assemblages occur on the shelf, slope, canyons, and basin floor. Superimposed on this depth variation was found a secondary control exerted by type of bottom and presence of local sewage discharge. An even finer depth variation was discovered by McGlasson (1957) in a study of the foraminiferans living on the shelf around Santa Catalina Island; although the shelf edge is only about 110 meters deep, four depth assemblages were noted. Depth facies also occur on offshore banks such as Coronado Bank off San Diego (Butcher, 1951). The differences that exist in the faunas of mainland shelves, island shelves, and bank tops are great enough that a critical comparison of the faunas from these environments should be profitable. A study and comparison of the foraminiferal faunas and their biozones in deeper water are being carried on, as discussed in the section on paleoceanography.

Pleistocene representatives of the shelf environment have been described by Woodring, Bramlette, and Kew (1946, pp. 86–103) in the Palos Verdes Hills. Since most of the Pleistocene mollusks are still living off southern California, an attempt was made to work out the depth relations of the strata by comparison with faunas collected from dredgings of the present sea floors. The oldest strata, the Lomita marl, contains calcareous algae

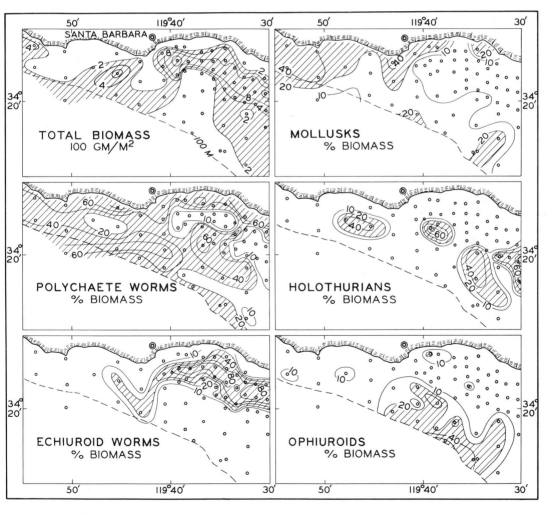

Figure 144. Comparison of biomasses of major animals living on the shelf near Santa Barbara. The holothurian is a single species of *Molpadia* and the echiuroid is a single species of *Listriolobus*. Based on unpublished data of J. L. Barnard. Compare with maps of the sediment character (Fig. 178).

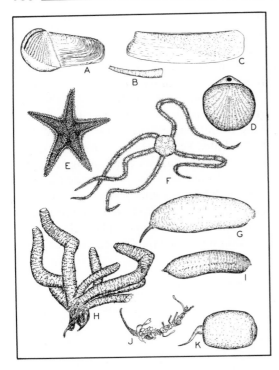

Figure 145. Some common animals of the shelf, slope, and basins: A, *Pholadidea* sp., common piddock (×0.3); B, *Dentalium* sp., tooth shell (×0.3); C, *Solen sicarius* Gould, razor clam (×0.3); D, *Terebratalia occidentalis* (Dall), lampshell—brachiopod (×0.3); E, *Astropecten californicus* Fisher, starfish (×0.3); F, *Ophionereis eurybrachiplax* H. L. Clark, brittle star—ophiuroid (×0.2); G, *Molpadia intermedia* (Ludwig), sea cucumber—holothurian (×0.3); H, *Chaetopterus variopedatus* (Renier), tube worm (×0.2); I, *Travisia pupa* Moore (×0.3); J, *Diopatra ornata* Moore (×0.2); K, *Listriolobus pelodes* Fisher, echiuroid worm (×0.3).

lowing to depths of 50 to 100 meters, although the northern aspect remains. Further shallowing that in some places reaches the intertidal zone characterizes the fauna of the next strata, the Palos Verdes sand. This study of the Pleistocene faunas of the Palos Verdes Hills serves to illustrate the close and valuable ties that exist between modern and ancient faunas. Other examples are Valentine's (1956, 1957) studies of fossils from Late Pleistocene terrace deposits near Santa Monica and just south of the United States–Mexico border. Modern representatives of the fossil species that are characteristic of exposed coasts live today farther north; in contrast, species that are characteristic of shallow embayments occur today to the south. This distribution suggests that the Pleistocene waters exhibited more temperature contrast than modern waters, possibly because upwelling was formerly more intense owing to stronger winds than those of today. When both fossil and modern faunas become better known and are more closely compared, it is evident that a much better knowledge of the ancient seas will be possible than has yet been reached.

Basin and Slope Environment (Bathyal)

Basins in the region may be classified into two groups according to their mega faunas, impoverished and populated. The three shallowest basins (Santa Barbara, Santa Monica, and San Pedro) have impoverished areas which cover a high percentage of their floors below sill depth (Hartman, 1955a; Hartman and Barnard, 1958). Impoverishment is believed to result from the low oxygen content of both bottom water and interstitial water. Low oxygen content of bottom water is a reflection of the position of the sills of these basins within the range of the oxygen minimum in the open sea. A parallel effect of low content of oxygen in the water is that much of the organic debris produced near the surface reaches bottom without having undergone much oxidation during settling; therefore, considerable oxidation continues

and associations of mollusks which indicate facies ranging from depths of less than 20 meters in some places, to between 50 and 100 meters in other places, and to between 100 and 200 meters elsewhere. The fauna is suggestive of the presence of water temperatures approximately the same as those of today, and it is strikingly similar to faunas and associated sediments now found around most of the offshore islands. The partly contemporaneous and partly later Timms Point silt contains mollusks that may be characteristic of greater depths than the Lomita marl, 100 to 200 meters, and it includes several species now found only off northwestern United States. The overlying San Pedro sand contains mollusks indicative of a shal-

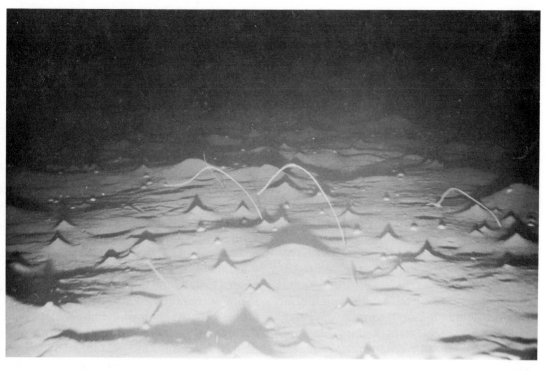

Figure 146. Surface of shelf east of Santa Catalina Island (lat. 33°19.0′, long. 118°17.7′, 90 meters). Sediment is fora-miniferal shell sand. Conical piles of sediment have been dumped at the mouths of holes by burrowing worms. Small white objects are sea urchins, *Lytechinus anamesus,* and long curved lines are sea whips, probably *Acanthoptilum* sp. Bottom edge is about 2 meters wide.

Figure 147. Upper slope of Santa Monica Basin off Santa Catalina Island (lat. 33°31.4′, long. 118°42.6′, 540 meters). Sediment is glauconitic foraminiferal shell sand. Note trails made by movements of sea urchin, *Allocentrotus fragilis.* Bottom edge is about 2 meters wide.

within the bottom sediments so that the dissolved oxygen in interstitial waters, originally low, becomes depleted. The production of hydrogen sulfide by anaerobic bacteria in the top layers of sediment in Santa Barbara Basin serves as an indication of the inhospitality of this bottom environment to animals that need access to free dissolved oxygen. Although measurements (Rittenberg, Emery, and Orr, 1955) show that oxygen is not depleted within about 50 cm of the bottom, it is possible that oxygen is depleted in a layer a fraction of a centimeter thick in contact with the bottom where it could inhibit small organisms that burrow in the sediment but have siphons or gills reaching to the sediment surface.

On the bottom of Santa Barbara Basin benthonic animals are few—a deep-water snail *Nitidella permodesta,* a clam *Macoma leptonoidea,* and some ophiuroids, sponges, and polychaete worms. Only four species are represented, and bioindices are only 1.5 and biomasses 2.0 grams/sq meter. On the side slopes, but still below sill depth, the fauna is richer with an average of 9 species per sample which include the same species present in the deep central area. Bioindices of these slope samples average about 4.0 and biomasses average 65 grams/sq meter. Santa Monica and San Pedro Basins are connected in such a way that the same

sill controls both. The bottoms of both basins are barren of living benthonic animals (Fig. 148); however, most samples contain empty tubes of the polychaete worm *Phyllochaetopterus* and the serpulid worm *Protis pacifica* and numerous tests of a large foraminiferan. The worms are probably vegetative or nonreproductive and reach the bottoms from large populations on the side slopes. That the scarcity of life at depth is not a normal situation is shown by its abundance at the same or even greater depths in other basins. The lower parts of the basin side slopes below sill depth resemble the flat basin floors in their deficiency of life, but at depths just greater than the sill many samples contain living animals, and at still shallower depths all samples contain living benthic animals (Table 10). Animals of the upper slopes are dominated by siliceous sponges and ampharetid worms but include many others such as ophiuroids, crustaceans, and mollusks. Biomasses increase from zero within 100 meters of the bottom of the slopes to probably about 80 grams/sq meter on the slopes shallower than the sill depth. The number of species and bioindices have not yet been worked out in detail, but they appear to be about 20 and 3.5, respectively, for the upper slopes.

The second kind of basin, having well-populated floors, has been sampled only in

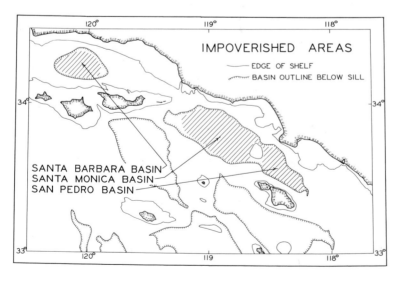

Figure 148. Impoverished basin areas. The floors of San Pedro and Santa Monica Basins have only occasional dead tubes of a polychaete worm, *Phyllochaetopterus* sp., a serpulid worm, *Protis pacifica,* and the dead shells of a scallop, *Cyclopecten* sp. That of Santa Barbara Basin has a few living gastropods, *Mitrella permodesta,* a clam, *Macoma leptonoidea,* and a few others. In contrast is a rich fauna living on the slopes of the basins above sill depth.

Table 10

SAMPLES WITH OR WITHOUT LIFE FROM SAN PEDRO AND SANTA MONICA BASINS
AT 50-METER INTERVALS ABOVE AND BELOW SILLS

Depth		Number of Samples			Biomass (wet),
Meters	Feet	Dead	Living	Dead, %	grams/sq meter
537	1762	0	11	0	30+
587	1925	0	6	0	30+
637	2090	0	12	0	30+
687	2254	0	11	0	30+
737	2418 (sill)	3	13	19	21
787	2582	7	13	35	15
837	2746	32	3	91	0
887	2910	12	0	100	0
937	3074				
Total Samples		54	69		

a reconnaissance way. The best-sampled one is Santa Catalina Basin with ten samples. Only one to three samples have been taken in Santa Cruz, San Nicolas, Tanner, West Cortes, and San Clemente Basins. Photographs have also been taken of the floors of several of the basins, and samples plus photographs serve as general guides as to the findings to be expected after more thorough sampling has been done. Photographs reveal an abundance of polychaete worms, ophiuroids, holothurians, and comatulid crinoids (probably *Florometra* sp.). Also frequent in the samples are brachiopods (*Laqueus* sp.), siliceous sponges, urchins, and sea whips. Most of the species are endemic, as is well shown by the fact that dredgings by *U.S.S. Albatross* in 1904 contained large numbers of new species. Only 2 of 182 species of annelid worms were cosmopolitan. The recent work aboard *R/V Velero IV* has recovered additional new and endemic species (Hartman, 1955a). Perhaps the high endemism is a result of the broad area in the bathyal depth zone as compared to the narrow belts present on most continental slopes of the world. Another factor doubtlessly is the physical isolation of the basins from other regions and even from each other by the ridges and island barriers. The rich population of the six outer basins as compared to the three impoverished inner ones is shown by their average biomasses of 9.9 grams/sq meter,

average of 15 species per sample, and average bioindices of 1.6. The abundant population is ascribed to the high content of dissolved oxygen in the bottom water, which in turn is the result of the position of basin sills well below the depth of the oxygen minimum in the open sea. Samples from the side slopes would probably be richer in life and comparable to samples from the slopes of the inner basins, but to date no samples have been processed.

Among the larger animals mollusks are of greatest interest to geologists because they almost alone have hard parts capable of being preserved in the geological column. Most important in this respect are the three classes, pelecypods, gastropods, and scaphopods (Fig. 149). Of the two other classes, amphineurans (chitons) are less easily preserved and cephalopods are rare. Examination of the graph of percentage of samples at various depths containing these mollusks shows that representatives of each class are more frequently encountered on the outer than the inner shelf and that all except amphineurans are less abundant with depth on the slopes of Santa Monica and San Pedro Basins. On the deep floors of these two basins they are absent. Perhaps a better comparison is that of the relative percentage of the total number of individual specimens in various depth ranges (Fig. 150). Such a comparison shows that amphineurans and gastropods are most fre-

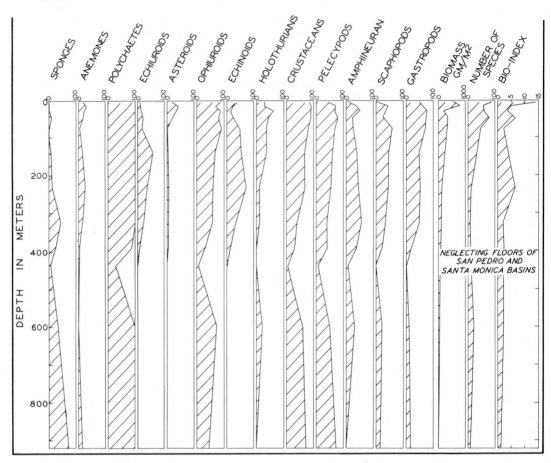

Figure 149. Graph showing percentage of 316 samples in various depth ranges which contain one or more specimens of siliceous sponge, of anemone, and of other kinds of animals. At right is depth distribution of average biomass (exclusive of algal bottoms), average number of species, and average bioindex of samples from all areas except the impoverished bottoms of San Pedro and Santa Monica Basins. Data from Hartman (1955a, 1956) and Hartman and Barnard (1957, 1958, and unpublished).

quent at great depth, pelecypods at shallow depths, and pelecypods and gastropods nearer the water surface. The absence of mollusks on the lower slopes and floor of San Pedro Basin was also noted by Natland (1957), who with Alex Clark studied small samples collected in 1932. Natland pointed out the fact that mollusks are seldom encountered in the shales of the now-filled Los Angeles and Ventura Basins; this absence may mean simply that these two basins were formerly similar to the San Pedro and Santa Monica Basins in having their sills within the depth range of the oxygen minimum of the open sea and thus containing bottom water inhospitable for mollusks, although not so for foraminiferans. Had their sills been deeper, these ancient basins might be expected to contain fossil mollusks like those now living in the deeper-silled Santa Catalina and other outer basins.

Although few of the animals from basin floors have hard parts capable of preservation, it is possible that evidence of their burrowing activities may remain in the geological record of the sediments as interruptions of bedding planes (Schäfer, 1956). Most photographs of the basin floors (Figs. 151, 152) show a hummocky microtopography made by hillocks about 15 cm high located at the mouths of burrows of large worms. These hillocks probably remain for centuries after the worm that made them dies—until they become buried under the slowly deposited sediment or perhaps erased by a rare turbidity current. Similar features were observed by Pérès and Piccard (1956) during dives in the bathyscaphe in the Mediterranean Sea; plowing through the hillocks uncovered no inhabitants, as though the burrows had long been abandoned. Hillocks of related origin are present on the shelves, where the concentration of animals is greater than in the basins, but there the hillocks are probably eroded away by the long-period swells entering the region from the Southern Hemisphere each summer. In the still shallower water of marshes, where animals and evidence of their activities are even more abundant, most of the burrow heaps are destroyed daily by the current and wave erosion at high tides.

Not to be overlooked are bacteria, which live in great abundance in the sediments of the basin floors—more abundant there than in the sediments of the shelves because of the higher percentage of organic matter in the fine-grained basin muds. The highest bacterial counts occur at the sediments surface where both organic matter and dissolved oxygen are most abundant. Plate counts of 100,000 to 100,000,000 cells per gram of wet sediment are typical, far greater than in the basin water. At depth in the sediment the counts decrease sharply at first and then more gradually; nevertheless, significant numbers have been found at all depths that have been sampled. Counts are usually made either by direct visual enumeration under the microscope or by a growth method. The direct count method is time consuming, cannot usually distinguish between dead and living cells, overlooks small cells, and is complicated by the presence of grains of sediment. More commonly used is successive dilution of samples, incubation, and counting of colonies. Dilution may be carried to extinction, dilution so great that not a single cell is present in a diluted fraction, or dilution may be less ex-

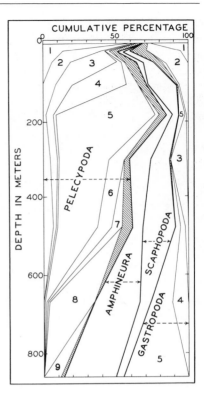

Figure 150. Graph showing frequency at various depths of dominant living mollusks in terms of percentage number of specimens. Averages were computed for following depth ranges: 7–14, 14–36, 36–73, 73–146, 146–220, 220–366, 366–550, 550–732, and 732–915 meters. Graph by O. L. Bandy (1958) from data of Wilson (1956).

Pelecypod faunas: 1, *Compsomya subdiaphana, Lucinoma annulata, Macoma yoldiformis, Protothaca tenerrima, Tellina buttoni;* 2, *Nuculana taphria, Parvilucina tenuisculpta, Solamen columbianum, Solemya panamensis, Solen rosaceus, Thyasira barbarensis;* 3, *Axinopsis sericatus, Lyonsia californica, Nemocardium centrifilosum, Nucula carlottensis;* 4, *Adontorhina cyclica, Aligena* sp., *Amygdalum pallidulum, Yoldia scissurata;* 5, *Acila castrensis, Cyrilla munita, Tellina carpenteri;* 6, *Cardita redondoensis, Saxicavella pacifica;* 7, *Dacrydium* sp., *Nuculana conceptionis;* 8, *Xylophaga washingtonia;* 9, *Kellia suborbicularis, Rochefortia* sp., *Xylophaga mexicana.*

Amphineuran fauna: *Chaetoderma* sp., *Leptozona catalinensis, Limifossor* sp., *Lepidopleurus nexus, Neomeniinid.*

Scaphopod fauna: *Cadulus fusiformis, Dentalium neohexagonum, Dentalium rectius, Cadulus tolmiei.*

Gastropod faunas: 1, *Halistylus subpupoides, Odostomia* sp., *Turbonilla* sp.; 2, *Balcis rutila, Cyclichna diegensis, Epitonium tinctum, Micranellum crebricinctum, Volvulella californica, Volvulella tenuissima;* 3, *Bittium catalinensis;* 4, *Amphissa bicolor;* 5, *Leptogyra* sp., *Nitidella permodesta.*

Figure 151. Base of slope at north side of San Pedro Basin(lat. 33°24.4′, long. 118°13.3′, 540 meters). Masses of rock are partly buried in silty sediment. Note ophiuroids (brittle stars), asteroids, and other organisms encrusting rocks and the mat of ophiuroid arms and worm tubes protruding from sediment surface. Bottom edge is about 2 meters wide.

treme; the cells are plated on a suitable medium so that the colonies that grow can be countered.

Either growth method, dilution or plate count, is beset by certain difficulties, mortality by transfer, dependence on kind of media, inability to distinguish growth from single cells or from clusters, and growth under artificial conditions. Unless the media are more favorable than that of the original bottom sediment and unless the temperature of incubation is higher than that _in situ_, the bacteria fail to grow in a reasonable length of time. In other words, if any growth in the laboratory is observable, the conditions must have been altered. Accordingly, for studies of diagenesis of the

sediments it is perhaps better to measure the cumulative effects of bacterial activity during thousands of years under natural conditions than it is to note the mere growth of colonies which occurs during the few weeks of artificial conditions in a laboratory (Emery and Rittenberg, 1952).

Many specific types of bacteria have been found in sediments off southern California (ZoBell, 1946c, p. 98) and elsewhere, even types that could not possibly be active in the environment in which they were found. Thus still another difficulty is presented by bacteria: although we can measure how many are viable in the laboratory, we do not know how many were dormant _in situ_. Thus we cannot form a satisfactory estimate of the biomass of active bacteria. Conceivably, it is larger than the biomass of the megafauna, as has been found true of some shallow-water sediments (ZoBell, 1946*c*, p. 96), but it could equally well be relatively negligible. Lacking more precise information on biomass of bacteria, it will have to be ignored in the following discussion.

The Organic Budget

Most of the effort in general marine biology during the past has been in the field of taxonomy, because it was necessary first of all to learn what organisms are present. Knowledge of the physiology and ecology of inhabitants of the more easily accessible biozones of the shore lagged only slightly behind taxonomic studies of these areas. However, little is yet known of the ecology of the deeper areas of the ocean, and still less is known of the physiology of the animals living in them. Some knowledge has been gained of the distribution and abundance of the few kinds of plants and the few animals used by man. Knowledge of others not directly used as food for man is far less complete. Nevertheless, there may be some gain in attempting to work out a budget of the organic matter contributed, produced, eaten, regenerated, and lost because such a budget can serve as a general framework into which many studies of biology, oceanography, and geology can be fitted in order to visualize their relationships to each other. The fact that the many uncertainties in this framework becomes glaringly obvious may serve to accelerate efforts to better evaluate them; thus, the following should be recognized only as an early attempt to form a general structure

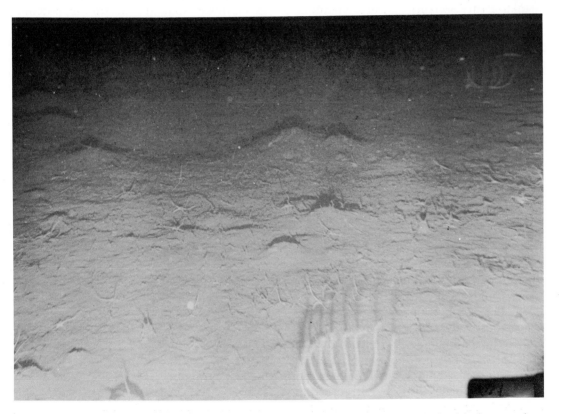

Figure 152. Bottom of Santa Catalina Basin (lat. 33°22.2′, long. 118°47.9′, 1326 meters). In the right foreground are the ten arms of a comatulid crinoid, probably *Florometra* sp. Small polychaete worm tubes and ophiuroids litter the surface. Two holothurians are present in the left center foreground. The bumpy bottom was produced by burrowing activities of large worms. The bottom edge is about 2 meters wide.

from pieces that range from fairly well known to guessed.

In any discussion of abundance of organisms it is necessary to distinguish clearly between standing crop and annual production. For phytoplankton the standing crop is much smaller than annual production, owing to the rapidity of cell division; in contrast, the large benthonic animals probably live for several years, so that their standing crop may be greater than their annual production. The abundance of some organisms is better known in terms of standing crop, whereas others have been measured chiefly in terms of annual production.

Phytoplankton production in the region amounts to about 500 grams/sq meter/yr of dry plankton, as discussed in the section on water currents at intermediate depth. For the entire area of 78,000 sq km inshore of the abyssal depths on Chart I, this productivity corresponds to 42 million tons of plankton (dry weight). Sessile plants are more difficult to assess, but they are most abundant along the 480 km of rocky coasts. Estimates of the total tonnage of kelp have been made by Crandall (1912), Cameron (1915), Wohnus (1942), M. C. Sargent (personal communication), and probably others. Sargent's estimate, the most recent one, is based on an area of 265 sq km of kelp beds having an average of one plant per 10 sq meters, an average of 40 kg per plant, and an average water content of 87 per cent. According to these figures, the standing crop is about 0.14 million tons dry weight. Sargent and others have found the production rate to be about 0.03 grams/gram-day, or 10 tons/ton-yr; thus the annual production of kelp must be about 1.4 million tons. To this must be added the production of smaller attached algae and *Phyllospadix* which mostly live nearer shore than kelp. If these total about one-fifth the production of kelp, the total production of attached plants must be about 1.7 million tons per year, a figure believed to be correct within a factor of 20 per cent. The total production for both floating and attached plants is then about 44 million tons (Fig. 153). Expressed in agricultural terms, the produc-

tion amounts to about 4500 pounds of organic matter per acre. This is about the same as the average production of wood, grain, grass, and other crops on good land of the United States.

Although this annual production appears to be very great, comparison with the energy of incident sunlight is sobering. At an annual average incidence of 0.232 g-cal/sq cm/min the total solar energy reaching the ocean off southern California is about 1×10^{17} kg-cal/yr. The annual production of plants, 44×10^6 tons, has a heat equivalent of about 4 kg-cal/gram (Albritton, 1953), or a total of 1.8×10^{14} kg-cal. The plant production then represents only about 0.18 per cent efficiency of conversion of solar energy into plant tissue, about the same as the 0.3 per cent determined by Riley (1941) for Long Island Sound. Although this is much greater than the 0.1 per cent efficiency of average oceanic water, it is far lower than the maximum potential yield of 27 per cent based on 10 quanta of red light needed for reduction of 1 mole of carbon dioxide (Ryther, 1957). Losses in efficiency come about because of reflection of sunlight by the water surface, absorption of light by water and suspended materials, presence of unfavorable wavelengths in sunlight, too great intensity of light near the surface, deficiency of nutrients, and respiration of the plants.

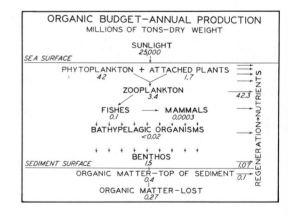

Figure 153. Approximate flow chart of organic matter and annual production of the various biozones of southern California.

Much of the organic matter produced by phytoplankton and sessile plants remains in an intermediate stage before regeneration is complete, as dissolved and suspended organic detritus, or leptopel. According to Fox (1957) this material is present in ocean water in concentrations of at least 1 ppm. At this concentration the waters in the area of Chart I should contain about three times the weight of organic matter annually produced by plants. The large size of this reserve should serve to soften the effects of temporary variations in production of phytoplankton on the food supply for animals. Because of the small grain size of the particles, they are readily absorbed on clayey sediments, but the proportion of organic matter in the sediments that arrived via adsorption is unknown. The role of leptopel as an intermediate decomposition product does not require its inclusion in the organic budget of Figure 153.

The primary grazers on phytoplankton are small herbivorous animals such as copepods. They in turn serve as food for the large omnivorous and carnivorous species of zooplankton and of pelagic fishes. Much of the material eaten is excreted undigested to serve as food for other animals, the scavengers. Digestion of the food results partly in its conversion into new animal tissue but probably mostly in supplying energy requirements. In the process of animal use, as well as of simple chemical oxidation, most of the organic matter is reconverted into the chemical nutrients that originally were brought together by the plants during photosynthesis. The tonnage of nitrogen and phosphorus used annually by phytoplankton is about 100 times the amount annually contributed to the ocean from land areas on a world-wide basis (Emery, Orr, and Rittenberg, 1955). Under steady-state conditions, the tonnage of nutrients annually lost to the sediments must equal the amount annually brought to the ocean from land, so it follows that about 100 times as much organic matter from plants is regenerated in the water or the bottom as is lost by permanent burial. Because the waters off southern California are shallower than the oceanic average, the ratio of loss to regeneration in the water column must be somewhat higher than the world average.

It is of interest to compare the standing crops and annual production of zooplankton, epipelagic fishes, marine mammals, and bathypelagic animals so as to note the losses involved during the conversion of organic matter in each successive step of the food chain. Unfortunately, however, too few basic data exist to permit drawing up of estimates that are much more than guesses.

Volumes of zooplankton have been measured at 15 to 20 stations in the region during monthly cruises since 1951 by the California Cooperative Oceanic Fisheries Investigations (1953–1956). Oblique tow net hauls have been made usually to depths of about 140 meters. Average zooplankton volumes for 1952 to 1955 expressed in cubic centimeters of displacement volume per 1000 cu meters ranged between 640 in June to 121 in December. The annual average is 281, a third to half the average values found on the shelf and in the bays of the East coast (Deevey, 1956), although at least part of the difference may result from the use of different mesh nets in the two regions. By using the conversion factor given by Sverdrup, Johnson, and Fleming (1942, p. 929), the annual average corresponds to 3.56 grams dry plankton per 1000 cu meters of water. This concentration taken throughout the region of Chart I and uniformly to an assumed depth of 200 meters yields a standing crop of zooplankton amounting to 0.09 million tons. Work by Harvey (1950) on food requirements suggests that zooplankton increases in weight about 10 per cent per day. This rate extrapolated over a year gives an approximate ratio of 35 between annual productivity and standing crop. From this ratio and the estimated standing crop, the annual production of zooplankton may be computed as 3,400,000 tons, about 7.5 per cent of the annual production of plants (Fig. 153).

The average annual commercial catch of fishes for the five years 1947, 1950, 1952, 1953, and 1954 was 160,000 tons, according to compilations by the Department of Fish and Game (Staff of Marine Fisheries Branch, 1956, etc.). The same average was obtained for the 16 years between 1926 and 1941 (Fig. 236, p. 305). To this must be added about 7000 tons of fish caught annually by men who fish for sport. At an average water content of 20 per cent, the total annual catch is 0.03 million tons dry weight. Tagging work with sardines indicates an exploitation rate of about 28 per cent (California Cooperative Oceanic Fisheries Investigations, 1955, p. 20). If we assume an average of 5 per cent exploitation for all fishes, the standing crop would be about 0.6 million tons. If the average life span (or turn over) is 6 years, the annual production is about 0.1 million tons, dry weight. This is only 3 per cent of the annual production of zooplankton and about 0.2 per cent of the annual production of plant tissue, somewhat lower than the generally assumed 10 per cent efficiency of conversion from phytoplankton to zooplankton to fish (Pequegnat, 1958).

Sea mammals serve as a further example of low efficiency, in their case of efficiency of conversion of fish to mammal tissue. The population of sea lions (both Steller and California) in southern California was estimated by Bonnot and Ripley (1948) to be 4000 in 1947, but it has subsequently increased to about 20,000. Assuming an average dry weight of 200 pounds, the total weight of sea lions living in the region is

about 2000 tons. Dolphins and porpoises comprise possibly an additional 1000 tons. Whales are not included because they are for the most part only transient. If the average life span of the mammals is 10 years, the average annual production is only of the order of 300 tons. This is negligible in comparison with the tonnage of fishes; however, it should be recalled that the balance between plankton, fishes, and mammals existing at present is not a natural one but is much influenced by the present and past hunting activities of man.

Fairly good estimates (to a factor of 2) can be made of the standing crop of invertebrates living on or in the bottom based on the work of Hartman (1955a, 1956) and Hartman and Barnard (1958 and unpublished data). A summary given in Table 11 shows that the standing crop is about 5.5 million tons (wet weight). The annual turnover of animals in shallow water is believed (but not known) to be about two times each year, judging from the average of 2.44 obtained by Sanders (1956) for both long- and short-lived components of the benthos in the shallower water of Long Island Sound. For those in deep water it may be once every 2 years; thus the annual production is computed to be about 7.4 million tons (wet weight). Analyses by Vinogradov (1953) show that the common benthonic invertebrates have water contents that average about 80 per cent. The total production of benthos off

Table 11

BIOMASSES OF BENTHONIC ANIMALS
(Wet weights)

	Area		Estimated Average Biomass,	Standing Crop, tons	Estimated	Annual Production, tons
	Sq miles	Sq km	grams/sq meter	$\times 10^6$	Turnover, %	$\times 10^6$
Mainland shelf	1,890	4,900	300	1.5	200	3.0
Island shelves	1,390	3,600	50	0.2	200	0.4
Bank tops	2,420	6,260	50	0.3	200	0.6
Basin and trough slopes and other deep irregular areas	15,350	39,700	80	3.2	100	3.2
Basin and trough floors	8,980	23,200	8	0.2	50	0.1
Continental slope	1,960	5,070	20	0.1	50	0.05
Total	31,990	82,730		5.5		7.3

southern California may then be estimated as 1.5 million tons dry weight. This is only about 3.4 per cent of the annual production of plants (Fig. 153).

Much of the organic matter that reaches the bottom escapes complete regeneration during digestion by benthonic animals and becomes buried under later layers of sediment. However, even after it is buried beyond reach of these animals, much of it is regenerated by bacteria living in the sediments. As a result about one-third of the organic matter present at the surface of the sediment is gone by the time it is buried a few meters. Essentially no losses of organic matter to the bottom occur on the mainland and island shelves and on bank tops because the percentage of organic matter is very low and the rate of deposition is extremely slow. Accordingly, significant losses occur only in the deeper areas of fine-grained sediment. Radiocarbon measurements of the rates of deposition and data on the organic content of sediment show that the loss of organic matter to the bottom is about 0.3 million tons per year (dry weight) as will be discussed in a later section. The annual infall of organic matter to the bottom and its fate may be summarized as follows:

$$
\begin{array}{ll}
0.4 & \text{million tons, buried in sediment} \\
-0.13 & \text{million tons, regenerated within} \\
& \quad \text{sediment} \\
1.5 & \text{million tons, benthic production} \\
\underline{1.0} & \text{million tons, energy loss of benthos} \\
2.8 & \text{million tons, total dry weight} \\
& \quad \text{reaching bottom}
\end{array}
$$

Thus it appears evident that 7 per cent of the organic matter produced reaches the bottom in deep water, but that only about 0.6 per cent is permanently lost to it (Fig. 153).

Sediments

Sediments contain within them the evidence of their origin. They are the end products of the interplay of water movements, life processes, and physiographic controls. Thus they are best considered only after their sources, agents, and processes are at least partly known. Since physiography is the easiest measured and best understood of the controls, the sediments have been arranged in a sequence of physiographic groupings. One of the most important properties of sediment is its role as host to petroleum; consequently, some of the threads of evidence for the origin, migration, and concentration of petroleum can be drawn together in a discussion of sediments.

General Composition and Minor Features

Marshes

The sedimentary characteristics of marshes in southern California as elsewhere are closely controlled by two factors, topography and vegetation. Topography is the primary factor, dividing the area into narrow winding tidal channels and broad, relatively smooth, intertidal flats. The flats are distinctive in that their surfaces are covered by patterns of vegetation (Fig. 154) as described earlier. Marshes are world-wide in distribution, and enough is known about them to

recognize that they closely resemble each other in most respects. A thorough study from the point of view of topography, water, flora, fauna, and sediments was made at Newport Bay by Stevenson (1954), and most of the following remarks are based on this study and particularly on one unit of the marsh for which about 160 sediment samples were analyzed. Another very complete study of marshes in several lagoons of Baja California by Stewart (1956) shows them to be similar in general to those of Newport Bay. In discussing the sediments of Newport Bay, it is important to realize that until about 1825 the bay was open to the ocean and contained a large population of oysters whose broken shells established the foundation for extensive sand bars within the bay. In 1825 a bar began to close the bay mouth, and finer sediments started to accumulate within the bay atop the sand bars. The fine sediments form the present marsh surface and are less than 1 meter thick (Table 12).

The coarsest sediment in the bay is on the floors of the deep tidal channels which have cut into the former sand bars. This sand averages about 320 microns in diameter. Along the banks of the channels are narrow beaches of fine sand and coarse silt existing in equilibrium with the currents and waves. Small tidal creeks that drain the water from the marsh surface during ebbing tide are also understandably coarser than the marsh sur-

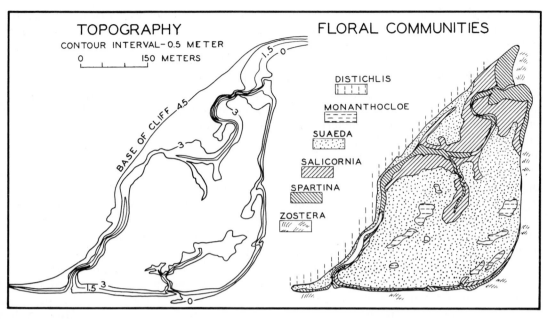

Figure 154. Topography and floral communities of marsh at Newport Bay. Adapted from Stevenson (1954) and Stevenson and Emery (1958, Figs. 32, 34).

Table 12

CHARACTERISTICS OF SEDIMENTS FROM VARIOUS ENVIRONMENTS

Environment	Median Diameter, microns		Trask Sorting Coefficient		CaCO₃,[1] %		Organic Matter,[2] %	
Coastal soils	80	*109*[3]	3.1	*109*	0.4	*109*	1.5	*est.*
Santa Ana dust	34	*8*	1.2	*8*	4.2	*1*	4.5	*1*
Dunes—El Segundo	330	*40*	1.3	*40*	1.1	*40*	0	*est.*
Stream beds	610	*44*	2.0	*30*	1.0	*est.*	0	*est.*
Stream suspended load	31	*23*	2.6	*6*	8.6	*3*	2.4	*3*
Marshes	32	*149*	4.2	*149*	1.2	*79*	18	*91*
Gravel beaches	60,000	*21*	1.3	*21*	0	*est.*	0	*est.*
Mainland sand beaches	240	*57*	1.2	*57*	6.3	*30*	0.05	*3*
Island sand beaches	290	*99*	1.2	*99*	12	*77*	0	*est.*
Suspended sediment in waves	160	*30*	1.3	*7*	0	*1*	0	*est.*
Mainland shelves	130	*1773*	1.6	*804*	9.2	*591*	0.9	*273*
Island shelves	260	*298*	1.7	*290*	27	*256*	.6	*168*
Bank tops	270	*284*	2.3	*164*	56	*166*	.8	*146*
Basin slopes	43	*107*	2.7	*71*	19	*63*	2.8	*30*
Submarine canyons	59	*247*	2.3	*225*	11	*22*	3.0	*27*
Basin floors[4]	5.3	*549*	3.9	*384*	20	*420*	7.0	*80*
Pliocene of Los Angeles Basin	14	*24*	3.9	*24*	4.9	*24*	2.6	*24*
Continental slope	8.0	*20*	4.4	*18*	44	*45*	4.1	*29*
Deep-sea floor	1.8	*19*	2.7	*9*	3.8	*27*	2.1	*11*
Totals		*3901*		*2515*		*1954*		*886*

[1] CaCO₃ from acid loss and from gasometric CO₃= determinations.
[2] Organic matter = nitrogen × 17, or organic carbon × 1.7.
[3] Italics indicate number of samples.
[4] Values for basin floors weighted according to relative areas of basins.

face, averaging about 90 microns. Bordering the tidal channels of some large marshes in other regions are low natural levees built of silts deposited by the flooding tide, but levees are only poorly developed at Newport Bay and on all other marshes of southern and Baja California. Sediments on the marsh surface have median diameters ranging between 100 and 1.6 microns, with an average of 10 microns. Actually, 97 per cent of the area is covered by sediments finer than 16 microns (Fig. 155). Sediments having median diameters in the clay size (finer than 4 microns) occupy about one-fifth of the area and occur mostly along the edges of the marsh where they are covered by nearly every high tide and thus are the places of most active deposition. Median diameters in this area mostly range between 1.6 and 1.9 microns. Sediments present a gradual coarsening inward from the margins of the marsh so that the coarsest (86 microns) occurs near the center. This reversal of the usual trend toward finer grain size near the center of a marsh is probably the result of absence of natural levees. When the marsh becomes older and levees develop, the finest

sediment may be expected to accumulate in the shallow basin behind the levees instead of largely being carried away by ebbing tides as at present.

The best sorted sediments of the bay are in the tidal channels, where the sorting coefficient averages about 1.5. The Trask sorting coefficient is

$$So = \sqrt{\frac{\text{coarse quartile}}{\text{fine quartile}}}.$$

Atop the marsh surface the sands near the center average about 3.7. The silts (4 to 62 microns) are also poorly sorted, averaging 5.4, with the worst sorting (7.0) for coarse silts. Clays are relatively well sorted, averaging 3.35. Because of their deposition in quiet water, the marsh sediments are not as well sorted as are those from many open-sea environments, as indicated by the gentle slope of the cumulative curves of their grain-size distribution (Fig. 156).

Organic matter derived almost entirely from the vegetation living atop the marshes is the most concentrated of any common sediment of southern California but not enough to be called peat. Contours of or-

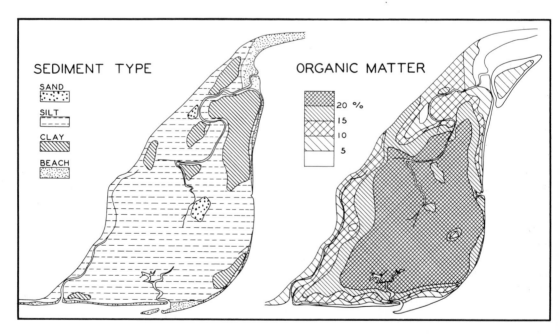

Figure 155. General sediment types and percentage organic matter of marsh at Newport Bay. Adapted from Stevenson (1954) and Stevenson and Emery (1958, Figs. 31, 36).

Figure 156. Typical cumulative curves of total sediment from various environments. Sediments subject to strong winnowing, wide lines: *A,* beach gravel, 3 km north of Encinitas; *B,* shell sand, shelf off Anacapa Island; *C,* foraminiferal sand, Santa Rosa–Cortes Ridge; *D,* red relict sand, shelf off San Diego; *E,* dune sand, El Segundo; *F,* beach sand, 6 km west of Santa Monica; *G,* detrital sand, Santa Monica Bay.

Sediments carried in suspension, narrow lines: *H,* waveborne sediment, Huntington Beach; *I,* wind-borne sediment carried by Santa Ana, El Segundo; *J,* river-borne sediment, Los Angeles River.

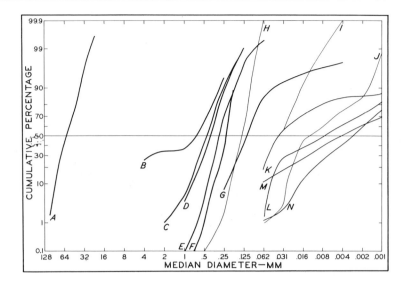

Sediment deposited in quiet water, medium lines: *K,* sediment from north slope of San Pedro Basin; *L,* sediment from floor of Santa Barbara Basin; *M,* marsh silt, Upper Newport Bay; *N,* Red clay, 80 km west of Northeast Bank.

ganic content closely correspond to boundaries of the various floral communities with average values for communities from above high tide to below low tide as follows: Distichlidetum, 29.8 per cent; Monanthocloetum, 28.0; Suaedetum, 24.1; Salicornietum, 14.7; Spartinetum, 8.4; and Zosteretum, 0.5. Because of the large productivity and burial of organic material, the interstitial water loses its dissolved oxygen and is characterized by a negative *Eh* (oxidation-reduction potential) and the presence of hydrogen sulfide and iron monosulfides that contribute toward the typical black color of the marsh sediment. Organic acids released to the interstitial water give it a low *p*H (hydrogen ion potential) that decreases from about 8.0 in the tidal channels through 6.9 in the Spartinetum and 6.7 in the Salicornietum to 5.7 in the Distichlidetum. Such *p*H's are sufficiently low to dissolve shells buried in the mud. As a result the average content of calcium carbonate in the marsh surface is only 0.6 per cent, as compared with about 80 per cent in the sands of the tidal channels.

Recognition of ancient marsh deposits must be made mostly on the basis of sedimentary characteristics owing to the general absence of fossils. Chief among the petrographic characteristics are fine grain size,

high organic content, dark color, and presence of marcasite. In addition, thin layers of muds deposited by floods or special high tides produce the well-known platy laminae of Paleozoic black shales, many of which have been considered to be former marsh deposits. Ripple marks and mud cracks are sometimes, but not invariably, present. Tracks and trails should be common in ancient deposits as they are in the modern marshes.

Gravel Beaches

Beaches consisting mostly of gravel fringe about 5 per cent of the coast, occurring at the base of many of the cliffed shores of the mainland and islands. They are most common at the sides of projecting points rather than at the very ends of the points where the exposure to waves is so great that gravels cannot remain. They are also especially likely to occur where the cliffs consist of conglomerate, mostly Eocene and Pleistocene, or where streams contribute large quantities of gravels (Fig. 157). These multiple-cycle gravels are believed to form about 75 per cent of the gravel beaches in the region. Most of the boulders, cobbles, and pebbles consist of dense igneous rock, but chert,

Figure 157. The longest gravel beach in southern California (about 1 km) forms a bar across an estuary located just north of Encinitas. The gravels are supplied by erosion of conglomerates in the cliffs at either side of the estuary mouth.

limestone, and schist are locally represented.

The median diameters of gravels at 21 mainland beaches (La Jolla, Encinitas, Carlsbad, Dana Point, Whites Cove, Vicinte Cove, Malaga Cove, Redondo Beach, Santa Monica, Corral Beach, Sycamore Point, Ventura, Rincon Point, Capitan, and Gaviota) were found to range between 24 and 650 mm (Emery, 1955a). Each station is characterized by low Trask sorting coefficients of 1.16 to 1.47 (average = 1.27) and symmetrical-size frequency curves (Table 12, Fig. 156). Within individual gravel beaches there usually exists a longshore decrease of grain size and a decrease of sorting coefficient away from the source of the gravels. This is well illustrated at Vicinte Cove, Palos Verdes

Hills, where basalt supplied by a sill is carried mostly to the east by wave action and is mixed with other boulders and cobbles of siliceous shale (Fig. 158). During their transportation these basalt cobbles become rounder (wearing of corners) and more spherical (volume approaching that of an enclosing sphere). An idea of the speed of transportion of cobbles is given by the fact that painted cobbles were moved 20 meters in 10 minutes by 1-meter waves striking the beach at Santa Monica.

Individual cobbles usually are round or subround, but they have only a moderate to low sphericity where they are flat and diskoidal. This is the original shape of some fragments because of control exerted by bed-

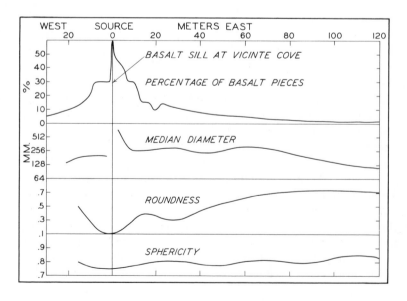

Figure 158. Variation in basalt cobbles and boulders with distance from source (a sill) at Vicinte Coves, southwest side of Palos Verdes Hills. Roundness and sphericity estimated visually from standard grain outlines by Krumbein (1941) and Rittenhouse (1943). Adapted in part from Baldwin (1956).

ding planes in sedimentary rocks, foliations in schists, and joints in some igneous rocks. However, the generally high degree of uniformity of shape gives rise to the long-pondered question of whether gravels are worn flatter on beaches or whether the originally flat pieces are selectively sorted away from their more spherical original companions. Arguments and evidence for both points of view exist. In order to check the erosional question, about 1000 cobbles were painted white and replaced on a sandy beach. After a few days the painted cobbles were sought out after undergoing heavy losses from wave action and little boy collectors. Although the results are statistically incomplete, the paint was the most worn off on the sides of flat pieces but more or less uniformly around spherical ones. In a later study Dobbs (1958) placed 375 painted cobbles on a gravel beach. After an hour only 10 specimens could be found. Counts were made of the number of impacts that these cobbles had undergone, with the following results: round rocks, 185/sq cm uniformly distributed; flat surface of flat cobbles, 125/sq cm; and rounded edges of flat cobbles, 292/sq cm. The hypothesis seems reasonable that on beaches consisting only of cobbles the cobbles tend to be tumbled over each other so that all sides are worn, especially the rounded edges, whereas cobbles scattered about a predominantly sandy beach rest on one side and are sand-blasted on their upper surface. In favor of the sorting point of view is the fact that even on beaches consisting only of cobbles flat pieces are prevalent high on the beach as though lifted by advancing waves, whereas spherical ones are commonest low on the beach as though they tend to roll seaward in the backwash of waves (Fig. 159).

Within the gravel beaches a preferred orientation of individual cobbles is usually well exhibited. The short axis dips landward because the force of wave impact tilts the discoidal specimens (Fig. 159). Since the beaches are highly permeable, most of the water in the waves seeps downward through the beach, leaving so little of it to return to the ocean atop the beach that it does not

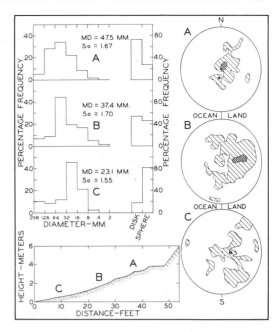

Figure 159. Some characteristics of gravel beach at Bluff Cove, west side of Palos Verdes Hills. Each histogram is based on a composite of 100 measurements at 11 stations located 15 meters apart along the beach. Note the increase of median diameter (intermediate axis) and decrease of sphericity from bottom to top of beach. Three berms are shown by the beach profile. Adapted from Briggs (1950). Petrofabric diagrams of C-axis (short axis) with land on right-hand side are adapted from West (1950) and are based on 100 to 125 cobbles at each of 3 stations, with cross-hatched area representing 1 per cent and double-hatched area 5 per cent of cobbles.

greatly modify the grain orientation on the higher levels of the beaches. The loud rattling of cobbles low on the beaches shows that modification of grain orientation does occur there, however, during the backwash of waves.

Gravel as well as sand beaches are commonly interrupted by two kinds of moderately large features. One, the berm, extends along the length of a beach (Fig. 160), whereas the other, the cusp, is transverse to the beach. Eight separate berms, or step-like flattenings of the foreslope, have been noted on a gravel beach at Punta San Telmo, in Baja California, but three or four appear to be the maximum in southern California. Because the berms usually extend the entire length of a beach, they must be produced by an agent that is uniform along much of the

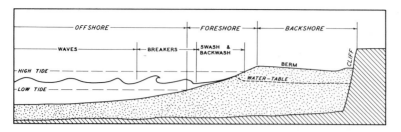

Figure 160. Terminology and some of the characteristics of water and topography of beaches. See also Shepard (1948, p. 82) and Wiegel (1953).

coast, such as storm waves at a particular stage of the tide.

The second feature, cusps, has been intriguing to many geologists. At Santa Monica Bay the gravel cusps range from irregular masses to isosceles triangles having points facing the ocean. They average 15 meters wide, 10 meters long, and 50 cm high. They are separated by sand embayments averaging about 20 meters wide. The cusps consist of well-sorted gravel with the smallest size at the apex. Several hypotheses have been formulated to account for cusps, among which are the following: breaching of a gravel bar (Jefferson, 1899), interference of two sets of waves (Branner, 1900), erosion of an embayment at an initial depression in a continuous gravel beach (Johnson, 1919, pp. 457–486), burial under sand followed by exhumation (Shepard, 1935), and erosion of embayments by swash followed by refraction of the swash to the sides and deposition of the eroded material as a cusp (Kuenen, 1948). None of these hypotheses appears to be based on actual observation of formation, probably because the cusps form quickly and then endure usually for at least several days. By a clever bit of detective work Schupp (1953) managed to photograph the development of a cusp from beginning to end (Fig. 161). Examination of the beach at the north end of Santa Monica Bay at intervals over a 2-year period showed that the cusps are most abundant during the summer and fall when waves are relatively small and during the neap stage of the tidal cycle. They also appeared to form at high tide. After several failures Schupp picked a favorable period, at night, and observed at first a bare sand beach (sloping 20° rather than the usual 12°), atop which a 4.5-hour rising tide

deposited a thin veneer of fine gravel that culminated in a 8-cm layer of medium-to-coarse gravel. During the first 2.5 hours of falling tide cusps were formed through erosion of the embayments by wave backwash which also deposited some of the eroded material at the seaward side of the embayment to build the apex of the cusp. The change from bare sand to gravel cusp required only 7 hours. Whether this explanation is true for other gravel cusps in the region is unknown, but quite possibly some others are of different origin.

Recognition of ancient gravel beaches is simple where shells are still present or where some of the cobbles contain pholad borings. If only unbored cobbles and pebbles remain, there may be some difficulty in distinguishing whether a large blanket conglomerate was of beach or alluvial origin. However, where former beach deposits are narrow, a sequence may be expected from angular talus debris at the base of the land side through spheroidal to diskoidal cobbles at the top of the deposit. Such a sequence is more or less completely represented in exposures of the raised terraces of the Palos Verdes Hills and elsewhere along the coast. Beach gravels (Fig. 81) also occur on the sea floor (Clements and Dana, 1944; Emery and Shepard, 1945); the sequence is less well exhibited than on land.

Sand Beaches

Unlike beach cobbles and pebbles, almost all beach sand grains are monomineralic with the maximum diameter limited by the original size of the minerals in the source rocks. The beach sands also usually have a lower degree of roundness and a higher degree of sphericity than the gravels. The low roundness is a result of both the low impact as compared with that of the heavier cobbles and the cushioning effect of the surrounding water film as compared with the negligible effect of air for wind-blown sands which are usually well rounded.

As pointed out long ago by Reed (1928), most of the Mesozoic and Cenozoic strata as well as unconsolidated recent sediments contain such a high percentage of feldspar that they should be termed arkoses or arkosic sands. Other supporting analyses of ancient sedimentary rocks of the region are given by Woodford (1925), Hertlein and Grant (1944), and Emery, Butcher, Gould, and Shepard (1952). Among the recent sediments the beach sands of Coronado Strand near San Diego consist of approximately 50 per cent feldspar and 50 per cent quartz, as compared with the 20 per cent minimum feldspar required by Krynine (1948) and the 25 per cent required by Pettijohn (1957, p. 291) for use of the term arkose. The high feldspar-to-quartz ratio is doubtlessly a reflection of the large proportion of feldspar in the source batholiths, the arid conditions of weathering, and the rapid transportation and deposition in the region.

More diagnostic of provenance are the heavy minerals, although unfortunately this branch of sedimentology has received less attention in the region than it deserves. Regional studies of the mineralogy of all southern California beaches have not yet been made, but some general information is provided by a comparison of several local studies. Trask (1952) found that the beaches between Monterey and Santa Barbara can be divided into three subequal units: the northern third with heavy minerals (62 to 125 microns) dominated by hornblende, the middle by augite, and the southern one by epidote. The latter third includes the entire coast between Point Conception and Santa Barbara, where the chief source of the minerals must be the Tertiary sedimentary rocks of the Santa Ynez Mountains (Fig. 162). Handin (1951) examined the minerals in the same size fraction of beach samples collected between Santa Barbara and Point Fermin

and found that heavy minerals in the central part of this span of beaches are dominated by augite. This span corresponds to the position of the Santa Monica Mountains, whose streams carry large percentages of augite. Near Point Fermin the chief heavy mineral is hornblende, which is even more dominant southward to Mexico (Inman, 1953) and San Diego (Emery, Butcher, Gould, and Shepard, 1952). It appears reasonable to divide the beaches of southern California into three heavy mineral regions: epidote between Point Conception and Ventura, augite between Ventura and Santa Monica, and hornblende between Santa Monica and Mexico. The presence of these zones is strongly suggestive of distinctive composition of the corresponding chief areas of provenance. Mineral composition can thus be used to identify the source of the beach sands. For example, Trask considered that the gradually diminishing content of augite in beach sands southward from the augite source area near Morro Bay indicates the downcurrent passage of sand around Point Conception to Santa Barbara.

Many studies of the grain-size distribution of beach sands have been made, but nearly all of these are for only small parts of the region and are of uneven quality and density of samples. In order to provide a more uniform basis for judging the character of the beaches, a special suite of samples was collected at 5-mile (8-km) intervals between Point Conception and the United States–Mexican border during a period of neap tide in late November 1956. These samples were composites of the zone between the high tidemark and the approximate midtide level. They exhibit a range in median diameter from 150 to 590 microns and average 240 microns (Table 12, Fig. 163). This is lower than the average of 350 microns obtained by combining the results of many independent beach studies (Emery, 1954e) but is a more valid representation for the region. Irregularities in grain size are apparent in the regional picture. Some areas of coarser-than-usual sand are present at the mouths of rivers such as the Ventura and Santa Clara and of Ballona Creek, as though these

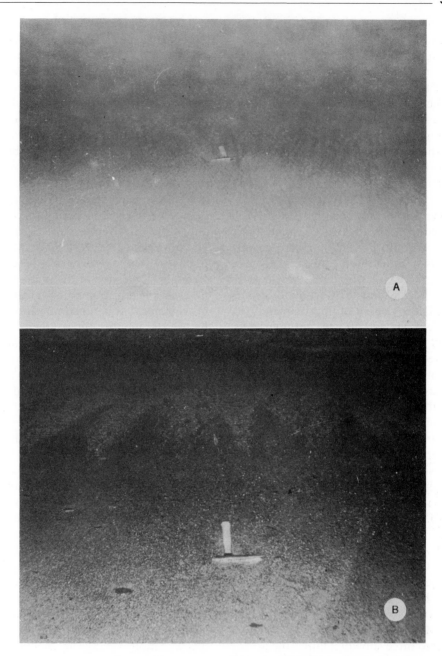

Figure 161. Series of photographs at Will Rogers State Park, north end of Santa Monica Bay, showing complete development of a gravel cusp, from Schupp (1953). A, bare sand, 1930 on June 26, 1952; B, thin veneer of fine gravel,

streams contribute a large proportion of coarse sands. In contrast, the mouths of the Santa Ana, Santa Margarita, San Diegueto, and San Diego Rivers are marked by finer-than-usual sands, perhaps in response to a finer caliber of load. These relationships may be purely circumstantial and the beach sands controlled by other factors in view of the scarcity of data on stream-borne sediments of the region. A closer spacing of samples would have revealed the presence of coarse sand confined to small pocket beaches like La Jolla Cove (Sample 51). An example of the ability of closely spaced sam-

2100; C, layer of coarser gravel, 0030 on June 27; D, complete cusp, 0730.

ples to reveal relationship to environment is exhibited at Newport Beach (Fig. 164) where fine-grained sand exists in equilibrium with the small waves that result from refraction away from the deep water at the head of Newport Canyon; in contrast, sand at both sides of the point where the waves are higher is coarser. Similar results were obtained here in summer and winter.

Variations in grain size also occur transverse to the beach. On coarse beaches it is common that the coarsest sand is present at the low-tide level where the wave turbulence is greatest; however, some fine-sand beaches

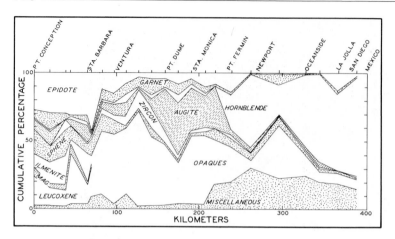

Figure 162. Distribution of chief heavy minerals along the coast as compiled from various sources given in text.

that are markedly concave upward in profile have the finest sand near the low-tide level, as though it had been winnowed out of the upper foreshore. As pointed out by Bascom (1951) the transverse variation of grain size requires a standardized sampling point in order to compare the characteristics of different beaches. The midtide level seems to be the most suitable place for collecting single samples because it is somewhat less subject to change of slope and of grain size than other portions. Analysis of many samples from that point by Bascom clearly shows a parallelism between coarseness of

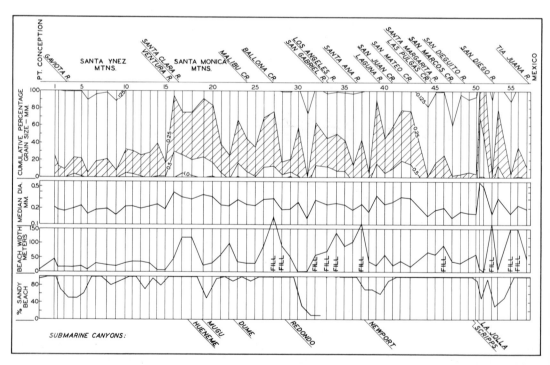

Figure 163. General characteristics of sand beaches from near Point Conception to Mexico based on observations and samples at approximately 5-mile (8 km) intervals during November 22–24, 1956 (Fig. 28). Top strip shows cumulative grain-size distribution of samples. Other strips show median diameter of sediment, width of beach, and estimated percentage of shore between sample localities that consists of sandy beach. The notation "fill" indicates areas where slight-to-large widening of the beach has occurred by artificial means, mostly by dredging the floors of adjacent bays.

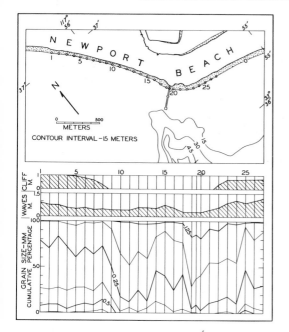

Figure 164. Relationship of grain size of beach sand to offshore topography, wave height, and reworking of beach. Note that the finest sand occurs near the pier built at the head of Newport Canyon where waves were smallest. Great increase of grain size is at left where beach was being cut by spring tides, leaving a concentrate of coarse grains at the surface. Samples were collected on July 22, 1957, about 30 cm above midtide level.

microns, owing to the unique interrelationship of settling velocity, roughness velocity, and threshold velocity for grains of that size. Silt (finer than 62 microns) is so fine that it tends to remain in suspension and be carried beyond the beach. Pebbles are so much coarser than most beach sands that they tend to be bypassed by moving sand, and when included in grain-size analyses they form a double maximum in the size frequency curve.

In addition to their geographical variations in grain size, beach sands undergo seasonal variations produced by winnowing away of finer grains by storm waves of winter and replacement of these grains by the smaller waves of summer (Kerr, 1938; Shepard and Inman, 1953). A side effect is the greater concentration of heavy minerals on some winter beaches by the "panning" action of wave erosion. A less extreme biweekly cycle probably also occurs as a result of cutting and filling of beaches during the lunar cycle of spring and neap tides (Fig. 30). Still another cycle results from differences in transporting ability of individual waves. The effects of this cycle are most easily seen in cross sections cut through the beach, where they show up as the thin laminae of alternating coarser and finer sands noted by Thompson (1937) and others (Figs. 165, 166). Because most of the dark and heavy minerals are concentrated in finer grain sizes, 50 to 200 microns, the fine layers are darker than the coarse ones. As pointed out by Emery and Stevenson (1950) the presence of the layers complicates precise sampling of beaches because a grab sample must have a grain size intermediate between the grain sizes of the many pairs of coarse and fine laminae that were penetrated and yet have a poorer sorting coefficient than either kind of lamina.

Preferred orientation of beach sands differs from that of beach gravels. As shown by Nanz (1955) and Curray (1956) elongate and particularly wedge-shaped grains tend to act as weather vanes, aligning their long axes with the water movement. Because the waves wash more or less directly across the beach, the grains tend to align themselves at right angles to the beach trend; the mean

grain, steepness of beach, and amount of wave energy. Some of the spread in results is attributable to the difference in slope of the beach when it is being eroded and when it is being built up during the biweekly tidal cycle, although the sand is nearly identical in both stages. Differences in slope at the two times can be detected from repeated field measurements of profiles and from the manner in which the laminae which compose the beach are truncated and overlain by later laminae.

One of the distinguishing characteristics of beach sands is their high degree of sorting. Rarely do appreciable quantities of sand fall into more than three Wentworth grade sizes. In the suite of samples collected along the mainland coast in November 1956 the sorting coefficient ranged between 1.11 and 1.40 and averaged 1.22. As pointed out by Inman (1949a), the median diameter likely to be most highly sorted in water is 180

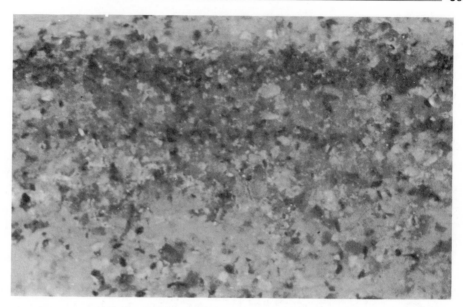

Figure 165. Section of beach sand from Newport Beach impregnated with a clear plastic and extending from the surface to a depth of about 4 mm. Two fine-grained dark laminae are present at depths of about 1 and 2 mm. From Emery and Stevenson (1950, Fig. 1).

departure of 2082 grains measured by Curray in thin sections at La Jolla's Scripps Beach was 15°, similar to results he obtained on beaches of the Atlantic Ocean and the Gulf of Mexico. Laboratory experiments by Scott (1954) showed that the sand grains on the foreshore tended to become tightly packed during their movement by waves; in contrast, grains washed onto the berm above were very loosely packed—presumably with

Figure 166. Laminated beach sand cemented in nature by travertine formed by seepage of ground water from sea cliff about 500 meters south of Casa Pool in La Jolla. Subsequent exposure and differential erosion caused some laminae to be recessed more than others. Similar cementation has been observed at Point Fermin.

little preferred orientation. A related phenomenon was studied by Bryson (1956),
who measured the permeability of beach
sands vertically, horizontally parallel to the
beach, and horizontally at right angles to the
beach. He used a constant-head permea-
meter and measured permeability according
to the equation $P = QL\mu/TAH$, where Q
is the quantity of water of viscosity μ that
passes through a column of sand of length L
and cross section A in the time T. The average of 24 sets of measurements at 9 stations
along the beaches of Santa Monica Bay was
36 darcys vertically, 61 darcys parallel to the
beach, and 75 darcys transverse to it; all
except two sets of measurements corresponded to this relative order. The lowest
permeability, in the vertical direction, is
doubtlessly due to the presence of horizontal
laminae, some of which are fine-grained and
thus of low permeability. However, *a priori*
we might have expected that the orientation
of long axes of grains at nearly right angles
to the beach would have produced the greatest permeability in that direction. The fact
that the greatest permeability is horizontal
and parallel to the beach may be due to
blocking of the seaward flow of interstitial
water by the grain imbrication as suggested
by a comparison of measurements of permeability and grain orientation and imbrication
by Rabinovitz (1958).

The horizontal direction of great permeability produces several unique minor features
on sand beaches. When waves on an in-
coming tide wash across a largely dry beach,
a high percentage of the water seeps downward into the sand. Where the sand is
coarse, the air readily escapes through small
holes that sometimes have been mistakenly
identified as animal burrows. Beaches composed of fine-to-medium sand having few
coarse layers and characterized by small
waves, such as in largely enclosed bays, trap
most of the air as subspherical pockets many
times larger in diameter than the sand grains
(Fig. 167). A porosity of 73 per cent was
measured in such sand, half of which was in
the form of large air pockets (Emery, 1945a).
Compaction of the sand underfoot leaves
footprints as deep as 20 cm and disturbance

Figure 167. Beach of fine sand near former entrance to
Mission Bay, San Diego, having a thickness of about 15
cm of highly cavernous sand with subspherical pockets
filled with air. From Emery (1945a, Pl. 3).

under water releases clouds of air bubbles.
On beaches having well-developed laminae
of alternating coarse and fine sand the water
drives the air ahead of it in the coarser and
more permeable laminae. Frequently, the
air is so compressed by the water movement,
probably aided by capillarity, that it is able
to lift up several centimeters of overlying
sand, forming a sand dome, a sort of air lac-
colith which usually has a diameter between
5 and 15 cm (Fig. 168). Later waves crossing

Figure 168. Double sand dome in sand of Scripps Beach
formed when air was driven along coarse laminae by
water seeping into the surface of beach.

the beach may truncate the dome so that outcropping dark laminae produce circular rings on the sand surface (Fig. 169). Although these are more capable of preservation in the geological column than other minor features known to have been preserved, no truncated domes have been reported.

Several other minor features of beaches are worthy of mention as indicators of probable marine environment and of the direction toward the ocean. One of these is swash marks, narrow lines of sand grains that are floated on a thin wedge of water at the front of an advancing wave (Evans, 1938; Emery, 1945b). When the wave reaches its point of farthest advance, the wedge seeps into the beach, leaving its load of sand filtered out at the surface (Fig. 170). Since the sand can be floated only from the semidry part of the beach, swash marks form only at levels above the outcrop of the beach water table. The swash marks usually contain a higher than usual percentage of Foraminifera and mica flakes owing to their low specific gravity or angularity. The highest swash mark is ordinarily a very irregular one, owing to the leaping of the foamy front of a wave produced by escape of interstitial air from the beach. Subsequent lower swash marks are broadly curving and convex toward land. Empirically it has been noted that swash marks are more closely spaced on steep beaches than on gentle ones (Fig. 171), suggesting a possible means of estimating the original slope of ancient beaches and the range of ancient tides. During the return of the water to the ocean, its movement scours around the sides of pebbles and leaves elongate markings on the seaward side of beach holes and bumps; these markings constitute supplementary means of orientating ancient beach deposits.

Four main kinds of ripple marks occur on beaches. Most common are rhomboid ripples which produce a diamond pattern of intersecting lines. The pattern shows best in sands that have a large percentage of dark grains (Fig. 172). Observations by Woodford (1935) and Demarest (1947) show that the pattern is a form of lee wave radiating seaward from coarser than usual grains or from centers of escaping interstitial water. Measurements by Moore (1951) and Keesling (1953) on southern California beaches showed that rhomboid ripples form only on

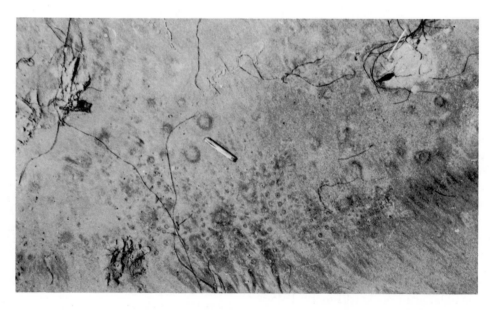

Figure 169. Rings of dark sand left when sand domes were truncated by subsequent waves. Scripps Beach with ocean at top. These rings are capable of preservation in the geological record but none has been reported.

Figure 170. Highest swash mark, scour around pebble, and elongate markings in the backwash lee of holes and other irregularities on Scripps Beach. Ocean is at bottom.

the saturated lower part of beaches and at angles of slope between 2 and 10°. They also found that the angle at the apex of the rhombs becomes progressively smaller with increased velocity of backwash, as predicted by Woodford. The next most common are erosional ripples—best developed on beaches that have pronounced laminations (Fig. 172). These ripples are broad, 30 to 60 cm, and are steeper where they cross the outcropping dark laminae. They have the appearance of a series of small cuestas and evidently are produced by erosion, possibly therefore they appear mostly during spring tides. Wind ripple marks are frequently present on the beach and are readily identified by their usually angular trend with respect to the beach and their presence on the backslope of a berm. Water ripple marks are unusual; current ripples do occur but rarely anywhere except at the mouths of bays (Fig. 173). Symmetrical wave ripple marks have not been reported, except of course on the underwater extensions of the sand beaches where they have been described by Inman (1957).

At low tide when the beach water table intersects the beach surface less than 1 meter above the low sea level (Fig. 118), much water drains from the sand. Runoff across the saturated lower part of the beach produces intricate badlands topography in miniature which would leave no question about orientation if seen in the geological column. Frequently, the water carries so much sand that it forms a braided pattern and builds a delta that progresses across the beach, obliterating previous minor features (Fig. 173). In some instances the sand also appears to flow en mass somewhat like a mudflow.

A larger feature present on sand beaches as well as on gravel beaches is the berm. Several sets may sometimes be observed. Although the observation is not well documented, it is believed that berms on sand beaches are more numerous in the early fall than at other times of the year because they form periodically during the spring and summer and are removed by storm waves during the winter. Their origin is not well understood, but one possible mode of formation is that started by cutting of the beach at spring tide so that a scarp a fraction of a meter high is left. As waves at later high tides reach higher and higher on the foreshore, they finally cross the top of the scarp and deposit their load of sand. In time a landward-sloping surface develops, a berm. Once established, a berm tends to

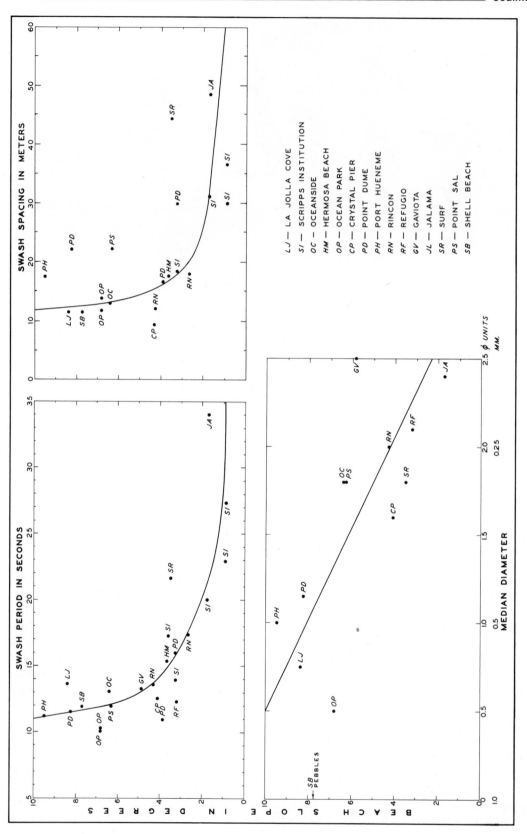

Figure 171. Relationship of beach slope to swash period, swash mark spacing, and grain size. From Emery and Gale (1951, Fig. 4).

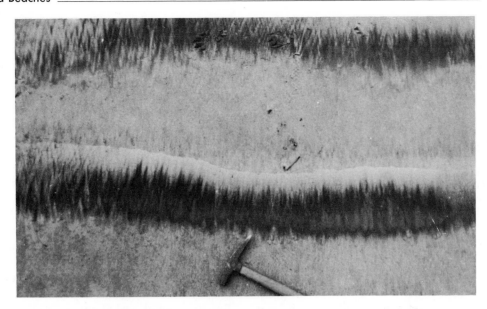

Figure 172. Erosional ripple marks produced by steep truncation of dark laminae and gentle truncation of thick, coarse, light-colored laminate. Note the rhomboid ripple marks with their usual diamond pattern. Scripps Beach with ocean side at top.

be self-perpetuating through the building of washover fans (Price, 1947), a delta-like blanket of sand left when waves cross the crest of the berm and the water soaks into the sand. Repeated accumulation of wash-over fans must add to the height of the berms's edge, thereby accentuating the usual landward sloping surface of the berm (Fig. 174). Sand beaches of southern California also commonly contain sand cusps that have shapes similar to those of gravel cusps. Distances from point to point of adjacent cusps commonly range between 3 and 30 meters. Preliminary studies show

Figure 173. Current ripples at former mouth of Mission Bay, San Diego. Note destruction of ripples by erosion and redeposition of sand at low tide through action of escaping interstitial water.

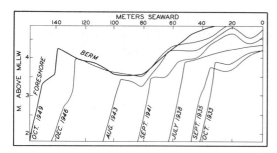

Figure 174. Growth of a sand beach and development of a long-lived berm at the north side of the shoreline bulge developed inshore of breakwater at Santa Monica Harbor. These profiles were measured by the Los Angeles City Engineer (Venice Office) during the years between construction of the breakwater in 1933–1934 and its first major dredging in 1949–1950.

that there is little or no difference in grain size between the cusp and its adjacent embayment.

Recognition of ancient beach deposits during the past has depended almost exclusively on only two criteria of vastly different size scale. One of these is the sediment texture, and the other is the general shape of the deposit. The minor features of intermediate size described earlier can also serve as reasonably certain criteria of beach environment when and if ancient representatives are found and adequately studied. Moreover, some of the features are diagnostic of a particular part of a beach. For example, above high tide on a beach we find berms, washover fans, wind ripples, and the uppermost irregular swash marks. Near midtide of the foreshore are cusps, ordinary swash marks, sand holes, sand domes, cavernous sand, and erosional ripples. Just above the low-tide level are rhomboid ripples and rills, and below low tide are oscillation ripples. The manner of preservation of the smaller of these features is not well understood, but the uniformity of laminae over distances of at least several meters indicates that deposition of sand by waves can occur without great erosion of the sediment surface. Preservation of delicate features such as swash marks is probably enhanced by the development of a rigid crust by growth of salt crystals in the interstices. In any event swash marks are known to have been

preserved in Paleozoic sandstones of eastern United States (Fairchild, 1901: Clarke, 1918). Partial impregnation of recent beach deposits in such a way that laminae can be separated would be of interest in showing just how and what features may be preserved.

Mainland Shelf

Approximately 5000, samples have been taken on the 1890 square miles (4900 sq km) of shelf bordering the mainland coast. Nearly 1700 of them were collected by the University of California Division of War Research in the San Diego region during World War II in a program of measuring the effects of bottom sediments on underwater acoustics (Russell, 1950; Emery, Butcher, Gould, and Shepard, 1952). About 1500 samples in a dense grid between Santa Barbara and Gaviota, by-products of oil company explorations, were studied by Thompson (1957). Most of the rest were taken by the University of Southern California along the entire shelf between Point Conception and Mexico, but with a concentration in Santa Monica Bay. This sampling was part of two large studies of sewage pollution, one for Hyperion Engineers (Terry, Keesling, and Uchupi, 1956) and the other for the California State Water Pollution Control Board (Stevenson and Terry, 1957). The densest and most systematic sampling is in the four widest places of the shelf: off San Diego, San Pedro, Santa Monica, and Santa Barbara. These areas comprise about two-thirds of the total area of mainland shelf.

Many methods can be used for describing the sediments in an area and have been used during the past. For depicting areas having many samples the ideal that is usually sought is a map on which a single completely descriptive parameter can be contoured or patterned. One obviously important parameter is grain size, usually expressed as median diameter of each of many mapped and analyzed samples. Such an isopleth map for the San Diego region (Fig. 175) reveals a complex pattern of coarse-to-fine median diameters, but it fails to show whether all areas of equal median diameter

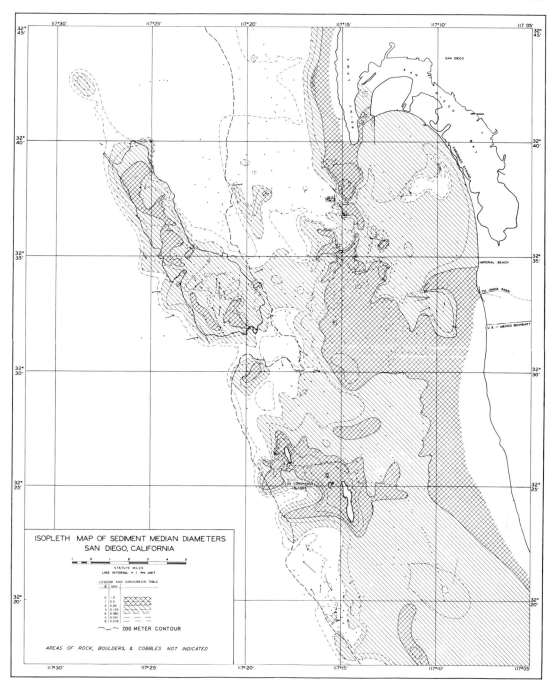

Figure 175. Map showing distribution of median diameter of 1660 surface sediment samples off San Diego. In some areas consisting chiefly of rock or boulder bottom the sand that is represented is only interstitial. From Emery, Butcher, Gould, and Shepard (1952, Fig. 8).

are equally well sorted. Sorting coefficients can be presented by another separate map, and comparison of the two maps provides new information. Still another map, of skewness, is required for a relatively full presentation of the grain-size distribution data. Moreover, the series of maps considers only the middle 50 per cent of the grain-size distribution included between the quartile percentages from which the sorting coefficient and skewness are computed. Broadening the base of computation to include the middle 68 per cent, as can be done by using Inman's (1952, 1953) method, improves the statistics but fails to increase appreciably the understanding of the general sediment pattern.

In order to improve on the median diameter–sorting coefficient–skewness method of presentation, a set of three maps showing the percentage of sand, silt, and clay may be used (Fig. 176). This presentation still requires some map-to-map comparison, but the results are simpler of comprehension than those by the first method; moreover, these maps can include virtually the entire grain-size distribution of the samples if close contour intervals of percentage are chosen. This method still requires several maps and fails to indicate relative amounts of calcium carbonate and other important and unique characteristics of some of the sediments.

A further improvement in easy visualization is that of classifying the sediments into types and mapping the distribution of each type. These types may be drawn on the basis only of the percentage distribution of grain sizes, using a triangular composition diagram to define the size terms. Several

variations of such diagrams have been used by different workers. Shepard (1954) suggested one based on sand-silt-clay relationships. A supplementary one used at University of Southern California (Fig. 177) is based also on gravel-sand-silt plus clay ratios as being more applicable to some shelf sediments of this region. An example of its use is given by Figure 178, a map of the sediments off Santa Barbara.

For special purposes the sands may be screened out of the whole sediment samples and examined separately with a binocular microscope to provide data on source of the sediment. The results can be plotted as contour maps of chief constituents (Emery. Tracey, and Ladd, 1954, Figs. 22, 43, 50, and 56), as pie diagrams (Shepard and Moore, 1954), or as mappable classes of sediment coarse fractions (Fig. 178).

A last sort of map of sediment types is one that combines grain size with a description of color and composition, for instance, green silty shell sand. Examples of such maps are given for the shelves off Santa Barbara (Fig. 178) and off San Diego (Fig. 179). Such a map of types indicates at a glance the general nature and distribution of sediments. In spite of the large variety of kinds of presentation, standardization of maps of sediments should not be attempted because each kind of map has its own ad-

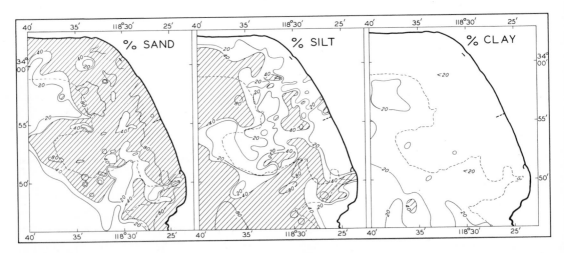

Figure 176. Percentages of sand, silt, and clay in Santa Monica Bay based on 510 samples. Dashed line is shelf-break, about 90 meters. Adapted from Terry, Keesling, and Uchupi (1956, Figs. 16, 17, and 18).

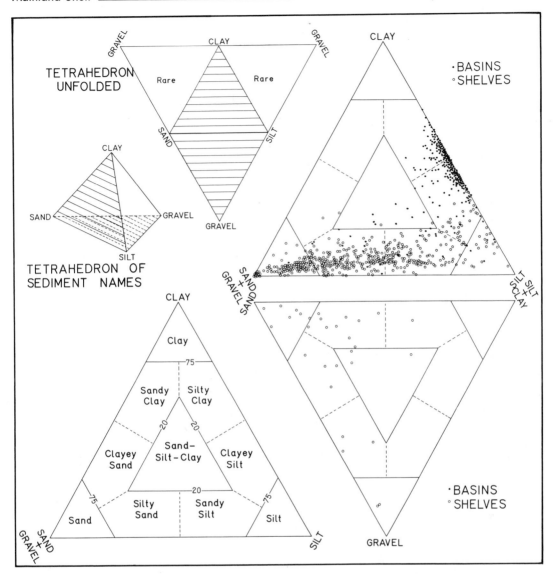

Figure 177. Triangular composition diagram for classifying sediments on the basis of their contents of gravel (>2 mm), sand (2–0.62 mm), silt (0.62–0.004 mm), and clay (0.004 mm). Circles and dots show many analyses for shelf and basin sediments of the region. Modified from Shepard (1954).

vantage for a particular situation and purpose.

Maps of shelf sediments, most of them with fewer details than Figure 179, have been made by many workers for many continental shelf areas of the world (see Lüders, 1939; Shepard and Cohee, 1936). Nearly all such maps exhibit irregularities in the distribution patterns that are difficult to explain. As a result the concept has arisen that sediments of the shelves are so haphazardly placed that the cause cannot be in-

terpreted, and thus the inference must be drawn that the patterns of similar ancient sediments cannot be predicted from incomplete sampling at outcrops or wells. An effort to reach an understanding of the chief distributive factors was made by Shepard, Emery, and Gould (1949), who found that many of the anomalous patterns can be related to bottom currents, exposure to large waves, nearby large river mouths, contiguous sand beaches, submarine basins and

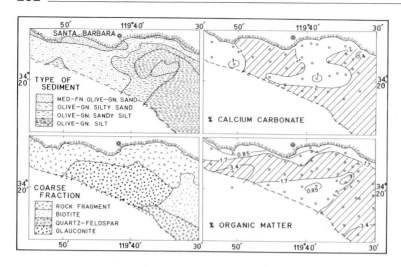

Figure 178. Sediments of mainland shelf off Santa Barbara. Contours of percentage calcium carbonate and of organic matter (1.7 × organic carbon) are based on samples indicated by small circles. Maps of grain size of total sediment and of composition of coarse fractions are based on approximately twice as many samples. Dashed line is 100-meter contour. Compare with benthic faunal distribution of Figure 144.

hills, abundance of calcareous organisms, recent explosive vulcanism, and presence of lag materials. Although these factors can be determined for the present ocean floor in well-known areas, they usually cannot be estimated for ancient strata.

As a further step toward reaching an understanding of the distribution of sediments and its causes, Emery (1952b) proposed that samples be classified according to the dominant cause of deposition and that sediments of similar origin be mapped as units. The major kind of sediment found on continental shelves is usually the present-day detrital material contributed to the ocean mostly by streams and sea cliffs. Having a similar origin but a longer and different history are relict sediments, material once deposited on the sea floor in equilibrium with then-existing waves and currents but now above or below that equilibrium position, owing to relative change of sea level. A third kind of sediment is residual inorganic debris left from *in situ* weathering of rocks cropping out on the sea floor; the relative roles of existing submarine and former subaerial weathering cannot usually be determined. Sediments of organic origin, a fourth type, consist of calcareous foraminiferal tests and shell fragments, siliceous skeletal debris, and organic matter. Fifth is chemical precipitates, or authigenic sediments, chiefly glauconite, phosphorite, and manganese oxide. In some regions other types of sedi-

ments occur in amounts large enough to be worthy of consideration. Among them are rafted sediments. Since ice is the chief mass rafting agent, these sediments are largely restricted to high latitudes and probably never occurred in southern California even during the Pleistocene Epoch. Another unrepresented kind of sediment is volcanic ash and cinders, which in Japan's Kagoshima Bay, for example, covers many hundreds of square kilometers. The five most important kinds of sediment in southern California (present-day detrital, relict, residual, organic, and authigenic) occur in varying proportions on the mainland shelves, island shelves, and bank tops. Each of these three areas will be described separately. In the well-known areas of the southern California mainland shelf the sediment distribution maps clearly reveal the reason for the apparently erratic distribution of grain sizes (Fig. 180). The areas of anomalous grain size correspond for the most part to areas of sediment derived from organic, authigenic, relict, and residual origins. They occur where the nature of bottom topography is such that modern detrital sediments cannot be deposited to bury older kinds of sediment.

Present-day detrital sediments are the most important in terms of area of the mainland shelf of southern California. The approximate percentage of area covered by them in the four best-known parts of the mainland shelf are as follows: off

Santa Barbara, 95; off Santa Monica, 53; off San Pedro, 87; and off San Diego, 78. These detrital sediments consist mostly of sands and silts which form seaward continuations of the beaches. They can be recognized by their seaward decrease in grain size, their low content of calcium carbonate, and the fresh unstained appearance of the grains. They consist chiefly of quartz and feldspar with an average ratio

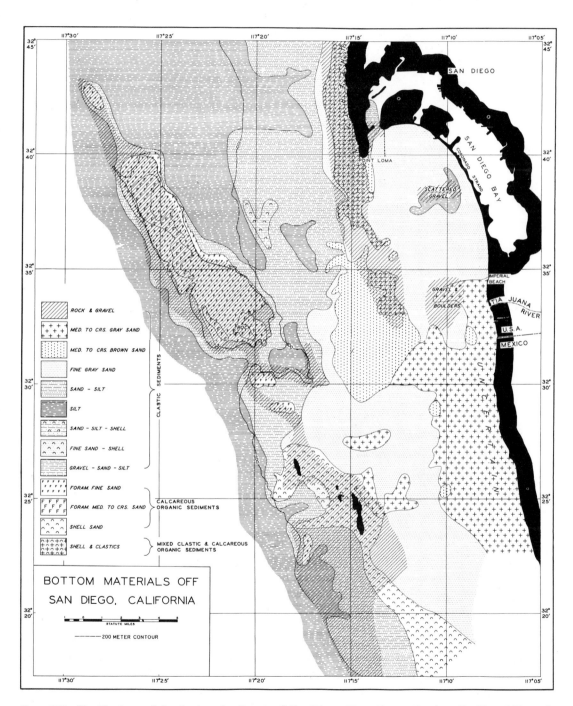

Figure 179. Classification and distribution of sediments off San Diego. From Emery, Butcher, Gould, and Shepard (1952, Fig. 7).

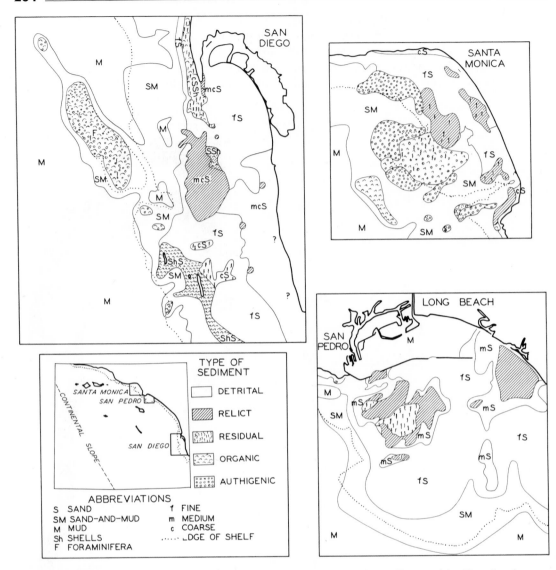

Figure 180. Sediments off San Diego, San Pedro, and Santa Monica classified according to origin. Note that the term "mud" is used here as a noncommital designation for various mixtures of silt and clay. Dotted line is shelf-break. Revised from Emery (1952b).

of 2.5–1 off San Diego and 1.05–1 off Santa Monica. Plagioclase is 4 to 100 times as abundant as orthoclase. Heavy minerals are dominated by hornblende off San Diego (67 per cent) and off San Pedro (65 per cent), but off Santa Monica hornblende takes second place to augite (29 versus 30 per cent), and off Santa Barbara both hornblende and augite are present only in traces whereas epidote averages 34 per cent and ilmenite 22 per cent. Thus, the heavy minerals in the detrital sediments of the main-

land shelf correspond closely with those of the adjacent beaches.

Detrital sediments in the nearshore parts of the mainland shelf also resemble the beaches in their mobility. This movement was first recognized when measurements made along the pier at Scripps Institution of Oceanography showed that seasonal and tidal cycle cutting and filling of the beach were reflected in simultaneous filling and cutting of the submerged areas to a water depth of at least 6 meters (Shepard and

LaFond, 1940). An extension of this work was made by eight separate surveys between April 1949 and May 1950 aboard amphibious vehicles in an area off 0.6 km of beach between Scripps and La Jolla Submarine Canyons and extending seaward 1 km to depths of about 30 meters (Shepard and Inman, 1951a, 1953). Later, checks were made of the surveys by repeated observation of the sand level against stakes driven into the bottom by divers (Inman and Rusnak, 1956). Comparison of the surveys showed definite cuts and fills to the outermost limits of the study, but with the greatest changes in depths shallower than 10 meters. Changes between the surveys in water depths greater than 3 meters averaged 8 cm and locally were ten times this figure. Estimates of the volumes and areas of change indicate that during times of large waves sand is lost from the shelf, presumably by southward lateral transport and accumulation in the head of La Jolla Canyon. During times of small waves the sand is believed to be replenished by southward lateral transport near the beach and around the head of Scripps Canyon. Support for the inferred movement of beach sand around the head of Scripps Canyon and into the intercanyon shelf area is provided by the similarity of grain size and mineralogy of the sediments on the shelf and the beaches north of the canyon (Inman, 1953). Sediments on the outer half of the shelf north of Scripps Canyon (Wimberly, 1955) contain a much larger percentage of silt and clay than those south of the canyon, indicating that southward transportation results in their being trapped by the canyon barrier.

In the absence of a submarine canyon trap, sediment might be expected to move downcurrent in a broad zone spanning the inner part of the shelf. The fastest movement and the coarsest sediment being moved should be at the shore because of greater turbulence there. Farther offshore the movement should generally be less rapid and involve progressively finer maximum sizes until at some point the greater depth and slight turbulence reduce the movement to negligible proportions. Longshore move-

ment past rocky coastal barriers such as Point Conception and Point Dume has been shown to exist by Trask (1952, 1955) on the basis of mineralogy, grain size, continuity of subsea slopes below 10 meters in front of these rocky points, and the presence of ripple marks on sand bottom to depths greater than 20 meters (Inman, 1957). If any rocky point extends to depths of 30 meters, there would be considerable doubt that sediment could move past it until the sea floor became built up enough by sediment to cover the deep barrier and thus permit subsequent passing of sediment. Observations by divers (Trask, 1955; others) show that in water deeper than about 30 meters the bottom is covered by a thin layer of fine brown sediment that could not be present if currents were appreciable. Similar material has been observed temporarily present after rainstorms, as though it were in the process of very slow seaward transport, bypassing sediments that form the more permanent sea floor mantle. In support of this hypothesis of movement is the fact that multilevel sediment traps placed on the shelf generally trap sediments that are finer than those constituting the bottom surface.

In addition to periodic changes in the nature of sediments on the shelves there are secular ones. Ancient changes are recorded by variations in grain size along the length of cores of shelf sediments. A more recent change is shown by a comparison of grain sizes of 200 samples collected from Santa Monica Bay by Shepard and Macdonald (1938) and 580 samples collected from the same area during a study of sewage pollution 20 years later (Terry, Keesling, and Uchupi, 1956). Almost the entire area of comparison is deeper than 20 meters. Contours of median diameter show that a definite decrease in grain size occurred between the dates of the two surveys that is greater than might be expected from differences in field collection and laboratory analysis techniques. This comparison of contours is made on the basis of whole suites of samples, few of which are at identical positions in the two surveys. For nine pairs that are essentially at the same positions, the average percentage of sand (coarser than 62 microns) in the earlier survey was 78 and in the later one 53. As pointed out by Terry, Keesling, and Uchupi, this decrease in grain size has probably been accompanied or caused by a decrease in the rate of contribution of sediments to the bay, owing to both natural and artificial factors. The chief natural factor is that of diversion of the mouth of the Los Angeles River from Santa Monica Bay (via Ballona Creek) to San Pedro Bay. This diversion began in 1825 and became permanent in 1884 (Troxell and others, 1942), thus diverting away from Santa Monica Bay large amounts of coarse flood-borne sediments. Artificial changes tending to reduce the amount of sediment contributed to Santa Monica Bay include construction of water supply reservoirs and flood debris basins in stream valleys, urban paving, installation of storm sewers and lining of river channels, building of highways and sea walls at the base of sea cliffs, and trapping of sediment behind breakwaters and groins. It is believed certain that the supply of sediment to the ocean has been reduced more by these factors than it has been increased by the minor amount of cultivation on the watershed. However, accelerated erosion in areas of brush fires locally causes such an enormous increase in the rate of erosion that reservoirs and debris basins fail to retain the materials and prevent them from reaching the shore.

In spite of the abundant evidence of movement of present-day detrital sediments on the mainland shelf, extensive areas remain uncovered by them. Some of these areas rise little if any above the general level of the shelf but remain uncovered, perhaps because wave turbulence is great enough to prevent the deposition of fine-grained detrital material but not great enough to remove coarser sediment of other origin. Most important in terms of area is relict sediment, ancient detrital sediment that is believed to have been deposited mostly during Late Pleistocene or Early Recent times when sea level was still far below its present position. Most abundant by far of these relict sediments are red sands which occur in patches between

at least San Francisco and Todos Santos Bay of Baja California. Most of the 550 samples and chart notations of red sand occur off San Diego, San Pedro, and Santa Monica where its mean depth is 36 meters, 23 meters, and 13 meters, respectively. This northward shoaling parallels that of the warping of shallow terraces on the shelf; also, the red sands occur on both the first and second submarine terraces and on the bordering slopes of each terrace, but nowhere are they as deep as the third terrace nor deeper than 60 meters. The red sand has an average median diameter of 480 microns, and thus it is considerably coarser than the present-day detrital sediments (Keller, 1957). The average sorting coefficient is 1.33, about the same as that of the present-day detrital sediments. Rounding is good, with values mostly between 0.4 and 0.6; sphericity also is high, 0.80 to 0.85. Calcium carbonate averages 3.2 per cent and heavy minerals about 3.1 per cent. The ratio of quartz to feldspar is 1.6:1 at Santa Monica Bay, 1.7:1 at San Pedro Bay, and 2.9:1 off San Diego and thus is similar to the ratios in the later detrital sediments. The red color is due to a thin stain of ferric oxide. Some of the samples from San Pedro Bay were found to contain a Pleistocene Timms Point foraminiferal fauna (Moore, 1954a). In addition, the sediment is lithologically closely similar to the Pleistocene semiconsolidated dunes that border Santa Monica Bay (Merriam, 1949), and it may also be related to a red sand that was reported from borings in the alluviated Tia Juana River valley. The fossil content, lithological similarities, iron stain, coarse grain size, good sorting, shape, and patterns of distribution indicate that the sand is an ancient deposit now being gradually buried beneath prograding detrital sediments. Clearly this coarse material cannot now be in the process of being carried over and past the finer present-day detrital sediment to its areas of abundance. Another relict sediment possibly related to the red sand is a rock fragment sand at Santa Monica Bay and other areas. As described by Terry, Keesling, and Uchupi (1956), this sand also is coarse-grained and weathered but was derived partly from local sea floor rock outcrops. Still a third kind of relict sediment is a dark-gray-to-black silt underlying red sand off Seal Beach at a depth of 13 meters. Hydrogen sulfide is present along with fibrous organic debris. R. E. Stevenson (personal communication) considers that this is probably a submerged marsh deposit.

Areas of nondetrital sediment (neither present nor ancient) are largely restricted to low hills that rise above the general level of the shelf and thus in a sense are islands surrounded by a flood of ancient and modern detrital sediments. Good examples exist in Santa Monica Bay, in San Pedro Bay, and off San Diego. Some nondetrital sediments also occur at or near the shelf break where the slope is so steep that fine-grained detrital sediments bypass. These nondetrital sediments have three origins, residual, organic, and authigenic. Commonly, nondetrital sediments have all three components mixed together, but in a few areas more or less pure single-origin sediment exists.

Sediments believed to be of residual origin are present at many places on the mainland shelf but are invariably present where bedrock is exposed on the bottom. They can be recognized by their poor sorting, angularity, and mineralogic similarity to the underlying or nearby rocks. However, recognition is not as simple as for residual sediments on land because on the sea floor these materials have been modified to some extent by water movements which have tended to winnow away the finer debris and to introduce new material. As a result there exists a broad gradation between true residual and true relict sediments that introduces an uncertainty of personal judgment in assigning a given sediment to a residual or a relict origin. For this reason, the areas of either type might be greater or less than shown by Figure 180.

Organic sediment is much simpler. On the mainland shelf it consists chiefly of broken and corroded shell fragments mostly of pelecypods and gastropods. The grain size is coarse and the sorting poor. Foraminiferal tests are included but serve only as a minor constituent, in contrast to the fact that they are more abundant than shell debris on most island shelves and bank tops. Mixtures with modern detrital, relict, residual, and authigenic sediments are usually present, depending on the origin of the nearby sediments, but a large area of nearly pure shell sand occurs at the shelf break just seaward of Los Coronados Islands off San Diego (Fig. 180).

Authigenic sediments are of two types, phosphorite and glauconite. The phosphorite consists mostly of small-to-large nodular masses which were described in the section on lithology and thus can be neglected here. In addition phosphorite comprises occasional small pellets, perhaps originally coprolites and named sporbo (*s*mall *p*olished *r*ound *b*lack *o*bjects) by Galliher (1931) from their similar occurrence in Miocene shales of the region. Chief of the authigenic sediments is glauconite, again a sediment that is usually mixed with other kinds of sediment, chiefly organic. Glauconitic sands are far more common on banks than on the mainland shelf, and so their description and discussion of origin will be deferred to the section on bank sediments. For some unknown reason neither phosphorite nor glauconite has been found in appreciable quantities in San Pedro Bay, in contrast to Santa Monica Bay, and off Santa Barbara and San Diego. The narrowness of the shelf elsewhere along the southern California mainland has led to mantling by present-day detrital sediments which have diluted or largely prevented the accumulation of much glauconitic sand on these parts of the shelf.

Examples of continental shelf sediments similar to those of the present mainland shelf are uncommon in the geological record, although their rarity may be merely a reflection of their having been overlooked by stratigraphers during the past. The shelf sediments off the Texas coast probably have their older counterparts in off-lapping Cenozoic strata of the coastal plain, but that region is one of more or less continuous deposition clearly different from off southern California. Here the existing shelf sediments form only a thin mantle atop the eroded shelf surface. Because of low supply of sediments and high turbulence, much debris bypasses, leaving behind on the shelf only sediments much different from those off Texas. Eventually, when the basins become filled, sediments can accumulate in broad off-lapping blankets over the shelf and the basin fillings. The thin layer of coarse sediment will then be found atop bedrock of the shelf and below a blanket of fine sediment. Possibly similar sediments exist in the geological record, but if the ancient shelves had been very narrow, owing to the limitation on erosion imposed by a constant sea level, the unique shelf sediments would have been deposited only in a narrow belt around the former shore. This restriction in area would certainly have contributed to failure to find and recognize ancient shelf sediments like the existing ones.

Island Shelves

Sediments of the island shelves have been studied less thoroughly than have those of the mainland shelf. Nevertheless, specific studies have been made for four island shelves: Santa Catalina (Shepard and Wrath, 1937; McGlasson, 1957), San Nicolas (Norris, 1951), Anacapa (Scholl, 1959), and Santa Barbara (Grady, in preparation). The type and distribution of their sediments can be presented in the same ways as for the mainland shelves, but only two methods will be used (similar to those of Figures 175 and 180 for the mainland shelves) for comparison with various other details of the sediments.

The earliest study of island shelf sediments, made by Shepard and Wrath (1937), was based on about 45 scattered samples plus many chart notations. The latter, however, failed to satisfactorily distinguish between organic and inorganic sands. A later study of McGlasson (1957) was based on 92 samples arranged mostly in 16 pofiles. Neither set of samples is very satisfactory for a real description, so Figure 181 is a composite of both. Here, organic sediment clearly is more abundant than along the mainland; moreover, the detrital sediment also contains fairly large percentages of foraminiferal tests, fragments of gastropods and pelecypods, and bryozoans. Although not

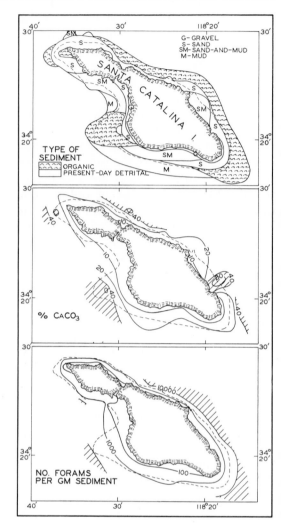

Figure 181. Sediments of shelf around Santa Catalina Island based on 137 samples. Maps show sediment types, percentage of calcium carbonate (acid-soluble material), and number of foraminiferal tests per gram of total sediment. Dashed line shows shelf-break 60 meters. Adapted from McGlasson (1957).

separated and plotted, the authigenic mineral glauconite forms an appreciable component, particularly on the outer parts of the shelf. When organic and authigenic sediments and minor amounts of residual sediments are ignored, the remaining present-day detrital sediments present a general seaward decrease in grain size. In these sediments the ratio of quartz to feldspar is about 1.1: 1, about the same as on the mainland shelves. Progressively greater dilution of detrital sediment by organic remains is indicated by a seaward increase in the percentage of calcium carbonate and in the number of foraminiferal tests per gram of sediment. This dilution supports grain size in indicating a seaward decrease in rate of deposition of present-day detrital sediment. The highly organic sediments on the shelf north of the east end of the island are likened by Woodring, Bramlette, and Kew (1946) to the Pleistocene Lomita marl that crops out north and east of the Palos Verdes Hills. General composition and depth of accumulation are similar. Calcareous algae in the Lomita marl also have their living counterparts in shallow water near the isthmus of the island.

Two other studies of island shelves warrant attention because of the dissimilarity of sediment patterns around them, even though both are small and consist dominantly of volcanic rocks. These are Anacapa Island (Fig. 182) and Santa Barbara Island (Fig. 183), studied by Scholl (1959) and Grady (in preparation), respectively. The maps of median diameters of whole sediments are strikingly different, with Anacapa Island being fringed by medium-to-coarse sand grading outward to very fine sand, and Santa Barbara being fringed by fine sand that grades outward to medium-to-coarse sand before again becoming fine-grained beyond the

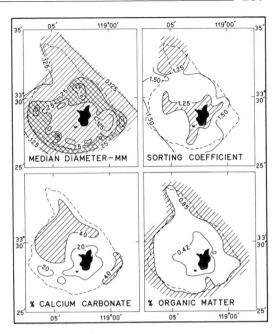

Figure 183. Sediments of shelf around Santa Barbara Island based on about 90 samples. Maps show median diameter, Trask sorting coefficient, calcium carbonate (gasometric analyses), and organic matter (17 × nitrogen). Dashed line is 200-meter contour. Adapted from Grady (in preparation).

shelf-break. The difference in the two patterns is largely due to faster erosion of Anacapa Island which provides coarser detrital sand for the area immediately adjacent to the island. Rapid modification of the sea cliffs was especially evident following a storm during the winter of 1957. In addition, the shelf south of Anacapa Island is so narrow that there is insufficient space for development of the ring of coarse shell sand found on the outer half of the wider shelf off Santa Barbara Island. Also, the strait between Anacapa and Santa Cruz Islands is the site of strong currents which prevent the deposition of sediments other than relatively coarse sands—chiefly debris of mollusk shells and calcareous red algae. Because of the strait, the area of coarsest sediment extends from the fringing area of the sea cliffs more or less due westward in line with the island. The organic content of the sediments around Anacapa Island is about double that around Santa Barbara Island, in spite of the fact that the total sediment of the en-

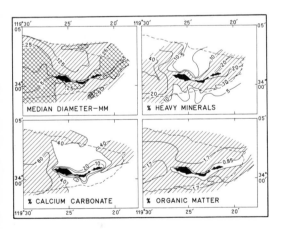

Figure 182. Sediments of shelf around Anacapa Island based on 100 samples. Maps show diameter, heavy minerals in insoluble residues, calcium carbonate (gasometric analyses), and organic matter (1.7 × organic carbon). Dashed line is 100-meter contour. Adapted from Scholl (1959).

tire shelf at Anacapa is slightly coarser than that off Santa Barbara Island. Perhaps this higher content is due to the greater production of diatoms in surface waters near Anacapa Island owing to its position within the chief area of upwelling off the coast.

The mineralogy of the detrital sediments at Anacapa Island is unique in its overwhelming abundance of feldspar, an average quartz-to-feldspar ratio of 0.09:1. Augite is the flood heavy mineral, as on the mainland shelf and beaches immediately to the east. Glaucophane is present, but not abundant, owing to reworking from land and sea floor outcrops of the San Onofre breccia. Sediments of both shelves, as on other island shelves, contain much glauconite.

Bank Tops

A few samples were collected more than 20 years ago from the tops of Thirtymile, Fortymile, and Sixtymile Banks, but they are sufficient only to show that the sediments of these banks are typical of those on other banks that were later studied more thoroughly. A more general study was made for Coronado Bank off San Diego by Emery, Butcher, Gould, and Shepard (1952) on the basis of about 250 samples collected in 1943–1944. Its sediments, shown in Figures 175, 179, and 180, are highly calcareous and contain abundant glauconite and phosphorite, minor amounts of weathered residual or relict grains, and little organic matter. They form a thin blanket atop thick Pleistocene strata which cap the bank. Inorganic grains are similar to those present on the nearby mainland shelf, but in all other respects the sediments of the bank are utterly unlike those of the shelf—an indication of the effect on sediments of the exclusion of present-day detrital materials.

A survey of sediments atop a completely isolated bank in the region was made in 1950 by Holzman (1952) for Cortes and Tanner Banks. The tops of these banks contain outcrops of rock, mostly basalt, probably larger in terms of percentage area than outcrops of rock on island and mainland shelves. Sediments are coarse, especially for the shallowest parts of the banks (Fig. 184). Calcareous organic debris comprises more than 80 per cent of the sediment at the top and lesser amounts at greater depth. In this respect the sediment is closely similar to that of the isolated Ranger Bank off Mexico (Emery, 1948). On both bank areas the calcareous debris is coarser than most of the detrital inorganic sediment. At Cortes and Tanner Banks the total sediment has an average median diameter of 310 microns in contrast to only 220 microns for inorganic sediment. Organic calcareous and siliceous material averages 47 per cent foraminiferal tests, 34 per cent broken gastropod and pelecypod shells, 7 per cent bryozoans, 7 per cent echinoids—mostly spines—and 5 per cent sponge spicules. Comprising most of the inorganic sediments are quartz and feldspar having an average ratio of 0.17:1, far lower than on the mainland beaches and shelves, doubtlessly because of the basaltic composition of most of the underlying rocks. In line with this source, the flood heavy mineral is augite which comprises about 45 per cent of the total crop. Most of the remainder of the inorganic sediment is of authigenic origin, with glauconite averaging 16 per cent and collophane 5 per cent. Because of the coarse grain size of the total sediment the average content of organic matter is low, less than 0.8 per cent on the bank top. This low organic matter and high calcium carbonate yields a gray color for that sediment in contrast to an olive color in surrounding deeper ones. In summary, the sediments of Cortes and Tanner Banks are dominantly residual, relict, and authigenic. Little or no present-day detrital sediments are present, owing to the absence of a nearby land source. Thus, the bank top sediment is greatly different in origin from that of the mainland and island shelves where most of it is present-day detrital.

The Santa Rosa–Cortes Ridge is a feature that is neither true island shelf nor true bank top. Because it is elongate at right angles to shore, the outer part can be expected to receive little island-contributed debris, so its sediment should resemble that of bank tops. A study of the ridge by Uchupi (1954)

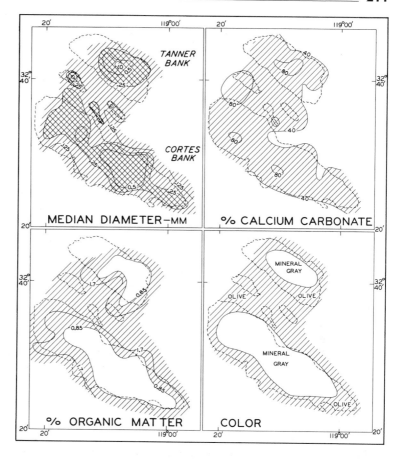

Figure 184. Sediments of Cortes and Tanner Banks based on 66 samples. Maps show median diameter, calcium carbonate (acid-soluble material), organic matter (1.7 × organic carbon), and color of sediment (dry). Dashed line is 200-meter contour. Adapted from Holzman (1952).

showed that indeed this is true. However, basalt pebbles and cobbles found at 52 stations north of the saddle that divides it into two parts and at only 1 station south of it indicate that coarse debris from the basalt outcrops on Santa Rosa Island was able to make its way across the top of the ridge until stopped by the saddle, presumably during a glacial stage of low sea level. The fine-grained material that accumulated subsequently presents a complex pattern of organic, authigenic, relict, residual, and present-day detrital sediments. The organic sediments consist of coarse shell sand in turbulent shallow water near shore and fine-to-medium foraminiferal sand in deeper water, particularly in the saddle. The occurrence of calcareous sediments in both shallow and deep water and their presence as a component in all sediments lead to a high content of calcium carbonate on the ridge—an average of 51 per cent of all sediments

and still higher percentages in the saddle, which is farthest from the source of inorganic sediments (Fig. 185). The coarse grain size of the calcareous sediments, matched also by most noncalcareous ones, leads to low contents of organic matter, as at Cortes and Tanner Banks, with average values of 0.85 per cent on the flat areas and about double that in the saddle with its finer-grained sediments. Relict and residual sediments occur in deep water atop the ridge, and present-day detrital sediments border the shore zone. The bulk of this sediment is quartz and feldspar with ratio of 6:1, a very high ratio as compared with that on Cortes and Tanner Banks. Among the heavy minerals magnetite is most abundant, 61 per cent, followed by hornblende, 18 per cent, of the total heavies. Glauconite occurs mixed with most of the other sediments but rarely in quantities great enough to be a major component. It averages about 5 per cent

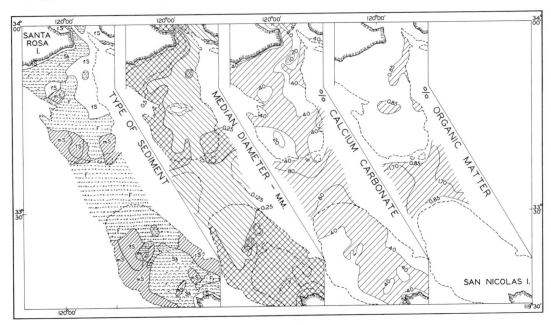

Figure 185. Sediments of Santa Rosa–Cortes Ridge based on 285 samples. Maps show sediment types (symbols as in Fig. 180), median diameter (symbols as in Fig. 175), calcium carbonate (acid-soluble material), and organic matter (1.7 × organic carbon). Dashed line is 200-meter contour. Adapted from Uchupi (1954).

in the samples from the flat areas and 20 per cent in the saddle, again doubtlessly a result of a slower rate of sedimentation there.

Glauconite warrants special discussion here because of its abundance on bank tops. So many papers have been written about glauconite that it is fruitless to attempt to summarize them even briefly. However, most of these papers have attempted to infer the environment of deposition from the scanty evidence remaining long after the enclosing strata had become lithified. Only a few authors have worked with sediments presently being deposited, among whom are Murray and Renard (1891), Galliher (1935), and Takahashi (1939). Although much additional X-ray and chemical work is desirable, the greatest lack at present appears to be field and laboratory studies of modern sediments. Where these contain glauconite now being formed, the chances of learning how it forms is far greater than by study of ancient sediments. For this reason some pertinent field and laboratory observations will be presented.

Field observations show that glauconite is abundant in the same places as phosphorite

(Fig. 63),—areas in which detrital sediments accumulate very slowly or not at all. The chief associated sediment is foraminiferal sand which with glauconite is enclosed in phosphorite nodules that grow on or in the sediment. Rarely does glauconite comprise more than about 20 per cent of the total sediment, but its color and coarse grain size impart such a unique appearance to the sediment, and its environment of deposition is so diagnostic, that it has an importance beyond that of its percentage abundance. Typically, glauconite occurs on bank tops, ridge crests, hills that rise above shelves, and some slopes. The depths of these environments range from 50 to more than 2000 meters. Secondarily, glauconite is present in minor quantities in sand layers interbedded with normal basin sediments; it is assumed that this glauconite has been reworked from shallow-water areas.

The environments in which glauconite is abundant are among the most oxygenated of the sea floor, areas of turbulent flow of currents and some movement by waves. Moreover, photographs and samples show the common presence of brittle stars, sea urchins, and some worms living on and in the glauconitic sediment. The benthic population is not dense, however, probably because the glauconitic sands are coarse and very low in their content of organic matter. Measurements show that the *p*H is typically about 7.8 and the *Eh* about $+300$ mv, both similar to the overlying sea water. Oxygen dissolved in the overlying sea water is as much as 90 per cent of saturation, depending on the water depth. These various facts show that the general environment in which glauconite is now found is one of oxidizing conditions, in contrast to the common statement that glauconite is restricted to anaerobic environments (Cloud, 1955; Lochman, 1957). Further chemical work may show that glauconite forms in a microreducing environment produced by decomposing protoplasm within foraminiferal tests or in faecal pellets, even though the interstitial and overlying waters are oxidizing.

It might be argued that the glauconite off southern California is not forming now but has been reworked from older sediments that were deposited under anaerobic conditions. In answer, it can be pointed out that the glauconitic sands form a fairly uniform blanket where present, that they are not covered by a different kind of sediment, that they overlie igneous and metamorphic as well as sedimentary rocks, and that the underlying sedimentary rocks belong to various parts of the Miocene and even to the Pleistocene (Coronado Bank). Additional evidence of age is provided by enclosing foraminiferal tests which include in addition to long-lived forms several of Pliocene to Recent age: *Angulogerina angulosa, A. carinata, Cassidulina californica, C. limbata, C. lomitensis, C. tortuosa, C. translucens, Cibicides mckannae, C. refulgens, Uvigerina hollicki, U. peregrina,* and *U. senticosa* (O. L. Bandy, personal communication; Pratt, 1956). Some of these species are rare in rocks older than Late Pliocene, and others are rare in Recent sediments, perhaps suggesting that they may really represent Pleistocene deposits. Comparison of enclosing Foraminifera with their normal depth range shows that at least some of the glauconite

formed at the depths at which samples containing it were taken. This is indicated by the presence of glauconite within tests of the shallow water species *Cassidulina californica, C. limbata, C. tortuosa,* and *Uvigerina hollicki* in samples from shelves and bank tops and of the deep-water species *Uvigerina peregrina* and *U. senticosa* at depths of 600 to 2000 meters on the continental slope off Point Conception (Bandy, 1953*a*).

Laboratory examination shows that the glauconite grains occur in several forms. Probably most of them are internal casts still concealed within foraminiferal tests, a type noted long ago by Murray and Renard (1891) for five species of Foraminifera. At least 17 species were found by Pratt (1956) to contain glauconite; further work will doubtlessly reveal many others. Casts are far more abundant in *Cassidulina* than in *Globigerina,* which has an aperture about half as large as that of *Cassidulina.* Casts also appear to be more common in weathered opaque tests than in fresh-looking ones and in larger specimens than smaller ones of a given species. Casts have also been observed in sponge spicules. A second mode of occurrence, rare, is as replacements of the calcium carbonate and silica of foraminiferal tests, echinoid spines, and sponge spicules. Thirdly, glauconite occurs as spheroidal, ovidal, or discoidal pellets, perhaps coprolites. Finally, there are irregular grains, lobed, cracked or layered, and smooth- to rough-surfaced. The color ranges from light green to dark green to black, some of the darker ones having brown cracks or surfaces. The light-green grains are much softer than the darker ones and have a lower index of refraction and a lower specific gravity. They also are mostly restricted to internal casts still protected by a foraminiferal test.

The origin of the glauconite is still uncertain, and very possibly several origins are involved. Grains presenting a continuous series from biotite to glauconite can be selected in the manner of Galliher (1935), probably indicating the formation of some glauconite from biotite. However, it should be pointed out that biotite is not as common in the bank areas of abundant glauconite as in the fine-grained sediments of Santa Monica and San Pedro Basins where glauconite is absent except for rare grains that are believed to have been reworked from areas of shallow water. Most of the glauconite lacks the gross internal structure suggestive of swelled flakes of biotite, and it lies within even the very small inner chambers of foraminiferal tests where biotite must be excluded by its size. Possibly this glauconite is derived from illite, the potassium clay mineral that has a chemical composition and X-ray structure similar to that of biotite and glauconite (Hendricks and Ross, 1941). Variation in chemical and molecular structure also suggests that several different origins are possible (Burst, 1958). The general appearance of many grains suggests that the glauconite swells before it hardens, permitting the inference that once the enclosing test is broken away or dissolved the freed glauconite may expand into a more or less shapeless grain. Completion of a study of glauconite in the approximately 1000 available samples that contain it should do much to uncover the origin or origins of this interesting mineral.

Glauconite is represented in ancient deposits of the region at several localities, among the most interesting of which are outcrops of the Pleistocene Lomita marl around the margins of the Los Angeles Basin. According to S. G. Wissler (personal communication), foraminiferal zones several thousand feet thick within the deep part of the basin are represented by only a few tens of feet in a glauconitic sand of Pliocene age at Palos Verdes Hills, testifying to the relative slowness of deposition of glauconitic sands.

Sills of Basins

A systematic study of the sediments covering the sills of basins has not yet been made; however, sixteen cores or surface samples have been collected at the sills of six of the basins incidental to other work. These samples show a wide range of types and grain sizes of sediments (Table 13). At the

sills of the nearshore Santa Barbara and San Pedro Basins the sediments are only slightly coarser than the average of the normal muds that cover the basin floors. One sample from another nearshore basin, Santa Monica, is much coarser, 25 microns. Two offshore basins, Santa Catalina and San Nicolas, have very much coarser sediments at the sills than on the floors, but the sediment at the sill of another offshore basin, Santa Cruz, is only slightly coarser than that on its floor. One sample in the sill of Santa Catalina Basin is 125 microns and one in San Nicolas Basin is 225 microns. Where coarse sediments are present, they consist largely of Foraminiferal tests, glauconite, and rock fragments; thus they are more analogous to sediments of bank tops than to those of basin floors. Obviously, the sediments in sills and saddles are so variable in both their horizontal and vertical distribution that a closely spaced sampling grid must be followed in order to learn the true patterns of distribution.

Table 13

GRAIN SIZE OF SEDIMENTS
IN SILLS OF BASINS

Basin	Average Median Diameter, microns			
	Basin Sill		Basin Floor	
Santa Barbara	7.7	*1*[1]	4.5	*36*
Santa Monica	16	*2*	8.5	*165*
San Pedro	8.0	*2*	7.5	*95*
Santa Cruz	5.3	*3*	3.9	*24*
Santa Catalina	33	*5*	4.0	*37*
San Nicolas	120	*3*	3.7	*35*

[1] Italics indicate number of sample analyses used for obtaining average values.

The presence of local areas of coarse-grained sediments in basin sills suggests the winnowing away of fine sediments or the prevention of their deposition by stronger currents than exist on the basin floors and side slopes. It is unlikely that currents required for the known replenishment of basin water are sufficiently fast to so control the sediments. Instead, it seems more reasonable to ascribe the currents to a periodic inward and outward flow that must be produced by the internal waves or deep seiches within the basins; these were revealed by periodic short-term temperature changes in Santa Catalina Basin (Fig. 114).

Slopes

Only a few studies of sediments on slopes have been made anywhere in the world, owing possibly to the small area of slopes as compared with those of shelves and deep floors. The general absence of data has given rise to speculation that fine-grained sediments should not be present because their angle of repose ought to be smaller than the steepness of some slopes. During 1929, however, Kuenen (1943, pp. 34, 35) found sediment at least a meter thick on slopes of 15° in the East Indies. Observations from the bathyscaphes *Trieste* (Piccard and Dietz, 1957) and *F. N. R. S. III* (Trégouboff, 1958) in the Mediterranean Sea during 1956–1957 also revealed many instances of sediment blanketing slopes as steep as 70° according to R. S. Dietz (personal communication).

Off southern California some sediment occurs on all slopes, but it is patchy on many slopes that are distant from the mainland, so that rock is usually exposed or only thinly mantled (Fig. 41). One nearshore slope which was studied in some detail by Emery and Terry (1956) is covered by sediment at least 6 meters thick. This sediment has an average median diameter of about 22 microns and is homogeneous. Distinct layers were penetrated by the corer only at the very top of the slope and beyond its base on the basin floor. The sediment has the usual high water content of freshly deposited mud, even though it lies on a slope of 9 to 18°, and exceptionally of 30°. Measurements showed the water content to be about 15 per cent higher than the Atterberg liquid limit (Fig. 186). Thus, the mud must be classed as a liquid rather than as a plastic or rigid material. Evidently, the water content tells only part of the story, and other properties permit the sediment to remain on the slope. Perhaps chief of these properties is shear strength produced by thixotropy, a

gel-like stiffening of the sediment. Resistance of clayey sediment to being cut by a wire was found by Emery and Rittenberg (1952) to decrease to less than 1 per cent of its normal value after being shaken. When the sediment is allowed to remain undisturbed for a few minutes after being shaken, its strength returns. Similar results were obtained by Moore (1956) using more elaborate equipment to measure shear strength. When sediments are deposited grain by grain on a slope, there clearly is ample time for them to become stiffened. However, if they start to slide or are shaken by an earthquake, their shear strength should largely disappear, permitting them to flow easily and to produce the elongate sea gullies described in the section on physiography (Fig. 43).

The sediments of still other basin slopes have been investigated briefly in connection with other problems. In most instances the main objective was the study of sediments on shelves and bank tops, but complete sampling included the tops of adjacent slopes (Figs. 175, 181, and 185). The more than 100 samples available from slopes show them to be intermediate in properties between those of the adjoining shallow areas and basin floors. Because of the large number of samples from the tops of basin slopes, the sediment parameters given by Table 12 are weighted somewhat too heavily toward sediments like those on the adjoining shelves and bank tops.

Fewer samples are available from the continental slope. Because the continental slope is farther from the source of detrital sediments than most basin slopes, its sediments might be expected to be different from those of the basin slopes. Sampling attempts indicate that almost certainly the percentage area of exposed rock is greater than on basin slopes; however, only two areas have been studied in any detail. One, near Point Conception, was investigated by Dill (1952) with a series of eleven short cores. Most were on the gently sloping and irregular upper part of the slope where the sediments are coarse with abundant glauconite, phosphorite, and rock fragments. Since

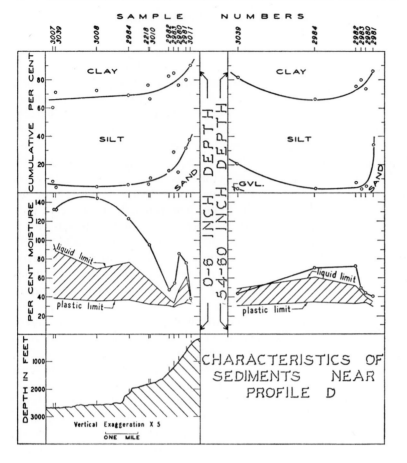

Figure 186. Sediments from Palos Verdes Slope, north side of San Pedro Basin (profile D of Fig. 43) (Emery and Terry, 1956, Fig. 6). Top, grain-size composition of surface samples and of ones at a core depth of 54–60 inches (137–152 cm), or an *in situ* depth of 108–120 inches (274–305 cm). Middle, relationship of water content of sediments to Atterberg limits. Note that the sediments have such a high relative water content that they must be classified as liquids, neglecting thixotropic effects. Bottom, positions of samples on the profile of slope.

these samples are probably more typical of shelves than of continental slopes, they will not be further described. Cores from the lower parts of this slope also contain glauconite but are fine-grained, about 9 microns, and contain an average of 22 per cent of calcium carbonate. The deepest core contains less calcium carbonate than the others, owing probably to the dissolving action of deep-sea water. The second area of investigation is west of Northeast Bank where two long cores have been taken chiefly for study of organic constituents. Because this area is about 150 km farther from the mainland shore than the area studied by Dill, the rate of deposition of detrital sediments is less, causing the calcium carbonate to be more than double that in the first area, 47 per cent. On removal of all calcium carbonate by acid treatment, the average median diameter decreased from 8 to 7 microns, showing that the foraminiferal tests, which

make up most of the carbonate, are coarser than the detrital sediment from shore. By strict definition (Revelle, 1944, p. 16) this sediment and that of some of the outer basins should be termed Globigerina ooze because calcium carbonate as foraminiferal tests constitutes more than 30 per cent of the sample. However, the gradational nature of the sediment from the more typical terrigenous green muds closer to shore suggests that the term calcareous green mud is more appropriate for this particular study.

A unique kind of sediment, barite concretions, was found on the steep basin slope of San Clemente Island in a single dredging made in 1938 (Revelle and Emery, 1951). Enclosed Foraminifera show that the concretions were formed in Pliocene sediments or more probably in Recent sediments containing many reworked Pliocene Foraminifera. Barite occurs in amounts of up to 77 per cent and consists mostly of small radial aggregates, although some larger clear crystals are within foraminiferal tests. The cylindrical shape of many concretions suggests that water containing dissolved barium, probably as the chloride, moved in tubular channels through the fine-grained sediment. Some thin flat pieces composed of coarser grains of plagioclase, glauconite, and foraminiferal tests were probably cemented by movement of the solution through the more permeable beds. It is believed that the baritic solution came from magma at an unknown depth and rose along the fault plane that produced the basin slope. On contact with the sulfate-containing interstitial water of the sediments that cover the fault trace, barite was precipitated in concretionary form. Similar barite concretions have been found elsewhere on the sea floor, notably off Ceylon and in the East Indies, in both instances on steep slopes of probable fault origin. Barite in the form of larger bladed crystals in veins as thick as 1 meter is well known from many exposures along the south side of Palos Verdes Hills where it is clearly of magmatic origin and is associated with a large fault zone.

Minor features are present in abundance on slopes, as shown by photographs (for example, Figure 42). Many of the smaller irregularities are produced by burrowing activities of animals; others may be effects of small local slides. Folds and crumplings associated with larger slides may be present but are concealed under later sediments; the uniformity of the sediment and the small diameter of core barrels prevent their detection by coring operations. Still larger slides have left scars that are detectable only by sounding surveys (Fig. 43). Some of these features are doubtlessly capable of preservation in the geological record. Features probably of related origin have been described by Fairbridge (1946), Rich (1950), Kuenen (1953b), and Crowell (1957) from various parts of the world. Others are known in the sedimentary rocks of Ventura Basin (Natland and Kuenen, 1951), where some of them represent ancient slope environments, although most are probably from the former basin floor. Similar features formed on the continental slope are probably rarely if ever brought to view in outcrops on land.

Submarine Canyons

Sediments of submarine canyons occupy an even more restricted environment than do those of slopes. Only one general textural study has been made, by Cohee (1938) on surface samples obtained by Shepard from many canyons. Also, only a single detailed study of sediments in an individual canyon is available, one by Inman (1950) for the shallow part of Mugu Canyon. All other data are incidental to work on organic matter (Trask, 1931), beaches (Marlette, 1954), basin sediments (Ludwick, 1950; Gorsline, 1958), or shelf sediments (Terry, Keesling, and Uchupi, 1956). As a result of this heterogeneity of source data, the canyon sediments are imperfectly known, particularly with respect to parameters other than texture. Even so, some generalizations can be formed (Table 12). At the heads of canyons that reach close to shore sediments are coarse-grained and similar in other respects to the adjacent beaches. In depths of 100 or 200 meters in the heads of at least some of these same canyons (Mugu, Redondo, Scripps, and La Jolla), sediments that are unusual in the marine environment have been discovered. These are black, smell of hydrogen sulfide, and contain masses of decomposing plant debris, mostly of kelp and surf grass. Clouds of methane bubbles have been observed rising from this sediment. Canyons whose heads are far from shore, such as Santa Monica, San Pedro, and San Gabriel, are floored by sandy green muds. In both kinds of canyons the surface sediments obtained farther down the canyon axes are more or less progressively finer-grained and grade into normal basin muds. Sediments on the side slopes are green muds like those on the usually less steep basin slopes.

Core samples in canyons show two distinct kinds of sediment at depth. On the canyon walls the few available cores reveal little change with depth of burial—again similar to sediments on basin slopes. Many of the more numerous cores along the canyon axes, however, contain sand layers, some of which are so thick and hard that core barrels have been bent on striking bottom. The sand layers in canyons that reach close to shore have textural and compositional similarities to beach sands and sediments of the nearshore parts of the shelf, as recognized long ago by Ritter (1902). Coarse sediments on the floors of canyons having heads farther from shore are more like the sediments of the outer part of the shelf, with common shell fragments and glauconite. The sequence of fine- and coarse-grained sediments in the canyon axes is probably a result of intermittent deposition of turbidity currents produced by mass movements at the head of the canyons, as discussed later. Included in the sediments of both kinds of canyons, but more abundant in canyons heading far from shore, are pebbles and cobbles similar to strata that constitute the canyon walls. Some pieces of rock were probably carried away by small mass movements of sediment, but others were probably dislodged by burrowing activities of organisms (Limbaugh and Shepard, 1957).

Basins and Troughs

A. Areal variation of grain size and percentage of calcium carbonate. More than 600 samples from about 250 stations in the various basins and troughs have been analyzed in the laboratory. These samples show that the bulk of the sediment consists of detrital materials and calcium carbonate of foraminiferal tests with only minor amounts of authigenic minerals and organic matter; thus grain size is controlled by the detrital and calcium carbonate fractions. Within individual basins there is some variation in grain size that is related to proximity to the basin side slopes (Fig. 187 top) and a greater variation that results from changes at depth. Owing to these variations and possibly also to alteration of the samples during preparation for analysis, the regional pattern of grain size is not easily recognized. A basin-

by-basin summary (Table 14) reveals no clear-cut trend of grain size, but when the basins are grouped into five series at progressively greater distances from shore and compared with the continental slope and deep-sea floor west of San Nicolas Island, the average median diameters may be seen to present the following general changes by group: (1) 14.0, (2) 6.5, (3) 4.0, (4) 4.0, (5) 4.6, (6) 7.8, and (7) 1.8 microns. Thus the grain sizes of whole samples decrease from the Los Angeles Basin to the middle basins, increase to the continental slope, and decrease again on the deep-sea floor. This is exactly the change that we would expect from an observed progressive increase in percentage of coarse foraminiferal tests of sediments in an offshore direction. We should also expect that removal of calcium carbonate by acid treatment of the samples would reveal that the insoluble residue does not increase in grain size near the continental slope. The corresponding average median diameters of insoluble residues are (1) none, (2) 8.1, (3) 9.4, (5) 6.7, (6) 6.7, and (7) 2.9 microns, a series that indicates a more uniform decrease of diameter with distance from shore than that exhibited by analyses of the whole samples. Comparison of the two sets of diameters (for whole samples and for insoluble residues), however, shows that the insoluble residues for most of the areas are coarser than the whole samples. Whether this is true, whether the acid treatment enlarged the grains (although flocculation did not occur), or whether the number of samples is too small to be statistically valid (121 insoluble residues versus 608 whole samples) is not clear.

Another way of investigating the effects of calcium carbonate on grain size of whole samples is illustrated by Figure 188, a plot of median diameter against percentage of calcium carbonate. With a continuous seaward increase in percentage of calcium carbonate, the median diameters of whole samples decrease from the Los Angeles Basin through the nearshore basins (Groups 2 and 3 of Table 14) to minimum diameters in the offshore basins followed by an increase in diameter in the outermost basins

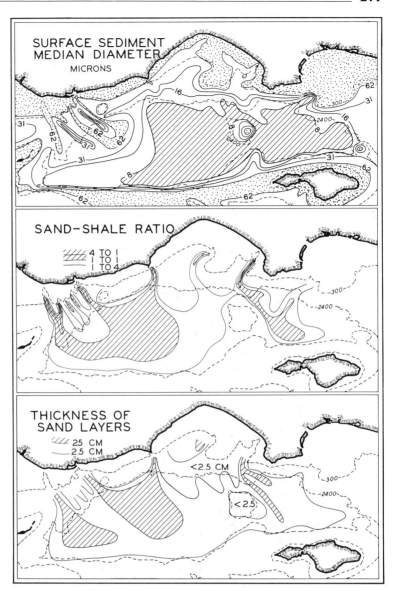

Figure 187. Areal variation of texture in Santa Monica and San Pedro Basins. From Gorsline and Emery (1959, Fig. 2). Top, median diameters of surface sediments (based on about 260 samples), showing general decrease of grain size away from shore, across continental and island shelves, down basin slopes, and toward center of basins. Data from coarsest sediment omitted in interest of simplification. Middle, sand-shale ratio computed on the basis of green mud eventually becoming compacted to half its present thickness. Note close relationship of high ratios to mouths of submarine canyons. Bottom, average thickness of sand layers in centimeters, showing seaward thinning.

and the continental slope. These data indicate that the high calcium carbonate from foraminiferal tests causes an increase in the median diameter of the sediments in the basins farthest offshore (Group 5) and on the continental slope, but the effects on basins closer to shore appear to be negligible owing to a smaller percentage of calcium carbonate and detrital grains. Histograms of sediments separated by decantation support the conclusions reached above (Fig. 189) and show in addition that grains of calcium carbonate in the sediments of near-

shore basins have nearly the same size distribution as do the detrital grains. This, of course, suggests that much of the calcium carbonate is itself detrital, reworked possibly from areas of shallower water. The alternative possibility, that the foraminiferal tests have been partly dissolved and the calcium redeposited, is refuted by the absence of solution even on delicate tests of hyaline forms and by the fact that there is no marked increase in percentage of fine fraction of calcium carbonate at depth in the cores, even though as much as 20,000

Table 14

SOME CHARACTERISTICS OF BASIN FLOOR SEDIMENTS

Group	Basin	Median Diameter, microns	Trask Sorting Coefficient	Calcium Carbonate, %	Nitrogen at Surface, %	Organic Matter, % (17 × N)	Green Pigments at Surface, ppm	Hydrocarbons, ppm	Insoluble Residue Median Diameter, microns	Insoluble Residue Trask Sorting Coefficient
1	Los Angeles	14.0 *24*[1]	3.9 *24*	4.9 *24*		2.6[2] *24*				
2	Santa Barbara	4.5 *36*	3.4 *33*	11.6 *43*	0.34 *10*	5.8 *10*	103 *2*	240 *5*	6.7 *9*	2.4 *8*
	Santa Monica	8.5 *165*	3.2 *54*	8.6 *42*	0.34 *13*	5.8 *13*	47 *11*	150 *1*	6.1 *1*	3.4 *1*
	San Pedro	7.5 *95*	3.6 *63*	10.2 *30*	0.39 *14*	6.5 *14*	40 *10*		12.5 *8*	2.6 *8*
	San Diego	5.6 *30*	4.6 *30*	10.8 *17*	0.43 *2*	7.3 *2*	23 *2*	200 *1*	8.2 *7*	2.4 *7*
3	Santa Cruz	3.9 *24*	3.6 *24*	15.5 *34*	0.50 *11*	8.5 *11*	28 *1*	180 *3*	8.5 *8*	2.2 *8*
	Santa Catalina	4.0 *37*	3.7 *35*	18.0 *48*	0.51 *8*	8.6 *8*	25 *4*	60 *4*	8.9 *15*	2.4 *15*
	San Clemente	4.0 *56*	4.2 *54*	14.4 *57*	0.34 *4*	5.7 *4*	5 *3*	43 *1*	10.9 *13*	2.4 *13*
4	San Nicolas	3.7 *35*	3.9 *33*	26.1 *29*	0.48 *4*	8.1 *4*	19 *3*		6.3 *8*	2.7 *8*
	East Cortes	3.7 *14*	3.2 *14*	26.1 *27*	0.38 *3*	6.4 *3*	8 *2*		4.7 *8*	2.5 *7*
	No Name	4.6 *1*	2.1 *1*	12.4 *10*	0.27 *1*	4.6 *1*	5 *1*		7.9 *9*	2.3 *9*
5	Tanner	4.8 *27*	3.4 *24*	34.4 *21*	0.68 *4*	11.7 *4*	39 *3*	98 *3*	5.6 *9*	2.8 *8*
	West Cortes	6.4 *13*	3.7 *13*	38.8 *32*	0.38 *4*	6.4 *4*	9 *3*		7.7 *10*	2.4 *9*
	Long	3.1 *16*	3.2 *16*	30.6 *30*	0.29 *2*	5.0 *2*	4 *1*	54 *1*	6.7 *5*	2.4 *5*
6	Continental slope	8.0 *20*	4.4 *18*	43.5 *45*	0.32 *2*	4.1 *29*	9 *1*		6.7 *8*	2.6 *7*
7	Deep sea	1.8 *19*	2.7 *9*	3.8 *27*	0.21 *1*	2.1 *11*	2 *1*		2.9 *3*	2.8 *3*

[1] Italics indicate number of sample analyses used for obtaining average values.
[2] At depth.

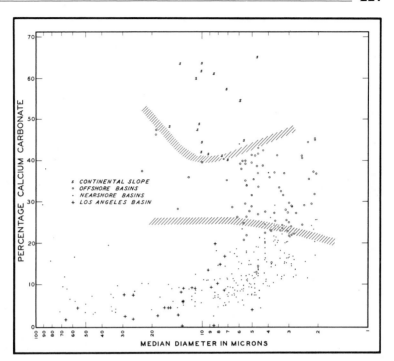

Figure 188. Relationship of median diameter and calcium carbonate of basin and continental slope sediments. Calcium carbonate was computed from determinations of carbonate ion, assuming all is combined with calcium. Note that calcium carbonate increases directly with distance from shore, whereas grain size decreases at first and then increases.

ears have elapsed since deposition of sediment now at depth. In fact, the percentage of calcium carbonate finer than 4 microns in most cores decreases with depth of burial (Table 15). Total calcium carbonate also decreases with depth in most of the cores, but comparison of the percentages of total calcium carbonate and calcium carbonate finer than 4 microns indicates that the decreases are not quite parallel. There is a slight concentration of calcium carbonate in the finer sizes of the nearshore basins and in the coarser sizes of the offshore basins, as though dilution by reworked calcium carbonate is most important in nearshore basins and dilution by foraminiferal tests is most important in offshore basins. Thus, the summary of Table 15 agrees with and amplifies the results shown in Figure 189.

B. Sorting of sediment. Median diameters and Trask sorting coefficients are available for several thousand sediment samples from the sea floor off southern California. When the two parameters are plotted against each other (Fig. 190), they present a pattern having a wide degree of scatter; nevertheless, the pattern shows a trend of finer sizes with poor sorting and coarser sizes with good sorting. In general, the former points denote

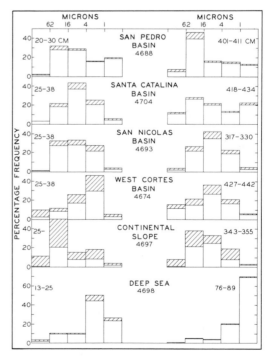

Figure 189. Histograms comparing grain-size distribution of whole sample with that of detrital fraction and calcium carbonate in each grade size that was separated by successive decantation steps. Note the general seaward decrease in grain size, the concentration of calcium carbonate in coarse grain sizes at and near the continental slope, and its similarity of grain size to detrital fractions in nearshore basins.

Table 15
Percentage of Calcium Carbonate in Cores

Area	Core Number	Depth of 13 to 38 cm		Bottom of Core, 280 to 460 cm	
		Total Sample	<4 microns	Total Sample	<4 microns
Santa Barbara	3503	10	11	12	13
Santa Monica	4647	3	3	11	37
San Pedro	4688	8	5	14	9
San Diego	4667	12	14	8	8
Santa Cruz	4700	5	4	14	15
Santa Catalina	4704	16	20	9	8
San Clemente	4670	18	18	11	14
	4672	9	12	5	5
San Nicolas	4693	19	24	19	17
East Cortes	4671	35	36	8	5
No Name	4673	37	43	9	7
Tanner	4696	29	23	24	24
West Cortes	4674	39	36	26	21
Long	4699	51	49	17	16
Continental slope	4697	61	53	51	56
Deep sea	4698	13	12	2[1]	2[1]

[1] 76 to 89 cm.

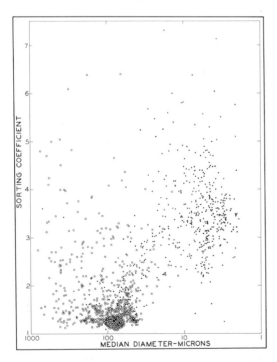

Figure 190. Plot of median diameter against Trask sorting coefficient for sediments from mainland shelves, island shelves, and bank tops (circles) and for sediments from basin floors, basin slopes, and continental slopes (dots).

sediments from basin floors and the latter sediments from mainland shelves, island shelves, and bank tops. Some overlap of points is caused by coarse sediments that have been carried from shelf areas by turbidity currents and deposited in the basins. Sediments from basin slopes and the continental slope (plotted as basin sediments in Fig. 190) also tend to be concentrated in the area of overlapping circles and dots of the plot. The poorly sorted shelf sediments are ones of mixed origin, most of them having large percentages of coarse shell fragments.

The relationship of sorting to median diameter is somewhat similar to that discovered by Inman (1949a) for beach sands wherein the best sorting occurs for sands of about 180-microns diameter and poorer sorting is typical of both finer and coarser sizes. In this plot, covering a much wider range of sizes and types of sediment than beach sands, the trends are not so clearly exhibited. However, even casual examination of Figure 190 shows a definite difference between shallow and deep-water sediments that indicate a difference in depositing agents.

C. Depth and age distribution of calcium carbonate. As shown by Table 15, core from most of the basins exhibit a decrease of calcium carbonate with depth. If this trend reflects changed conditions of deposition during the past, the date of change can be estimated from a plot of calcium carbonate against time instead of depth. Such a plot allows for the different rates of deposition of sediments in different basins. As will be discussed more completely in the section on rate of deposition, radiocarbon dates at the bottoms of cores from each basin and from the tops of some cores have been made by Dr. T. A. Rafter of New Zealand as part of a University of Southern California project financed by the National Science Foundation. Knowing the date at which the sediment at the bottom of a reasonably uniform core was deposited and the fact that similar sediment still is being deposited, we can make a first approximation of the date at which any part of the core was deposited by assuming a uniform weight of new sediment added each year per unit area. Obviously this date is subject to error if the rate of deposition was not uniform throughout the length of a core. Use of weight instead of thickness corrects for the normal compaction or decrease in water content with depth. Occasional layers of sand deposited rapidly by turbidity currents and containing abnormally high or low percentages of calcium carbonate must be eliminated from consideration.

The change of calcium carbonate concentration with time is shown by Figure 191, constructed as outlined in the previous paragraph. Most of the cores exhibit a definite decrease of calcium carbonate with depth earlier than about 3000 years ago. Two cores (Santa Barbara and Santa Monica) show no change because sediments at their bottoms were deposited only 2000 years ago. One (San Pedro) shows no change, and two (Santa Cruz, and west end of Santa Catalina) show an increase with depth. The curves, plus the data of Table 15, appear to be sufficient to indicate that calcium carbonate exhibits a sharp decrease at depths corresponding to a date 3000 years before the present.

Related studies of cores from the floor of the deep sea have been made by various workers. Hough (1953) found an alternation of layers of red clay and globigerina ooze which he ascribed to alternations of glacial and interglacial stages of the Pleistocene. Arrhenius (1952), working with cores of the Swedish Deep-Sea Expedition, believed that the percentage of calcium carbonate in sediments of a large area of the deep-sea floor is inversely related to the temperature for

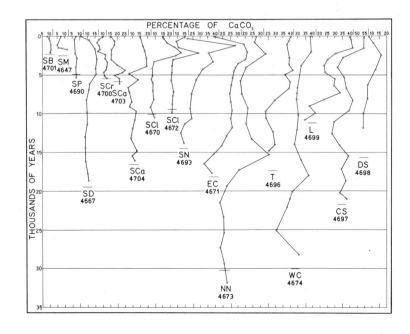

Figure 191. Variation of calcium carbonate in cores from several basins during past time. Data include corrections for radiocarbon zero age, core shortening, sand layers, and variation in water content of sediment with depth, as discussed in text. Calcium carbonate was measured from volumes of carbon dioxide produced by treatment of sediment with acid. Aged sections are indicated by short horizontal lines. Sample sites are given in Figure 205 and Table 20.

core depths ranging throughout most of the Pleistocene; he attributed this relationship to a high rate of production during times of temperature minima. Foraminiferal studies by Ericson and Wollin (1956b), on the other hand, showed that in the Atlantic a change from low to high percentages of calcium carbonate corresponds to a change from cold- to warm-water species. Verification was given by oxygen isotopes as reported by Emiliani (1955). Radiocarbon dates (Ericson, Broecker, Kulp, and Wollin, 1956) showed that the change from low to high carbonate content occurred about 11,000 years ago. Using these and additional radiocarbon dates, Broecker, Turekian, and Heezen (1958) proved that, although the percentage of calcium carbonate in an Atlantic deep-sea core was less prior to 11,000 years ago than afterward, the absolute rate of deposition was more than twice as great prior to 11,000 years ago than later. Clearly, the problem is a complex one.

Changes in sediments taking place more than about 15,000 years ago cannot be inferred from many of the cores off southern California because few of them are long enough to reach so old a date. Only three (West Cortes, No Name, and the continental slope) are much older than that, but all these cores show an increase of calcium carbonate at about 10,000 to 15,000 years ago, perhaps similar to that exhibited by some deep-sea cores. On the other hand, sediments were deposited in the basins off southern California much faster than were those of the deep-sea floor, so trends exhibited by them yield detailed data for the past few thousand years that cannot be obtained from the very thin layer of sediment deposited on the deep-sea floor during the same period. The change at about 3000 years, interpreted in the light of studies of deep-sea sediments, may suggest that the oceanic temperature increased 3000 years ago and has remained high since then. However, other factors that may well have influenced the rate of deposition of calcium carbonate are (1) the blocking of the circulation pattern of surface water by exposure of the Santa Rosa–Cortes Ridge when sea level was lowered during glacial stages (and

reduction of upwelling and thus of production of plankton), (2) the reworking of calcareous sediments on the then exposed shelves and bank tops, and (3) the great restriction in total area of shallow-water sites for population by the highly calcareous mollusks during glacial stages. Owing to the complexity of the problem and the insufficiency of existing data, further speculation on the cause of the decrease of calcium carbonate with depth in cores of basin sediments is considered too hazardous to be justified.

D. Depth distribution of grain size. As soon as long cores began to be collected, sand layers were noted interbedded between greater or lesser thicknesses of the normal green mud of the basins (Revelle and Shepard, 1939). Except for these layers the muds are nearly uniform throughout the length of cores. The positions of cores taken up to 1950 that showed the layers were compiled by Shepard (1951b); subsequent work revealed the sand layers in more than 150 new cores, mostly from the San Pedro and Santa Monica Basins. Sand layers have been found now in cores from all except Santa Barbara Basin where their place is taken by gray silt layers.

Some of the coarse-grained layers are thick enough to provide good echoes from below the mud-water interface. A traverse across the San Diego Trough made by a Scripps Institution of Oceanography ship using a Precision Depth Recorder clearly reveals the presence of two sound-reflecting layers, doubtlessly sandy. Both layers are covered by later sediments to a greater depth nearshore than offshore (Table 16), as a result of faster deposition of mud atop the sand layers on the mainland side of the San Diego Trough than farther offshore. Two somewhat less distinct layers are also shown in a sounding traverse across the north end of San Clemente Basin at about the same depths below the mud-water interface.

Detailed analyses of cores from nearly all basins (Emery and Rittenberg, 1952; Orr, Emery, and Grady, 1958) reveal that each sand or silt layer has a lower content of water and of organic matter (expressed either as organic carbon or nitrogen) than the finer-grained muds that overlie and underlie it (Fig. 192). For basins bordering the mainland, calcium carbonate is less abundant in the coarse-grained layers than in the finer muds; for Santa Catalina, San Nicolas, and San Clemente Basins at intermediate distances from shore some layers have more and some less carbonate than the muds; and for the far-offshore basins carbonate is generally more abundant in the sand layers than in the muds. Shallow-water Foraminifera (Crouch, 1952) and glauconite in sands from the offshore basins closely resemble these components in sands from bank tops and island shelves. Detrital heavy minerals of West Cortes Basin are dominated by augite as are sands on the nearby Cortes Bank, but heavy minerals in sands from San Pedro and Santa Monica Basins are dominated by hornblende like the sands from the adjacent

mainland shelf. Among the light minerals feldspar is so abundant that the sands are properly termed arkose.

Table 16

APPARENT DEPTH OF BURIAL OF TWO SAND LAYERS (APPARENTLY SAND) IN SAN DIEGO TROUGH WEST OF SAN DIEGO AS READ FROM PRECISION DEPTH RECORDER

Distance West of Base of Slope, km	Depth of Burial, meters	
	First (Top) Layer	Second Layer
0	6.7	13.1
2	4.0	9.1
4	3.0	8.2
6	2.0	7.5
8	0.0	6.1
10	0.0	5.2
12	0.0	6.1
14	0.0	4.9
16 base of west slope	0.0	indefinite

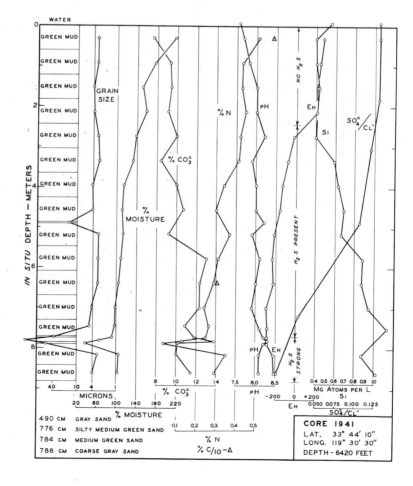

Figure 192. Analytical data for core from Santa Cruz Basin. Note the effects of grain size on other parameters. From Emery and Rittenberg (1952, Fig. 9).

The most complete information on sand and silt layers is from San Pedro and Santa Monica Basins where a detailed study was made in 1956–1957 (Gorsline, 1958; Gorsline and Emery, 1959) with financial aid from California Research Corporation, La Habra. This study was initiated after five or six coring attempts during one day of 1955 at the west end of San Pedro Basin failed to produce more than bent core barrels having a few grains of sand sticking to them. The 86 piston cores that were collected, together with 30 earlier simple gravity cores and about 170 surface samples, provide a reasonably dense grid of samples for both San Pedro and Santa Monica Basins. The results reveal the presence of sand and locally o fine gravel layers at the mouths of Hueneme Mugu, Dume, and Redondo Submarine Canyons (Fig. 193). Farther basinward the layers become thinner, are separated b thicker interbeds of normal green muds, and are irregularly finer-grained (Fig. 187, middle and bottom). The sands are most abun dant on the subsea fans and the area traversed by deep-sea channels which extend basinward from the mouths of at least Hue neme, Mugu, and Redondo Submarine Can yons. Cores from the basin slopes contain no sand layers and consist of sediment tha is coarser than the muds and finer than th sands of the basin floors. At the foot of th

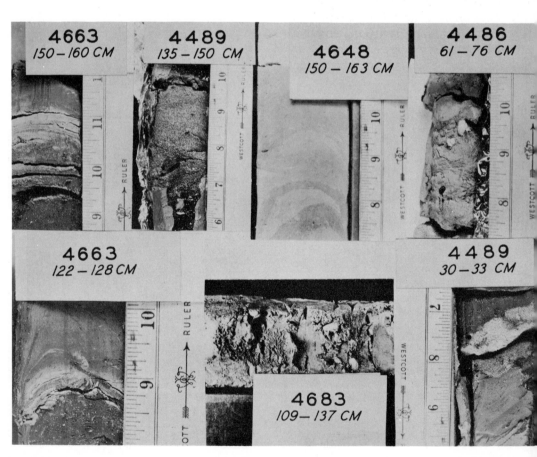

Figure 193. Photographs of typical sedimentary features in cores of basin sediments. From Gorsline and Emery (195? Pl. 1). Core 4663 (150–160 cm and 122–128 cm), laminated silty sand layers with flow structures in their upper portions from basin floor. Core 4489 (135–150 cm), thick graded medium-to-coarse sand layer, from a subsea fan. Core 464? (150–163 cm), gray silt layers (downswept ends are result of coring operation), from basin floor near base of steep side slope. Cores 4486 (61–76 cm) and 4683 (109–137 cm), massive sandy silt with gravel and shallow-water mollusks from upper parts of subsea fan. Core 4489 (30–33 cm), graded coarse-sand layer with sharply defined top, from uppe part of a subsea fan.

lopes on the mainland side of the basins are prons of hummocky character (Fig. 43) which are believed to consist of debris lumped there by mass movements from the upper parts of the slopes (Emery and Terry, 956). Many cores from the aprons contain ections that are highly contorted and have ome mud clasts, both of which features are onsidered indicative of deposition from mass movements. Some cores from the base of the slope north of Santa Catalina Island how features that are similar but far less ommon than in cores from the base of the mainland slope. Beyond the aprons and in reas marginal to the subsea fans, many ores have silt layers, counterparts of sand ayers on the fans and basinward of the fans. A schematic representation of the various ore features and their areal distribution Fig. 194) shows a definite relationship to ubmarine canyons and marginal slopes. The most reasonable agency for depositing he coarse-grained layers is believed to be urbidity currents that develop from mass novements of nearshore sediment at the teads of submarine canyons or down the upper parts of basin slopes, as will be dis-ussed more fully in a later section.

Support for turbidity currents is provided by the common upward decrease of grain ize of sands within many individual layers, is though in response to slower settling of iner grains carried by turbidity currents after most of their coarse load had been de-posited. Some of the layers grade into silt; others have sharply defined top surfaces of and. Commonly, charcoal-like sticks, twigs, .nd leaves are also incorporated into the top parts of the graded layers. Near the mouths of canyons some of the sands are banded or aminated as though deposited at intervals oo short for accumulation of green muds vhich elsewhere intervene between the ands.

Additional examples of abundant deep-vater sands are provided in the San Diego Frough at the mouths of La Jolla and Coro-1ado Submarine Canyons (Fig. 195). The Pliocene shales of the Los Angeles Basin also contain many sand layers, particularly in the niddle area of originally deep water and to

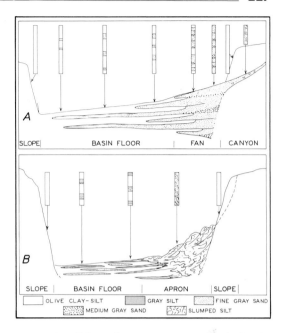

Figure 194. Schematic representation of typical sedimentary features in basin sediments. From Gorsline and Emery (1959, Fig. 5). A, canyon-fan-basin sequence; B, slope-apron-basin sequence.

the northeast of it (Slosson, 1958; Conrey, 1959). Still other deep-water sands are well known in the Pliocene shales of Ventura Basin where they have been described by Natland and Kuenen (1951) and Baldwin (1959). The areal distribution and minor characteristics of the sands in both of these ancient basins correspond very closely with those of the modern basins and doubtlessly were produced by similar processes.

E. Organic matter. Trask (1932) and Emery and Rittenberg (1952) found that California basin sediments contain large percentages of organic matter as compared with most other marine sediments, values locally exceeding 10 per cent by dry weight of whole sediment. Determinations of nitrogen by Kjeldahl analysis reported by Emery and Rittenberg, supplemented by a nearly equal number of additional analyses, 350 altogether, are given in Figure 196 for both surface and subsurface samples. These nitrogen values may be converted to total organic matter by multiplying by the factor 17, as will be discussed more fully in a later section on composition of organic matter.

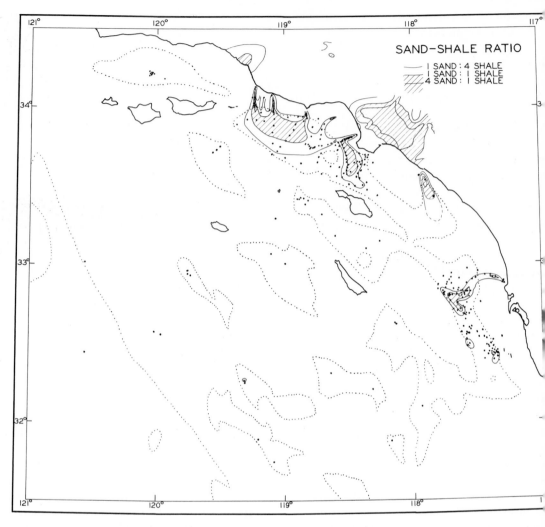

Figure 195. Sand-shale ratio of sediments in present basins and in the now-filled Los Angeles and Ventura Basin. In order to make the two sets of data comparable, the thickness of "shale" in existing basins was taken as half th thickness of the uncompacted green muds. Note the restriction of high sand-shale ratios to nearshore basins and the close relationship to submarine canyons. Compiled in part from Slosson (1957), Gorsline (1958), and Baldwin (1959

The accumulated data verify earlier conclusions that organic matter is present in the basins adjacent to the mainland in percentages equal to or slightly greater than percentages in shales of the now filled Los Angeles Basin. Farther offshore, in Santa Catalina, Santa Cruz, San Nicolas, and Tanner Basins (Table 14), organic matter rises to the highest percentages found in the entire continental borderland. Still farther seaward organic matter decreases in the outermost basins, and this decrease is continued by the very low percentages found in sediments on the continental slope and the

deep-sea floor beyond. The peak concentra tion of organic matter at intermediate dis tance from the mainland is attributed to very rapid rate of deposition of detrital sed ments near shore, resulting in the dilution o masking of organic matter there, and to very slow rate of deposition far from shore resulting in extensive oxidation of organi matter before it can become protected b burial. Thus the highest concentration oc curs under optimum conditions of neithe too rapid nor too slow a rate of depositio of detrital sediments.

Viewed in vertical section, the organi

matter of basin sediments may be seen to exhibit a general downward decrease upon which are superimposed minor irregularities related to grain size (Fig. 192). The coarse-grained layers found in all basins have a low organic content which evidently results from the much more rapid deposition of these layers than of the intervening finer green muds. Such a rapid deposition must serve to dilute the organic matter, which is de-

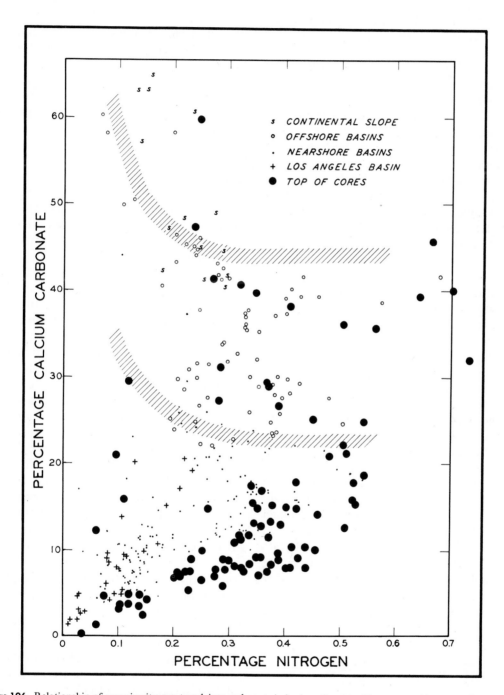

Figure 196. Relationship of organic nitrogen to calcium carbonate in basin sediments. Note seaward increase of nitrogen from nearshore basins to ones at intermediate distance from shore and then decrease in basins far from shore and continental slope. Values of nitrogen in Los Angeles Basin should be increased about 50% to be comparable with sub-surface data from present basins, to adjust for late diagenetic losses of nitrogen.

posited at a more uniform rate than is the detrital component of the sediment. When only the green muds are considered, organic matter shows a downward decrease in percentage which is rapid for the first meter or so and gradual at greater depth. The transition between rapid and slow rate of decrease occurs near the depth of zero oxidation-reduction potential (*Eh*), signifying that oxidation must be slower after all the dissolved oxygen originally present in the interstitial water has been consumed by oxidation of organic matter soon after deposition while it is still in the upper, recent, layers of sediment. Approximately one-third the total content of organic matter is gone by the time it becomes buried to the depth of zero *Eh,* zero to more than 6 meters, depending on the particular basin.

Reference to Figure 86 reveals that the standing crop of diatoms (the chief producers of organic matter) varies by a factor of 1000 in the region, much more than the variation of organic matter in the basin sediments; moreover, the areas of greatest production are not necessarily the areas of greatest abundance in the sediments. Evidently, the areal and depth variation of organic matter in the sediments is more a function of dilution and oxidation than of production in the overlying water.

The control of organic content by grain size of whole sample is borne out by analyses of organic nitrogen present in different-size fractions of samples. Samples from the tops and bottoms of ten basin cores were separated by decantation into five size fractions. After carbonates were determined (Fig. 189, Table 15), nitrogen was measured by Kjeldahl analysis on each of the 100 fractions. The results were somewhat erratic, probably because of some solution and other minor losses of organic matter during handling of the samples, but average nitrogens for the size fractions are as follows:

>62 microns	0.25 per cent
62 to 16	0.29
16 to 4	0.33
4 to 1	0.42
<1	0.48

The progressive increase of average nitrogen content with decreasing grain size of the fractions shows the existence of a definite affinity of organic matter for fine-grained sediments. This may be a result of similarity in their settling velocities or of adsorption of organic matter on clay minerals. Although the finest grain-size fraction contains the highest percentage of nitrogen, the total weight of this size fraction is small compared to the weight of coarser fractions (Fig. 189). As a result, about 65 per cent of the nitrogen is associated with grains having diameters between 1 and 16 microns.

In addition to variations in the percentage of total organic matter, the basins also present variations in composition of organic matter. Since these are rather involved, they are described in a separate and later section.

F. Mineral composition. The bulk of the sediments of clay size (<4 microns) usually consists of clay minerals, members of the kaolinite, montmorillonite, illite, or chlorite groups. It is generally considered that kaolinite is characteristic of an acid environment in which leaching of calcium, magnesium, and iron is active. Montmorillonite forms in an alkaline environment having magnesium, calcium, and ferrous iron. Illite requires a similar environment but one that includes potassium; chlorite needs a similar one but with especially high magnesium (Grim, 1951, 1953; Keller, 1953). According to G. Millot (Grim, 1951), in lake sediments kaolinite is dominant, except that if much calcium carbonate is present illite may be important instead; in brackish lagoonal sediments illite or montmorillonite is dominant; and in marine sediments illite is dominant. Because of the presence of abundant potassium and magnesium in sea water, some of the kaolin and montmorillonite brought to the ocean is converted during diagenesis to illite and chlorite.

Although these are the general environmental relationships that can be expected through physical-chemical factors of the environments, many complications prevent strict interpretations of environments from clay mineralogy alone. Perhaps chief of the complicating factors in the marine environment is that of the variable composition of the source materials; for example, stream-borne sediments in an area of weathering Tertiary marine shales may contain much illite. Another factor is that of differential flocculation and deposition of clay minerals (van Andel and Postma, 1954), whereby illite may be precipitated closer to shore than montmorillonite. Rate of deposition with respect to rate of diagenesis can also control the ratio of illite to montmorillonite. Another general limitation is the low degree of precision in determining the composition of complex mixtures of fine-grained clay minerals, even though all available methods are used, such as X-ray diffraction, differential thermal analysis, chemical and base-exchange analyses, and optical and electron microscopy. These various factors clearly require caution in the interpretation of environments of deposition for ancient shales on the basis of their clay mineralogy.

The only comprehensive study of the clay minerals on the sea floor off southern California was made by Dietz (1941) and reported also in part by Grim, Dietz, and Bradley (1949). Samples were analyzed from the Colorado River and Mission Bay (near San Diego), from cores of the mainland shelf off Encinitas and Oceanside, from cores of some slopes and the bottoms of Santa Barbara, San Pedro, Santa Monica, San Diego, Santa Cruz, Santa Catalina, East Cortes, and Tanner Basins, and from cores of the continental slope and the deep-sea floor. In general, kaolinite, montmorillonite, and illite were found to be about equally abundant in the Colorado River and Mission Bay. Samples from the mainland shelf showed a relative loss of kaolinite. In the basins there appeared to be a further seaward decrease in kaolinite accompanied by an increase in illite, so that in offshore basins kaolinite averaged about 20 per cent, montmorillonite 30 per cent, and illite 40 per cent. Presumably, this change in ratio means that illite is being formed in the basin sediments at the expense of kaolinite. The seaward decrease of the kaolinite-to-illite ratio can be an effect of the rate of deposition which is slower in the offshore basins than in near-

shore ones, thus providing more time for diagenesis during burial of the sediments; the decrease may also be influenced by the higher percentage of calcium carbonate in offshore than in nearshore basin sediments, giving rise to lesser stability of kaolinite offshore. A slight seaward decrease of the montmorillonite-to-illite ratio indicates that montmorillonite is also being lost by diagenesis.

In 1955 X-ray analyses of core samples from Santa Barbara, Santa Monica, and Santa Catalina Basins were made by the Petroleum and Oil-shale Experiment Station, U. S. Bureau of Mines (H. M. Thorne, personal communication of November 10, 1955). The results showed that illite is dominant but that kaolinite, montmorillonite, and chlorite are present in minor amounts, probably less than 10 per cent each. Again no change of relative proportions of the clay minerals with depth, to as much as 360 cm, could be detected. Two more analyses of clays from Santa Barbara Basin by Grim (Orr and Emery, 1956a) yielded the following results: montmorillonite 55 per cent, illite 30 per cent, and chlorite 15 per cent. The dissimilarity between the three sets of clay mineral analyses must be due to differences in techniques of analysis.

In addition to their content of clay minerals, the clay-sized sediments in the basins contain much fine-grained calcium carbonate, as discussed in an earlier section. The X-ray analyses by the U. S. Bureau of Mines indicate that it is in the form of calcite. These analyses also show the presence of fine-grained feldspar, quartz, dolomite, and pyrite in order of decreasing abundance. More detailed X-ray diffraction determinations of quartz, plagioclase, and orthoclase were made by E. D. Goldberg aided by D. S. Gorsline (personal communication). Analysis for quartz was an extension of studies made by Rex and Goldberg (1958), in which the quartz content of deep-sea sediments was determined with a reproducibility of 3 per cent. Analysis for feldspar is less certain because of dependence of the diffraction pattern on the type and history of the feldspar, as pointed out by Smith and Yoder (1956).

Nevertheless, the relative heights of the peaks for quartz, plagioclase, and orthoclase were found to be approximately proportional to the percentage of the three minerals present in several natural sand samples that had been examined by staining and optical methods. Thus the ratios of peak heights on the diffraction record were assumed to serve as measures of the weight ratios in samples of basin muds. A total of sixteen samples were studied from San Pedro Basin, seven from Santa Monica Basin, and one each from nearly all the other basins, the continental slope, and the deep-sea floor. The results of all analyses, averaged by basins, yield a quartz-to-feldspar ratio of 2.2:1, similar to the average ratio obtained optically for many samples of sands from the beaches and mainland shelves. There appears to be no systematic regional variation, and individual samples varied from the average by no more than a factor of 2. By the same method the average plagioclase-to-orthoclase ratio was found to be 4.5:1, again within the range characteristic of the sands from the mainland beaches and shelves. Particularly in nearshore basins biotite is common, locally in excess of 10 per cent. Its flat shape permits easy transportation in suspension from beaches and other areas of winnowing.

G. Chemical composition. Spectrochemical analyses were made of 58 samples from 6 cores by California Research Corporation in 1953. Since the only preanalysis treatment was drying to 140°C, these bulk analyses include mineral solids, sorbed solids, and dissolved solids of the pore water. The percentage of silicon was determined gravimetrically and of carbonate ion gasometrically. The results (Fig. 197) show only a slight dependence on grain size for the range of grain sizes of these particular cores. Had the size range included both sands and clays, there would have been a clearer relationship to grain size.

The most abundant cation is silicon, except in the core from the continental slope (Table 17) in which calcium is greater. Both silicon and calcium lie in the region of values found by Murray and Renard (1891) for green mud and are somewhat different from their value for blue mud. Reference to Figure 197 shows a clear relationship of calcium to carbonate ion; however, an over-all average of 0.44 per cent more calcium (in terms of total sample weight) was found by spectrochemistry than is needed to satisfy the carbonate ion as calcium carbonate. This excess is probably the calcium present in clay minerals, as indicated by the average of 0.63 per cent calcium in analyses of clay minerals of the offshore region after removal of calcium carbonate by acid digestion (Grim, Dietz, and Bradley, 1949). Aluminum is the second or third most abundant cation, yielding an average silicon-to-aluminum ratio of

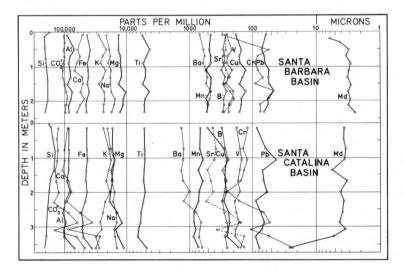

Figure 197. Chemical composition of cores from basin floors. Most are spectrochemical analyses by California Research Corporation after drying to 140°C; gasometric carbonate ion and grain size were previously reported by Emery and Rittenberg (1952) on the same cores (Santa Barbara Basin, AHF 1856; Santa Catalina Basin, AHF 1633); silicon was measured gravimetrically by Griffin-Hasson Laboratories on later cores (AHF 2622E and AHF 2187-8), 0.1 mile and 13 miles distant, respectively.

Table 17

CHEMICAL COMPOSITION OF SEDIMENTS, PER CENT

	Spectrographic Analyses				Chemical Analyses			
	Santa Barbara Basin (Cal Research Corp.), 1 core (to 244 cm), 11 samples	Santa Catalina Basin (Cal Research Corp.), 1 core (to 315 cm), 32 samples	Continental Slope (Cal Research Corp.), 4 cores (to 386 cm), 15 samples	Red Clay (Goldberg and Arrhenius, 1958), 3000± samples	Red Clay (Steiger, in Clarke, 1920, p. 510), 51 samples	Blue and Green Muds (Steiger, in Clarke, 1920, p. 510), 52 samples	Shale (Stokes, in Clarke, 1920, p. 544), 78 samples	Igneous Rocks (Clarke, 1920, p. 28), 111 to 1789 analyses
Si	19.9[1]	17.3[1]	11.9[1]	23.0	25.3	26.6	27.2	28.0
Al	8.1	7.7	5.5	9.2	8.4	9.1	8.2	8.0
Ti	0.50	0.50	0.36	0.73	0.59	0.76	0.39	0.46
Fe	4.3	4.5	2.8	6.5	6.7	5.3	4.8	4.6
Mg	1.2	2.1	1.2	2.1	2.0	1.3	1.5	2.3
Ca	5.7	8.6	22.4	2.9	1.4	1.5	2.2	3.5
Na	1.8	1.6	1.5	4.0	1.5	0.76	0.94	2.5
K	2.4	2.0	1.7	2.5	2.4	1.9	2.7	2.5
Sr	0.024	0.040	0.11	0.071	0.047	0.025	–	0.034
Mn	0.048	0.064	0.036	1.25	0.76	0.093	tr.	0.078
Cu	0.015	0.026	0.037	0.074	0.019	0.013	–	–
V	0.023	0.015	0.015	0.045	0.24	0.020	–	0.017
Ba	0.054	0.12	0.13	0.39	0.18	0.054	0.045	0.093
Cr	0.007	0.015	0.010	0.0093	0.0082	0.034	–	0.034
B	0.028	0.017	0.025	0.030	–	–	–	–
Pb	0.0081	0.0095	0.0079	0.015	0.0074	0.0004	–	–
Ni	–	0.02[2]	–	0.032	}0.031	}0.050	–	0.020
Co	–	–	–	0.016			–	–
P	0.10[3]	0.08[3]	–	–	0.12	0.09	0.074	0.13

[1] Silicon from Griffin-Hasson Laboratories, Los Angeles (11, 9, and 10 samples, gravimetric).
[2] Nickel from Richfield Oil Corporation, Wilmington (4 samples).
[3] Phosphorus from Rittenberg, Emery, and Orr (1955) (colorimetric).

2.3, lower than the average of 2.5 for red clays reported by Goldberg and Arrhenius (1958), probably because of the lower percentage of siliceous organic debris and of wind-borne quartz in the basin sediments than that in red clay. Aluminum averages about 1.9 times iron in the basin sediments as compared to 1.4 in red clay, perhaps because of the concentration of iron in the fine-clay sizes, as suggested by Grim, Dietz, and Bradley. Although about half the sodium reported from the basin sediments is in the form of dissolved solids of the interstitial water, very little of the potassium is of that origin. Instead, the potassium must be chiefly from illite clay minerals. Grim, Dietz, and Bradley reported an increase of potassium with depth in basin cores, as though in response to progressive formation of illite from other clay minerals during diagenesis, but the present six cores show no such trend, being evenly divided between decrease, increase, and no change. The calcium-to-magnesium ratio averages 4.7, 4.1, 1.9, and 1.3 in the sediments of Santa Barbara Basin, Santa Catalina Basin, continental slope, and deep sea, respectively. Because most of the magnesium is clearly part of the clay mineral structure, these ratios cannot be compared with those of limestones reported by Chilingar (1956) to have an average calcium-to-magnesium ratio of 40 in Quaternary and Recent sediments and, of course, they are also unrelated to temperature of accumulation of the sediments (Chilingar, 1953; Chave, 1954).

Among the trace elements titanium clearly bears a close relationship to iron (Fig. 197) with a Fe_2O_3-to-TiO_2 ratio of 7.5 (Fig. 198), slightly lower than that for red clays (Revelle, Bramlette, Arrhenius, and Goldberg, 1955, Fig. 8). Barium relative to titanium is much less abundant in basin than in deep-sea sediments. Although the barium-to-titanium ratio may serve as an index of surface organic productivity in the deep-sea region (Arrhenius, 1952; Goldberg, 1954), this use in the continental borderland is complicated by other as yet unknown factors. In fact, the ratio of barium to titanium presents a rapid and continuous seaward increase and thus is inversely proportional to both productivity of surface waters and rate of deposition of detrital sediments. Strontium, with its nearly constant CaO-to-SrO ratio of 230 (Fig. 198) (or Ca/Sr = 195), is more abundant relative to calcium than in limestones (Kulp, Turekian, and Boyd, 1952) and less abundant than in deep-sea sediments. Manganese is understandably much less than in red clay. The abundance of chromium with depth in several cores (Fig. 197) closely parallels calcium and strontium, but no reason for this behavior is suggested. Lead also roughly parallels manganese in basin as in deep-sea sediments (Goldberg, 1954). Vanadium, as discussed by Krauskopf (1955), is probably present in clay minerals rather than in organic matter; this source is also suggested by its greater abundance in red clay than in basin sediments.

Comparison of the analyses of basin muds with averages for shales and igneous rocks (Tables 17 and 18) reveals many similarities, with few cations differing by a factor more than 2 and only calcium by one of more than 3.

H. Color. The terrigenous marine sediments that include Blue Mud and Green Mud were named and described by Murray and Renard (1891, pp. 229–230, 236–237) on the basis of samples obtained aboard _H.M.S. Challenger._ Blue Mud was described as blue or slate-colored owing to organic matter but having a red or brown oxidized surface layer. Calcium carbonate ranged from a trace to 34.3 per cent and averaged 12.5 per cent. Hydrogen sulfide was characteristically present. The rate of deposition was considered fairly rapid. Blue Mud of this definition covers 46,000,000 sq km, occurring in the deeper water surrounding continents and in enclosed or partially enclosed seas. The depth for 58 samples ranged from 230 to 5100 meters and averaged 2580 meters. In contrast, Green Mud was defined as green to gray in color, possibly owing to green amorphous matter and glauconite that formed because of the slow rate of accumulation of detrital sediment. Calcium carbonate ranged from a trace to 56.2 per cent, averaging 25.5 per cent. It covers an area of less than 2,200,000 sq km off bold exposed coasts with no large rivers. The depth for 22 samples ranged from 200 to 2320 meters and averaged 940 meters.

Rather than having to refer to the basin sediments only as green or yellow-green,

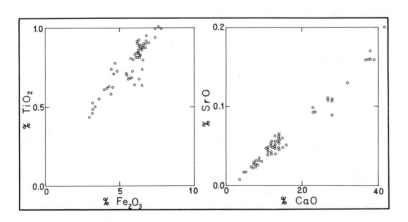

Figure 198. Plots showing close relationship between TiO_2 and Fe_2O_3 and between SrO and CaO in basin and continental slope sediments.

Table 18

CHEMICAL COMPOSITION OF SEDIMENTS EXPRESSED AS OXIDES, PER CENT

	Santa Barbara Basin (Cal Research Corp.), 1 core (to 244 cm), 11 samples	Santa Catalina Basin (Cal Research Corp.), 4 cores (to 315 cm), 32 samples	Continental Slope (Cal Research Corp.) 1 core (to 386 cm), 15 samples	San Clemente I Slope (Revelle and Emery, 1951), 1 sample	Green Mud (Murray and Renard, 1891, p. 239), 1 sample (164B)	Blue Mud (Murray and Renard, 1891, p. 232), 2 samples (213 and 323)	Green and Blue Muds (Steiger, in Clarke, 1920, p. 510), 52 samples	Shale (Stokes, in Clarke, 1920, p. 544), 78 samples
SiO_2	42.55	37.18	25.53	23.18	31.27	63.78	58.38	59.12
Al_2O_3	15.40	14.60	10.45 ⎱	7.16 ⎰	4.08	14.32	15.40	15.34
Fe_2O_3	6.13	6.51	3.98 ⎰		12.72	9.80	5.45	5.90
MgO	2.04	3.55	2.07	1.80	0.38	0.72	2.45	3.49
CaO	8.00	12.10	31.40	29.40	26.91	3.99	3.12	5.08
Na_2O	2.48	2.29	2.09	2.62	–	–	1.31	3.84
K_2O	2.88	2.46	2.08	0.58	–	–	3.25	3.13
CO_2	7.20	7.90	22.62	22.03	20.71	1.54	2.64	0.10
Organic	5.80	8.60	5.40	4.56	3.30	5.26	7.66	1.25
Total	92.48	95.19	105.62	91.33	99.37	99.41	99.66	97.25

sections of many still-wet core samples were assigned color symbols using the National Research Council's Rock-Color Chart developed by Goddard and others (1948). Nearly all the color measurements fell in the range between $5Y$ 3.5/2 [$5Y$ = hue, 3.5 = value (lightness), 2 = chroma (saturation)] and $3GY$ 4/3. However, some samples from Santa Monica Basin were assigned to the color region near $4BG$ 3/1. Few of the "values" were higher than 4 or lower than 3, and the "chromas" ranged between 1 and 3. These colors might best be described as gray yellow-green to gray bluish-green. No relationship to oxidation-reduction potential or to hydrogen sulfide was evident; in fact, the bluish-green cores were the only ones free of hydrogen sulfide throughout. When the muds are dried, the only obvious color change is one of value, which increases about two points (becomes lighter). When wetted again, the color returns approximately to the original.

Sediments of all the basins off southern California are green, they are high in calcium carbonate, hydrogen sulfide is present in some sediments at the surface or at least at depth but it does not influence the color, the basins are areas of somewhat restricted circulation, and the coast is bold with few rivers. Thus it is evident that the characteristics of Blue Mud and Green Mud as indicated by Murray and Renard are not definitive or even mutually exclusive, a conclusion that has been reached in other studies of marine sediments. As suggested by Revelle (1944, p. 15), these names should not be used any longer as genetic terms but only as descriptive of the actual color of muds. In this sense all the fine-grained sediments off southern California must be termed green muds.

Among the factors usually considered as yielding the greenish color of many marine sediments are clay minerals, fine-grained green minerals such as glauconite and chlorite, reduced iron, and pigments. The latter, pigments, is most easily eliminated as a factor because little or no color change could be detected in sediment samples after more than 90 per cent of the green pigments had been extracted during laboratory studies of the distribution of green pigments (Orr, Emery, and Grady, 1958). Fine-grained glauconite has not been reported in the basin silts and clays, although sought by

Grim, Dietz, and Bradley (1949). Chlorite is present in some analyses but is not abundant. Probably far more important are the clay minerals, illite and montmorillonite, which together make up the bulk of the sediment. Both may be green, and according to Grim (1951) and Keller (1953) both are responsible for the green color of many shales.

It is possible that some contribution to the green color may be made by some ferrous iron compound, but probably the chief color effect of iron is in providing a red masking effect at the sediment-water interface. Sediment at this position for a variable thickness of 1 to 10 mm is soft, mobile, and brown. Because this sediment is in contact with the overlying water containing dissolved oxygen, its iron can be present partly as a hydrated ferric oxide (Strakhov, 1958). Later, when this layer becomes buried a few centimeters, it reaches a reducing environment and its iron changes to a ferrous form, such as the siderite reported by Grim, Dietz, and Bradley (1949) to be present in the basin sediments. The iron would then lose its red color and allow the normal green of the clay minerals to dominate. Supporting evidence for this role of iron is the development of a brown surface on samples of green mud stored for a few days or weeks in incompletely filled bottles and its easy removal by treatment with stannous chloride.

Deep-Sea Floor

Only a few cores have been taken from the deep-sea floor in the area of Chart I beyond the base of the continental slope, but these are of interest because of their contrast to sediments of the continental borderland. The sediments are red clay that is typical of red clays elsewhere on the Pacific Ocean floor (Table 12). One core, representing 5 meters of section, is uniform throughout in general appearance—fine grain size, high pH, positive Eh, and low contents of calcium carbonate and organic matter. Another, 1 meter long, is red clay at the bottom but is capped by 15 cm of gray mud believed to be a turbidity current deposit

from shallower water. Globigerina ooze has been reported nowhere in abyssal depths in the region, but it does occur in impure form at several localities sampled near the top of the continental slope. Since deep-sea deposits are outside the field of concentration of this study, the interested reader is referred to the following papers on deep-sea sediments: Revelle (1944), Arrhenius (1952, in press), Menard (1955), Revelle, Bramlette, Arrhenius, and Goldberg (1955), and Goldberg and Arrhenius (1958).

Source

Sediments on the sea floor off southern California are restricted to the following possible sources: streams, wind, sea cliff erosion, organic remains, and chemical precipitates. The first three of these sources are terrestrial and the last two marine. Even though most of the computations must be only approximations, estimates of the quantities of sediment supplied by the various sources are needed in order to be able to determine their probable order of importance.

Sediment supplied to the ocean by wind is appreciable only during the Santa Anas, the hot dry winds that blow seaward from the desert for a few days each year. During these days R/V *Velero IV* and other ships become coated with a layer of tan dust that even works its way into closed cabinets. Appreciable dust fall aboard ship has been noted even as far offshore as San Nicolas Island where 135 mg/sq yd was collected on November 4, 1950. On several occasions off Newport Beach the dust was seen floating on the water. In an attempt to learn more about this dust, Babcock (1957) collected samples from eight cities in the Los Angeles region after a Santa Ana windstorm by carefully sweeping 1 square yard of the tops of automobiles in used car lots in which the cars had been polished on the previous day. The median diameters ranged between 30 and 38 microns and averaged 34 microns (on a weight basis). The average weight of dust at three stations near the coast was 2.4 grams/sq yd, or 0.3 mg/sq cm. If an equal fall occurs on each of 5 days per year (a typical number), the annual dust fall would be about 1.5 mg/sq cm/yr. Owing to an offshore decrease in wind velocity, this dust fall diminishes in a seaward direction but at a rate unknown at present. Assuming that the rate dropped steadily from shore to zero at the continental slope, the contribution of eolian dust would total about 0.6 million tons annually. However, X-ray and optical studies of pelagic red clays by Rex and Goldberg (1958) revealed the presence of considerable numbers of chips and shards of quartz between 1 and 20 microns in diameter; they are thus coarser than the accompanying clay minerals. The percentage is greatest on the floor of the northeastern Pacific Ocean between latitudes 25 and 45° where the average is about 16 per cent quartz. The similarity of this distribution with the latitudes of desert areas and of the high-altitude jet stream gave rise to the suggestion that the quartz is of eolian origin. Accompanying wind-blown feldspars and other minerals yield a total of about 40 per cent wind-blown grains in the deep-sea sediments west of southern California. At an average rate of deposition of nonbiogenous sediment in pelagic clays of 0.073 grams/sq cm/1000 yr (Revelle, Bramlette, Arrhenius, and Goldberg, 1955), the rate of deposition of eolian sediments in the deep sea is about 0.03 mg/sq cm/yr. Thus the estimated rate near the coast of southern California is about 50 times the estimated rate for the deep-sea region.

The waves striking rocky shores are so spectacular during storms that there is a natural tendency to consider wave erosion of cliffs as providing a major proportion of the sediment available for distribution on the sea floor. Although a precise measure of the contribution of sediments by cliff erosion cannot be provided, a rough estimate can be formed. In the chapter on physiography it was estimated that cliffs averaging 25 meters in height line about 360 km of the mainland coast and cliffs averaging 55 meters in height line 500 km of island coasts. A comparison of old and new photographs by Shepard and Grant (1947) shows that erosion of cliffs formed of consolidated rocks was inappreciable during past periods of 30 to 50 years. On this basis we may guess that the average present-day rate of cliff retreat is about 30 cm/500 yr. Almost certainly it cannot have been faster. At this rate about 22,000 cu meters of cliff is removed in the region each year, an annual average of about 0.054 million tons, a rate that is only about 10 per cent of that estimated for wind-contributed sediment. If we deal with larger units and assume that an average thickness of 30 meters was stripped from the 14,800 sq km area of shelves and bank tops during the Pleistocene Epoch (1 million years), an average annual contribution of about 1.1 million tons is obtained. Although this Pleistocene rate is also small, it is about 20 times greater than the rate computed from present-day cliff erosion, a comparison that supports physiographic data in suggesting that the present rate of cliff erosion is less than that obtaining during the past.

Figures for the grain size and quantity of sediments annually contributed to the ocean by streams are very unsatisfactorily known, primarily because of the brevity of periods of violent stream flow and their separation by very long intervals of no or only slight flow. Many analyses have been made of the grain size of sediments that cover the floors of dry stream beds; as summarized by Table 12, the average median diameter of many samples is 610 microns, or coarse sand. These sediments, however, represent material that was left by the stream and was not contributed to the ocean. To be sure, every flood moves some of it to the stream mouth as a sort of plug, but the percentage of this material that reaches the ocean is probably very small compared to that carried in suspension. For example, Gould (1953) found that bed load constitutes less than 2 per cent of the total load carried by the Colorado River. The grain size of material carried in suspension by streams is much less well known. Revelle and Shepard (1939) reported that the median diameters of sediments from all streams (about 20) that were sampled during the heavy rain of March 1939 ranged between 1 and 50 microns but that the sediments of the larger streams were more uniform, ranging mostly between 20 and 35 microns. During a more typical moderate rainfall in early 1957 samples of sediment collected from just below the surface of the approximately 3-meter-deep San Gabriel, Los Angeles, and Dominguez Rivers had median diameters of 13, 12, and 5 microns, respectively. Similar samples collected in early 1958 at the San Gabriel, Los Angeles, and Santa Ana Rivers yielded median diameters of 5, 14, and 54 microns, respectively. Lindsay (1957b) found a unique method of determining the grain size of sediment discharged to the ocean by a small intermittent stream near Ventura. After the first major rain of the 1956–1957 season the stream discharged water and sediment atop a berm that lay in front of the stream mouth. Since no channel was cut through the sand, the water was trapped behind the crest of the berm and much of it seeped out through the sand, leaving behind a filter cake of sediment. Eventually a wedge-shaped layer of stream-contributed sediment having a maximum thickness of 60 cm accumulated, but wind-blown sand contaminated the top portion which remained soupy for several weeks. Five samples from the lower uncontaminated half of the deposit had median diameters ranging from 1.7 to 43 microns and averaging 19 microns.

On the basis of supply of sediment by streams Revelle and Shepard (1939) prepared an estimate of the rate of deposition in basins. They assumed that about 10 per cent of the regional average of 50 cm of rain (in a drainage area of 31,000 sq km) reached the ocean with an average concentration of 0.5 per cent sediment. This estimate corresponds to 7.8 million tons per year. A different kind of computation by Handin (1951) was based on the rate of accumulation of sediment in artificial reservoirs and debris basins. He obtained a figure of 1.2 million cu meters of sand contributed to the ocean by streams between Point Conception and San Pedro. For the entire coast this might be extrapolated to about 2.4 million cu meters, or 5 million tons of sand annually. If the average stream-discharged sediment consists of one part of sand to three parts of silt and clay, the total discharge of sediment would amount to about 20 million tons annually.

Neither Revelle and Shepard's nor Handin's estimate can be very firm, owing to lack of precision of the necessary basic data. Clearly, a different method is needed. This has recently been provided by radiocarbon methods of age determination of sediments that will be discussed in more detail later. For the present, it is sufficient to give only a brief summary. For each basin the rate of deposition of inorganic detrital sediments ranges between 6.3 and 117 mg/sq cm/yr; for the basin slopes and other deep irregular areas, 4.0 mg/sq cm/yr; for the continental slope, 3.0 mg/sq cm/yr; and for the abyssal sea floor of Chart I, 3.3 mg/sq cm/yr. Using these rates weighted according to the area of each unit (Tables 1 and 5), we find that about 5 million tons of land-derived sediment are deposited annually in the basins. To this must be added an estimated 5 million tons for the basin slopes and other deep irregular areas, the continental slope, and the abyssal sea floor. The total is 10 million tons per year. This is close to the other two estimates but is based on much firmer data. It seems probable therefore that the streams contribute more than ten times as much sediment to the ocean as do wind and sea cliff erosion combined.

Sediments of organic origin are dominated by calcium carbonate, but they also include siliceous tests, frustules, spicules, and organic matter. Calcium carbonate, mostly as recognizable foraminiferal tests, averages about 24 per cent of total sediment on the basin floors with the highest values in the basins having the lowest rate of deposition of inorganic detrital sediments. Radiocarbon measurements of age at the bottoms of basin cores show that the average rate of deposition of calcium carbonate in the basins is about 3.5 mg/sq cm/yr. This, of course, is the total for calcium carbonate derived directly from pelagic and benthonic organisms and for that which is reworked from shallow-water areas; however, probably nearly all the latter is also of organic origin, mostly comminuted mollusk shells. A somewhat greater rate of deposition of calcium carbonate may exist on the shelves and bank tops owing to the additional contribution of calcareous algae in the euphotic zone, but negligible deposition of detrital sediments in these areas causes the calcareous sediments to be exposed to the overlying water for so long that resolution is important. One result of solution is the observed high concentration of coarse shell fragments in these areas, the more delicate tests having been largely or wholly dissolved. Another result is the frequent exposure of ancient rocks. Where rocks have not been buried the net rate of accumulation of calcium carbonate is zero. Elsewhere on the shelves the rate may be greater or less than that in the basins by factors that are unknown but doubtlessly highly variable.

That solution of calcium carbonate is possible during its period of settling through the water column or during exposure on the bottom before burial is suggested by the apparently unsaturated condition of the water. The percentage saturation of calcium carbonate in sea water is given by the ratio of the ion product and the apparent solubility product:

$$\text{Per cent saturation} = \frac{[Ca^{++}] \times [CO_3^{=}]}{K'_{CaCO3}} \times 100$$

The carbonate ion concentration may be computed from temperature, chlorinity, hydrogen ion concentration, and alkalinity, using equations given by Harvey (1955). Measurements of these parameters were made at various depths in the water over several of the basins in connection with a study of the dissolved nutrients in the water (Rittenberg, Emery, and Orr, 1955). Calcium ion in sea water bears a constant ratio to chloride ion and was so computed. The apparent solubility product was based on Smith's (1941) values corrected to the observed chlorinity and temperature by Wattenberg's coefficients (Sverdrup, Johnson, and Fleming, 1942, pp. 206–207). The resulting values of percentage saturation of calcium carbonate (Fig. 199) show typical oversaturation at the surface and undersaturation below 100 meters. Below the basin sills the water is 30 to 60 per cent saturated, and it exhibits a slight increase in percentage saturation at the bottom as would be expected from solution of calcium carbonate at the water-sediment interface. Great reliance, however, should not be placed on these curves, owing to uncertainty of the solubility product and the great dependence of the computations on measurements of pH— never as precise as desirable.

Siliceous organic remains are present in quantities that are unknown because of the difficulty of making adequate separations. They probably constitute a good deal less than 1 per cent of the total weight of sediment. The organic matter in the basin sediments averages about 7 per cent by dry weight of total sediment, actual percentages

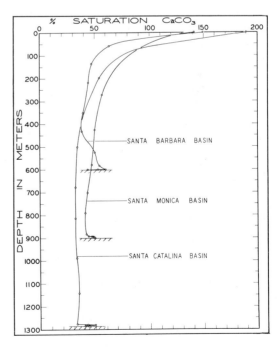

Figure 199. Curves showing computed percentage saturation of calcium carbonate in the water above several basins. Arrow indicates depth of basin sills and crosshatched line shows the bottom depth at the sampling sites.

being dependent on productivity, depth of water, rate of deposition of other sediments, and nature of interstitial water. The roles of these factors in controlling the amount and composition of organic matter will be discussed in a later section. Radiocarbon age measurements indicate that the organic matter accumulates at an average rate of about 1.5 mg/sq cm/yr at the basin floors.

Chemical precipitates are recognizable chiefly in the areas of slow deposition, where glauconite, phosphorite, and manganese oxide are characteristically present. Either these minerals do not form in the environment of the basin floors or they form such tiny grains so diluted by other sediments that they have neither been recognized nor separated from the other sediments. Even in the areas dominated by them, these authigenic sediments accumulate at a nearly negligible rate. Possibly more important in the basins, but impossible to evaluate at present, is the direct chemical formation of clay minerals in sea water. Goldberg (1954) suggested this as the origin of some of the clay minerals in the deep-sea sediments, but it must be far less important in the continental borderland where the nearby land is a ready source of clay minerals.

Transportation

Most of the sediments of the continental borderland have been derived from land; thus the methods by which they are transported from shore to final resting places are of prime importance to an understanding of them. There are only four possible zones of transportation of sediments in the sea: over the water, on the water, through the water, and under the water. Transportation over the water is of course the method for wind, whereby fine sediments can be carried in suspension far out to sea and coarser ones moved in saltation must be left at the shoreline.

Several agents can transport sediment on the water. Most important of these quantitatively is the flotation of sediment-laden fresh water atop the denser (higher salinity

and lower temperature) sea water. After heavy rains this "epithalassis" spreads its brown color many miles offshore. The layer is thin and sharp-bottomed, as indicated by measurements of light transmission at various depths and by the fact that boats traversing it stir up the underlying clear water and leave a semipermanent dark trail through the discolored area. Secchi disk readings in an area where 10 meters is normal may be reduced to 2 meters or less. Excellent photographs of the discolored areas are given by Bell (1942) and Natland and Kuenen (1951). Eventual mixing with the underlying sea water causes the fine-grained sediments to become flocculated so that clusters settle out of the layer and to the bottom. Other agents of transportation at the surface of the water are most effective for coarse sand, pebbles, and cobbles. All these are forms of rafting: kelp, sea lions, and driftwood (Emery and Tschudy, 1941; Emery, 1941b, 1955b). The quantities of sediment moved are small compared with those carried by floating fresh water, but rafting has the unique ability of explaining the occasional presence of erratic pebbles and cobbles in otherwise fine-grained sediments. Two pebbles with remnants of kelp holdfasts still attached were dredged with mud from a depth of 220 meters south of Palos Verdes Hills, and other such erratic pebbles are well known in Paleozoic and other shales of the United States and elsewhere. Sea lions carry as much as 5 kg of pebbles and cobbles, some of which are up to 10 cm in diameter. Rock identifiable as to source almost invariably shows local derivation and presumably therefore a short distance of transportation by the sea lions.

Probably even more important is transportation through the water in a sort of diffusion action. Sediment stirred up by the waves or contributed by streams is coarsest and most concentrated in shallow areas where waves break and create high turbulence. Marlette (1954) sampled the zone from shore outward about 55 meters to a depth of 1.7 meters by wading out with empty quart Mason jars and then opening and recapping them at measured depths and distances from shore. Waves at the outer plunge zone were 75 cm high and at the inner plunge zone 25 cm during the sampling period. The results (Fig. 200) show an increase from about 75 grams of sediment per liter of water at the shore to about 0.004 grams/liter at the water surface 55 meters seaward. Median diameters also decreased outward from 185 to 160 microns. Sediment was more concentrated and coarser near the bottom than higher above it. A similar vertical variation was found by Inman (1949b) who placed multisock sediment traps in 1 to 4 meters of water near the surf zone off Scripps Institution of Oceanography. The socks 10 cm above the bottom caught 2 to 20 times as much as those at 30 cm, and 5 to 50 times as much as those at 78 cm, with the amount and vertical distribution of sand dependent on the size and period of the waves. Another multisock sediment trap placed in 1.4 meters of water off Huntington Beach by Terry (1951) collected 5 times as much sediment in a sock near the bottom as at 1.2 meters above it, and the median diameters decreased regularly from 180 microns in the bottom sock to 130 in the top one. Measurements of suspended sediment along a pier at Mission Beach near San Diego were made by Watts (1953), who used a submersible electric pump that forced measured volumes of water through a sediment filter. The results again showed a dependence of the amount and

grain size of suspended sediment on the wave height and water depth. According to Watt's computations the wave-induced longshore current is capable of transporting several hundred thousand cubic meters of sand past the pier annually. Stirring of sediments in the surf zone is of course the result of high turbulence there. According to orbital current meter measurements by Inman and Nasu (1956), these velocities are as much as 100 times the settling velocity of sand grains present on the floor of that zone.

Work on suspended sediment was carried farther seaward by Gorsline (1954) by sampling from several depths using a pump and hose lowered from a boat to bring water to the surface where the sediment was allowed to settle out. At a station in 7.5 meters of water 1700 meters off Seal Beach, he found at depths of 7, 5, and 2 meters concentrations of 0.24, 0.12, and 0.05 grams/liter and median diameters of 70, 32, and 15 microns. The sediment near the surface was finer than that flooring the shelf between the sampling site and the shelf break, so we might conclude that suspended sediment in appreciable quantities is able to make its way across the shelf to the basin beyond. Supporting evidence is provided by reports by divers of a kind of haze near the bottom in shelf areas. In addition to traveling across the shelf-break to deep water, some of the suspended sediment slowly makes its way down submarine canyons. A sediment trap left in La Jolla Canyons for 2 months (Revelle and Shepard, 1939) was covered with about 2 mm of sediment that graded upward from 75 microns for median diameter in a bottom tray to 41 microns in a top one, in contrast to 110 microns for the underlying sediment surface.

The fact that diffused sediments reach deep water by crossing the shelves or moving down canyons is shown by the discovery of fine silt particles in water samples taken in Nansen bottles between the water surface and a depth of 300 meters in surveys made in October and December 1957 (Gunnerson, 1957b). Concentrations at the north side of San Pedro Basin were found to be as great as 200 grains/ml decreasing to 20 grains/ml farther offshore. Commonest among the

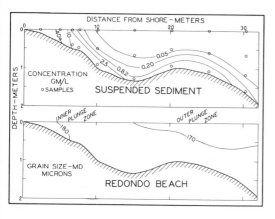

Figure 200. Concentration and grain size of suspended sediment in surf zone off Redondo Beach. Adapted from Marlette (1954).

grains are flakes of biotite, thus pointing out the route by which the abundant biotite in nearshore basins makes its way there. Conceivably this suspended sediment can be carried by currents throughout the area of the nearshore basin before its settling velocity will allow it to reach bottom.

Lastly, much sediment is transported seaward at the bottom in the form of turbidity currents. Evidence presented in other sections shows that the submarine canyons which reach close inshore intercept sands that travel along the beaches; the canyons thus divide the mainland beaches into a series of semi-independent sections (Fig. 28). Finer sediments that move longshore atop the inner half of the continental shelf are also intercepted. High sand-shale ratios in the bottom sediments of nearshore basins reveal the resting place of these sandy sediments by their concentric pattern around the mouths of the submarine canyons that debouch at the sides of the basins (Figs. 194, 195). In these areas the sands are thicker than elsewhere and the topography has the shape and slope suggestive of alluvial fans, subsea fans. Similar deposits of Pliocene age are known in the now-filled Los Angeles and Ventura Basins (Natland and Kuenen, 1951; Slosson, 1958; Conrey, 1959; Baldwin, 1959), and these basins commonly have graded bedding as do the sea floor deposits. They also have deep-water current ripples which have not yet been detected on their sea floor counterparts. Although turbidity currents have not been seen in action off this coast, these pieces of circumstantial evidence are very persuasive of sediment transportation in the form of turbidity currents. Both sedimentary and physiographic evidence indicates that turbidity current deposits occur in every basin off the coast but that they are far more important in the nearshore Santa Monica and San Pedro Basins and the San Diego Trough than elsewhere. The high sand-shale ratios in Santa Monica and San Pedro Basins show that the volume of sediment deposited in them by turbidity currents is about equal to that contributed by all other means, chiefly diffusion through the water column. Not until the two basins become filled to their sills can turbidity currents move completely through them and reach the next basins farther seaward (Fig. 54). This is the situation in the now-filled San Diego Trough which is spilling turbidity current sediments into the adjacent San Clemente Basin (Fig. 201).

Deposition

The composition and grain size of accumulated sediment are not a simple function of derivation, transportation, and deposition. Instead, there is a complex interplay of sources, one dominant here and another there. Transportation may be by several agents, each separated by shorter or longer periods of rest followed by physical or chemical reworking. We can cite examples of complexity in sediments of many kinds of areas, but it is especially well documented for the sea floor off southern California.

Most detrital sediments reach the ocean from land in a wide spectrum of grain sizes. In general, the beaches act as a sort of filter that allows the finer sizes to continue seaward and retains the coarser sizes until they too are worn fine enough to be transported seaward in suspension, or, in a few special cases, such as mass movements and turbidity currents in submarine canyons, they may be carried seaward en mass as sands. At the same time that detrital sediments are being transported seaward from land, even less well-sorted sediments are extracted from solution in the water. The coarsest of these are mollusk shells grown on the bottom; the most abundant are foraminiferal tests grown throughout the overlying water column, and probably the finest is organic matter formed by phytoplankton living near the water surface. All these organic materials experience changes parallel to but different from those undergone by detrital sediments. These changes consist of chemical alteration by herbivores, carnivores, and scavengers, and by simple contact with sea water. Mechanical comminution also occurs through organic activities and water motions. Again, the sediments undergo a filtering action by water

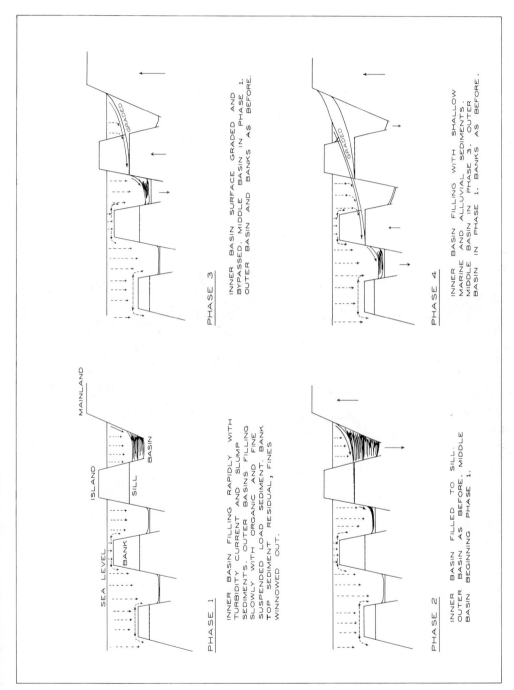

Figure 201. Phases of filling of basins by sediments, showing relative roles of deposition from general suspension and from turbidity currents. Note that latter deposits fill nearshore basins before they can spill over into adjacent basins. From Gorsline and Emery (1959, Fig. 6).

movements so that only a narrow range of sizes and compositions can remain in any single environment.

Many examples of the interplay can be given, but one for a shallow bank top will be enough. Only the finest detrital sediment from shore can reach the top of a bank, except for rare kinds of rafting. If deposited there, the detrital sediment joins coarser detrital sediment derived mostly from the immediately underlying rocks by slow submarine weathering or perhaps by former erosion and deposition as a now relict beach. Most of the loose material atop the bank, however, is of organic origin. Shells when newly grown are coarser than the sediment of either distant or near sources, and some of them also are fairly resistant to comminution

by whatever means, so that even the broken fragments are larger than most other sediment grains. Wave action on shallow banks is capable of moving most of the sediment there, and by its action the coarser grains are formed and reformed into ripple marks (Fig. 202). Finer sediments remain longer in suspension, and so they come under the influence of tidal and other currents. By this means whatever fine-grained material from shore that managed to reach the bank top is removed. Also the fine-grained and low-density organic matter is removed almost entirely. Coupled with this mechanical action is solution of shell fragments and organic matter by the moving sea water. Finely broken shells offer a larger surface area per unit volume, and therefore their rate

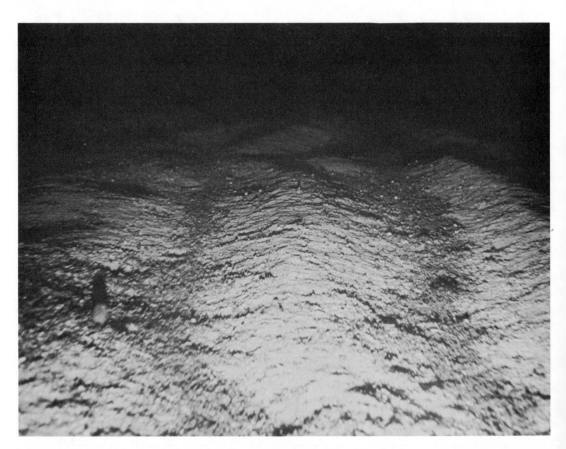

Figure 202. Ripple marks atop Osborn Bank (lat. 33°22.0′, long. 119°02.9′, 58 meters). The sediment is coarse-grained glauconitic shell sand. Ripples of about 1-meter wave length probably formed at least several months before the photograph was taken in November 1951. A time lapse is indicated by the partial destruction of the ripples by organic activity and perhaps by slow water movements. Turbulence when ripple marks form must account for much of the known winnowing away of finer grains. (AHF 2086.)

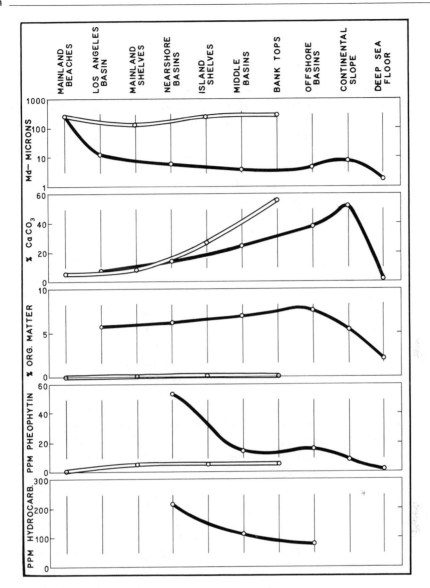

Figure 203. Curves showing variation with facies or generalized distance from shore of several components of the sediments. Nearshore basins are Santa Barbara, Santa Monica, San Pedro, and San Diego; middle basins are Santa Cruz, Santa Catalina, San Clemente, San Nicolas, East Cortes, and No Name; offshore basins are Tanner, West Cortes, and Long.

of solution accelerates as they become smaller. Because the rate of deposition is approximately equal to the rate of solution and mechanical removal of grains, bedrock is exposed for long periods of time, thereby allowing slow-growing authigenic minerals to accumulate if they form immovable coatings on the rocks such as manganese oxide and phosphorite, or large grains such as glauconite and phosphorite nodules. Owing

to these various processes, it is no surprise that the sediments of shallow bank tops are coarse-grained, highly calcareous, and contain much glauconite and phosphorite but little organic matter.

The full sequence of major environments and their sediments can be related by a series of curves (Fig. 203). Grain size is coarsest for the shallow sediments that are most exposed to wave turbulence—beaches, shelves, and bank tops. Sediments of the basins (and also marshes) accumulate in quiet water, and accordingly they mostly are fine-grained. A decrease of grain size occurs from the now-filled Los Angeles Basin to existing basins halfway across the continental borderland in response to the size control exerted by diffusion and to the restriction of important turbidity currents to nearshore basins. The far-offshore basins and the continental slope have somewhat coarser sediments owing to a relatively high percentage of coarse foraminiferal tests, which nearer shore were masked or diluted by the more rapidly deposited detrital components. On the deep-sea floor the grain size falls to its lowest values because of great distance from shore and nearly complete dissolution of the calcareous component.

Reference to the curves for calcium carbonate (Fig. 203) shows the relationship required by the variation of grain size: A steep and continuous increase of percentage of calcium carbonate is presented by the shallow areas because access to them by coarse-grained detrital sediments is less than that by shell debris. Probably the low calcium carbonate content of beaches is due also to the fact that the resistance of calcite to the intense abrasion there is less than that of quartz and feldspar. The content of calcium carbonate in fine-grained basin sediments also increases seaward until a peak of abundance is reached in offshore basins and on the continental slope. Inshore of these areas the rate of deposition of detrital sediments is so great as to dilute the calcium carbonate, and offshore of them the rate is so slow as to permit the calcareous material to be exposed long enough for it to be dissolved in the bottom water, which is more corrosive at these depths than at shallower depths anyway.

Organic matter is of low percentage in coarse-grained sediments for several reasons, one of which is that it is easily winnowed away. Moreover, the low rate of deposition on shelves and bank tops permits nearly complete oxidation of organic matter. Only in the basin sediments do physical processes permit it to remain, but in nearshore basins the rapidly deposited detrital sediments greatly dilute organic matter, and far from shore the slowly deposited detrital sediments fail to bury it before it becomes oxidized. Comparison of the curves for calcium carbonate and organic matter in the basin sediments suggests immediately that organic matter is more susceptible to solution or chemical regeneration than is calcium carbonate. Even more susceptible are pheophytin and hydrocarbons, minor components of the organic matter, as revealed by the relative positions of the points of highest concentration of these materials (Fig. 203). Obviously, the optimum concentrations of all four organic substances are also dependent on the positions of areas of greatest productivity for all overlying water, yet although the area of greatest productivity for all should be identical or nearly so, their curves of abundance in bottom sediments differ markedly. Details regarding pheophytin and hydrocarbons are reserved to a later section.

It may be profitable to think of the sediments in terms made familiar by economists, supply and demand. The greatest supply of detrital sediments is the shore. The supply of organic sediments is more involved. For pelagic organisms the supply is related to productivity of overlying waters, which is greatest in areas of upwelling, for example (Fig. 86). Benthic production of organic matter occurs only where the bottom is shallow enough to be in the euphotic zone, but benthic production of calcium carbonate may also occur much deeper, except in basins that because of low oxygen content are nearly barren of life. Demand for sediments is also complex. Mechanical demand is of course greatest where there is the most turbulence, in shallow water, and it may be nearly nonexistent at the bottoms of basins. In all areas chemical demand causes some regeneration, but this demand is minor relative to supply where the supply is very great or where toxic conditions markedly reduce both biological and abiological chemical demands. The varying roles of supply and demand factors are responsible for the curiously contorted curves of grain size plotted against calcium carbonate and organic matter (Fig. 204). In only a simple area can the curves approximate straight lines, and possibly no large area can be that simple, certainly not the continental borderland off southern California.

Rate of Deposition

Methods

Many geochemical computations require information about the rate of deposition of sediments. In order to satisfy this need, several estimates have been made during the past, mostly on the basis of supply. Revelle and Shepard (1939) based their estimate on supply for the entire region, obtaining a rate of 0.13 mm/yr, or 60 mg/sq cm/yr in the basins. Using the same basic data, Emery and Rittenberg (1952) assumed a greater-than-average rate for the nearshore Santa Barbara Basin—2 mm/yr, or 91 mg/sq cm/ yr. Handin (1951; Luplow, 1950) estimated that streams between Santa Barbara and San Pedro discharge about 1,300,000 cu meters of sand per year. If all eventually made its way onto the floors of Santa Monica and San Pedro Basins by turbidity currents, the

rate of deposition of sand throughout the 2720 sq km area of flat floors of the two basins (Table 5) would average about 0.48 mm/yr. Since the ratio of sand to shale in the basins averages about 1:1, and since compaction of mud to shale results in a 50 per cent decrease in thickness, the total rate of deposition would be about 1.44 mm of total sediment per year, or 91 mg of sediment grains per square centimeter per year. Lastly, the relative rates of deposition across the floor of a basin can be determined by differences from place to place in thickness of sediment between subsurface sands; these differences are detected by echo sounding. By this stratigraphic method, deposition at the east side of San Diego Trough was found to occur more than twice as fast as on the west side (Table 16).

A different method is needed for obtaining absolute rates of deposition in individual basins or at different localities in the same basin. The best of such methods available is that of radiocarbon dating. Because of the importance of proper dating, the National Science Foundation provided funds for collecting cores, determining radiocarbon ages, and measuring necessary sediment

Figure 204. Complex relationship of grain size with contents of calcium carbonate and organic matter in sediments of continental borderland. In a generalized way the curves connect points at progressively greater distance from shore. The complexity results from the interplay of supply and demand for sediments in the various environments.

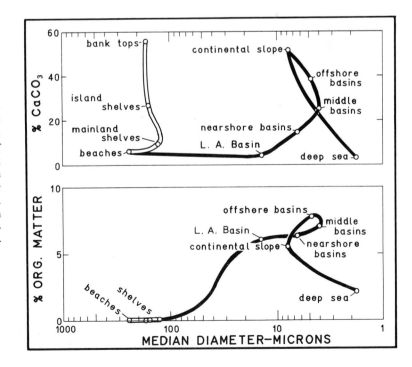

parameters. Eighteen cores were collected
from thirteen basins, the continental slope,
and the deep-sea floor (Fig. 205). For comparison, the rate of deposition of sediments
at the top of the San Pedro Basin slope off
Palos Verdes Hills based on radiocarbon age
determinations by the Magnolia Petroleum
Company (Emery, 1958a) and the rate in
Ventura and Los Angeles Basins since the
Miocene Epoch are included.

All cores were obtained with a piston
corer (Kullenberg, 1947) weighing 500 kg
and having a core tube 6.5 meters long and
about 10 cm in inner diameter. Piston cores
are far superior to simple gravity cores for

this kind of work because of the shortening
of the sediment section produced by gravity
cores during their penetration of the bottom
(Emery and Dietz, 1941). The tripping device for the piston core was adjusted in such
a way that it tripped above the bottom,
allowing as much as a meter of water to be
drawn in before the core tube reached the
sediment surface. This procedure insured
that the topmost layer of sediment was
cored, although at the expense of not obtaining the maximum possible core length.
Evidence of recovery of the sediment surface was provided by typical high contents
of interstitial water and even better by the

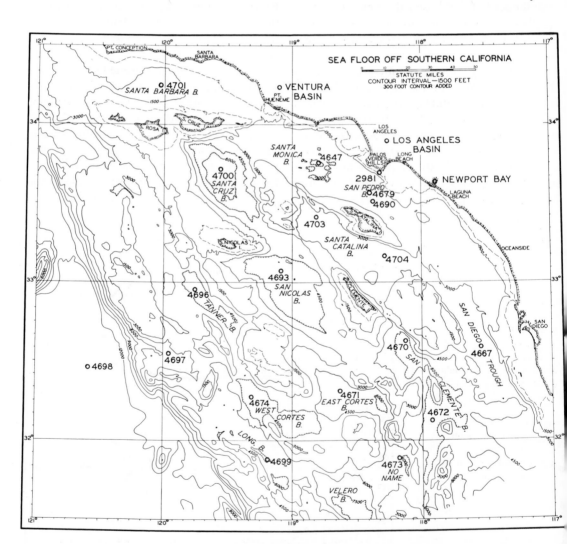

Figure 205. Positions of cores used for determining rates of deposition of sediments from radiocarbon age measurements. Rates of deposition in Ventura Basin, Los Angeles Basin, and Newport Bay are based on other data.

similarity between contents of green porphyrin pigments in sediment at the top of the piston core and at the top of a small open gravity core used as a tripping weight for the large piston core device. Since water content and especially porphyrin content decrease rapidly with depth in the sediment, failure to core the topmost layers would have resulted in great differences between the piston and the simple gravity cores, which always contain surface layers. As soon as the cores were brought aboard ship, they were extracted from the core tubes, split, described, and cut into about fifteen sections which were sealed in glass jars. Measurements of *p*H and *Eh* were made within a few hours. On return to the laboratory, the bulk of the bottommost section and commonly of the surface section of each core was sent away for carbon-14 age determination. Sections were chosen so as to avoid sandy turbidity current layers. All sections were analyzed in the laboratory for their percentage contents of water, nitrogen, and calcium carbonate (by gasometric analysis).

Radiocarbon age determinations were made in New Zealand by Dr. T. A. Rafter, whose radiation-counting technique is based on carbon dioxide referred to wood (Rafter, 1953, 1955*a*, 1955*b;* Fergusson, 1955). The results of 37 age determinations are shown in Table 19, along with measurements of the contents of nitrogen and organic matter (17 × nitrogen) near the surface (Orr, Emery, and Grady, 1958) and composite calcium carbonate for each core. Unfortunately, not all the 37 age determinations could be used for direct measurement of rate of deposition. Three separate problems basic to the work had to be investigated first, and half the analyses were used for these problems.

The first problem was that of whether the ages should be based on carbon from organic matter or carbon from calcium carbonate. Pairs of organic carbon and carbonate ages were determined for eleven core sections at various depths in different basins. The results (Table 19) show close agreement between the two ages only for Santa Barbara, San Clemente, and East Cortes Basins. In Santa Monica, San Diego, Santa Catalina,

and San Nicolas Basins the carbonate age exceeds the organic carbon age by an average of 25 per cent. Thus, except for Santa Barbara Basin, the greatest differences occur in the nearshore basins. The differences are believed to result from erosion of old calcium carbonate from shallow-water areas and redeposition of it on the basin floors. Reworking can of course occur in any basin at any depth, but it is probably most frequent in the nearshore basins which have steep side slopes and deeply indented submarine canyons. In addition, it will be recalled (Table 15, Figs. 188, 189) that the sediments of the nearshore basins (again except for Santa Barbara Basin) have a concentration of calcium carbonate in the finer grain sizes, which are similar to the sizes of the grains of detrital sediment. This contrasts with a concentration of calcium carbonate in the coarser sizes of sediments in offshore basins where it is mostly in the form of recent foraminiferal tests. Thus the ages support the grain-size data by indicating the presence of more reworking of calcium carbonate in nearshore basins than in offshore ones. Similar reworking was inferred by Rubin and Suess (1955) and Ericson, Broecker, Kulp, and Wollin (1956) from the greater age of fine-grained (<74 microns) than of coarse-grained calcium carbonate in cores from the Caribbean Sea. Santa Barbara Basin is somewhat unusual because the organic carbon near the surface is of greater age than the carbonate. There, reworked calcium carbonate may be minor because the side slopes are gentle, no large submarine canyons enter the basin, and the shelf along the mainland to the north contains little calcium carbonate. Conceivably some reworked organic carbon is present in the form of bits of tar carried by currents from oil seeps near Point Conception; however, since the age discrepancy is not great, it probably can be neglected in the problem of rate of deposition. The organic carbon dates appear to be far less subject to error from reworking than the carbonate ones, so all subsequent age determinations are based on carbon from organic matter.

The second problem is that of the zero

Table 19

RADIOCARBON DATES IN BASINS[1]

Basin	Core	Depth, cm	Age	Basis	Surface Nitrogen	Surface Organic Matter	Composite CaCO₃
Santa Barbara	4701	0–19	3000 ± 700	C	0.340	5.77	10.5
		0–19	2260 ± 250	$CO_3^=$			
		228–241	3500 ± 150	C			
		406–419	5150 ± 80	C			
		419–432	5600 ± 180	$CO_3^=$			
Santa Monica	4647	386–396	4900 ± 140	C	0.378	6.42	5.7
		386–396	6260 ± 250	$CO_3^=$			
San Pedro	4679	300–310	9450 ± 250	C	0.392	6.66	10.1
	4690	5–25	2400 ± 150	C	0.441	7.50	7.85
		330–348	7050 ± 120	C			
San Diego	4667	343–356	21900 ± 700	C	0.424	7.20	10.2
		343–356	27300 ± 1500	$CO_3^=$			
Santa Cruz	4700	343–356	9000 ± 200	C	0.460	7.81	11.0
Santa Catalina	4703	267–279	8250 ± 200	C	0.520	8.83	18.0
	4704	3–13	1970 ± 150	C	0.527	8.95	12.8
		3–13	2320 ± 130	$CO_3^=$			
		13–25	2820 ± 140	C			
		13–25	4270 ± 130	$CO_3^=$			
		406–419	18400 ± 600	C			
		406–419	23100 ± 1000	$CO_3^=$			
San Clemente	4670	305–318	12500 ± 250	C	0.343	5.82	12.8
		305–318	12400 ± 300	$CO_3^=$			
	4672	267–279	11800 ± 300	C	0.262	4.45	9.0
San Nicolas	4693	0–5	2560 ± 110	C	0.513	8.72	22.3
		0–5	3100 ± 100	$CO_3^=$			
		330–343	16900 ± 350	C			
		330–343	18600 ± 400	$CO_3^=$			
East Cortes	4671	5–13	3250 ± 300	C	0.393	6.67	22.6
		441–454	21000 ± 550	C			
		441–454	21200 ± 500	$CO_3^=$			
No Name	4673	401–414	32600 ± 1700	C	0.281	4.77	15.7
Tanner	4696	330–343	20200 ± 600	C	0.644	10.92	33.0
West Cortes	4674	3–13	4800 ± 200	C	0.408	6.93	28.2
		419–432	32800 ± 1300	C			
Long	4699	343–354	13600 ± 500	C	0.269	4.56	29.2
Continental Slope	4697	381–396	24100 ± 1000	C	0.386	6.55	37.6
Deep sea	4698	102–112	17100 ± 1100	C	0.212	3.60	5.5
Top of basin Slope off Palos Verdes Hills	2681	300–325	20000 ± 1000	$CO_3^=$	0.048	0.82	13.2

[1] Dated by T. A. Rafter, New Zealand Department of Scientific and Industrial Research, Lower Hutt except for the sample from top of basin slope, which was dated by the Magnolia Petroleum Company, Dallas.

age of the sediments, or the radiocarbon age of the organic matter now being deposited at the sediment-water interface. Six organic carbon age determinations were made of the surface samples (Table 19), but since a length of core amounting to 10 to 15 cm was needed in order to obtain enough carbon for age measurement, the age obtained was for a composite sample centered several centimeters below the sediment-water interface. Surface ages were computed by extrapolation upward from this depth according to the age of a sample near the bottom of a core. The extrapolated ages of surface sediments are as follows:

Santa Barbara Basin	2900 years
San Pedro Basin	2200 years
Santa Catalina Basin	1800 years
San Nicolas Basin	2400 years
East Cortes Basin	2800 years
West Cortes Basin	4200 years

The age for West Cortes Basin is much greater than those for the other basins, and it will not be further considered except for that particular basin. The remaining surface ages average 2400 years. Radiocarbon dates at various depths in eight suitable cores from the deep-sea floor of the Atlantic Ocean are given by Kulp, Feely, and Tryon (1951), Suess (1954, 1956), Ruben and Suess (1955), and Broecker and Kulp (1957). Extrapolation to the sediment surface yielded zero ages of 1000 to 5800 years, with an average of 2900 years, not much different from the average for the basin sediments off southern California.

The great age of the surface sediment in the basins off southern California cannot be ascribed to a lack of deposition during the past 2400 years, for the surface sediments are not different from those at depth. Great radiocarbon ages for surface sediment have sometimes been considered to result from mixing of sediments by burrowing organisms, but it is evident that mixing would have to occur to depths of several meters to make the surface sediments appear to be so old as 2400 years. In Santa Barbara Basin the presence of many thin, probably annual, laminae testifies to the absence of mixing, as does the fact that benthonic animals have not been found in samples and photographs of this basin floor. Some other mechanism is responsible for the great apparent age of the surface sediment. Evidently the age is in some way related to the nature of the organic matter which falls onto the floor of the basin. The time required for organic matter to reach the bottom from the euphotic zone must be a matter of not more than a few months, certainly not 2400 years.

Measurements of the radiocarbon ages of six water samples from depths in the Atlantic Ocean greater than 3000 meters yielded values between 450 and 1950 years according to Kulp (1953), but these values are now considered erroneous (Ewing and Gerard, 1956). Recent measurements have shown a complex pattern of apparent ages (Broecker, Ewing, Gerard, and Heezen, in press) that is related to the degree of equilibrium reached by carbon dioxide between atmosphere and ocean when the water was last at the surface. Although measurements off southern California are lacking, analogy with similar areas of the Atlantic Ocean indicates that the radiocarbon age of the water must be only a few hundred years at most. Average surface water is considered by Craig (1953, 1957) to have a radiocarbon age of about 400 years on the basis of equilibrium values of carbon 14 suggested by C^{13}/C^{12} ratios in surface water. In areas of upwelling, of course, the age of the water may be greater than that at the surface elsewhere, but since the depth of upwelling is only a few hundred meters, the increased age should not be as great as the 2400 years in question. Except for possible biological fractionation of carbon 14 with respect to carbon 12, the age of organic matter in phytoplankton should be the same as the age of the surface water in which it grows. Additional fractionation may occur through the activity of animals and bacteria which repeatedly attack the original tissue of phytoplankton during its fall through the water column and subsequent exposure on the bottom before burial.* It is also possible that selective oxidation of organic matter takes place whereby components having high C^{14}/C^{12} ratios are preferentially lost from the sediments, giving the remaining organic matter an apparently greater age than originally present. Since we really do not know why the organic matter now being deposited has so great a radiocarbon age, the safest way of using the age information for determining rate of deposition is probably by taking the lapsed time for accumulation as the difference between the radiocarbon ages at the bottoms and tops of the cores.

The third problem is the question of uniformity of rate of deposition throughout the length of cores. A simple way of determining this is by measuring the ages at several depths and learning how closely they correspond to a straight-line function of time against depth. The most complete data for this problem come from Santa Barbara Basin where eight ages are available, distributed between organic carbon and calcium carbonate source materials. The data (Fig. 206) show reasonably good straight-line relationships for both organic carbon and carbonate to a depth of about 3 meters. Below that depth the sediment

appears to have been deposited more slowly than afterward. Additional ages for each of the other basins were desirable but could not be obtained with the funds that were available.

In the outer basins, where sediments have accumulated less rapidly than in Santa Barbara Basin, there is of course a greater chance of irregularity in past rates of deposition. Numerous radiocarbon dates made for a core of deep-sea sediments in the Atlantic (Broecker, Turekian, and Heezen, 1958) revealed a decrease in rate of total sedimentation and especially of the clay fraction beginning about 11,000 years ago. This date also corresponds to a change from cold- to warm-water species of foraminifers (Ericson and Wollin, 1956b). According to studies by Bandy (in press), the foraminifer *Globigerina pachyderma* exhibits a change in coiling direction from left to right in the cores of Table 19. This change appears to have occurred about 11,000 years ago (from comparison with the radiocarbon dates). Thus the depth of change in coiling direction might be taken as a dated depth. Computation of the rates of deposition before and after 11,000 years ago based on these measurements suggests that the rate after 11,000 years ago was greater in some basins and less in others than the over-all rate based only on radiocarbon measurements at the bottoms of the cores.† Owing to the un-

---

* After this book had reached the galley proof stage, some additional carbon-14 age determinations (on organic carbon) by Rafter became available. Those that bear on the question of zero age of the sediment are:

1. Sample 6094: Dried deep-sea fish, genus *Myatophus*, obtained in trawl at 640 meters in San Pedro Basin where bottom depth is 840 meters (lat. 33°28', long. 118°17'). Carbon-14 age is Modern (probably less than 200 years).

2. Sample 6034: Santa Catalina Basin at same site as sample 4704 (Table 19); living benthos, mostly worms and echinoids. 1670 ± 150 years.

3. Sample 6034: Sediment scraped from top centimeter of large orange-peel bucket sample. 2100 ± 300 years.

4. Sample 5993: Santa Monica Basin (lat. 33°50.7', long. 119°13.6', 825 meters); sediment scraped from top centimeter of large orange-peel bucket sample. 1230 ± 150 years.

These ages suggest that the great increase in apparent age from Modern of water and nekton to between 1700 and 4200 years for surface sediments is somehow produced during the growth of benthonic animals or shortly afterward.

---

† Two additional carbon-14 ages from intermediate depths in cores became available after the book had reached galley proof stage. These are:

1. Sample 4671: 89 to 102 cm. 15,200 ± 500 years.

2. Sample 4704: 280 to 292 cm. 15,600 ± 600 years.

After correction for the 2800-year zero age at the sediment surface, sample 4671 is 12,400 years, unaccountably far different from the 4100 years interpolated from data of Table 19. The age (corrected by 1800 years) for sample 4704 is 13,800 years, a smaller departure from the 10,800 years interpolated from data of Table 19. Both samples were selected to determine whether a change from right-hand to left-hand coiling direction of *Globigerina pachyderma* corresponds to a date 11,000 years ago. Differences of measured ages from those inferred from straight interpolation and from foraminiferal counts indicate that still more age measurements are needed for a complete understanding of rates of deposition of sediments in the basins.

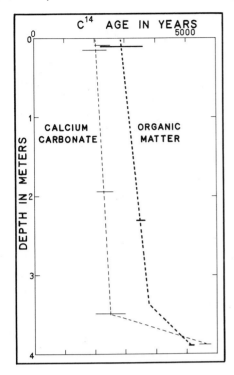

Figure 206. Radiocarbon ages at several depths in sediments of Santa Barbara Basin. Most ages were determined by T. A. Rafter (Table 19) with depths corrected for turbidity current silts. Curve for carbonate includes three dates measured by Magnolia Petroleum Company on simple gravity cores. Note the uniformity of rate of deposition for the top 3 meters. No correction was made for effects of compaction.

certainty introduced by use of both foraminiferal and radiocarbon dating, however, the following discussion on rates of deposition will be based only on radiocarbon measurements.

Computation

Compaction of the normal basin muds at depth and their interruption by occasional rapidly deposited sand layers introduced minor complications in the computations of rate of deposition. The object was to determine the total weight of all normally deposited (grain by grain) muds in a 1 sq cm column between the sediment surface and the depth of the bottommost radiocarbon date. Use of weight per unit area (mg/sq cm/yr) avoids the uncertainties of compaction inherent in the use of thickness of annual layer as an expression of rate of deposition.

Examination of the field descriptions and of grain-size analyses permitted recognition of the turbidity current sands and silts and their rejection from the following computations. The remaining sediments exhibit a downward decrease of water content and, by inspection of the curve of water content versus depth, the average percentage water content was determined for sections of core ranging from 10 to 75 cm long. After applying a 0.25 per cent correction for sea salts left in the sediment during drying at 110°C, the percentage volume of solid grains in each core section was computed, using an average measured grain density of 2.65. These figures are readily converted to absolute volumes in 1 sq cm columns of the same length as each core section. By totaling the volumes of all sections between the sediment-water interface and the depth of the deepest radiocarbon age determination, the total volume of sediment was obtained. When this was converted to total weight of solid grains in a 1 sq cm column and divided by the difference between the deepest radiocarbon age and the extrapolated age at the surface, the weight of solid grains deposited on each square centimeter per year was found.

The main constituents of the total sediment are detrital grains, calcium carbonate, and organic matter. Composite values of calcium carbonate and surface values for organic matter were measured for the same cores used for age determinations (Table 19), and these percentages multiplied by the weight of total sediment deposited each year yielded the annual weight per unit area of calcium carbonate and of organic matter. The remainder is the weight of normal detrital sediments. It will be remembered that sand layers were omitted from the computations; these were then reintroduced and their average rate of accumulation computed according to the relative weights of total normal sediment and of sandy layers. The over-all average weight of sediment deposited each year is the total for all normal sediment and all turbidity current deposits. The results, given in Table 20, are supplemented by figures for green porphyrin pigments and hydrocarbons measured mostly on other samples in the same basins (Table 14).

Results

The rate of deposition for total sediment varies throughout the region by a factor of 34, from 123 mg/sq cm/yr in Santa Monica Basin to 3.6 on the deep-sea floor (Table 20). The rate for the latter is slightly more than the 2.8 mg/sq cm/yr computed for the same eight Atlantic Ocean cores mentioned earlier, and the difference is reasonable in view of the differences in distance from sources of supply for the two areas. An estimate of 0.073 mg/sq cm/yr by Revelle, Bramlette, Arrhenius, and Goldberg (1955)

for the nonbiogenous component of deep-sea sediments in the central Pacific Ocean is far lower and is also lower than other general oceanic estimates made by Kuenen (1950, p. 384). Rates of accumulation for calcium carbonate vary by a factor of 45, from 0.2 to 8.9 mg/sq cm/yr, but if the deep-sea floor is excluded, calcium carbonate varies by a factor of only 8. Organic matter is deposited at rates of between 0.1 and 4.9 mg/sq cm/yr, a factor of 50. About one-third of the organic matter is regenerated before burial to a depth of 3 meters.

Plotted in map form (Fig. 207), the rates of deposition of the various components of the basin sediments given in Table 20 form interesting patterns. Both normal detrital and total sediments (chiefly normal detrital and turbidity current deposits in nearshore cores, plus some calcium carbonate and organic matter) are deposited fastest in the nearshore basins and formerly in those

Table 20
ABSOLUTE RATE OF DEPOSITION OF SEDIMENTS
(mg/sq cm/year)

Basin	Core	CaCO$_3$	Organic Matter[1]	Normal Detrital	Total Normal	Turbidity Current	Pheo-phytin[1] X 10^3	Hydro-carbon X 10^3	Over-all Total
Santa Barbara	4701	8.9	4.9	71.2	85.0	5.0	8.75	20.40	90.0
Santa Monica	4647	4.3	4.9	67.0	76.2	47.0	3.58	11.40	123.2
San Pedro	4679	2.7	1.7	22.0	26.4	8.8	–	–	35.2
	4690	4.1	3.9	44.5	52.5	0.4	2.10	–	52.9
San Diego	4667	1.3	0.9	10.4	12.6	0.0	0.29	2.52	12.6
Santa Cruz	4700	3.1	2.2	23.2	28.5	3.5	0.80	5.14	32.0
Santa Catalina	4703	4.8	2.3	19.5	26.6	1.3	0.67	1.60	27.9
	4704	1.8	1.3	11.0	14.1	1.4	–	–	15.5
San Clemente	4670	3.0	1.4	19.1	23.5	0.1	0.12	1.01	23.6
	4672	1.4	0.7	13.7	15.8	1.6	–	–	17.4
San Nicolas	4693	2.8	1.1	8.6	12.5	0.6	0.24	–	13.1
East Cortes	4671	3.4	1.0	10.6	15.0	0.0	0.12	–	15.0
No Name	4673	1.3	0.4	6.8	8.5	0.0	0.04	–	8.5
Tanner	4696	3.1	1.0	5.4	9.5	1.7	0.37	0.93	11.2
West Cortes	4674	2.8	0.6	6.0	9.4	0.3	0.08	–	9.7
Long	4699	5.7	0.9	13.0	19.6	0.0	0.08	1.06	19.6
Continental slope	4697	4.9	0.8	7.3	13.0	0.0	0.12	–	13.0
Deep-sea floor	4698	0.2	0.1	3.3	3.6	0.0	0.01	–	3.6
Top of basin slope	2981	1.1	0.1	7.5	8.7	0.0	0.05	–	8.7
Ventura Basin		6.5	5.1	121.1	132.7	37.5	–	–	170.2
Los Angeles Basin		2.6	3.2	47.7	53.5	53.5	–	–	107.0

[1] Data for organic matter and pheophytin is for surface of sediments; all other parameters are for sediments at depth.

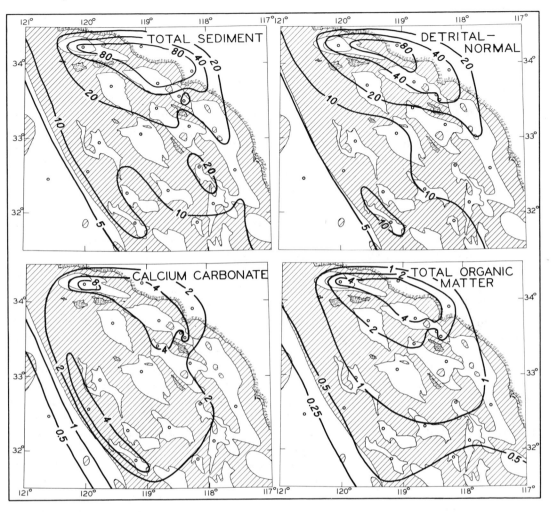

Figure 207. Rates of deposition in mg/sq cm/yr of the major constituents in basin sediments. The rates are based on radiocarbon ages of cores at localities indicated by circles, except for Los Angeles and Ventura Basins on land where the rates are based on the thickness of all post-Miocene strata. Contours have been drawn independently of basin boundaries but of course refer only to the basin, continental slope, and deep-sea sediments. Total sediment includes normal detrital grains, turbidity current deposits, calcium carbonate, and organic matter at the surface.

basins now on land because of their nearness to the chief source of sediments—the Transverse Ranges (Santa Ynez, Santa Monica, San Gabriel, and San Bernardino Mountains). At greater distances from shore the rate for normal detrital and for total sediment diminishes, except for minor erratic variations. Calcium carbonate is also being deposited most rapidly in nearshore basins, probably partly because of inclusion of reworked calcium carbonate from shelf areas and because of greater productivity of surface waters near Santa Barbara

Basin. On the deep-sea floor the rate of deposition of calcium carbonate, or rather the rate of its accumulation, is low because of solution in the corrosive deep oceanic waters before it can become safely buried. Organic matter is being deposited much faster in the nearshore basins of rapid burial than in offshore basins and on the deep-sea floor where it becomes oxidized before burial. Again high productivity near Santa Barbara Basin is probably partly responsible for high values there.

The lapsed time for deposition of the

column of sediment in Core 4701 in Santa Barbara Basin to a depth of 412 cm is 2250 years according to the radiocarbon analyses. The thin laminae present throughout the core counted and estimated where necessary by Polski (1957) total about 2510. Since the radiocarbon time span of deposition differs by only about 10 per cent from the count, the laminae should probably be considered annual, a kind of varve. The dark member of each varve consists of detrital clay and silt deposited after the winter rains, and the light-colored member consists mostly of diatoms deposited probably during the subsequent spring period of abundant plankton in surface waters (Fig. 131). More exact counts and measurements of thicknesses of varves will be made in future cores taken specifically for that purpose, in an effort to learn whether variations in the varves correspond with variations in past rainfall and tree rings.

Since the rates of accumulation of organic materials and calcium carbonate are controlled partly by the rate of deposition of inorganic detrital sediments, it is reasonable to expect some similarity in rates of accumulation for all the materials. Reference to Figure 208 does reveal a striking parallelism of the curves for rates of deposition for normal detrital sediments, organic matter, porphyrin pigments, and hydrocarbons. All these materials except detrital sediments are highly susceptible to oxidation where they are not protected by burial soon after reaching the bottom. The curve for calcium carbonate is similar to the others only near the deep-sea floor, which also is the only area where calcium carbonate is known to be subject to much dissolution (excepting of course shelves and bank tops). In the grouped basins the rates of accumulation of calcium carbonate vary by a factor of less than 2, perhaps supporting other lines of reasoning that it undergoes little solution there. Considerable differences exist in the curves for rate of accumulation of organic matter in basin sediments (Fig. 208) and for its percentage in the sediments (Fig. 203). However, the two sets of curves for green porphyrin pigments and for hydrocarbons are very similar.

A question of considerable geochemical interest is that of just how much of each of the various components of the sediments is lost to the bottom each year throughout the entire region. Data for the basins are the most complete (Tables 5 and 19); measured rates of deposition on basin slopes, the continental slope, and the deep-sea floor are available for only a single core in each environment. The core for the continental slope, if used directly, would yield a rate probably too great to be typical, owing to its position in a broad sag near the top of the slope. Similarly, the only core for a basin slope is in an area close to the mainland where the rate of deposition is probably faster than elsewhere. The rate on shelves and bank tops has not been adequately determined, but in many places rock is exposed, showing that the rate of accumulation is negligible at these places and probably very low at most other places. After all known factors were considered, estimates of average rates for total sediment were taken as follows: shelves and bank tops, 2.0 mg/sq cm/yr; basin floors, 42.0; basin slopes, 7.0; continental slope, 5.0; and deep-sea floor, 3.6. By taking into consideration the data on sediment composition (Tables 12, 14, and 19) and areas (Tables 1 and 5), figures for annual losses to the bottom for all five kinds of environment were computed as summarized in Table 21. Although this is not as accurate as desired, particularly for the important and large area of the basin slopes and other fairly flat nonbasin areas, it is the best that is obtainable with existing data.

It will be noted that the total of 10 million tons deposited annually (Table 21) differs by a factor of only 2 from the figure obtained from the supply of sediments by streams: 5 million tons of sand, plus about three times this weight of silt and clay, yielding a total supply of about 20 million tons per year. It is surprising that the figures should be so close in view of the uncertainties in basic data for each. In addition, an unknown percentage of the calcium carbonate was deposited from supplies brought into the region by ocean currents. As can be noted from Table 21, the regional

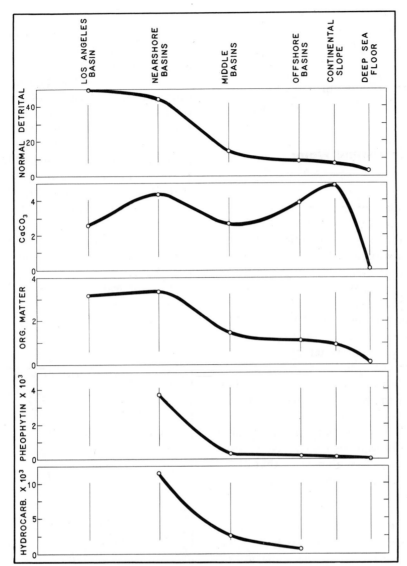

Figure 208. Curves showing rates of accumulation of the various components of basin, continental slope, and deep-sea floor sediments. The same grouping of basins is used here as in Figure 203. Note the similarities and differences between curves for absolute rate of deposition and for the percentage compositions given in Figure 203. Values for organic matter are at surface of sediment.

Table 21

ESTIMATES OF ANNUAL LOSSES TO BOTTOM IN AREA OF CHART I
(10^3 tons)

	Total Sediment	Calcium Carbonate	Organic Matter Surface	Depth	Pheophytin Surface	Hydro-carbon
Shelves and bank tops	290	95	2	1	0.015	0.045
Basin floors	5,600	480	290	190	0.220	0.690
Basin slopes	3,500	660	100	65	0.031	0.100
Continental slope	250	75	7	5	0.012	0.040
Deep-sea floor	450	17	9	7	0.001	0.003
Total	10,090	1327	408	268	0.279	0.878

percentage composition of all sediments deposited annually is as follows:

Detrital	84.2 per cent
Calcium carbonate	13.2
Organic matter (at depth)	2.6
Total	100.0 per cent

Interstitial Water

Percentage

Usually water content is expressed as percentage dry weight of sediment, paralleling the expression of concentration of other chemical constituents. Values in excess of 100 per cent are common, so for some purposes water content may be preferred in terms of percentage of wet weight of sediment. Conversions are simple: $W = 100D/(100 + D)$, or $D = 100W/(100 - W)$, where W is per cent water by wet weight and D is percent water by dry weight.

The simplest and most accurate method of measuring the water content of fresh sediment samples is to find the weight loss on drying to $110°C$. An alternate method that can be used for samples which have become partially dried before analysis is that of extracting the chloride ion with hot distilled water and titrating it with silver nitrate. Tests of this method made on five fresh cores showed that the chlorinity of the interstitial water averaged 19.3‰ (Emery and Rittenberg, 1952), nearly the same as the chlorinity of the overlying basin water, 19.1‰. Evidently, changes in the chloride content of interstitial water are absent or minor during diagenesis.

The top 5 to 20 mm of most cores of fine-grained sediments exhibits a thin soupy character. This material flows so readily that it sometimes is referred to as the mobile layer. Its mobility makes proper sampling difficult, and frequently it is entirely lost from core samples. The water content in samples of the top 5 cm from twelve typical cores ranged between 180 and 670, with a mean of 230 per cent by dry weight. Thus water at the mean value has a weight more than twice that of the sediment grains and a volume about six times as great.

At depth the water content decreases markedly just below the surface and more gradually farther down. Little similarity, however, is exhibited by water-depth curves for sediments of different areas (Fig. 209). For simplicity the curves of this figure omit the irregularities produced by sand layers, which consistently have less water than overlying and underlying clays and silts, as illustrated by Figures 192 and 224, as well as by many others presented by Emery and Rittenberg (1952) and Orr, Emery, and Grady (1958). Quite clearly, water content is inversely related to grain size. However, comparison of the curves given in Figure 209 shows that at a depth of 3 meters, well below the surface region of rapid change, the water content must also be controlled by the rate of deposition, varying directly with it. For example, even though

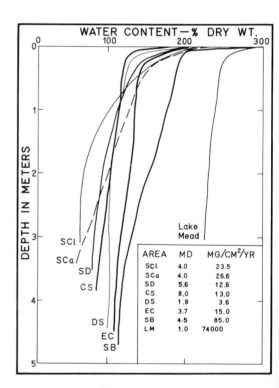

Figure 209. Typical curves of water content versus depth in basin sediments. For comparison a curve from the very rapidly deposited sediment of Lake Mead near Hoover Dam is included (Gould, 1954). Note the sharp decrease of water content near the sediment surface and the fact that the water content at depth is a function of grain size, rate of deposition, and probably of other factors.

the core from Santa Barbara Basin is slightly coarser than those from San Clemente and Santa Catalina Basins, its water content is far greater. Even more extreme is the very high water content of a core from Lake Mead near Hoover Dam (Gould, 1953; 1954, Fig. 95), which is very fine-grained and was deposited much faster than were any of the marine cores. Rate of deposition is a reasonable factor if time is required for the grains to become reoriented and deformed before water can be forced out during compaction. An empirical formula relating water content, grain size, and rate of deposition could not be developed, possibly because of errors in basic data, but more likely because of the presence of other complicating factors such as extent of burrowing activity by animals and amount and kind of clay minerals.

An approximate relationship between porosity and median diameter (Fig. 210) shows the range of values that have been determined for several hundred samples. Data for sediments coarser than 30 microns are from measurements on the shelf off San Diego (Hamilton, Shumway, Menard, and Shipek, 1956); those for finer sediments are from basin cores below the depth of marked decrease of water content—at 3 meters. Since the water content of sandy sediments does not decrease much with depth, data from surface samples of them are satisfactory. Experimental data for both coarse- and fine-grained sediment reported by Trask (1932, p. 82) fall within the range depicted on Figure 210. It is well known that simulated sediments composed of similarly packed spheres of uniform size have identical porosities, regardless of what that size is. However, actual sediment grains are not spherical, nor are they so well sorted as to be all of a single size. The presence of flat grains tends to increase the porosity, and the presence of small grains between large ones tends to reduce the porosity. In addition, as the grains become smaller, their total surface area increases markedly, so that for small grains the surface film of water may comprise a far larger volume than that in the main interstices. Because clayey sediments have a large surface area, poor size sorting, and a predominance of flat flakes, their water content (and porosity) greatly exceeds that of sands.

Effects on Physical Properties

Porosity and bulk density are parameters of the sediment that are closely related to the water content, from which they may easily be computed if the grain specific gravity is known. Values of porosity and bulk density based on the average of several score

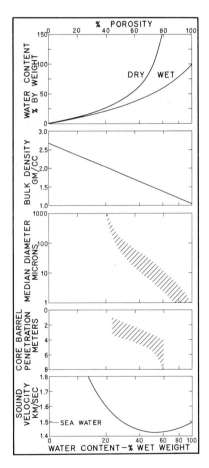

Figure 210. Dependence of several physical properties of sediments on porosity. The relationship of porosity to water content and bulk density was computed from an average measured grain specific gravity of 2.65. Data on porosity versus median diameter are from measurements of shelf sands by Hamilton, Shumway, Menard, and Shipek (1956) and from many basin cores collected by the University of Southern California. Penetration of core barrels relative to porosity is from Emery and Dietz (1941) plus many later measurements. Sound velocities are from Hamilton (1956).

measurements of specific gravity, 2.65, are presented by the curves of Figure 210.

Even though a core sample may contain more than 100 per cent water by dry weight (or a porosity greater than 72 per cent), a section of silt-clay core 10 cm in diameter and 30 cm long may be stiff enough to be held at one end in a horizontal position for several minutes without collapsing. Although water may easily be extracted from the top of a core by suction through a microfilter or by twisting it in a cloth, water is much more difficult to extract from the stiffer sections of a core at depth.

The resistance to bulk deformation is a function of water content and can be expressed in at least two ways, plasticity and shear strength, both of which are influenced by thixotropy. The plasticity of sediment is measured in terms of Atterberg limits (Terzaghi and Peck, 1948, pp. 32–33). The liquid limit is the water content (percentage dry weight) at which two sections of a standard pat of sediment flow to barely touch each other when subjected to sharp blows under standard conditions. The plastic limit is the lowest water content at which the sediment can be rolled into 3-mm diameter threads

without crumbling. A sediment is considered to be liquid, plastic, or semisolid according to whether its water content is greater than the liquid limit, between the liquid and plastic limits, or less than the plastic limit, respectively. Measurement of Atterberg limits on several cores (Emery and Rittenberg, 1952; Emery and Terry, 1956) showed that the limits decrease with depth in cores, but the decrease for the plastic limit is commonly less than that for the liquid limit and the decrease for the liquid limit in turn is less than that for the actual water content (Fig. 211). Thus the basin sediment usually must be classed as liquid at the top, plastic at depth, and semisolid at greater depths than is reached by ordinary cores. Certainly the sediments are semisolid when compacted to shale. Atterberg limits for the basin cores are higher than those obtained by White (1949) for pure illite and kaolinite but lower than his values for montmorillonite, conforming with the known mixed clay mineralogy of the basin sediments.

Even though the tops of cores are liquid, as defined by Atterberg limits, in nature they may not be mobile until after they become disturbed. Lack of mobility is exhibited by

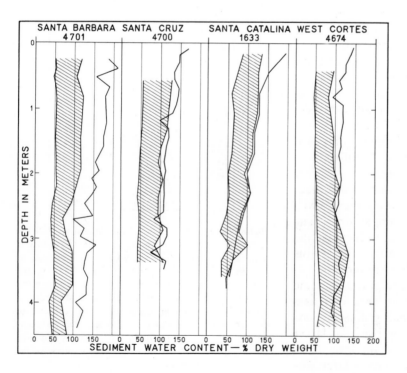

Figure 211. Atterberg limits measured on cores from several basins as compared with actual water contents of the same cores. Left side of crosshatched area is plastic limit; right side is liquid limit; separate line is actual water content.

the fact that much sediments mantle slopes at least as steep as 20°. Evidently grain-by-grain accumulation can occur on slopes until some disturbance converts the mass into a fluid-like suspension that must then flow downslope, incorporating more and more similar sediment as it moves along and perhaps finally developing into a turbidity current. The property of remaining stiff until jarred is called thixotropy. In oil well drilling muds thixotropy is promoted by addition of montmorillonite clays which have this gel-like property to a high degree; and the basin muds consist of about one-third montmorillonite. The property is difficult to measure precisely for muds other than watery suspensions, but a wire cutting method devised by W. R. Heiner and described by Emery and Rittenberg (1952) yielded semi-quantitative results. A weighted 0.5-mm diameter wire was able to cut the same cross-sectional area of sediment at the top of a core from San Nicolas Basin nearly 400 times as fast after the sample was kneaded as before. For a section near the bottom of the core, 3 meters, the rate after kneading was about 200 times as great as before. After 24 hours the thixotropic strength had largely returned.

Shear strength of sediments can be measured by devices such as shear boxes (Terzaghi and Peck, 1948, p. 79), torsion plummets (Romanovsky, 1948), or torsion vanes (Moore, 1956). Each of these devices, and especially the latter two, is capable of measuring the shear strength of samples before and after kneading so as to show the effects of thixotropy. The results of such shear tests provide direct data for computing the angles of rest of sediments and the depths to which objects can sink in sediments. Another method of obtaining shear strength is that of measuring directly the depth to which coring devices penetrate different kinds of sediment. A summary of coring data by Emery and Dietz (1941), supplemented by more recent measurements, shows that a corer which weighs 270 kg in water when dropped into the bottom at a speed of about 5 meters/sec penetrates as far as 8 meters in muds as porous as those of Santa Barbara

Basin but only about 1 meter in sands of the shelves (Fig. 210).

The velocity of sound in sediments is also controlled by the percentage content of water. As pointed out by Hamilton (1956) and others, although the velocity of sound is greater in solid mineral grains than in water, a sediment containing more than about 40 per cent by dry weight (54 per cent porosity) has a sound velocity lower than either water or mineral grains alone (Fig. 210). This dip in the porosity-velocity curve comes about because the velocity varies inversely with the square root of the product of bulk density and compressibility of the mixture, and the bulk density of a mixture increases faster than the compressibility decreases within the porosity range between 100 and about 75 per cent. Knowledge of the sound velocity in sediments is necessary for converting the data on subbottom reflections obtained by strong echo sounders from lapsed time to sediment thickness.

Permeability and Natural Compaction

Permeability of granular materials is defined as $K = QL\mu/TAH$, where K is permeability in darcys, Q is the quantity of water of viscosity μ passed in time T through a sample of length L and cross-sectional area A with a hydrostatic head of H atmospheres, all dimensions being in cgs units. Samples of sediments of nearly uniform grain size from various depths in a core from Santa Cruz Basin were introduced into the bottom 5 cm of a 120-cm-long glass tube which was then filled with sea water and stood on end. As described more fully by Emery and Rittenberg (1952), the resulting measurements showed that the permeability ranged between 6×10^{-3} and 30×10^{-3} darcy (Fig. 212).

Under steady-state conditions the curve of water content versus depth should be the same today as it was a thousand years ago or will be a thousand years hence. The rate of deposition of sediments is the same from year to year, and the characteristics of the sediment must also be the same. Such an assumption of steady state is probably justi-

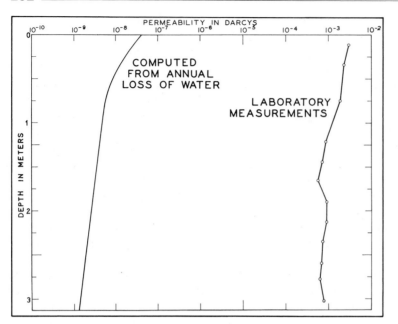

Figure 212. Measured permeability of Core 1941 from Santa Cruz Basin (right) as compared with "permeability" computed from decrease of water content with depth in typical core (Fig. 213). From Emery and Rittenberg (1952, Fig. 23).

fied for the basins containing sediments that are very uniform with depth, except for occasional abnormally coarse layers deposited by turbidity currents. Santa Barbara Basin is one of the best examples. The typical decrease in water content with depth of burial in basin sediments (Fig. 213B and C) must mean that each annual layer becomes more deeply buried it is progressively thinned; the same volume of sediment grains is present in a given area of each layer, but the volume of water in each layer decreases with depth. According to Table 20, normal sediment in Santa Barbara Basin is deposited at a rate of 85 mg/sq cm/yr. At a water content of 67 per cent by wet weight (200 per cent by dry weight, or 82.5 per cent porosity), a year's deposit has an original thickness of 0.200 cm. At depth the layer becomes thinned in accordance with the decrease of porosity at depth, so that at a depth of 500 cm the thickness is $0.200 \times (100 - 82.5)/(100 - 73.0) = 0.130$ cm thick (Fig. 213D). Knowing the present thickness of annual layers and their porosity, we can easily compute the volume of water in layers at any depth; it decreases markedly—from 0.168 ml at the surface to 0.095 ml at a depth of 500 cm (Fig. 213E). Obviously, this decrease means that water has been lost upward, as

this is the shortest escape route, but the difference between 0.168 and 0.195 ml represents only a net decrease of water content because, while the annual layer now at 500-cm depth was losing its original water upward by compaction, other still deeper layers were also losing some of their water upward to overlying layers. The annual loss for a layer at any depth is essentially the slope of Figure 213E at that depth, and it is expressed in Figure 213F. Clearly, the greatest annual loss should occur in that part of the core having the greatest decrease in water content with depth.

As shown by Emery and Rittenberg (1952), if permeability limits compaction we may compute the permeability for annual layers at any depth using the foregoing data, where the quantity of water annually discharged Q is given by Figure 213F, length of column L is given by Figure 213D, viscosity μ for the temperature and salinity is 1.61 centipoise, time T is the number of seconds in a year, area A is 1 sq cm, and the pressure difference H is the weight of grains in a layer corrected for their buoyancy in water and expressed in atmospheres— 5.8×10^{-5}. The permeability computed in this way varies between 5×10^{-10} and 500×10^{-10} (Figs. 212, 213G). Since this

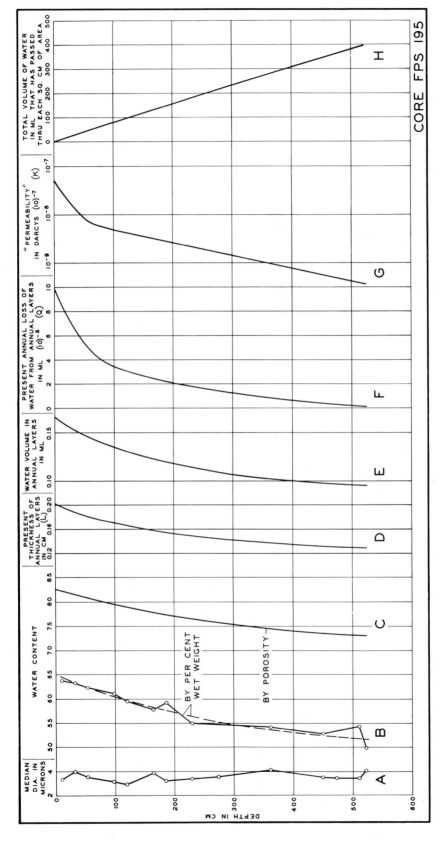

Figure 213. Compaction of sediments as computed from a core in Santa Barbara Basin for which the rate of deposition of normal sediments is assumed to be 85 mg/sq cm/yr. From Emery and Rittenberg (1952, Fig. 21).

value is about five orders of magnitude smaller than the direct measurements of permeability, it is obvious that permeability does not limit the expulsion of water during compaction and that compaction must instead be limited by the characteristics of the solid phase of the sediment. The most reasonable of these characteristics is the resistance of the grains toward repacking and deformation, both of which are controlled by pressure transmitted from grain to grain and thus by weight of overburden or depth of burial.

Under steady-state conditions last year's layer originally had the same water content as this year's layer, and next year it will have the same content as now held by the layer deposited the year before last. Thus, every year each layer discharges its water to the overlying layer and receives the water that was held by the layer under it. If the sediment at some depth were compacted to zero water content, the same water would move endlessly upward in the sediment column, and the total amount of water which passed through any given annual layer would equal the total volume of water above that layer and to the left of the porosity-depth curve (Fig. 213C). This volume is shown for all depths by Figure 213H, from which we can see that during the time since the layer now at 500-cm depth was deposited, about 3500 years ago, a total of 385 ml of water has passed through every square centimeter of its area. Using an extension of the porosity-depth curve to a depth of 1500 meters, we learn that about 32 liters of water would have passed through each square centimeter of a layer deposited about 3,800,000 years ago. It is not unreasonable to suppose that such a vast flushing of water through the sediment may have caused some chemical alteration of it.

From this view of the process of compaction we can recognize that if the sediments at some great depth have a zero water content, there need be no escape of water from the surface and no entrance of new water. In reality, however, even at great depth the sediment retains some water (in the Los Angeles Basin, about 5 per cent by volume).

As a result of this loss from the bottom of the steady-state curve of water content versus depth there must be a continuous addition of some new water at the top of the sediment column. The annual amount of new water could be as small as the amount of water at final compaction contained in an annual layer, about 0.0017 ml. To trace a given average molecule of interstitial water through space, we can visualize it as rising upward with respect to sediment layers, owing to its expulsion from the layers by compaction, but as slowly sinking with respect to the rising sediment surface. In other words, none of the interstitial water need ever escape into the overlying water. In reality, however, some of the water does escape—through the stirring activities of burrowing organisms, through channeling, through following along sandy, more permeable, layers that crop out. In Santa Barbara Basin neither burrowing organisms nor sandy layers nor channels have been discovered in cores. According to Kullenberg (1952) the coefficient of diffusion of salts in sediments of the Baltic Sea is about 20 per cent of that in the overlying water, about 2×10^{-6} sq cm/sec. Although the coefficient of diffusion for interstitial water is not known for the basin sediments, the existence of differences in concentration of some salts between interstitial water and overlying water must cause movement of the salts across the sediment-water interface by diffusion, even if there is no bodily movement of the water itself.

pH and Eh

The symbol pH stands for the negative logarithm to the base 10 of the hydrogen ion concentration in moles per liter, being 0 to 7 for acids and 7 to 14 for bases. The oxidation-reduction potential Eh is a measure of the tendency of the system to accept or give up electrons relative to the standard hydrogen electrode, being either positive or negative. Both pH and Eh were measured in sediments (usually slurried with freshly boiled distilled water) by means of a Beckman pH meter. For pH a calomel and a glass electrode are used, and for *Eh* a calomel and a platinum electrode. Details of the measurements are given by Emery and Rittenberg (1952).

Values of *p*H in the water column generally decrease from about 8.3 at the surface to 7.7 at some depth between 400 and 1000 meters, below which it again rises to about 7.8 (Rittenberg, Emery, and Orr, 1955). Bottom water collected just above the cores averages 7.5, indicative of a *p*H minimum just above the sediment-water interface. Usually the *p*H of the topmost layer of sediment is slightly greater than that of the immediately overlying water, averaging 7.6. At depth in the sediment the *p*H typically rises, in many cores to values of 8.5, although in others it is lower or irregular with some obvious dependence on grain size (Fig. 192).

Values of *Eh* in the water column are invariably positive with values mostly between +200 and +300 millivolts. The surface of the sediments of all except parts of two basins (Santa Barbara and Tanner) is also characterized by positive values. At depth the *Eh* decreases sharply or gradually to zero values reached at depths averaging about 2 meters except in San Pedro and Santa Monica Basins and the deep-sea floor, where, except for rare instances in the first two areas mentioned, the *Eh* is never negative within the depths reached by coring. Below the depth of zero *Eh* values become as low as −100 mv and even −300 mv.

The variations of *p*H and *Eh* in the sediments are attributed to diagenetic changes produced by both biogenic and abiogenic agents. For example, low *p*H's, to 7.5, can be produced by carbon dioxide liberated during oxidation of organic matter, particularly of carbohydrates and fats. Oxidation of protenaceous and fatty organic matter forms ammonia and hydrogen sulfide, both of which tend to raise the *p*H, the latter because a strong acid (sulfate ion) is changed into a weak one. If the ammonia and hydrogen sulfide work their ways to near the sediment-water interface, they may be further oxidized to nitrate and sulfate, thus lowering the *p*H in that area. Because of the complexity of the question of which prod-

ucts are formed first in the sediment and of how they become altered, it is useless to speculate on the cause of changes of *p*H at depth at the present low state of factual knowledge.

The decrease of *Eh* at depth in the sediments is also a very complicated problem. Probably the chief cause of the decrease is the oxidation of organic matter. The easiest available oxidizing agent is the free oxygen dissolved in the interstitial water, but as soon as this has been used up the chief remaining source is oxygen in sulfate ions. This is used by sulfate-reducing bacteria whose activity is revealed by a decrease in the ratio of sulfate ion to chloride ion (Fig. 192), beginning at the same depth as the first appearance of hydrogen sulfide and of negative values of *Eh*. Because *Eh* depends on the ratios of the concentrations of the oxidized and reduced forms of many chemical systems in the sediment, the state of equilibrium, temperature, *p*H, and other factors (ZoBell, 1946*a*), little use can be made of absolute measured values; however, the depth of zero *Eh* is so closely identified with the first appearance of hydrogen sulfide that it can safely be taken as an indicator of the replacement by hydrogen sulfide of dissolved oxygen in the interstitial water, and thus of the change from aerobic to anaerobic conditions, even though it is impractical to determine oxygen on water squeezed from cores. Measurements of *Eh* on nearly 400 samples from 30 cores show that more than 90 per cent of the samples have either a positive *Eh* with no hydrogen sulfide or a negative *Eh* with hydrogen sulfide (Fig. 214). Most of

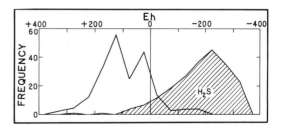

Figure 214. Frequency distribution of *Eh* measurements in 30 cores. Note the grouping into two modal ranges, 0 to +300 and −100 to −300 mv and the close dependence of hydrogen sulfide on negative *Eh*.

the anomalous samples are immediately above or below the depth where hydrogen sulfide first appears in the cores.

Data to be presented in later sections indicate that both Santa Barbara and Tanner Basins contain higher percentages of easily oxidized components of organic matter than do other basins. Partial oxidation of these materials has evidently exhausted dissolved oxygen in interstitial waters and, because of the absence of burrowing animals in at least Santa Barbara Basin, new supplies of oxygen are not made available. In other basins the slow rate of accumulation of organic matter relative to inorganic sediments and the presence of burrowing animals result in more complete loss of the easily oxidized components of organic matter, without exhausting the supply of dissolved oxygen in interstitial water until enough time has passed that the organic matter is buried to a depth of several meters. Lack of dissolved oxygen in interstitial water, or negative _Eh_ there, represents a hostile environment for burrowing and possibly for small surface-living animals and for aerobic bacteria. Thus a mutual interrelationship exists between animals and oxygen content such that as long as the ox-

ygen content permits burrowing animals to live, their stirring activities increase the oxygen content and this oxygen plus the ingestion of sediment markedly reduce the organic content of the sediments. Probably a decrease of oxygen to a level just below the threshold value for burrowing animals would produce an immediate catastrophic decrease in oxygen content to zero values that would cause difficulty in repopulating the bottom.

A plot of _p_H against _Eh_ for 23 well-distributed basin cores (Fig. 215) shows that the points occupy a rather restricted area with a general tendency at depth for _p_H to increase and _Eh_ to become more negative. In contrast, values from marshes, chiefly in Newport Bay (Fowler, 1957; Stevenson and Emery, 1958), are more widely scattered but are usually of lower _p_H than the basin sediments. There is some slight overlap with values for sea water, which generally is of more positive _Eh_ than are the sediments. Comparison with similar plots and other data of Krumbein and Garrels (1952) shows several fields of apparent chemical stability in the basin sediments. For example, the stable forms of iron should be

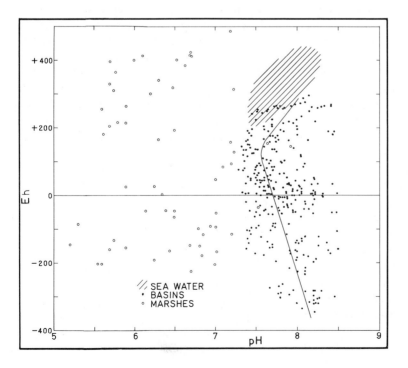

Figure 215. Interdependence of _p_H and _Eh_ in basin (dots) and marsh (circles) sediments and in the overlying sea water.

hematite near the sediment surface, siderite at intermediate depth, and pyrite nearer the bottoms of many cores. Organic matter should be stable at all negative *Eh*'s. In reality, however, conditions are not so simple as suggested by the geological fence diagrams, because of the presence of microenvironments so small as to defy precise measurements with existing equipment and because of the activity of biogenic processes that cause organic matter, for example, to continue to break down in spite of its presence in an environment of negative *Eh*.

A good example of the importance of microenvironments is given by pyrite. In the tops of cores above the level of zero *Eh* pyrite forms internal casts of foraminiferans, diatoms, and radiolarians. These casts are highly porous and very fragile. Evidently, local spots of negative *Eh* produced by decomposing protoplasm of these organisms are more or less insulated from the positive *Eh* of the matrix. Issatchenko (1929) also noted the development of minute crystals of pyrite within cells of sulfate-reducing bacteria, and Le Calvez (1951) found iron sulfides forming within foraminiferal tests, some developing into muriform masses like those pictured in Figure 216. At depths below the level of zero *Eh* in the cores the pyrite forms in addition large irregular masses as though it had grown beyond the confines of shells and filled the interstices of grains as a type of cement. Both sorts of pyrite are grouped in Figure 216. A few octahedrons served to identify the material as pyrite rather than marcasite, agreeing with experiments of Allen, Crenshaw, Johnston, and Larsen (1912) which show the characteristic deposition of iron disulfide as pyrite in alkaline-to-neutral media and as marcasite in acid media.

Dissolved Nutrients

Nutrients are chemical compounds that are needed for plant growth but are sometimes present in such small concentrations in sea water that growth is limited. Chief of these are dissolved nitrate, phosphate, and silica. Although plants require much

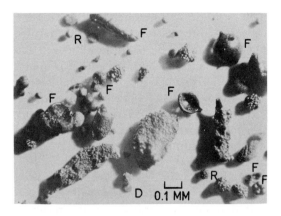

Figure 216. Grains of pyrite from zone of negative *Eh* in Core 1983 from East Cortes Basin. Present are large irregular masses and internal casts of foraminiferans F, diatoms D, and radiolarians R.

larger quantities of carbon, oxygen, and hydrogen, these elements are always so abundant that they do not limit growth. Still other elements such as zinc, iodine, and copper are also needed by organisms, but in such minute quantities that growth is not limited even though they are very minor constituents of sea water. Animals need the same building materials, but they obtain them mostly from plants and plant debris. The ultimate source of the nutrients is the land (Emery, Orr, and Rittenberg, 1955), but the plants each year use more nutrients than are newly contributed to the ocean. A balance is provided by the fact that most of the nutrients extracted from the water by plants are returned on the death of the organisms. According to Riley (1951), 90 per cent of the organic matter produced by plants is regenerated in the top 200 meters. And additional regeneration occurs at greater depth in the water column and from the bottom sediments during the period after deposition and before burial to great depth.

An examination of the distribution of nutrients in basin sediments and overlying waters was made by Rittenberg, Emery, and Orr (1955). Three basins were selected as representative of all basins: Santa Catalina because of its change from aerobic to anaerobic conditions at a depth of about 2

meters in the sediment, Santa Monica because its sediments vary from slightly aerobic
to slightly anaerobic with no hydrogen sulfide, and Santa Barbara because it is anaerobic with a strong odor of hydrogen sulfide
from the surface to the bottom of cores.

The first product of oxidation of the nitrogenous portion of organic matter, ammonia, was found in the interstitial waters
of the sediments in all three basins. It is
most abundant in Santa Barbara and least
so in Santa Catalina Basin and increases
with depth except for irregularities resulting
largely from depth changes in grain size of
the enclosing sediment (Fig. 217). Concentrations reach a maximum of 11,400 μg-

atoms/liters. The next stage of oxidation,
nitrite, is well exhibited in sediments of
Santa Catalina Basin with concentrations as
great as 6μg-atoms/liter in the aerobic zone
but none below. It was found in only the
topmost sample of the core from Santa
Monica Basin, and only doubtful traces
were noted at Santa Barbara Basin. Even
in Santa Catalina Basin nitrite is too minor
to be shown in Figure 217, probably because it is a transitory intermediate compound. The next stage of oxidation, nitrate,
is much more abundant in sediments of
Santa Catalina than in those of the other
basins, reaching a value of 240 μg-atoms/
liter at the top of the core and markedly

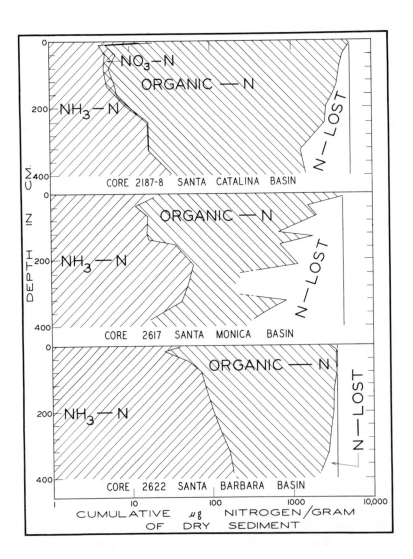

Figure 217. Depth distribution of nitrogen compounds in sediments and overlying water of three basins. Note the use of logarithmic scale of concentration. From Rittenberg, Emery, and Orr (1955, Fig. 4).

less in the anaerobic zone at depth. Nitrate was doubtfully present near the top of the core from Santa Monica Basin and was not detected at Santa Barbara Basin. More abundant by 15 to 1000 times than the total nitrogen present in all dissolved components is the nitrogen of particulate organic matter. It decreases in abundance with depth, causing the total for all nitrogen constituents also to decrease with depth.

Interpretation of this depth distribution of nitrogen components is simplified by assuming the existence of steady-state conditions throughout the period of deposition of the cores; that is, in a relatively constant environment a study of the change in a property with depth of burial is essentially the same as a study of the alteration of the property with time in an isolated mass of sediment. By this method changes produced in the sediments by bacterial activity can be traced for thousands of years, rather than for the brief periods that are possible in laboratory experiments. As soon as sediment containing organic matter is deposited, ammonia begins to form as the first stage of oxidation. Where ammonia is released into an aerobic environment such as the tops of some of the cores, it is further oxidized to nitrite and thence to nitrate by a specific group of bacteria, *Nitrobacteriacea,* obligate aerobic forms that cannot nitrify in reducing environments. Because aerobic conditions exist only at the top of the core from Santa Catalina Basin, this is the only core having appreciable dissolved nitrate. The amount of new nitrate formed here is greatly amplified by the introduction of large new supplies of oxygen by the activities of burrowing animals. These supplies total many thousand times the original supply of oxygen as shown by Emery and Rittenberg (1952), and thus the newly produced nitrate is many thousand times the original amount. Nitrate in Santa Catalina Basin persists to all depths reached, although there is only a small remnant below the depth of zero *Eh,* which is reached by a layer of sediment about 5000 years after it it first deposited. Under the reducing con-

ditions of sediment in Santa Barbara Basin nitrate is not formed, and even the nitrate present in the sea water that is originally trapped within the interstices of the sediment is soon reduced or denitrified to ammonia. Because the sediments of Santa Monica Basin are less anaerobic, the original supply of nitrate may remain for several years before it is reduced. In addition to reverting back to ammonia, nitrate may also be denitrified to molecular nitrogen by activity of some bacteria and by abiogenic reactions. This denitrification is slow and requires nitrate or nitrite as starting materials, so it can be expected only in sediments of Santa Catalina Basin or of similar basins.

The decrease with depth of the total nitrogen present in all forms means that nitrogen must have escaped from the sediment into the overlying water if steady-state conditions existed during the time of deposition of the entire length of core. In other words, the original nitrogen content of the bottommost annual layer must have been the same as that of the layer that is being deposited now. From the sediments of Santa Barbara Basin nitrogen could have escaped only in the form of ammonia, but from Santa Catalina Basin it could have escaped as ammonia, nitrite, nitrate, and molecular nitrogen. Possibly some in both basins could also have escaped as dissolved organic matter.

Typically, the basin waters contain about 40 μg-atoms/liter of nitrate and no detectable nitrite or ammonia. Near the bottom, however, nitrate may be present in greater or smaller concentrations than this, and small amounts of nitrite may also be present, as shown by Rittenberg, Emery, and Orr (1955). At the bottom of Santa Catalina Basin nitrate reaches a value of 45 μg-atoms/liter, having been augumented by supplies from the sediment by diffusion or perhaps by some bodily movement of interstitial water through channels (Fig. 218). At the bottom of Santa Monica and Santa Barbara Basins nitrate is impoverished to concentrations of only 35 and 30 μg-atoms/liter, respectively, indicating its passage from overlying water into the sediment. Reduc-

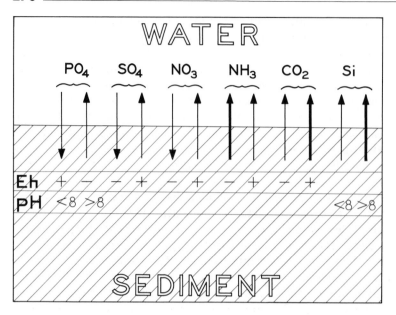

Figure 218. Diagram showing the control exerted by pH and *Eh* on the movement of certain ions across the sediment-water interface. Width of arrows indicates relative quantities for different conditions. From Emery (1958*b*, Fig. 14).

tion of nitrate by the sediment should also be reflected by a concentration of ammonia and nitrite in the bottom waters of these basins; however, surveys of these effects are incomplete.

If the decrease of total nitrogen at depth in the sediment of Santa Barbara Basin is ascribed to ammonia alone, the rate of escape of ammonia from the top 4 meters of sediment is 1.6 μg-atoms/sq cm/yr. If all is oxidized to nitrate in the basin water between bottom and sill, it would increase the nitrate content of the water 5 μg-atoms/liter in 20 years. Because the nitrate of this water is actually within 5 μg-atoms/liter of the concentrations in the water that enters at sill depth, the water of the basin must be completely replaced in less than 20 years. Ammonia from layers deeper than 4 meters in the sediment must also escape, so the turnover time of the basin water may be much shorter than 20 years. This short period of overturn is supported by the related depletion of dissolved oxygen in oxidation of organic matter in the sediment as discussed by Emery and Rittenberg (1952). About one-third of the organic carbon originally deposited in an annual layer (3.5 per cent by dry weight) is oxidized to carbon dioxide by the time it has been buried to a depth of 4 meters, about 2300 years.

At this rate of oxidation, 2.0 ml of oxygen must annually diffuse through each square centimeter of sediment from the overlying basin water. Loss of this much oxygen from the basin water corresponds to 0.13 ml/liter/yr for the whole water column between sill and bottom depth. Since the oxygen content of the basin water is within 0.1 ml/liter of that which enters, the basin water must be completely replaced at least once each year.

The cycle of phosphate in the interstitial waters is less complex than the cycle for nitrogen, because there are no intermediate forms between the phosphorus of organic matter and the orthophosphate dissolved in the water. Again, however, an examination of the amount of dissolved phosphate in interstitial water shows differences between the three basins (Fig. 219). By far the greatest concentration occurs in Santa Barbara Basin where phosphate reaches nearly 200 μg-atoms/liter in the sediment in contrast to typical values of only 3.0 to 3.5 μg-atoms/liter in the basin water. In sediments of Santa Monica Basin phosphate ranges from slightly more to slightly less concentrated than in basin water. In sediment of Santa Catalina Basin the dissolved phosphate of the aerobic zone has a concentration similar to that in Santa Monica

Basin, whereas in the anaerobic zone beneath it is similar to that in Santa Barbara Basin. Thus the concentrations of dissolved phosphate in the sediments of the three basins closely parallel the *Eh*'s. The nature of the chemical control is not known, but the parallelism of phosphate and *Eh* has been noted in other kinds of sediments (Rittenberg, Emery, and Orr, 1955). Probably *p*H also plays a role through its control of the solubility of calcium phosphate. Comparison with immediately overlying water shows some enrichment at the bottoms of all three basins, as though regenerated phosphate is diffusing or otherwise moving upward out of the sediment into the overlying waters. Precipitation must, however, be occurring at certain depths in Santa Monica Basin sediments because the concentration of phosphate at those depths is less than that of the sea water which originally occupied the interstices between the sediment grains. Variations of total phosphorus at depth are probably more related to grain size (and thus to composition of the sediment) than to solution or deposition of phosphate, because the content of phosphorus in detrital sediments far exceeds the amount present in organic matter deposited in the sediments. Unlike that for the nitrogen components, the concentration of dissolved phosphate is controlled by solubility equilibria rather than by bacterial oxidation of organic matter. Nevertheless, the uniformity with depth of the ratio of dissolved nitrogen (mostly ammonia) to dissolved phosphate (Fig. 219) shows that the rates of regeneration of phosphate and ammonia at all depths are similar.

Silica, the third nutrient, is even more concentrated in detrital sediments than in the organic matter that is deposited with the sediments. Its release, even more than that of phosphate, is a pure solubility problem. In the sediments of each basin the dissolved silica increases with depth to maximum values of 2300, 2030, and 1400 μg-atoms/liter in Santa Barbara, Santa Catalina, and Santa Monica Basins, respectively. These concentrations bear a direct relationship to *p*H: 8.20, 8.05, and 7.64, respectively; evidently the amount of dissolved silica is closely controlled by *p*H, as might be expected. Even at the tops of the cores dissolved silica is several times more concentrated in interstitial than in basin waters, which reach about 160 μg-atoms/liter. Somewhat greater values occur in the water immediately overlying the bottom (Fig. 218). A comparison with the concentration of silica in other kinds of waters (Fig. 220) shows that dissolved silica in interstitial waters of basin sediments is far more concentrated than in waters of the ocean or of fresh-water lakes. Only in some ground water, streams, and alkaline lakes does silica become so concentrated. This relationship is such as to suggest that dissolved silica can become

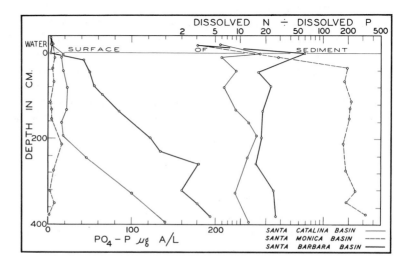

Figure 219. Depth distribution of dissolved phosphate and of nitrogen-phosphate ratio in sediments and overlying water of three basins. From Rittenberg, Emery, and Orr (1955, Fig. 5).

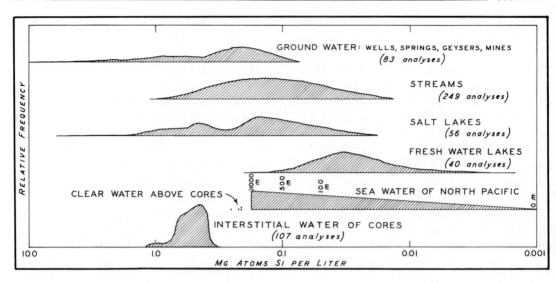

Figure 220. Concentration of dissolved silica in various kinds of waters. Note high concentrations in interstitial waters of basin sediments. From Emery and Rittenberg (1952, Fig. 29).

concentrated only where it is not rapidly removed from solution by plant growth. Possibly, therefore, it has reached saturation values in the interstitial waters of the basin sediments.

Although not a nutrient, strictly speaking, sulfur in sediments has a cycle of regeneration somewhat like those of nutrients, and so it is worthy of mention here. Sulfur is deposited in the sediments chiefly in the form of dissolved sulfate ion of interstitial water and as sulfur in the protenaceous and fatty parts of organic matter. In the aerobic zone it changes little, but at greater depths, beginning at the top of the anaerobic zone, the sulfur-reducing bacteria *Desulfovibrio* reduces it to hydrogen sulfide. Some sulfide ion reacts with iron of organic matter (Issatchenko, 1929; Le Calvez, 1951) or of minerals, depositing iron sulfides. Iron monosulfide, hydrotroilite, has not been found in the basin sediments, although it imparts the characteristic dark-gray-to-black color to marsh sediments. The control as to whether hydrotroilite or pyrite is present may be rate of deposition, whereby more iron is made available in marshes than in basin sediments to react with the hydrogen sulfide to form the monosulfide; in addi-

tion, if pyrite is formed from hydrotroilite as an intermediary, the slower rate of deposition in basins may allow complete conversion to pyrite in the time required for only a few centimeters of sediments to be deposited, whereas great depth of burial may be required in marshes before the conversion occurs.

Most of the hydrogen sulfide works its way toward the surface, probably by diffusion. When it enters the aerobic zone of sediment or the overlying water, some of the hydrogen sulfide is oxidized to molecular sulfur, which is deposited, and some is oxidized to sulfate ion. Some sulfate doubtlessly escapes to the overlying water into which it mixes. Probably precise work will show a higher sulfate-chloride ratio in the bottom water than in shallower water in response to this movement—just as is the situation for regenerated nitrate and phosphate. A sulfate-chloride ratio in deep-sea sediments off Brazil twice as high as normal (F. W. Locher *in* Ahrens, Rankama, and Runcorn, 1956, p. 206) may well be the result of such oxidation. In estuarine areas some sulfate ion also replaces carbonate in shells, converting them to gypsum, and authigenic gypsum crystals form locally.

Deposition of gypsum by replacement or crystal growth has not yet been noted in the California basin sediments, but it has not been carefully sought. Because of losses of hydrogen sulfide from the surface of sediments, we can expect to find that the total sulfur in all forms decreases with depth in the sediment in a fashion similar to that observed for total nitrogen. Some of the stages of this regeneration have been observed by Sugawara, Koyama, and Kozawa (1953, 1954) in fresh, brackish, and marine sediments of Japan. The cycle is also being studied at the University of Southern California by I. R. Kaplan, who uses isotopes of sulfur to measure the nature of the changes.

Regeneration of nutrients from the bottom is minor in comparison with regeneration in the overlying water, amounting to less than 1 per cent of the annual requirements of phytoplankton, but this regeneration is an important factor modifying the nature of organic materials that are permanently lost from the ocean by burial in sediments. Evidence of the gross effect of regeneration on the sediments is exhibited by the decrease with depth of total nitrogen (Fig. 217), and by probable but unmeasured losses of phosphate, silica, and sulfur from organic materials. Losses are especially great in oxidizing environments such as those of Santa Catalina Basin where only about one-half the original amount of organic matter survives to a depth of 2 meters, about 8000 years. Losses are smaller in the anaerobic environment of Santa Barbara Basin where more than two-thirds survive to the same depth, although its age is only about 600 years. The surviving material is more stable and resistant to further change than is that originally deposited.

Organic Constituents

General

Information about the source of organic matter and the biogenic and abiogenic losses that it undergoes before and after reaching the bottom have been discussed in previous sections, with the more important stages evaluated in Figure 153. Factors that control the extent and nature of the losses between plant growth and burial of the remnant in sediments, such as oxygen content of the water, activity of bacteria and animals, and *Eh* of the sediments, have also been described. The percentages of organic matter that occur in bottom sediments of various kinds of areas of the sea floor, such as shelves and basin floors, are summarized in Tables 12 and 14 and Figures 155, 178, 182–185, 196, 203, and 204. In addition, the rate of deposition of organic matter in basin sediments based on radiocarbon age determinations is presented, with a summary in Tables 20 and 21 and Figures 207 and 208.

Total organic matter usually constitutes less than 1 per cent by dry weight of the sediment on the mainland shelf, island shelves, and bank tops. In the basin and trough sediments it is mostly between 5 and 10 per cent. Intermediate values occur on basin slopes and sills and on hills that rise above the general level of the basins and troughs. These relationships were observed long ago by Trask (1931, 1932, Fig. 16) on the basis of about 50 samples and were extended by Revelle and Shepard (1939, Fig. 8), who analyzed about 210 additional samples. They are shown in still more detail by the 886 samples of Table 12 that have been plotted in map form for the various areas of detailed study.

Throughout all previous discussions organic matter was considered *in toto,* although it is well known to have a complex composition. There are many reasons to suppose that the various constituents have different resistances to decomposition. Accordingly, a knowledge of the composition of organic matter that has accumulated on the sea floor under various conditions of oxidation and rate of burial should go far toward explaining the cause and effect relationship of environment and percentage of organic matter in the sediments. If we are ever to learn how petroleum forms, a knowledge of the effects of environment on the early stages of diagenesis must be obtained. This has long been recognized, but the approach has been more that of speculation based on ancient sediments than of collection of facts from modern sediments and environments.

Elemental Composition and C/N Ratio

The elemental composition of organic matter in sediments has so far proved impossible to obtain with any accuracy, owing to the difficulty of separating the organic matter from its enclosing sediment. A method that has sometimes been used is to dissolve away the inorganic grains with hydrochloric and hydrofluoric acids and to analyze the residue, correcting for the pyrite, excess ash, and chlorine that also remain. An example of such an analysis from Core 2989 in Santa Catalina Basin (Table 22) was provided by the Petroleum and Oil-Shale Experiment Station, U. S. Bureau of Mines, Laramie, for comparison with analyses of oil shales. The final total organic content was 3.17 per cent by dry weight of the original sample, nearly as much as the original 3.32 per cent organic carbon alone before treatment. Carbon in the residue is 15.6 times nitrogen, whereas in the original sample it was only 9.5, indicating that at least 63 per cent of the nitrogen was lost during the removal of inorganic grains. Although we might expect many comparable analyses of phytoplankton to be available, all that could be found were a

rather unsatisfactory tabulation of analyses by Vinogradov (1953) and some older analyses of 1898 by K. Brandt (in Trask, 1937). Vinogradov's data were supplemented in Table 22 by the rather well-known composition of the human body. In spite of the deficiencies in source data, comparison of the various items in Table 22 shows that natural alteration of the original organic debris causes a progressive increase in the relative contents of carbon and hydrogen and a decrease in oxygen and nitrogen. Similar general changes were noted by Trask (1939), ZoBell (1945), and Porfiriev (1955). With coal the change from wood to anthracite is accompanied by a progressive relative decrease in hydrogen as well as in oxygen and nitrogen (Clarke, 1920, p. 763; Rankama and Sahama, 1950, Table 8.7).

The uncertainty in composition of total organic matter in sediments is reflected by an uncertainty in the ratio of total organic matter to organic carbon. Trask (1932, 1937, 1939; Trask and Patnode, 1942, p. 43), who studied the problem extensively, has at various times advocated use of different ratios (1.7, 1.8, and 1.8 to 1.9) for Recent sediments and 1.6 for ancient rocks. In discussing the problem he pointed out that the true ratio for any given sediment depends on the nature of the source material and the state of oxidation of the organic matter. Emery and Rittenberg (1952) found that at least the second factor is important for the

Table 22

ELEMENTAL COMPOSITION OF TOTAL ORGANIC MATTER
(Per cent dry weight)

	Diatoms[1]	Man[2]	Colorado Oil Shale[3]	Santa Catalina Basin[3]	Petroleum[4]
Carbon	45.9	48.4	66.2	77.6	82.2–87.1
Oxygen	35.7[5]	23.7	21.8[5]	9.5[5]	0.1– 4.5
Hydrogen	9.4	6.6	5.3	9.6	11.7–14.7
Nitrogen	9.0	12.7	4.2	2.6	0.1– 1.5
Sulfur	n.d.	1.6	2.5	0.7	0.1– 7.5

[1] Vinogradov (1953, Tables 83, 84).
[2] Rankama and Sahama (1950, Table 8.4).
[3] After solution of detrital sediment, Orr and Emery (1956a).
[4] ZoBell (1945); Ball, Whisman, and Wenger (1951).
[5] Oxygen by difference.

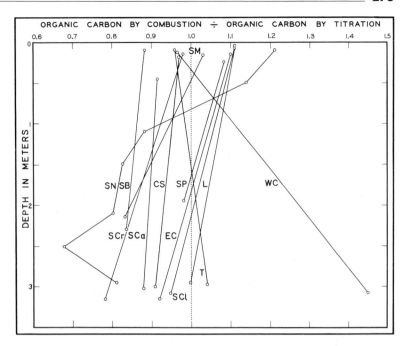

ORGANIC CARBON BY COMBUSTION ÷ ORGANIC CARBON BY TITRATION

Figure 221. Variation of the state of oxidation of organic matter with depth in basin sediments. From Emery and Rittenberg (1952, Fig. 25).

basin sediments by comparing the results of organic carbon analyses by wet combustion and by an empirical titration method. The top sections of twelve cores (Fig. 221) had an average content of organic carbon 2 per cent lower when determined by titration than by combustion, whereas at 3 meters the average was 11 per cent higher. These differences indicate that organic carbon near the sediment surface is in a slightly higher state of oxidation, and at depth it is in a lower state than in average soil for which the method was calibrated by Schollenberger (1927) and Allison (1935). Thus a larger amount of reagent is required to oxidize the carbon at depth than nearer the surface. Because of the various uncertainties, no particular ratio of total organic matter to organic carbon can be accepted as correct; however, for the sake of consistency the factor 1.7 has been used throughout the work on southern California sediments.

Analyses for organic carbon by combustion are time consuming, and analyses by titration are subject to error because of uncertainty of the state of oxidation for any particular sample; accordingly, many analyses have been made by the rapid and accurate Kjeldahl method for another measure of total organic matter, nitrogen. In using this measure, however, we must remember that the ratios of carbon to nitrogen and of total organic matter to nitrogen are not fixed. In fact, their variations provide some information about the history of the organic matter. Easiest to determine is of course the C/N ratio.

Some of the first workers to make much use of the C/N ratio were Trask and his associates, using a titration method for organic carbon. Trask's (1932) average for 86 samples from the region off southern California was 8.3 and for 13 surface samples from basin floors 8.0. A plot of carbon versus nitrogen for 79 samples from 13 later basin cores (Fig. 222) shows a higher ratio, averaging about 12.2. However, this average is complicated by the presence of at least two variables: (1) some samples are from near the surface (mostly shallower than 35 cm) and some are from depth (mostly between 275 and 325 cm), and (2) the carbon of some samples was determined by wet combustion but for most it was by titration which is known to depend on the state of oxidation which changes at depth. Based on only the more reliable combustion carbons, the C/N ratios of the surface samples average 11.3

and for those at 300 cm 13.0. Both values exhibit a progressive increase over Trask's 8.0, which was for samples mostly between 0 and about 10 cm. This increase of C/N ratio continues through the Pliocene and Miocene strata of Los Angeles Basin (Table 23) and through older sedimentary rocks elsewhere. For general computations of the content of total organic matter in sediments the C/N ratio at the surface has been taken as 10, an approximate average of Trask's and our values.

Table 23
AVERAGE C/N OF VARIOUS SEDIMENTARY MATERIALS

Diatoms [1]	5.1
Basin sediments	
0–10 cm [2]	8.0
0–35 cm [3]	11.2
275–325 cm [3]	13.0
Los Angeles Basin [4]	
0–610 meters	13.2
610–1220 meters	13.8
1220–1830 meters	14.1
1830–2440 meters	14.2
Ancient sedimentary rocks [5]	14.8
Crude oil [6]	212

[1] Table 22, combustion.
[2] Trask (1932, pp. 282–284), average of 13 analyses—titration.
[3] Emery and Rittenberg (1952), average of 10 analyses—combustion.
[4] Trask and Patnode (1942, pp. 423–461), average of 3600 analyses—titration.
[5] Trask and Patnode (1942, p. 34), average of 6865 analyses—titration.
[6] ZoBell (1945).

Carbons by combustion for the surface and the 3-meter levels of nine of the cores of Figure 222 plus three later cores (Orr and Emery, 1956a) yielded averages of 4.23 per cent carbon at the surface and 2.76 at depth. If steady-state conditions obtained during the period of deposition of these materials, the sediment now at 3 meters originally contained 4.23 per cent organic carbon. Evidently, during its burial to 3 meters, 35 per cent has been lost by regeneration. Since the C/N ratio increases with depth, more nitrogen than carbon has been regener-

ated, 45 per cent. Lacking data on losses of oxygen and hydrogen, we might round off the regeneration of total organic matter in the top 3 meters of sediment at one-third of the near-surface concentration for basin sediments (Table 14, Fig. 196). This is probably a better basis for estimating regeneration than the carbonate-to-nitrogen ratio used by Emery and Rittenberg (1952) by which a 50 per cent regeneration was computed. The latter method depends on the now-realized change in rate of deposition of carbonate during the past and on the greater rate of regeneration of nitrogen than of carbon.

As pointed out by Trask (1932, p. 181), Bader (1955), and others, the C/N ratio is controlled by the kind of materials deposited in the sediments and by the nature of its decomposition. The C/N ratio alone then

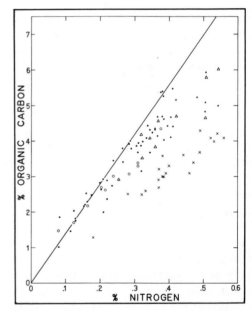

Figure 222. Organic carbon versus nitrogen (per cent by dry weight of total sediment) for samples from basins. Triangles and circles are for carbon based on wet combustion for samples at depths between 0–35 cm and 275–325 cm below water-sediment interface, respectively. Dots are for carbon based on titration for samples at all depths. For comparison, crosses show data obtained by Trask (1932, pp. 282–284) for samples in basins mostly between 0 and 10 cm for which carbon was determined by titration. The line is the best fit for 3600 analyses based on carbon titration for Los Angeles Basin (Trask and Patnode, 1942, pp. 423–461).

has only limited application in revealing the history of organic matter in sediments, and it must be supplemented by other kinds of chemical analyses. Some that have been used are general proximate analyses; others are specific for particular kinds of organic materials.

Proximate composition

Most of the published data on proximate composition of organic matter in sediments was done by Trask (1932). The most detailed of his analyses of recent sediments were made for two samples: one from Lake Maracaibo and one from his station 418 at 580 meters in Santa Barbara Basin located within 10 km of the positions of the later cores collected by the University of Southern California. Results for these two samples were similar and are averaged together in Table 24. Also Table 24 lists the average results that Trask obtained for two Miocene

and one Eocene shale from California and his (1939) tabulation of analyses of sessile algae and zooplankton by Waksman, Carey, and Reuszer (1933). Comparison of the four sets of data shows a decrease in hemicellulose, cellulose, nitrogenous compounds (largely proteins), nonnitrogenous water-soluble compounds, and nonnitrogenous acid-soluble compounds during the transition from algae through sediments to rocks. Resistant lignin-humus complexes show a complementary increase with time, and other materials are little changed. The changes, decrease of nonresistant and increase of resistant compounds, are about what we would expect from chemical and geological considerations of oxidation. Relatively rapid regeneration of proteins is also supported by the increase with depth of the C/N ratio of the sediments and by the measured release of ammonia from the sediments.

Since the completion of Trask's studies,

Table 24
PROXIMATE ANALYSES OF VARIOUS MATERIALS[1]

Fraction of Organic Matter	Sessile Algae	Zooplankton[2]	Marine Sediments	
			Recent	Past
Ether extract—includes oils, fats, pigments, and sulfur compounds	2	10	1	3
Alcohol extract—includes waxes, alkaloids, pigments etc.	9	5	5	4
Hemicellulose	11	0	2	–
Cellulose	5	2	1	–
Nitrogenous compounds	7	56	40	27
Simple proteins and amino acids			1	1
Complex proteins and simple compounds			19	4
Resistant compounds			17	15
Urionic acid	16	0	–	–
Simple nonnitrogenous water-soluble compounds	23	5	3	3
Acid-soluble nonnitrogenous compounds	29[3]	0[3]	7	6
Lignin-humus complexes	5	3	31	48

[1] From Trask (1932, p. 200; 1939, p. 443).
[2] Does not include 6 per cent chitin as reported by Waksman, Carey, and Reuszer (1933).
[3] Reported as pentosans (Trask, 1939).

many new chemical techniques and instruments have been developed that permit the detection and measurement of specific chemical materials which had to be grouped 30 years ago. Among the materials from the basins and other areas of sea floor off southern California that have been studied are amino acids, pigments, hydrocarbons, and gases.

Amino Acids

Living organic matter contains a large number of proteins that range from simple to complex in structure. Many are unstable and difficult to separate; however, hydrolysis leads to the formation of amino acids that are common to many proteins (Doty, 1957). The 21 types of amino acids that occur in living tissue exhibit varying degrees of resistance toward oxidation. Eight that include the most resistant ones (alanine, aspartic acid, glutamic acid, glycine, isoleucine, leucine, proline, and valine) were detected by Abelson (1956, 1957) in bones of Cretaceous dinosaurs and Devonian fish and in shells of Miocene mollusks and an Ordovician brachiopod. Ten (alanine, arginine, aspartic acid, glutamic acid, glutamine, glycine, leucine, phenylalanine, proline, and serine) were found by Dr. Paul Saltman (personal communication) in a preliminary examination of a sample of surface sediments from Santa Cruz Basin. Others may also be present. Among those found are several relatively unstable amino acids, arginine, aspartic acid, phenylalanine, and serine. These relationships suggest that a spectrum of amino acids occurs in cores with many at the surface and only the more resistant ones at depth. More detailed studies should reveal depth variations of the number and quantity of amino acids that should relate to the known increase of C/N ratio at depth in the sediments.

Pigments

Many different kinds of pigments are present in sediments, but the ones that have been investigated most thoroughly are the green porphyrin pigments—derivatives of chlorophyll (Treibs, 1934)—in a study made possible by a grant from Shell Development Company, Houston. Pigments obtained in acetone extractions (Orr and Grady, 1957) include pheophytin a and pheophorbide a identified through paper chromatography, absorption spectra, and acid numbers. Pheophytin b, pheophorbide b, and higher intermediates appear to be absent. For convenience the mixture will be referred to as simply pheophytin. Pheophytin a is derived from chlorophyll by replacement of the magnesium nucleus with two hydrogens; a further replacement of a phytol group by a propionic acid side chain converts pheophytin a into pheophorbide a (Fig. 223). Such changes are known to be caused by the acid fluids of animal digestive tracts. Further changes are required before the porphyrin becomes similar to porphyrins found in petroleum, none of which seems to be present in the sediments. Vanadium and nickel, which commonly form the porphyrin nucleus in petroleums, have not been detected in the extracts from sediments, even though the sediments contain more than ten times enough vanadium and nickel to satisfy the porphyrin requirement (Table 17).

Pheophytin was found in each of more than 200 sediment samples that were analyzed, ranging from beach sand to deep-sea red clay (Orr, Emery, and Grady, 1958). In beach sands it amounts to 0.02–0.09 ppm dry weight of sediment, in mainland and island shelf and bank top sediment 1–13 ppm, in basin sediments 4–103 ppm, and in red clay 0.02–1.6 ppm. The basins with their great range of values (Table 14) are most interesting. Pheophytin has its highest concentration (40 to 103 ppm) in Santa Barbara, Santa Monica, and San Pedro Basins, all of which are close to shore and have the highest rates of deposition of detrital sediment (Table 20). It is also abundant, 39 ppm, in Tanner Basin which has a low rate of deposition but is in a favorable position for receiving organic debris from the area of high productivity near the Santa Rosa–Cortes Ridge (Fig. 86). Cores from southern San Clemente, No Name, and Long Basins

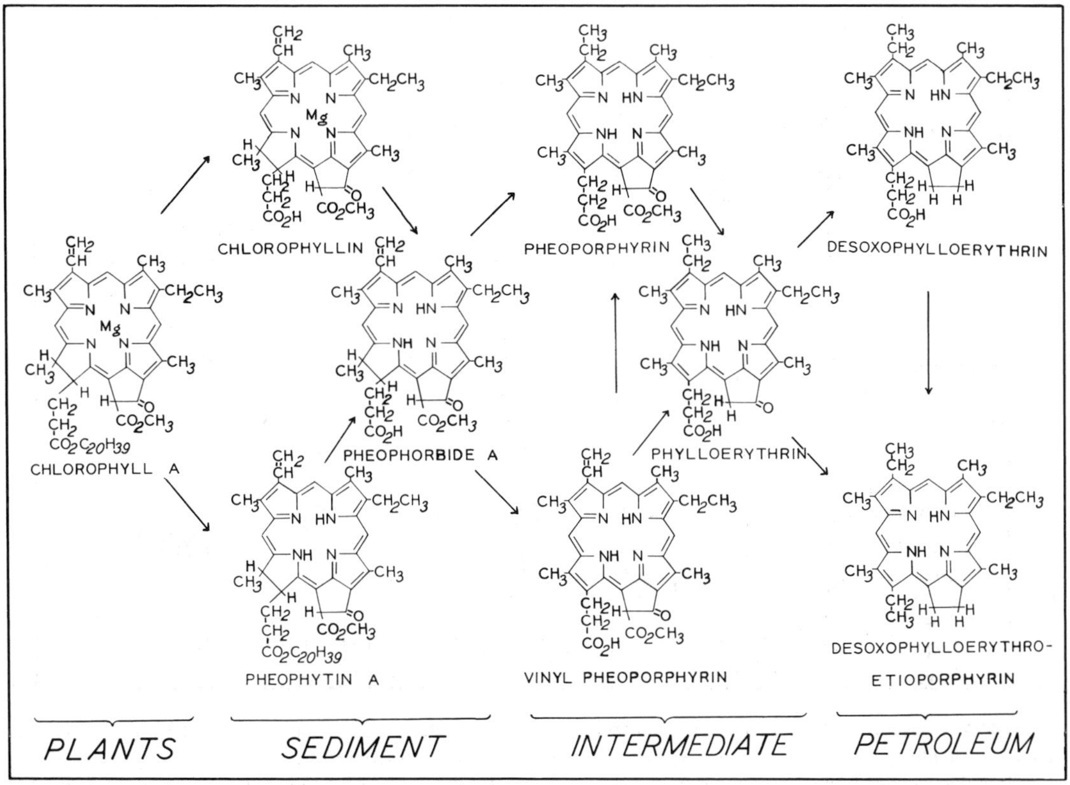

Figure 223. Relationship of chlorophyll to pheophytin a and pheophorbide a in sediments and to porphyrins in petroleum. From Orr, Emery, and Grady (1958, Fig. 16).

contain less than 5 ppm of pheophytin. Within individual basins the areal distribution of pheophytin is directly related to content of nitrogen and inversely related to grain size. In vertical sections provided by cores it also exhibits a very close relationship to grain size, and thence to water content, carbonate, and nitrogen (Fig. 224). These changes are superimposed on a general decrease in concentration with depth of burial.

Pheophytin reaches its greatest abundance in sediments found at a depth of about 600 meters, in contrast to nitrogen which is most abundant at about 1500 meters. Its relationship to both nitrogen and depth is so close that if the contents of nitrogen and pheophytin in a sample are known, an estimate of the depth of water accurate to within a few hundred meters can be formed (Fig. 225). The rate of deposition of pheophytin in muddy sediments throughout the area of Chart I ranges from more than 0.001 mg/sq

cm/yr in the northeastern nearshore basins to less than 0.00001 mg/sq cm/yr in deep-sea red clays (Fig. 226, Table 20). For the entire region about 280 tons of pheophytin are deposited annually (Table 21), but about three-fourths of it is regenerated before burial to a depth of 3 meters, leaving only about 70 tons annually buried to that depth and still less to greater depths.

The relationship of pheophytin to nitrogen provides information about its regeneration. In phytoplankton nitrogen is about 1.5 times as abundant as pheophytin, at the surface of the sediment in Santa Barbara Basin nitrogen is 35 times pheophytin, and at 3 meters it is 60 times pheophytin. Even greater differences exist in some other basins; for example, at 3-meters depth in a core from San Clemente Basin nitrogen is 400 times pheophytin. It is evident that even though nitrogen is lost in the water column and during burial in the sediments, pheo-

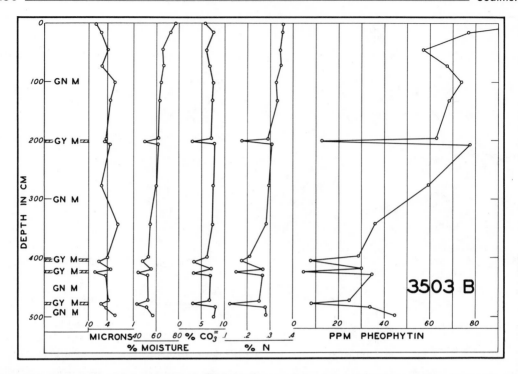

Figure 224. Concentration of pheophytin and other sediment parameters in core from Santa Barbara Basin. The gray muds are slightly coarser than the more typical green muds and are considered to be turbidity current deposits. Note the close dependence of pheophytin on grain size and its general decrease with depth. *Eh* is negative throughout the core. From Orr, Emery, and Grady (1958, Fig. 9).

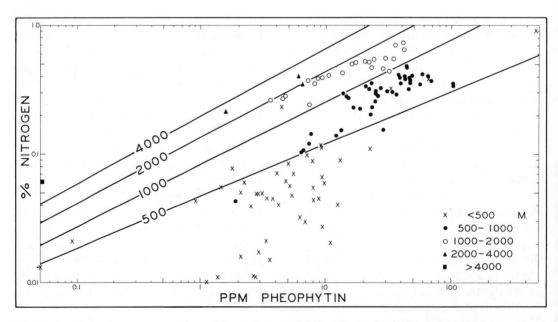

Figure 225. Plot of pheophytin versus nitrogen concentrations in surface sediments with points for different ranges of water depth indicated by different symbols. Note the close grouping of the symbols between depth lines. From Orr, Emery, and Grady (1958, Fig. 7).

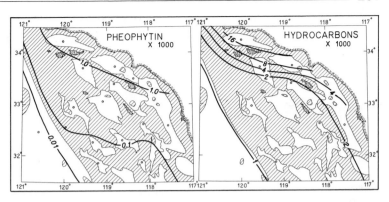

Figure 226. Rate of deposition of pheophytin and hydrocarbons in surface sediments of basins expressed in mg/cm²/ yr. Compare with Figure 207 for rates of deposition of other constituents of sediments.

phytin is lost much faster, indicating its greater susceptibility to oxidation. The nearshore basins where the least oxidation should occur, owing to their shallow water depth, low oxygen content, rapid rate of deposition of detrital sediments, and low or negative *Eh* of interstitial water, are the ones in which pheophytin is buried most rapidly in terms of weight per unit area per unit time (Fig. 226). The greater preservation more than makes up for the greater dilution by detrital sediments in these basins, so that pheophytin also reaches its highest concentration there in terms of percentage weight of total sediment (compare Figures 203 and 208). In summary, the pheophytin content of the sediments must be influenced by differences in its production by phytoplankton, dilution with inorganic sediments, and oxidation in the water and sediment. Production in the area varies by a factor of about 1000 (Fig. 86), about four times the range of pheophytin concentration in the basin sediments, and it is probably responsible for high values, especially in Tanner Basin. The rate of deposition of total sediment varies by a factor of 15 in the basins (Table 20), but dilution does not lower the pheophytin content in the nearshore basins, aside from the effects of turbidity current deposits (Fig. 224). Oxidation appears to be the main factor that controls pheophytin, permitting the highest concentrations in sediments where oxidation is reduced by low *Eh* and rapid burial.

Another group of pigments, the carotinoids, or yellow pigments, were noted in the extracts for pheophytin. More com-

plete studies were made by Fox, Updegraff, and Novelli (1944), whose data indicate that the carotinoids are more easily oxidized than even pheophytin. Of the carotinoids investigated, carotenes (hydrocarbon form) and xanthophylls (oxidized form), the latter appears to be the more easily oxidized. In plants and animals xanthophyll is commonly several times more abundant than carotene, but the reverse is true in sediments owing to the more rapid rate of oxidation of xanthophyll. Values in various materials (Table 25) indicate the relative importance of the two pigments, but measurements are few in number and distribution and thus are of uncertain relationship to environment. When more study has been made of these pigments, they may prove to be excellent supplements to chlorophyll derivatives in serving as measures of environment. Although carotinoids do not occur in petroleum as pigments, the carotenes may contribute directly to the hydrocarbon content of petroleum.

Hydrocarbons

In 1952 Smith reported the presence of hydrocarbons in Recent sediments of the Gulf of Mexico. Samples of a core from Santa Cruz Basin were sent to him, and the results of his study of these were also published (Smith, 1954). The abundance of hydrocarbons showed a clear dependence on environment with especially high concentrations in the sediments of the southern California basins, so Smith's work was followed up at the University of Southern California

Table 25

CAROTINOID PIGMENTS IN PHYTOPLANKTON AND SEDIMENTS[1]

Location	Depth of Water, meters	Depth in Sediment, cm	Ppm (Dry Weight)	
			Carotene	Xanthophyll
PHYTOPLANKTON				
Prorocentrum micans			2.6	22.6
Nitzschia closterium			659	5785
Rhizosolenia styliformis *Biddulphia sinensis*			350	650
SEDIMENTS				
Loma Sea Valley	194	0– 5	1.3	0.4
		5– 61	2.0	0.4
		61–122	0.5	0.1
		122–183	0.4	0.1
		183–244	0.2	0.1
San Diego Trough	1190	488–518	2.4	0.5
San Clemente Basin	2005	5– 20	1.3	0.2

[1] From Fox, Updegraff, and Novelli (1944).

first with a grant from the Geological Society of America and later with a larger one from Shell Development Company. The procedure was the rather conventional chromatographic technique as used by Hunt (1953) on petroleum, by Hunt, Stewart, and Dickey (1954) on various organic minerals and extracts from sedimentary rocks, and by Smith (1952, 1954) on extracts from Recent sediments. In this technique the paraffin-naphthene hydrocarbon fraction is eluted with *n*-heptane, the aromatic hydrocarbon fraction with benzene, and the asphaltic fraction, which contains the bulk of the oxygen, nitrogen, and sulfur compounds with pyridine, acetone, and methanol. The strongly absorbed materials, which are not eluted from the chromatographic column under the conditions of the analysis, are determined by difference and reported as "remaining on alumina."

Infrared spectra of the paraffin-naphthene and the aromatic fractions are typical of these materials and are closely similar to spectra of the same fractions separated from a Pliocene crude oil from Los Angeles Basin

(Fig. 227). Checks were also made of ultraviolet spectra and elemental composition (Table 26). In the first work (Orr and Emery, 1956*a*) the hydrocarbon fractions (paraffin-naphthene and especially aromatic) included some sulfur as an impurity that had to be removed or corrected for. In later work sulfur was removed by treatment with sodium cyanide before chromatography, and improvements were also made on the method of extraction of soluble organic matter from the sediment (Orr and Emery, 1956*b*). Invariably the asphaltic fractions are black tarry solids. Aromatic fractions are pale-yellow waxy solids fluorescing strongly under ultraviolet light. The paraffin-naphthene fractions are colorless waxy solids that at 50°C melt enough to flow. Only one sample (294 to 340 cm in Santa Catalina Basin) was a liquid at room temperature; this paraffin-naphthene fraction amounted to only 8.6 ppm of dry sediment, according well with the observation of Trask and Wu (1930) that liquid hydrocarbons in Recent sediments are rare and less than 30 ppm. Optical activity, rotation, may be

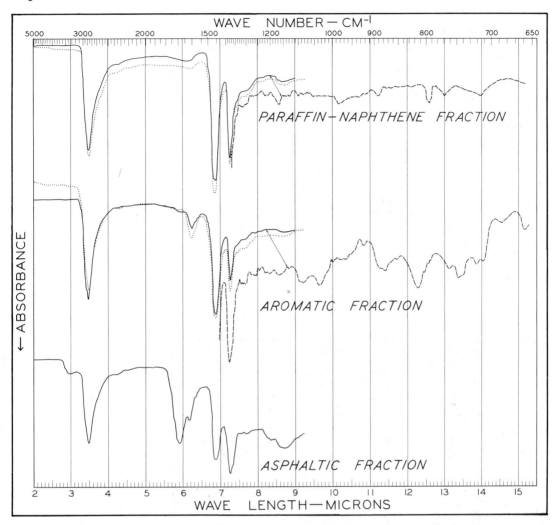

Figure 227. Infrared spectra for paraffin-naphthene, aromatic, and asphaltic fractions of samples of organic matter present between 418 and 478 cm in Santa Barbara Basin and of Pliocene crude oil from Los Angeles Basin. From Orr and Emery (1956a, Fig. 2).

present as it is in petroleum (Oakwood, Shriver, Fall, McAleer, and Wunz, 1952) and in chromatographic fractions from Recent sediments of the Gulf of Mexico (Smith, 1954), but it could not be measured, owing to the small size of the hydrocarbon fractions. The elemental composition, molecular weight, spectra, waxy nature, and the degree of rotation indicate that the paraffin-naphthene fractions are largely straight chains 15 to 30 carbon atoms long.

Data on the depth distribution of hydrocarbons are provided by three to five samples in cores from four basins (Table 27),

some of which are presented in Figure 228. Total extract decreases with depth in all four basins, indicating the loss of less resistant organic materials during the course of burial if steady-state conditions existed throughout the period of deposition. The paraffin-naphthene fraction decreases with depth in Santa Barbara and Tanner Basins, the two basins in which it is most abundant. It presents only an irregular depth variation in the other two basins, although conceivably if hydrocarbons could have been run on a very thin surface layer of sediment, they would have been found quite abundant there. The

Table 26

ELEMENTAL ANALYSES OF CHROMATOGRAPHIC FRACTIONS OF A SAMPLE FROM 248 TO 274 CM
IN SANTA BARBARA BASIN[1] AND OF OTHER ORGANIC MATERIALS[2]

	Carbon	Hydrogen	Sulfur	Nitrogen	Oxygen	H/C
Paraffin-naphthene	86.26	13.66				190
Aromatic[3]	87.54	12.45				1.71
Asphaltic	68.01	10.17	2.32	1.09	18.40[4]	1.79
Carbohydrates[2]	44.50	6.20			49.30	1.67
Lipids[2]	76.60	12.65			11.35	1.98
Proteins[2]	50.0–55.0	6.5–7.3	0.0–2.4	12.0–15.0	21.0–24.0	
Pigments[2]	76.03	8.41		6.45	9.11	1.33
Lignins[2]	60.00	5.50			28.50	1.10
Resins[2]	70–80	5–10	2–3	1–2	2–20	

[1] Orr and Emery (1956a).
[2] Porfiriev (1955).
[3] Recomputed omitting sulfur as a contaminant.
[4] Oxygen by difference.

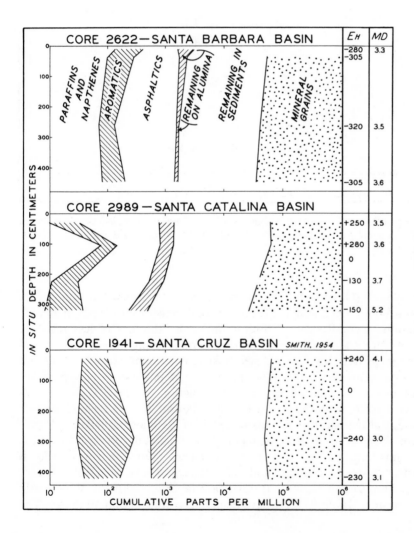

Figure 228. Cumulative composition of organic matter in sediments of three basins. Note the logarithmic scale. From Orr and Emery (1956a, Fig. 1).

Table 27

HYDROCARBONS IN BASIN SEDIMENTS OFF SOUTHERN CALIFORNIA

Basin and Depth in Sediment, cm	Core No.	N, %	C, %	Organic Extract, grams/ 100 grams dry sediment	Paraffin-Naphthenes, ppm in dry sediment	Aromatics, ppm in dry sediment	Asphaltics, ppm in dry sediment
Santa Barbara Basin							
0– 16	2622B	–	(3.75)[2]	0.301	132	247	1200
32– 60	2622B	–	3.24	0.239	100	172	1460
100–152	3503D	–	–	–	91	121	–
248–274	2622B	–	2.40	0.175	72	61	1420
418–478	2622C	–	2.06	0.166	81	119	1230
Santa Monica Basin							
0– 40	5002	0.291	–	0.195	51	99	1210
San Diego Trough							
5– 30	4667	0.430	–	0.220	64	136	1360
Santa Catalina Basin							
0– 60	2989	–	3.63	0.141	10	23	746
60–148	2989	–	3.66	0.138	77	69	668
206–250	2989	–	(3.50)	0.092	11	18	485
294–340	2989	–	1.63	0.048	9	22	196
Santa Cruz Basin[1]							
24– 36	1941	–	3.76	0.188	36	64	277
274–304	1941	–	2.91	0.152	29	254	272
396–442	1941	–	3.36	0.149	38	125	408
Tanner Basin							
3– 38	4696	0.412	–	0.144	129	38	483
64–152	4696	–	–	0.126	21	68	–
305–331	4696	0.335	–	0.094	14	25	595
San Clemente Basin							
0– 5	4669	0.385	–	0.065	21	22	233
Long Basin							
0– 30	4699	0.269	–	0.097	20.4	34	398
Soledad Valley Marsh[1]							
0– 5		–	–	0.76	501	296	–

[1] Smith (1954).

[2] Numbers in parentheses taken from other nearby cores.

cores from both Santa Barbara and Tanner Basins had negative *Eh*'s to the sediment-water interface, whereas the depth of negative *Eh* in cores from Santa Catalina and Santa Cruz Basins was at about 270 cm. The aromatic fraction is irregular at depth in all four basins, with perhaps the nearest approach to a decrease in Santa Barbara Basin. Irregularity of depth trends in hydrocarbons are also present in five cores, 2 to 3 meters long, from the Gulf of Mexico as described by Stevens, Bray, and Evans (1956) where, however, concentrations are much lower than in the California basin cores, averaging about 3-ppm paraffin-naphthenes and 7-ppm aromatics. Irregular concentrations with a tendency toward higher values at depth were also present in some longer drill cores described by Smith (1954) from the Gulf of Mexico.

The areal distribution of hydrocarbons based on analyses of eight basins (Tables 14 and 27) reveals the highest concentrations in Santa Barbara Basin, which has the most reducing conditions, and the lowest concentrations in San Clemente and Long Basins, which are among the most oxidizing of the basin sediments. When compared with the better-known distribution of green porphyrin pigments (Fig. 229), a general parallelism can be noted. The parallelism also extends to marsh sediments where Smith (1954) found hydrocarbons present in amounts more than twice as great as in any basin sediment (Table 27) and where pheophytin, with a concentration of 476 ppm (Orr, Emery, and Grady, 1958), is more than four times as abundant as in any basin.

Evidently the same factors of production, dilution, and oxidation affect hydrocarbons as affect pheophytin. Oxidation appears to be the most important factor controlling the concentration of hydrocarbons in sediments, as it is for pheophytin. This conclusion is supported by the similarity of the areal patterns of rates of deposition for the two organic materials in basin sediments (Fig. 226 and Table 20). As shown by Table 21, about 880 tons of hydrocarbon accumulate in the sediments each year, with 80 per cent of it in the basins that comprise only 17 per cent

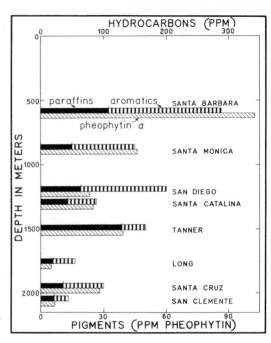

Figure 229. Comparison of concentrations of hydrocarbons and pheophytin in sediments of eight basins. Note the use of different scales for the two materials.

of the sea floor area of Chart I. Lipids in phytoplankton that can be extracted with the same methods used for hydrocarbons in sediments amount to about 3200 ppm by dry weight (Smith, 1954, 2000 ppm; Stevens, Bray, and Evans, 1956, 4000 ppm; Orr, 3200 and 3500 ppm). These materials are almost exclusively paraffin-naphthenes with virtually no aromatics. Since the annual production of phytoplankton in the region is about 42 million tons (Fig. 153), about 135,000 tons of hydrocarbon-like materials are produced annually in the area of Chart I. About 0.65 per cent of this annual production is buried in the bottom, mostly in basins, representing a percentage loss almost exactly the same as that for total organic matter and 250 times less than that for pheophytin.

In the basin sediments hydrocarbons vary between 0.05 and 0.60 per cent of total organic matter and average 0.30 per cent. Additional hydrocarbons can be produced from the sediment by pyrolysis. Assays at 500°C by the Petroleum and Oil-Shale Experiment Station, U. S. Bureau of Mines, Laramie, on samples from Santa Barbara,

Santa Monica, and Santa Catalina Basins yielded oil amounting to 9.5, 7.7, and 9.5 per cent of the total organic matter, respectively. This is 19 to 36 times the amount extracted by solvents from otherwise untreated sediments.

Gases

In addition to their solid and liquid constituents, sediments also contain greater or lesser quantities of gases of various kinds. Detailed studies of these gases awaited the development of mass spectrometer techniques during the past decade. Sampling also presented a problem because gases bubbling up from the bottom consist only of the gases that had not yet dissolved in the water, and they provide no measure of gases present in the sediments. Recently Emery and Hoggan (1958) combined a special collecting device and use of a mass spectrometer to analyze gases present between the surface and a depth of 375 cm in sediments of Santa Barbara, Santa Monica, and Santa Catalina Basins and between the surface and 45 cm in marshes at Newport Bay and Seal Beach. A weighted coring device made of short lengths of steel pipe coupled together was dropped into the bottom sediment, recovered aboard ship, and disassembled and capped inside a large plastic bag in which atmospheric gases had been replaced with helium. At the laboratory of Richfield Oil Corporation, Wilmington, California, the gases were extracted under vacuum from the capped lengths of pipe. The most abundant gases were determined directly in the mass spectrometer; the rest of them had first to be concentrated in a liquid nitrogen bath. Percentages of various gases were converted to milliliters per liter of interstitial water using nitrogen as a standard gas with a concentration assumed to be the same as in overlying water. Ammonia, not determined by mass spectrometer, was added from earlier measurements on nearby cores by Rittenberg, Emery, and Orr (1955); hydrogen sulfide was also present in some samples but was not measured. Carbon dioxide was measured, but probably not reliably because of complexities of the carbon dioxide–carbonate system.

The results for Santa Barbara Basin (Fig. 230) show that ammonia and methane dominate at depth, but higher representatives of the methane series and even some aromatic volatile hydrocarbons are also present. At depth the weight of methane is about equal to the weight of all heavy nonvolatile hydrocarbons that were separated by chromatography (Table 27). In oil fields also the weight of hydrocarbon gases is about equal to the weight of petroleum. However, in the Recent sediments of Santa Barbara Basin the ratio of methane to ethane is about 100,000 to 1, in contrast to the 4-to-1 ratio that is typical of oil field gases. Results in the other basins showed an increase of methane with depth but to maximum concentrations of less than 0.2 per cent of those found in Santa Barbara Basin. Evidently the negative *Eh* and other conditions are more favorable for the production of hydrocarbon gases in Santa Barbara Basin than in the other basins or in marshes. None of the hydrocarbon gases was detected in samples of sea water above the basins, so they must have been produced by diagenesis of organic matter at the bottom. In support of this conclusion, bacteria and fungi have recently been discovered to be capable of producing hydrocarbon gases higher than methane

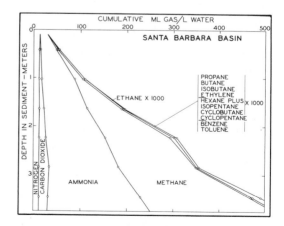

Figure 230. Composition of dissolved gases and volatile organic materials in interstitial water of sediments in Santa Barbara Basin. Note the increase with depth of most gases.

from sewage and other media (Young, Pratt, and Biale, 1951; Davis and Squires, 1954).

Carbon Atoms

A comparison of the nature of carbon atoms in organic matter and in extracts of it provides information about diagenetic changes not obtainable only a few years ago. Data on three aspects are available: number of carbon atoms per molecule; radiocarbon isotope, C^{14}; and stable carbon isotope, C^{13}.

When samples of hydrocarbons are examined with a mass spectrometer, the number of carbon atoms per molecule can be measured. Using this method, Stevens, Bray, and Evans (1956) discovered that the normal paraffins (*n*-heptane fraction of chromatography) from soils and marine muds of the Gulf of Mexico have a decided predominance of molecules containing an odd number of carbon atoms. Frequency peaks are highest for 29 and 31 carbon atoms but are present for 27, 25, and 23 also. The odd-even ratio over this range for the sample of marine mud that was figured is 3.4. In contrast, no such preference is exhibited by petroleums that were studied. The paraffin fraction from a plankton sample collected off the east coast of Florida exhibited only a slight predominance of odd numbers of carbon atoms, the odd-even ratio being 1.1. Thus, the odd carbon atoms are accentuated in marine muds and soils over those in plankton, and no preference seems to be present in petroleum. A similar variation of odd-even preference in sediments from the southern California basins has been found by Mr. Ellis Bray of Magnolia Petroleum Company, but results have not yet been published.

The radiocarbon isotope, C^{14}, has been measured in a few hydrocarbon extracts from organic matter in sediments. First was the discovery by Smith (1954) that hydrocarbons present in a 33-meter core of Recent sediments at Grande Isle, Louisiana, had radiocarbon ages of 11,800 to 14,600 ± 1400 years. A composite sample of nonextractable organic matter had an average age of 9200 ± 1000 years, and of carbonate 12,300

± 1200 years. Similarly recent ages of 3100 to 9300 years were obtained by Stevens, Bray, and Evans (1956) for hydrocarbons extracted from muds flooring the continental shelf of the Gulf of Mexico. Age determinations of hydrocarbons from sediments of the California basins are not available, but Magnolia Petroleum Company (N. P. Stevens, personal communication) made measurements on 15 organic extracts with resulting ages ranging between 4310 and 13,880 years and averaging 8550 years.

The stable isotope C^{13} is far more abundant than the radioisotope C^{14}, but it is only about 1 per cent as abundant as C^{12}. The difference in atomic weight permits measurements of the relative abundance of C^{13} and C^{12} by means of a mass spectrometer. Studies of the C^{13}/C^{12} ratio by Craig (1953) and others have shown a range of values for different materials. Because of the aid that C^{13}/C^{12} ratios might provide in understanding the diagenesis of organic matter, part of a grant from the National Science Foundation was used to defray the costs of their measurement along with the radiocarbon ages of basin sediments by T. A. Rafter of New Zealand Department of Science and Industrial Research. His analyses (Table 28) are accurate within about 1‰. Special analyses of extracts and hydrocarbon fractions were kindly made by S. Silverman of California Research Corporation with an especially sensitive mass spectrometer considered to be accurate to 0.1‰. The results, given in Table 28, are expressed as

$$\delta \text{ in per mil}(‰) = \frac{C^{13}/C^{12} \text{ sample} - C^{13}/C^{12} \text{ standard}}{C^{13}/C^{12} \text{ standard}} \times 1000$$

The standard to which all values have been adjusted is the one in use at the University of Chicago, a Cretaceous belemnite. Values of δ in nature range mostly between +5 and −50, with the more negative ones indicating lower contents of C^{13} with respect to C^{12} (or lighter carbon).

Craig (1953) showed that δ in marine plants (measured mostly for sessile algae) ranges between −7.6 and −16.5‰, about the same as in marine invertebrates but far higher than in petroleum, for which δ lies mostly between −22.2 and −29.4‰ according to Wickman (1956) and Silverman and Epstein (1958) (Fig. 231). The latter is nearly the same as for terrestrial plants, −21.1 to −26.7‰. Values in the 24 basin and other southern California marine sediments that were analyzed range between −19.9 and −24.8‰ for total organic matter. These values are closer to those for petroleum in general and to two southern California petroleum samples reported by Silverman and Epstein (1958), −23.0 and −23.1‰ in particular. The values in the sediments are similar to others reported for organic matter in deep-sea sediments by Landegren (1954) and to two samples of shale from the Los Angeles Basin. This correspondence indicates either that fractionation with relative loss of C^{13} has occurred between the synthesis of tissue by phytoplankton and deposition of the debris in the sediment, or that the organic matter in sediments is dominated by a part of the organic matter that is both resistant to oxidation and has a lower C^{13}/C^{12} ratio than the bulk of the original tissue. Some data suggest that the latter is more likely because a hydrocarbon chromatographic fraction prepared from phytoplankton was found by Silverman to have a δ of −30.4‰. Organic matter extractable by solvents from three depths in Santa Barbara Basin sediments and hydrocarbon fractions from the same basin also have slightly lower δ values (−23.3‰) than does total organic matter in the sediments, falling more nearly in the range of petroleum than even the organic matter. For comparison, δ values for carbonate in the sediments are far higher, +0.9 to −1.9‰. This difference between δ values for carbonate and organic matter is well known from studies by Craig and others.

At depth in the basin sediments δ values based on organic matter present a consistent decrease (carbon becoming lighter) in each of five cores for which values at several depths are available (Table 28). Differences between top and bottom core samples range up to 2.3‰, well beyond the error of analysis.

Craig (1953) and Parks (1957) reported

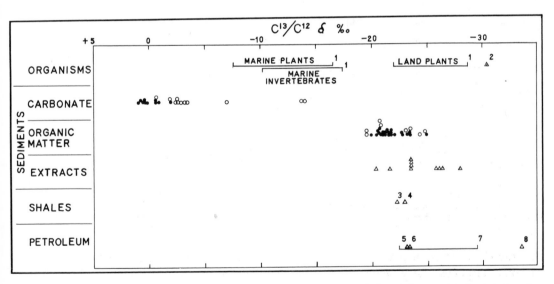

Figure 231. Distribution of C^{13}/C^{12} δ values in ‰ for different materials: 1, Marine and terrestrial plants and marine invertebrates (Craig, 1953). 2, Paraffin fraction from phytoplankton consisting of 97% dinoflagellates. 3, Extract from Pliocene shale, Los Angeles Basin. 4, Total organic matter in Miocene shale, Los Angeles Basin. 5, Pliocene-Miocene petroleum, Los Angeles Basin. 6, Oligocene petroleum, Ventura Basin. 7, Various petroleums, Tertiary on left and Paleozoic on right. 8, Natural gas. Triangles and range bar for petroleums indicate analyses reported by Silverman and Epstein (1958) or by Silverman (personal communication), circles indicate analyses reported by Landegren (1954), and dots indicate analyses on California basin sediments made by T. A. Rafter financed by grant from National Science Foundation.

Table 28
C^{13}/C^{12} δ ‰ VALUES FOR BASIN SEDIMENTS[1]

Basin	Core	Depth, cm	Carbonate	Organic Carbon	Total Extract	Paraffin-Naphthenes	Aromatics
Santa Barbara	4701	0– 19	+0.3	−20.4			
	4701	228–241		−21.2			
	4701	406–419	−0.7	−21.6			
	3503	102–162				−23.3	
	2622C	31– 41			−23.3		
	2622C	183–193			−23.3		
	2622C	386–396			−23.3		
Santa Monica	4647	386–396	−1.9				
San Pedro	4679	300–310		−22.0			
	4690	5– 25		−21.0			
	4690	330–348		−23.3			
San Diego	4667	343–356	+0.2	−21.5			
Santa Cruz	4700	343–356		−22.7			
Santa Catalina	4703	267–279		−21.7			
	4704	3– 13	+0.5	−20.8			
	4704	13– 25	+0.9	−21.7			
	4704	406–419	−0.7	−22.6			
San Clemente	4670	305–318	−0.9	−23.1			
	4672	267–279		−24.8			
San Nicolas	4693	0– 5		−20.6			
	4693	330–343	+0.4	−21.0			
East Cortes	4671	441–454	+0.7	−19.9			
No Name	4673	401–414		−21.2			
Tanner	4696	2– 38				−27.9	−26.3
	4696	330–343		−20.5			
West Cortes	4674	3– 13		−21.3			
	4674	419–432		−21.5			
Long	4699	343–354		−23.3			
Continental slope	4697	381–396		−20.6			
Deep sea	4698	102–112	−9.9				
Average			−0.1	−21.7			

[1] Values for carbonate and organic carbon by T. A. Rafter, New Zealand Department of Scientific and Industrial Research, Lower Hutt; other values by Silverman and Epstein (1958) and Silverman (personal communication).

that the C^{13} content of plant lipids (hydrocarbons, terpenes, fatty acids, and other ether soluble components) are about 10‰ lighter than the rest of the plant. The typical oxidation and loss to the sediment of carbohydrates and proteins at a rate faster than for lipids must then result in a decrease of the C^{13}/C^{12} ratio, in agreement with the observed progressive change from plants and animals to sediments at the surface to sediments at depth to petroleum. According to a single analysis of a natural gas by Silverman and Epstein (1958), the sequence may continue beyond petroleum to oil field gas. This whole sequence accords with the belief that petroleum is derived from fatty acids (Brooks, 1952) or hydrocarbons in plankton (Smith, 1954), rather than that fractionation and faster loss of C^{13} than of C^{12} has occurred during diagenesis. However, data on parts of the sequence, especially on extracts from phytoplankton and sediments, are still too scanty for the process to be considered certain as yet.

Craig (1954) suggested that variations in C^{13}/C^{12} be used to correct ages based on C^{14}/C^{12} measurements. However, such corrections were not applied to the ages of the sediment from the basins (Table 19) because the original C^{14}/C^{12} ratio may be independent of C^{13}/C^{12}, owing to the nature of the water media of growth (Rafter, 1955a) and because the C^{13}/C^{12} ratio in the sediments may be a function of selective oxidation rather than of fractionation.

Origin of Petroleum

Petroleum and asphalt, because of their uses as fuel, building material, and medicine, have been known to man from ancient times, being mentioned in the Bible and in other ancient literature. The origin of petroleum was considered a great mystery, although by the middle of the nineteenth century Lyell (1850, p. 252) could write the half-truth that petroleum seems to be formed by the action of subterranean fires on vegetable substances buried in the sedimentary strata. A few years later in 1866 M. Berthelot produced an inorganic theory of origin of petroleum by reaction of carbon dioxide with free alkaline metals in the earth's interior, and in 1877 D. Mendeléef developed his famous theory of reaction between water and carbides in the earth's interior (Clarke, 1920). Since then theories of organic origin have generally prevailed over inorganic ones. However, during the past few years the possibility of inorganic origin of petroleum has received renewed attention. As discussed by Link (1957), Fred Hoyle and Immanuel Velikovsky recently have published opinions that petroleum was brought to Earth by meteorites, a reiteration of an 1890 theory by N. V. Sokoloff. Even more recently, Kropotkin (1957) strongly favored the inorganic origin of petroleum on the basis of its presence in stony meteorites and in fractured igneous and metamorphic rocks and its rarity in some areas of abundant coal. Because of the strong stands taken by proponents of the inorganic versus the organic theories of petroleum genesis in the U.S.S.R., a large symposium on the question was convened there during late 1958 (Committee on Origin of Oil, 1958).

Evidence most frequently cited in favor of the organic origin of petroleum is its nitrogen content, the presence of porphyrins, and its optical rotation, all being otherwise typical of organic substances. In addition to these chemical and physical properties is the general restriction of petroleum to strata rich in fossils, usually only of marine types. For most oil fields, particularly those of southern California, there is little disagreement to the statements that the temperature of the sedimentary source rocks has always been low (probably less than 150°C) and that the pressure has been low (probably less than 500 kg/sq cm). Evidence for the first point is the presence of porphyrins in petroleum—desoxophylloerythrin would be destroyed by prolonged heating to even 150°C. Evidence for the second point is the presence of petroleum in strata of Los Angeles Basin that have never been buried deeper than they are now and have not been subjected to great lateral pressures of folding. There is much more disagreement on the question of distance of migration of petroleum, owing to both geological and chemical uncertainties in identifying the source rock for any particular petroleum accumulation.

If petroleum is accepted as having an organic origin, the important question of how it is derived remains. Two different general methods are worthy of consideration: whether it is a survival or a product of diagenesis or both. Favoring survival is the fact that hydrocarbon-like lipids are present in phytoplankton and their C^{13}/C^{12} ratios are like those of the hydrocarbon fractions of organic matter in sediments and of petroleum. Also favoring survival is the general decrease with depth of paraffin-naphthenes in the basin cores (although increases have been noted in some cores from the Gulf of

Mexico). Favoring production is the fact that between the times of secretion of lipids by phytoplankton and deposition of organic matter in the topmost layers of sediments, aromatic fractions and longer chain paraffin fractions formed. The latter may occur by hydrogenation of lipid molecules or partial regeneration of proteins. Production of methane and other gaseous hydrocarbons also occurs after deposition. Aromatics and gases evidently are products of diagenesis in the sediments and may owe their origin to breakdown of complex organic molecules by radiation developed within the organic matter or associated mineral grains (Whitehead, 1950–1951; Burton and Sullivan, 1951). The slight odd-even carbon atom preference of phytoplankton lipids is accentuated in the sediments but lost in petroleum as though survival had been followed by diagenetic and post-diagenetic changes. Liquid hydrocarbons that develop only deep in the sediment must be products of diagenesis, and the process continues for a far greater time than has so far been reached at the bottoms of basin cores. Chlorophyll of phytoplankton survives in the sediments and petroleum as porphyrins, with the particular type changed to pheophytin a, pheophorbide a, and others in the sediments and to more complex ones in petroleum. Thus porphyrins, as well as the types of hydrocarbons, indicate survival in forms modified by diagenesis. It appears evident then that neither survival alone nor production alone is sufficient to explain satisfactorily the changes that have been observed between phytoplankton, sediments, and petroleum. Both survival and production occur together in ways that are not yet fully understood throughout the period that organic debris sinks through the water column and is buried to depths of several meters in the basin sediments, and they continue even at greater depth (or time) where (or when) their relative roles become further confused by changes produced by migration.

When liquid hydrocarbons are present in the sediments and the interstitial water of the sediments becomes largely squeezed out by compaction, it is reasonable to expect that the waters will carry with them some of the liquid hydrocarbons. During their migration the liquid hydrocarbons must become modified by at least the effects of natural chromatography of adsorption on the clays through which they filter. This migration very much intensifies the difficulty of learning about the origin of petroleum—both through the changes that occur en route and through the uncertainty of identifying the sites of the source and of the stages of change in the migrated hydrocarbons. Problems of establishing the causes and sequences of changes in coal are relatively simple because the coal does not migrate (Fig. 232). Quite possibly the lipid fraction of organic matter supplies the bulk of the petroleum components, and so the organic materials remaining in the source rocks are not a true measure of the source materials of petroleums. Besides hydrocarbons, petroleum contains many sulfur, nitrogen, and oxygen compounds and metals. Study of these materials and of their origins and sources may provide new information about petroleum genesis as outlined by Stevens (1956). It appears probable that much more will be learned about petroleum genesis in the future by such chemical studies than by geological ones, although evidence from either discipline must be reasonable in terms of the other one.

Many of the changes in organic matter leading to petroleum occur at depths greater than can be reached by cores of basin sediments, so it is of interest to examine the Pliocene strata that fill Los Angeles Basin. These Pliocene and Miocene marine sediments approach a thickness of 4 km and according to Edwards (1951) have a volume of about 8450 cu km. The basin itself has an area of about 3750 sq km, some of which has been folded, leaving a 2500 sq km area which is flat at present (Table 5). The sediments consist of shales interbedded with sands deposited by turbidity currents (Slosson, 1958; Conrey, 1959), particularly for the Pliocene part of the section. The sands are coarsest and thickest in the northeastern part of the basin, closely resembling the nature and distribution of sands in the adjacent but not yet filled Santa Monica and San Pedro Basins

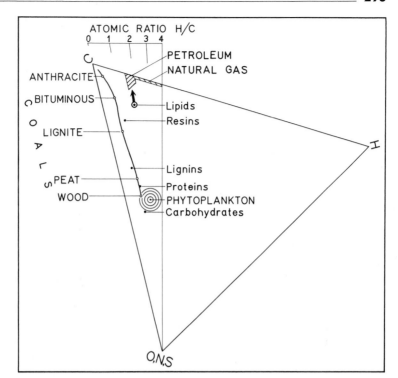

Figure 232. The chemical composition of various organic materials. Averages for coal are from Clarke (1920, p. 763). Those for phytoplankton, organic chemical groups, petroleum, and natural gas are from various tables in this work. Corners of triangle indicate 100% carbon, hydrogen, and combined oxygen, nitrogen, and sulfur, respectively. Diagram adapted partly from Kropotkin (1957). Note the differences in evolutionary trend of coal and petroleum.

(Fig. 195). The shales, which make up about half the section, have an average median diameter of about 14 microns (Table 12), decreasing irregularly with depth (Fig. 233). Calcium carbonate in the shales averages about 4.9 per cent and total organic matter about 2.6 per cent (Tables 12 and 14). These values of median diameter, calcium carbonate, and organic matter form reasonable continuations of the trends from offshore to nearshore basins (Figs. 188, 196, 201, 203, and 204), as do their rates of deposition (Figs. 207 and 208). It is evident from the foregoing that the sediments of Los Angeles Basin are so closely related to those now being deposited in the present nearshore basins that many of the small differences which do exist can serve as measures of the changes taking place at depths (or times) beyond the reach of cores of basin sediments, provided of course that the environment of deposition during the Pliocene Epoch was not very different from that existing at present.

The sediments of Los Angeles Basin, having a 2.6 per cent content of organic matter

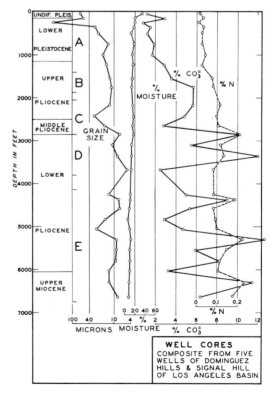

Figure 233. Sediment data for composite section near middle of Los Angeles Basin. From Emery and Rittenberg (1952, Fig. 30).

at depth, originally had a higher content. Emery and Rittenberg (1952) attempted to estimate the original organic content on the basis of the carbonate-nitrogen ratio, unaware that much of the carbonate in nearshore basins had been reworked from older sediments and thus was not deposited from the same plankton source as the nitrogen. A better method is to assume that the original content of organic matter in the surface sediments was the same as the average for the present Santa Monica and San Pedro Basins, about 6.1 per cent. This value is close to the 5 per cent estimated by Emery and Rittenberg. At a depth of about 3 meters the content of organic matter would typically be reduced one-third to about 4 per cent. A further loss to 2.6 per cent at great depth is not unreasonable, especially in view of the fact that the 2.6 per cent total organic matter is based on analyses of nitrogen, which is lost faster than is organic carbon in the sediments.

Approximate figures for supply and deposition of total organic matter (Table 29) can be worked out for the area of Los Angeles Basin, 3750 sq km, assuming that conditions during the past were the same as those of the present Santa Monica and San Pedro Basins. Rates of deposition of porphyrins and hydrocarbons in Los Angeles Basin were taken in the same ratios to total organic matter as they have in Santa Monica Basin (Table 14). Up to 1952 the Los Angeles Basin oil fields had produced 3.8 billion barrels of petroleum and had 1.1 billion barrels of proved reserves, giving a total ultimate recovery of 4.9 billion barrels (Emery and Rittenberg, 1952). About two-thirds, or 3.3 billion barrels, is

from Lower Pliocene strata. If the latter had a duration of 5 million years, the annual production of exploitable petroleum would have been 660 barrels, or 100 tons. Annual amounts of hydrocarbons and porphyrins required for this weight of petroleum are based on reasonable figures for composition of petroleum (Orr, Emery, and Grady, 1958).

Although no great weight can be given the estimates of Table 29, they do show trends which probably are reliable. Only about 6.4 per cent of the organic matter that is produced by phytoplankton was deposited in the bottom sediments of Los Angeles Basin. Somewhat less than half of this, 2.8 per cent of production, still remains in the shales, and only 0.005 per cent is likely to be exploited as petroleum. Thus, one barrel of petroleum required the growth of organic matter equivalent to 19,000 barrels. The hydrocarbons, of which petroleum for the most part consists (about 80 per cent), are more efficiently preserved, so that 1.3 per cent of the original production by phytoplankton is recovered as petroleum. Of course, we must recognize that this is only a net figure and that some of the original hydrocarbon molecules were lost and replaced by others probably broken out of more complex organic materials by bacterial and abiological processes. Quite evidently, chlorophyll is produced by phytoplankton in far greater quantity than its derivatives are needed to satisfy the requirements of petroleum produced in Los Angeles Basin. At present the annual production of petroleum in Los Angeles Basin is about 100 million barrels per year, a rate roughly

Table 29

PRODUCTION AND DEPOSITION OF ORGANIC MATERIALS IN LOS ANGELES BASIN, TONS PER YEAR

	Total Organic Matter		Porphyrins		Hydrocarbons	
	Tons	%	Tons	%	Tons	%
Production	1,900,000	100.0	112,000	100.0	6000	100.0
Deposition	120,000	6.4	95	0.8	300	5.0
At 3 meters	80,000	4.2	15	0.1	200	3.3
In shale	52,000	2.8	?	?	?	?
In petroleum	100	0.005	0.2	0.0001	80	1.3

150,000 times faster than it was formed. The sunlight required to make this petroleum also had about 10 million times the energy that is presently being recovered as petroleum. Nature's storage of the solar energy has been inefficient, but it is in a form that is cheaper and easier to tap and use than solar energy at our present level of technology. Some idea of the magnitude of solar energy is provided by a computation of Ayres and Scarlott (1952, pp. 187, 313), who showed that the entire stock of combustibles on Earth (wood, coal, petroleum, natural gas, oil shale, uranium, and thorium) can altogether provide only as much heat as is received by Earth from the sun in 3 days.

Economic Aspects

The classical sequence—observation, understanding, prediction, and utilization—implies that economic development should be the last stage in knowledge of a region. However, perhaps more often it come first by chance or by empirical methods. Even then we may try to discover the reasons for an economic resource by rationalization. Thus the discovery of future resources or the understanding of present ones must be based on the first three steps of the sequence. Accordingly, it seems desirable to end this study with a discussion of some potential and existing economic resources and their causes.

Water

Fresh Water

Prior to the intensive settlement of southern California with its attendant need for large supplies of water, the water table and the pressure surfaces of aquifers sloped seaward and fresh water flowed underground to the ocean. Fresh-water springs along the shore and springs rising locally through sea water from shallow depths were known to fishermen and others. By 1905 Mendenhall reported a general shrinkage in extent of artesian area and a lowering of water levels unrelated to deficiencies in precipitation. By 1933 overpumping had reversed the slope of the water table so that in the area north-east of Palos Verdes Hills it was more than 8 meters below sea level (Eckis, 1934). Progressive lowering continued until the water table fell as much as 30 meters below sea level in some coastal areas. Falling coastal water tables are reported by Upson (1951b) for Santa Barbara, by Thomas, Marliave, James, and Bean (1954) for the Oxnard-Ventura Plain, by Eckis (1934), Poland, Garrett, and Sinnott (1948), Kramsky and others (1952), Baumann and Laverty (1956), and Bookman (1957) for the Los Angeles Plain, and by Poland, Piper, and others (1956) for the Long Beach–Santa Ana Plain.

With the reversal of the water table, a reversal of flow took place, leading to serious contamination of water wells by sea water. The first indication of approaching sea water may be a change in ion ratios, but not the same changes that would be expected of simple mixing of sea water and ground water. Contact with clay minerals may produce alteration of cation ratios in the intruding sea water through base exchange (Revelle, 1941). Calcium, magnesium, and potassium have a far higher base exchange activity than sodium, but, because of the much greater concentration of sodium than of the other cations in sea water and the typical dominance of calcium and magnesium as replaceable bases on the clays that are deposited by streams in the region, the intrusion of sea water usually leads to some loss of sodium and a pickup of calcium and magnesium by the water (Fig. 234). Contact with organic matter in the sediments may result in reduction of sulfate ion to sulfide and its partial disappearance from the water. Chloride is the only common anion of sea water that is unlikely to be affected during movement through an aquifer. Bicarbonate (with carbonate) is usually the most abundant anion in ground water, particularly in southern California. Accordingly, an increase in the chloride/bicarbonate ratio may signal imminent serious contamination by sea water. When

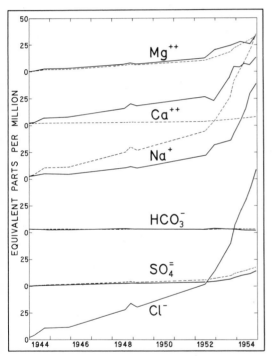

Figure 234. Change of water composition in Manhattan Beach well no. 7 (701E)—about 1.5 km inland—as a result of sea water intrusion. Computations made before 1949 are from Kramsky and others (1952); analyses for later computations are from files of Los Angeles County Flood Control District, courtesy E. J. Zielbauer. Between May 1950 and February 1951 the well served as an injection point for recharging the Silverado zone. The solid line represents observed values; the dashed line represents values that would have existed if the native ground water had simply become mixed with sea water in proportions such as to produce the observed chloride contents. Note that observed values are higher than simple mixing ones for calcium and magnesium, but lower for sodium, sulfate, and usually bicarbonate ions.

the latter occurs, the total salt content rises to unmistakable concentrations that make the water unfit for domestic, agricultural, and most industrial uses. Serious contamination has occurred in many of the coastal ground-water basins (Richter and Marliave, 1952; Slater and Richter, 1952), including Mission Valley, San Luis Rey Valley, Santa Margarita Valley, Orange County Coastal Plain, Los Angeles County Coastal Plain, Malibu Creek Valley, and Trancas Creek Valley. Contamination is threatened at many other areas and can eventually occur at still more.

The useful life of a well may be prolonged by less intensive pumping at the first sign of approaching sea water intrusion. Reduction of pumping resulted in a rise of water table of as much as 5 meters in much of the Los Angeles Coastal Plain between 1955 and 1958. However, water needs in this area are so great that more drastic measures are needed to prevent intrusion. An experimental fresh-water barrier along 3 km of the coast of Santa Monica Bay was constructed in 1950 by injection of fresh water into wells spaced about 150 meters apart 600 meters inland from the shore (Banks, Richter, and Harder, 1957). By this method the water table in the aquifer was built above sea level as a long ridge, reportedly with little loss of fresh water to the sea. Additional fresh-water barriers are to be constructed in the Long Beach and the Redondo Beach areas in 1960. Other methods of preventing intrusion of sea water that have been used or considered here and elsewhere in the region are recharge of aquifers by spreading or pumping into recharge wells large quantities of treated or raw fresh water or of treated sewage effluent, development of a pumping trough adjacent to the coast to remove landward-flowing sea water, and construction of artificial semipermanent barriers of sheet piling, asphalt, cement grout, or puddled clay.

The need for ever larger supplies of fresh water in southern California, coupled with the insufficiency of local ground water and the high cost and political problems of importation from Lake Mead, Owens Valley, and elsewhere, has focused attention on schemes of converting sea water into fresh water. Because of the gravity of the situation here and elsewhere, the California Legislature in 1951 appropriated funds for the University of California to undertake research in conversion, and the U. S. Congress in 1952 passed a Saline Water Conversion Act authorizing a program of research and development administered by the Office of Saline Water in the Department of the Interior. More than a score of laboratory investigations are underway and several pilot plants are now being operated. Very good outlines of the various methods being investigated are given by Howe (1952) and Jenkins (1957, 1958).

The simplest conversion method is that of using solar energy to evaporate sea water under glass or plastic covers, but the efficiency is low, only about a quarter of a gallon per square foot per day. If all the fresh water required within Los Angeles County alone, about 300,000,000 gallons per day, were produced in this way, an area of about 2 square miles (5 sq km) of solar stills would be needed. The cost of the land alone prevents the use of solar stills for development of urban water supplies. Obviously a more concentrated source of energy than sunlight is needed. Energy as heat, electricity, and pressure has been applied in a variety of ways. Multieffect stills also use the latent heat released by condensation of water vapor from each stage to evaporate the brine from the next stage. Reductions in pressure at each successive stage reduce the boiling point in accordance with the lower temperature of the brine at each stage. In vapor-compression stills improved efficiency results from compression of the water vapor to raise its temperature and the transfer of heat from the vapor to the brine to aid in evaporation. A great improvement over either type of still, especially for small supplies of water, is the spinning top in which a thin film of sea water sprayed on the inside surface partly evaporates. This vapor is drawn off, is compressed to raise its temperature, and is condensed on the outside surface, thus yielding heat that is transmitted through the thin metal of the

spinning top to evaporate the film of sea water on the inside surface. Another method operates on temperature differences existing between the ocean surface and depth, using the colder water from depth to condense vapor from the warmer surface water or vapor from a flash chamber. This method has the advantage of producing power as well as fresh water, but it has a low yield for the capital outlay.

Ion exchange with zeolites and various resins was used in war-time survival kits for life rafts. In principle, the unwanted ions are exchanged for less offensive ones; for permanent installations the unwanted ions are washed off the exchange medium which can then be reused. Thus the method is similar to that of the family water softener, but it is expensive and useful for making only small quantities of fresh water. A more complex ion exchange method, electrodialysis, makes use of selective membranes, whereby membranes permeable to cations alternate with ones permeable to anions in subdividing a long tank into compartments. When an electric current is passed from one end of the tank to the other, alternate compartments become fresh, having yielded their salts to the intervening compartments. By another method, reverse osmosis, water is forced through a semipermeable membrane which screens out the salts. Freezing has long been known by oceanographers to purify sea water because sea ice when melted is relatively fresh. As shown by Thompson and Nelson (1954), increased efficiency of converting salt into fresh water can be obtained by freezing from the top of a water column and by discarding the first 70 per cent of the meltwater. Because the latent heat of fusion is less than the latent heat of evaporation, freezing when properly applied may become cheaper than distillation as a source of fresh water. All these and other methods are being intensively tested, some in southern California.

Only the multieffect distillation and vapor compression distillation methods have reached a commercial level, but both are too expensive at their present stages of development (Howe, 1958). The costs of distillation are approximately $2.00/1000 gallons for a Pacific Gas and Electric Plant at Morro Bay which produces about 144,000 gallons per day. According to Howe (1958) recent developments suggest that costs may soon be reduced for large-scale distillation to something like $0.35/1000 gallons. This is less than the $0.40/1000 gallons commonly paid by southern Californians for municipal water; the cost at the source for the latter is only about $0.10/1000 gallons. It is also much more than the $0.02 to $0.12/1000 gallons paid by farmers for irrigation water. As pointed out by Howe (1952), production by distillation of all needed domestic water in the United States would more than equal the total fuel now burned in power plants. With the imminent depletion of reserves of petroleum, natural gas, and high-grade coal in the United States, it is evident that large-scale distillation using these fuels is impractical. However, waste heat from industry might well be utilized. As pointed out in the section on man-made oceanography, about 2.8×10^{10} cal/day of heat is wasted to the ocean from power plants in the Los Angeles region. Additional heat is put into the air or ocean by the numerous oil refineries of the region. Possible reduction in costs may also be permitted by use of atomic energy. In 1958 the U. S. Congress and the California Legislature granted $100,000 to the Fluor Corporation of Whittier to study this problem. Plans call for the design of a low-level low-cost nuclear reactor to produce 1,000,000 gallons per day, with later ones to be rated at as much as 50,000,000 gallons per day at a cost of perhaps $0.50/1000 gallons (Brice, Dusbabek, and Townsend, 1958). Since the evaporation will be at low temperature and use only half the introduced sea water, scale formation should be avoided. The fresh water, condensed by cold sea water, should carry less than 60 ppm of salts, about one-fifth the maximum for drinkable water.

Still other supplies of fresh water can be obtained from treated sewage effluent. If pumped from the Hyperion Sewage Treatment Plant, delivery to the desert for irrigation would cost about $0.30 to $0.40 per 1000 gallons; even then the chemical composition would be such as to restrict its uses (Gunnerson, 1958a). For local domestic and industrial use the effluent must be treated to maintain the dissolved solids below accepted concentrations (U. S. Public Health Service, 1946), requiring about half the flow to be discharged to the ocean. The cost of reclaiming Hyperion effluent is estimated at only $0.03 to $0.12 per 1000 gallons; thus, increased demands for water will probably require its eventual use in spite of popular resistance to use of reclaimed sewage effluent. Reclaimed sewage effluent has long been used in some European cities (Tolman, 1937, p. 186).

Pollution

In addition to their problem of obtaining, treating, and distributing water, urban areas must provide for the collection, treatment, and disposal of the same water and of other materials as sewage after use by the inhabitants. Some of this sewage can be reclaimed through treatment and return of water to the ground or to water mains, but popular prejudice and the high content of salts limit the amount that can be recovered. A large percentage of the solids can also be reclaimed as fertilizer, but the cost is about $14/ton (Hume, Bargman, Gunnerson, and Imel, 1958), nearly four times the cost of fertilizer from other sources. About 24 per cent of the solids are being recovered at Los Angeles City's Hyperion Sewage Treatment Plant, an amount almost exactly the same as the synthesis due to algal growth in the sewage during its purification treatment (Gunnerson, 1958b). The bulk of the water and solids from this and other coastal treatment plants is discharged to the ocean in the belief that the ocean is a limitless reservoir and that concentrations are quickly reduced by stirring and other processes. Even with the minimum treatment permitted by discharge to the ocean, the costs of collection and handling are approximately $0.12/1000 gallons, about one-third the original cost of the water.

Some idea of the magnitude of the disposal problem is given by the mere figures for average volume of sewage in millions of gallons per day: 4 for Santa Barbara, 4 for Oxnard, 265 for Los Angeles City (at Hyperion), 180 for Los Angeles County (at Whites Point), 35 for Orange County (near the mouth of the Santa Ana River), 40 for San Diego, and about 15 for all other coastal communities. When discharged to the oceans, these wastes must not constitute a hazard to health of bathers, or be a threat to commercial shipping and fishing, or be esthetically offensive. Criteria set up by the California State Water Pollution Control Board must be met; chief of these is that the coliform bacteria cannot exceed 10 per mil in three consecutive samples or in more than 80 per cent of 20 consecutive water samples tested. During the past this limit has occasionally been exceeded, mostly because of leakage from outfalls, requiring the adoption of measures such as chlorination of the sewage and closing of beaches to the public.

Because of the rapid growth of Los Angeles between 1945 and 1955 plans had to be made to construct by 1960 new facilities capable of handling an average of 420,000,000 gallons of sewage per day with storm peaks of 720,000,000 gallons per day. The complex question of whether Santa Monica Bay might become seriously polluted by such a great discharge of unchlorinated sewage led to a thorough study by the University of Southern California in 1955–1956 of oceanographic conditions and the behavior of sewage discharges. This is probably the largest oceanographic program ever conducted to secure data for engineering purposes. On its completion, a regular monitoring program was set up for Santa Monica Bay by the City of Los Angeles Bureau of Sanitation using its own ship and facilities. Other general pollution problems which arose from the intensive study of the bay are being further investigated by the University of Southern California in a 5-year study of the mainland shelf between Point Conception and Mexico in a program supported by the California State Water Pollution Control Board.

The findings in Santa Monica Bay that are of particular interest with respect to sewage disposal may be briefly summarized. Cur-

rents in the bay are slow, 80 per cent of the observations by current meters, drift cards, and drogues being about 0.2 knot (10 cm/ sec) (Stevenson, Tibby, and Gorsline, 1956). At an average concentration at discharge of 400,000 coliform bacteria per milliliter, dilution alone could not reduce the count to below the acceptable limit; however, experiments with patches of sewage tagged with fluorescene dye and finally with radioactive scandium showed that the T-90 (time for 90 per cent decrease in coliform count) varies between 1.5 and 4.5 hours for primary effluent and between 3.0 to 6.5 hours for secondary effluent. Almost identical results were obtained by the University of Southern California and Los Angeles City investigations (Rittenberg, 1956; Gunnerson, 1958a, 1958b). For primary effluent the decrease is due mostly to sedimentation of solids to which bacteria adhere, and for secondary effluent it is due about equally to sedimentation, dilution, and mortality. When the new effluent outfall is built 8 km from shore, the time required for effluent to drift inshore will be 13 to 30 hours, so that after an initial dilution of about 1 to 60 in the area of the outfall the reduction en route to the shore should be more than enough to comply with state standards. An interesting side effect of sedimentation was the finding of concentrations of more than 10,000 coliform bacteria per square centimeter on bottom off Whites Point and Orange County outfalls which discharge unchlorinated sewage and maxima of 250 per square centimeter in Santa Monica Bay where chlorination is still practiced (Rittenberg, 1956; Rittenberg, Mittwer, and Ivler, 1958). A linear area of high counts of bacteria on the bottom bordering the entire southwest side of Palos Verdes Hills marks the route followed by sewage from Whites Point. The same area is characterized by black sediment, locally containing either (but not both) free hydrogen sulfide or *Chaetopterus variopedatus*, a polychaete worm that serves as a pollution indicator (Fig. 235). These studies of coliform bacteria in the water and in the bottom are among the first that have been conducted in nature—avoiding the uncertainties inherent in the use of laboratory experiments.

Figure 235. Top, mean probable number of coliform bacteria per square centimeter of bottom sediment in vicinity of Whites Point outfall of Los Angeles County, from which the average sewage discharge is 177 million gallons per day. Note the presence of high counts at more than 10 km from the outfall. Bottom, distribution of black sediment (solid dots) versus ordinary green or gray sediment (circles), free hydrogen sulfide (S), and *Chaetopterus variopedatus* (C). Transparency of overlying water, shown by Secchi disk readings in meters, exhibits a pronounced decrease near outfall. Redrawn from Rittenberg, Mittwer, and Ivler (1958, Figs. 3 and 4).

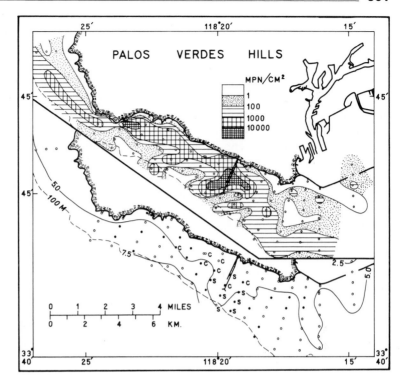

Sewage discharge alters sea water in other ways than addition of bacteria. One way is the addition of suspended solids which markedly reduce the transparency of the water (Fig. 235). Reduction has been noted to a distance of at least 4 km from outfalls. A close inverse correlation exists between Secchi disk readings (depth at which a 30-cm white disk disappears from view) and the contents of chlorine and ammonia. A transparency meter for measuring horizontal transparency of light at various depths through 1 meter of water served to track the movement of effluent, which sometimes spread out at an intermediate depth near the thermocline.

The low salinity of the effluent dilutes the sea water about 5 per cent directly over the outfalls and progressively less at greater distance, but, owing to limitation in accuracy of measuring chlorinity, the effects of dilution by sewage effluent cannot be traced as far as can reduction of transparency. The contents of phosphate and fixed nitrogen in the effluent are of the order of 1000 times their concentrations in average surface sea water. However, collections of plankton show only a slight average increase of dino-

flagellate populations, uncertain increases of diatoms, copepods, tunicates, tintinnids, and annelid larvae, and no increase of other forms. No blooms have been related to sewage discharge. Perhaps the minor effect of the great concentration of nutrients on plankton populations results from the rapid dispersal of nutrients by currents and diffusion as compared with the time required for much plankton growth. Abundant heavy metals discharged in sewage have no identifiable effect on the sea water or its life. Oxygen demand of the sewage is great, about 70 times the oxygen normally present in the same volume of surface sea water, when the oxygen demand is taken as the total of the ordinarily measured 5-day biological oxygen demand (160 ppm) plus the oxygen required to oxidize the ammonia and particulate organic matter that is discharged. Nevertheless, little effect has been noted in the receiving waters and certainly no stagnation occurs, probably because of the rapid mixing and the liberation of oxygen during photosynthesis by photoplankton.

With respect to benthos, greater effects of sewage discharge are discernible. As noted by Hartman (1956), within 3 km of the

Hyperion outfall the benthos in 1956 was much changed, with the development of an impoverished pollution-tolerant fauna composed mostly of detritus feeders. Between 3 and 6 km the benthos were enriched, particularly in detritus feeders, predators, and scavengers, probably because of the greater-than-normal food supply there. At 6 to 9 km away the benthos present a gradual transition to the normal faunas of the shelf and slope. Bottom fishes were found to reflect the changes in benthos, with maximum catches over the area of enriched benthos, evidently in response to an increase in their own food supply. At Whites Point a marked decrease in the abundance of kelp has been attributed to sewage discharge, and a decrease in abalone may be related to loss of their food supply, the kelps.

Wastes considered too harmful to be pumped to sea through outfalls are barged farther out and dumped. Such materials include overage military explosives and used acids and caustics from oil refineries. The explosives are dumped by Navy ships, presumably mostly in the prescribed areas: San Diego Trough 30 km west of Point Loma and Santa Catalina Basin at its west end. In northern California other dumping areas are located 30 km west of the Farallon Islands and, formerly, 75 km west of Pigeon Point. Most chemical wastes in southern California are dumped in Santa Cruz Basin or en route to it from San Pedro. One company weekly disposes of a barge load of acid, mostly sulfuric, and a barge load of caustic, mostly sodium hydroxide. Since most of the material is easily soluble in water, it is usually slowly dumped at the surface as the barge is being towed, in order to avoid forming large spot concentrations.

Potentially more dangerous to man than sewage discharge, although invisible, is the disposal at sea of radioactive materials. A small quantity of these have been and will continue to be introduced intentionally as tracers to aid in the study of movements of water and sediment. Only radioisotopes of short half-lives and low intensity are selected so as to constitute no nuisance or danger. One example is the introduction of 20 curies of 85-day scandium 46 into 5 million gallons of sewage at the Los Angeles Hyperion Sewage Treatment Plant to permit tracing the discharge from the outfall and to measure its dilution with sea water to about 1 part in 10,000; a single such experiment combined with other field studies served to evaluate the reduction in concentration of discharged coliform bacteria by dilution, sedimentation, and mortality (Nuclear Science and Engineering Corporation, 1956; Rittenberg, 1956). Another example is the irradiation of sand from Scripps Beach at La Jolla and its replacement on the beach to learn the rate and direction of movement (Inman and Chamberlain, in press). About 5 millicuries of the radioisotope, phosphorus 32, that was formed had a half-life of 15 days but could be detected even after several months with a sensitivity of 1 grain in 1 million by using photosensitive paper. Waves caused the 860 grams of irradiated fine sand to be dispersed over an area of about 2 sq km in only 24 hours.

Of far greater importance than tracer tests is the disposal at sea of radioactive wastes. Some disposal is indirect—the fallout from bomb bursts. Since all explosions before 1959 were at least several hundred kilometers distant from the coast of southern California, the fallout has doubtlessly been reasonably uniform throughout the area except probably nearshore where some concentrations must be produced by stream discharge. Measurements by the Los Angeles Department of Water and Power (Ree, 1958) show that counts in streams and rains immediately following Soviet bomb bursts are higher by a factor of about 10 than prior to them. Little or no effect is noted for the much closer but smaller American tests, except for one in October 1958. Because the beta gamma activities are reduced in about 60 days to one-tenth of their original values, the radioactivity supposedly represents no known danger to users of the water. However, it is conceivable that a single large widespread rainstorm coming during the first week or two after a large dirty test would bring as much as a thousand curies of fission products down to the ocean throughout the area of Chart I. Probably most of the longer-lived fine-grained fallout debris that is not dissolved becomes concentrated at the floors of the basins with the clays and silts normally deposited in these areas.

Many radioactive waste products have been intentionally introduced on the assumption that the ocean is a convenient and limitless receptacle for atomic garbage. Two plans have been followed, containment and dilution. Material disposed by containment is packed in 55-gallon or smaller steel drums, mixed and weighted with concrete, and sunk in deep water. Atomic Energy Commission wastes so disposed in the Atlantic consist of material irradiated by reactors, liquids solidified by mixing with cement or gels, contaminated solids, and combustible solids (Carritt, et al., 1958). The officially designated dumping area for southern California is Santa Cruz Basin in depths greater than 2000 meters, and for northern California it is the continental slope off San Francisco at more than 2000 meters. According to Faughn, et al. (1957), between 1946 and 1956 the San Francisco area received 10,000 packages totaling about 10,000 curies (probably mostly from reactors), and the southern California area received at least 825 drums containing about 40 curies, mostly of the sort discarded by smaller research laboratories.

Ordinary steel drums are not very strong and, unless all the air spaces of their wastes are displaced by concrete, some of the drums can be damaged or ruptured during descent. Rusting at the bottom within probably less than 10 years releases some of or all the material, as does leaching of concrete in time. Nevertheless, even the temporary holding in containers permits reduction of radioactivity, particularly of short-lived isotopes; slow leakage from the containers also reduces peak concentrations in the water. Once released, the waste products become diluted by diffusion and currents in much the same way as would low-level wastes introduced directly into the ocean, the second mode of disposal. This mode has not been used in southern California, except for accidental and intentional disposal of radioactive wastes from laboratories and hospitals into public sewage systems in quantities that are estimated to total about 4 curies per year of gamma radiation at the Hyperion Sewage Treatment Plant (W. A. Schneider, personal communication) and consist mostly of short-lived isotopes of iodine and phosphorus. However, according to Carritt et al. (1958), one British nuclear power plant has been authorized to dump 10,000 curies per month into the Irish Sea through a 5-km pipeline. Maps show that nine existing and proposed British plants are located along the coast (Hinton, 1958) in such a way that probably all intend disposal at sea of low-level waste products. Disposal is planned only on a much smaller scale in the United States, where high-level wastes are being held in tanks or pumped underground into presumably tight reservoirs. Doubtlessly, there must eventually be an end to both tankage and underground storage so that disposal at sea of large quantities of even high-level wastes must be considered. Thus we face the major problem of nuclear energy, for which the equilibrium level of waste products has been estimated at 3×10^{13} curies by the year 2000.

Once the radioactive wastes are mixed with sea water, their concentrations are reduced by natural decay, dilution, adsorption on sediment particles, and uptake by organisms. Two of the most common radioisotopes shipped by the Atomic Energy Commission, iodine 131 and phosphorus 32, have half-lives of only a few days, so they soon become unimportant as compared with other elements. Most important is strontium 90, followed by copper 64, cesium 137, and iron 59 (Carritt et al., 1958). Dilution is the next most important factor and it occurs by diffusion and currents. The main point of interest here is that the currents must not sweep unfavorable concentrations into recreational areas along the shore. Adsorption of radioactive materials on suspended and bottom sediment particles should withdraw some of them from availability to sea water, but in areas of disposal, such as the floors of basins, the bottom is not greatly disturbed by currents so there is little suspended sediment, and the shallow shelves with their high turbidity due to suspended sediment are not at present areas of disposal. Selective pickup of dissolved radioisotopes by both plants and animals is important, particularly with reference to human food supplies from the ocean. The well-known autophotographs of fishes collected from Bikini Atoll following the 1946 bomb tests are examples of such pickup. As shown by Martin (1957) the pickup is more important for minor constituents of organisms than for major ones, because the major elements such as calcium and carbon are naturally present in such large concentrations in sea water that the added radioisotopes are nearly negligible in comparison with the total available to organisms. Radioisotopes among trace elements, such as zirconium 95, rubenium 106, zinc 65, and cobalt 60, were observed to become concentrated up to thirteen times by *Discorbis floridana,* a benthic foraminiferan. Even larger concentrations were measured in fresh-water organisms by Krumholz and Foster (1957).

In order to obtain data for future control of radioactive contamination of the ocean, surveys of present and future levels of radioactivity have been and will continue to be made. A survey in April 1956 over Santa Cruz Basin by Scripps Institution of Oceanography (Faughn, et al., 1957) failed to detect radioactivity in the water, although large water samples from the surface and from 1000 meters deep were concentrated by precipitation of salts and by evaporation. The organisms collected at various depths had far greater radioactivity at the surface than at depth, presumably because of concentration of fallout of bomb fission products. The level of artificial radioactivity at the sediment surface was below that of natural radium and its daughter products in the sediment. Negative results were also obtained for the much greater dumping area off San Francisco. In 1956–1957 measurements of radioactivity in the water over the mainland shelf off southern California were made in connection with a survey of the area by University of Southern California for the California State Water Pollution Control Board, again with negative results. Negative results for both surveys indicate either that no appre-

ciable contamination of the water has occurred or, more reasonably, that methods of detection are not yet sensitive enough.

Repeated monitoring should be done in areas where radioactivity is most expected after leakage of containers. The bottom and surface currents near Santa Cruz Basin are such that detection near the surface ought to be expected in the part of the area of upwelling that is just south of Santa Cruz Island. Sampling is probably simplest in the shallow-water column of the north half of the Santa Rosa–Cortes Ridge. Probably a better area for disposal of containers than Santa Cruz Basin is Santa Barbara Basin, even though it is shallower. Small containers should settle farther into the softer mud of that basin and, if not first ruptured or corroded, they should be buried faster by deposition of subsequent sediments owing to the three-times-faster rate of deposition in Santa Barbara Basin. Corrosion should also be relatively slower in Santa Barbara Basin because of the low content of oxygen in the bottom water and its absence in interstitial waters. Once the container is buried, it is probable that future release from it would not mean release to the water above the bottom, because burrowing organisms are not present and water driven upward by compaction should never reach the surface of the sediment, as discussed in the section on permeability of basin sediments.

Fisheries

Fishing constitutes one of California's major industries and it takes on both commercial and sportfishing aspects. The value of the total commercial catch and importation for the whole state has increased from about $7 million in 1926 to $19 million in 1939 to $60 million in 1947 to $83 million in 1956. These figures are influenced more by the rise in price of fish than by increased landings. About three-quarters of this total value represents landings at the ports of Los Angeles and San Diego, about one-third of which consists of fish caught in waters off Mexico and even farther south. In 1946, 4450 commercial fishing boats were active with about half based in southern California. Similarly, about half the state's 10,000 commercial fishermen were licensed in southern California.

Since 1926 statistics on the fish catch have been tabulated and published by the California Department of Fish and Game in a series of reports entitled Fish Bulletins. Periodically the Fish Bulletins also contain summary statistics and detailed information about each of the approximately 70 important species of commercial fishes, crustaceans, and mollusks (Staff of Bureau of Marine Fisheries, 1949). Data for catches made in waters off southern California were extracted from the Fish Bulletins and presented graphically for the years 1926–1957 in Figure 236.

Except for the years since 1952 two-thirds or more of the tonnage of commercial fish catch off southern California was sardines, of which about 90 per cent were landed at Los Angeles. Prior to about 1952 nearly as many sardines were landed at Monterey as at southern California ports, but afterward the northern catch practically vanished. Few sardines are imported from waters off Mexico; thus they are concentrated in the area off southern California. As pointed out by Pinkas (1951) and Clothier and Greenhood (1956), the best catches of sardines (and of many other fishes) occur over areas of particular kinds of bottom topography, shelves, submarine canyons, and escarpments. Each of these areas is characterized by high productivity of sessile plants or phytoplankton owing to shallowness of waters or to relatively intense upwelling. According to John Radovich of the California Department of Fish and Game (personal communication), areas of shallow water such as the Santa Rosa–Cortes Ridge serve as avenues of migration of sardines, possibly in response to their need for food. After the tremendous catch of sardines in 1950 (Fig. 236) the annual catch decreased markedly and was nearly negligible in 1952 and 1953. A price rise from about $35/ton in 1950 to $114/ton in 1953 did not produce more fish, of course, but merely reflected the demand in the face of a short supply. The small catch since 1950 has also resulted in more intense competition for fish, as indicated by the laying up of many boats and the testing and adoption by some of the surviving boats of new techniques such as aerial reconnais-

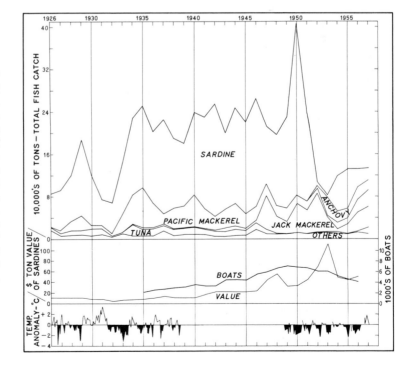

Figure 236. Catches of chief commercial fishes in waters off southern California between 1926 and 1957 as compiled from statistics in Fish Bulletins of California Department of Fish and Game. For comparison, note the graphs of the number of fishing boats and price to fishermen of sardines, compiled from the same source. The monthly anomaly from average water temperature for the region (30° to 35° latitude and 115° to 120° longitude) is from Reid, Roden, and Wyllie, 1958).

sance, sonar, and other devices. This same short supply of sardines resulted in an increased catch of anchovy and jack mackerel as sardine substitutes.

The tunas are also well-known products of the California fishery, with the bulk of those caught in the southern California region being albacore. Others that occur here but are usually obtained more abundantly in Mexican and more southerly waters are the bluefin, yellowfin, and skipjack tunas. Large number of tunas, chiefly albacore, are caught by sportfishing party boats; these are not included in Figure 236, but they usually constitute only about one-tenth of the commercial catch. Because the tuna fishery decreased markedly about the same time as did the sardine fishery, a Scripps Tuna Oceanography Program sponsored by the U. S. Fish and Wildlife Service was initiated in 1957 to learn more of these fish and the factors that control their abundance.

Among the "other fish" of Figure 236 are croaker, halibut, rockfish, salmon, sea bass, shark, sole, swordfish, crab, lobster, abalone, and squid, each of which totaled more than 100 tons for waters off southern California in 1956. Abalone, a marine gastropod, is more or less characteristic of southern California and has been landed commercially in amounts that have increased from 9 tons in 1926 to 2100 tons in 1956, mostly at Santa Barbara. An unknown but probably larger catch of abalone has been made by skin divers whose activities have largely eliminated abalones in easily accessible areas and depths off the mainland shores. A similar depletion of lobsters has resulted from skin diving by the large number of week-end enthusiasts.

The decrease in sardine catch, paralleled by other fishes, since 1950 cannot reliably be ascribed to either overfishing or to natural variation produced by population cycle or migration induced by changes in water temperature or other water characteristic. In order to determine the cause and thence to predict the return of sardines, a program of study of oceanographic and fishery factors was initiated in 1947 as the California Cooperative Oceanic Fisheries Investigations,

financed by a special tax on fish landings and by appropriations of the California Legislature. This is a combined project of Scripps Institution of Oceanography, the California Department of Fish and Game, the California Academy of Sciences, and the U. S. Fish and Wildlife Service. The six progress reports published between 1950 and 1958 (Marine Research Committee, 1958) summarize many data on oceanic temperatures and currents, plankton crop, and fish eggs and size classes. However, in general the findings so far have been inconclusive. An estimated 15 to 20 per cent of the total standing population is caught annually, regardless of effort beyond a certain point, but it is still not clear whether variations in the standing population are due to man's fisheries or to other causes. An example of the difficulty of evaluation is the fact that low temperature of water is commonly related to intense upwelling and high concentrations of nutrients which should produce much phytoplankton, zooplankton, and finally sardines, but the same low temperatures may inhibit spawning of sardines if spawning occurs in the same areas as feeding. Empirical relationships between water temperature and sardine catch may indicate that the two are directly related, particularly for 1958 when the high water temperatures (Fig. 120) (Stewart, Zetler, and Taylor, 1958; Marine Research Committee, 1958) are reflected in unusually large catches of sardines, which are evident even though the catch data are incomplete. Coupled with the return of warm water, high sea level, and sardines was the first appearance off southern California for many years of many tropical fishes such as dolphin fish, sailfish, manta rays, hammerhead sharks, and green turtle. When placed on a longer time scale (Fig. 236), the temperature of the water is less clearly related to the catches of sardines. It is evident that new efforts, perhaps with a new orientation, are needed to solve the problem of sardine populations.

Recent studies of the sea floor topography aboard *R/V Velero IV* using the Precision Depth Recorder (Luskin, Heezen, Ewing, and Landisman, 1954) showed the common presence of echoes, probably from schools of fish. The most frequent site of the echoes is basin slopes, a reasonable one in view of the known local upwelling in such areas. However, the most common depth is 80 to 120 fathoms (146 to 220 meters), far below the near-surface zone of commercial fishing in deep water. Conceivably these echoes represent a heretofore unexploited fishery that warrants further investigation.

Shipping

In 1805 the small trading ship *Leila Byrd* out of Boston anchored at San Pedro to barter cloth, sugar, and household goods for hides, tallow, and horns. A graphic account of this trade was given by Dana (1945), who described his experiences in loading cattle hides during the years 1835 and 1836. At that time half a dozen ships *(Pilgrim, Alert, California, Ladoga, Ayacucho,* and *Loriotte)* were engaged in the trade, although port facilities were very primitive: in the words of Dana, "Two days brought us to San Pedro, and two days more (to our no small joy) gave us our last view of that place, which was universally called the hell of California, and seemed designed in every way for the wear and tear of sailors. Not even the last view

could bring out one feeling of regret. No thanks, thought I, as we left the hated shores in the distance, for the hours I have walked over your stones barefooted, with hides on my head; for the burdens I have carried up your steep, muddy hill; for the duckings in your surf; and for the long days and longer nights passed on your desolate hill, watching piles of hides, hearing the sharp bark of your eternal coyotes, and the dismal hooting of your owls." Twenty years later the first records of the Port of San Pedro after California became a state showed that 61 ships of an average 100 tons visited the port in 1855. By the years 1867–1870 about 90 per cent of the cargo was carried by steamships that had an average tonnage of 1200, as compared to 160 for the remaining sailing ships. Records of the port for each of these four years show 100 to 200 entrances of coastwise ships mostly discharging coal, prominent among which were *Oriflamme* and *Orizaba.*

The number of entrances of ocean-going ships at San Pedro remained below about 500 per year until the year 1900, when it rapidly rose to about 3000 by 1920 (Fig. 237). Subsequently, the number has fluctuated between 2000 and 8600 with a peak between the years 1925 and 1935 (Board of

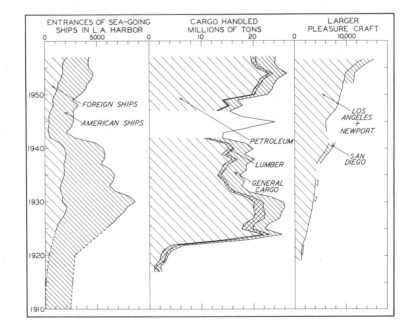

Figure 237. Annual number of ocean-going ships entering Los Angeles Harbor since 1910 with tonnage of different general types of cargo handled each year (from 49th annual report of Board of Harbor Commissioners, Los Angeles, 1957). Rise in number of pleasure craft (undocumented vessels) is also shown for Los Angeles, Newport, and San Diego (from files of U. S. Coast Guard, 11th District).

ENTRANCES OF SEA-GOING SHIPS IN L.A. HARBOR

CARGO HANDLED MILLIONS OF TONS

LARGER PLEASURE CRAFT

FOREIGN SHIPS

AMERICAN SHIPS

PETROLEUM

LUMBER

GENERAL CARGO

LOS ANGELES + NEWPORT

SAN DIEGO

Harbor Commissioners, City of Los Angeles, 1957). The smaller number of ships entering since 1935 is merely a reflection of the increase in average size of modern ships; for example, some tankers now using the port have a capacity of about 700,000 barrels. Since 1923, when the period of great oil production began in the Los Angeles Basin, about 85 per cent of the cargo tonnage has been petroleum or petroleum products, imported and exported. Most imports are from Venezuela, the Persian Gulf, and Canada. About two-thirds of the ships are of American registry, although 80 per cent are in foreign trade as opposed to coastal shipping. This growth of shipping has required a high state of development of port facilities at San Pedro and Long Beach —the Los Angeles Harbor—which has 150 acres of wharves and sheds and more under construction. A parallel but much smaller increase in shipping occurred at San Diego for which, instead of petroleum, Navy activities are chiefly responsible, with cotton being the main commercial cargo.

Larger commercial fishing craft in Los Angeles Harbor number about 878, a figure that represents a slow and steady increase from 847 in 1946 (Mr. E. W. Park, Los Angeles Harbor Department, personal communication). About 125 are purse seiners, and most of the rest are jig boats. The lack of rapid increase is probably a reflection of competition from foreign supplies of tuna, sardines, and mackerel. More than a hundred sportfishing craft are chartered for catches of rockfish, bass, mackerel, albacore, and barracuda. In addition, many pleasure craft are used for occasional private fishing.

Since about 1920 the increased population, leisure, and interest in the ocean have produced a rise in the number of sail and inboard powered pleasure craft in southern California from less than 1500 to more than 15,000 (Fig. 237). Although this represents only about 3 per cent of the total number in the United States, most of the others are in areas having large enclosed bays. Facilities for docking are at a premium, and new small-boat harbors and marinas are rapidly being developed at many places along the coast (Patterson, 1950; numerous press notices). In part to avoid docking charges, innumerable other small pleasure craft powered by outboard engines are kept in garages and moved by trailers. During the early years of yachting in the region the many islands off the coast provided destinations at convenient distances and of sufficient interest that many pleasure cruises were made to them (Holder, 1910). As a result of competition from other forms of entertainment, military restrictions, and smaller average size of pleasure craft owing to high taxes and high cost of operation, the islands are now less frequently visited (Warren, 1958; Hillinger, 1958) and many boats are used only in the restricted waters of the small enclosed bays of the region.

Some rather unusual craft have sailed the waters off southern California in recent years. One is the raft _Lehi_ built by DeVere Baker and sailed after several false starts from Redondo to the Hawaiian Islands in 69 days between July 13 and September 20, 1958, as a sort of reverse test of Mormon history. Another is the 50-ton submarine, _Cetacean,_ built by Edmund Martine, the builder of diving bells at Santa Monica, Santa Catalina Island, and elsewhere. Launched in 1955 with the intention of being used to great depth, it was soon modified by installation of a large window for picture taking, thus destroying its depth capabilities. During late 1958 the bathyscaphe _Trieste_ and its builder Jacques Piccard (Piccard and Dietz, 1957) were brought to San Diego to begin a Navy-sponsored program of investigation of the water, life, and bottom in great depths off southern California. In water shallower than 100 meters a type of small two-diver craft called a Minisub has been developed and used in scientific studies of the mainland shelf off San Diego by the U. S. Navy Electronics Laboratory. This trend toward the undersea region may be followed by cargo ships that have their cigar-shaped hulls under water and expose only a navigational cabin atop a vertical fin. Such a ship now being studied would avoid much of the motion induced by waves and could at the same time be a more efficient shape than conventional hulls for moving through water.

Dredgings of rock and sediment often contain artifacts lost or discarded from ships. Chief of these are cinders and pieces of coal, but occasionally broken chinaware and glass have been found. Even steel cable and bits of iron and brass, a tar bucket, paint cans, beer cans, bottles, rubber, cloth, and paint brushes have been noted, although most of this rubbish is highly perishable in sea water. Much more interesting as artifacts are wrecked ships where all or part of the ship still remains.

The earliest wrecks in the southern California region may be of Spanish ships, one of which is reported by Coffman (1957) to have been a galleon carrying $2,000,000 in gold which struck Ship Rock off Santa Catalina Island in 1598. Another worth $700,000 is supposed to have sunk on Cortes Bank in 1701, another with $2,000,000 sunk at the north end of San Clemente Island in 1754, and another carrying silver sunk at San Miguel Island in 1801; and lastly a Spanish frigate supposedly with $1,200,000 in gold ran aground at the northwestern tip of Santa Catalina Island in 1852. Solid verification of these reports is lacking, and it should be recalled that charts of the period prior to 1800 left much to be desired in accuracy, so even if the ships were wrecked there is considerable doubt about the exact localities. Possible support for the 1598 wreck off Santa Catalina Island is provided by the mention in Vizcaíno's diary of seeing two pieces of figured China silk during his visit to the island in 1602 (Bolton, 1916, p. 85). The Indians told him that a ship carrying people like the Spaniards and also Negroes was driven ashore on the island and wrecked; however, circumstances prevented Vizcaíno from visiting the wreck site.

During the last century many well-established shipwrecks have occurred on the islands and mainland, owing to stranding and breaking up at night or in fog or in narrow entrances of bays, to fire, and to collision and foundering. Many of the larger wrecks have been tabulated by Mason (1955) through compilation from Coast Guard and Hydrographic Office bulletins and from generally unverified newspaper stories (Fig. 238). His map was later copied and published by McKinney (1956). The largest ship reported wrecked was the *Cuba,* 3168 tons, stranded high on San Miguel Island on September 8, 1923. Little loss of life has been incurred by the wrecks off southern California; in contrast, north of Point Conception where winds are strong and waves are high, as many as 250 casualties have occurred in a single shipwreck. Chief losses in southern California have been in Navy ships. A gunboat, *U.S.S. Bennington* blew up off San Diego in 1905 killing 65 men, and a submarine, *U.S.S. F-1,* was rammed and sunk off San Diego with 19 men in 1917. Famous in the annals of California was the driving ashore just north of Point Arguello of nine destroyers, one after the other, during ten minutes of the same foggy morning in 1923 that the *Cuba* was stranded. The cause was a navigational error, a reversed radio compass bearing (Hadaway, 1957). Twenty-three men were killed, and the seven destroyers that finally were lost were more combatant ships than were accounted for by enemy action during all of World War I. During the first month of World War II a tanker, *Montebello,* was torpedoed and sunk about 130 km north of Point Conception (Gibbs, 1957). A lumber schooner, *Absaroka,* was also torpedoed off Point Fermin, but the buoyancy of its cargo permitted it to make port. In May 1942 a Japanese submarine was rumored to have been sunk in the outer San Pedro Bay; a magazine story even mentioned its salvage (Wellman, 1950), but Admiral King's (1946) official Navy summary of sinkings indicates that no Japanese warships were sunk east of the Hawaiian Islands. Evidently, the rumor was false though recurrent, and no sinkings related to enemy action occurred in southern California.

In spite of increased navigational aids the number of shipwrecks off southern California presents a steady increase each decade (Table 30), more or less paralleling the increase in number of ships, fishing boats, and

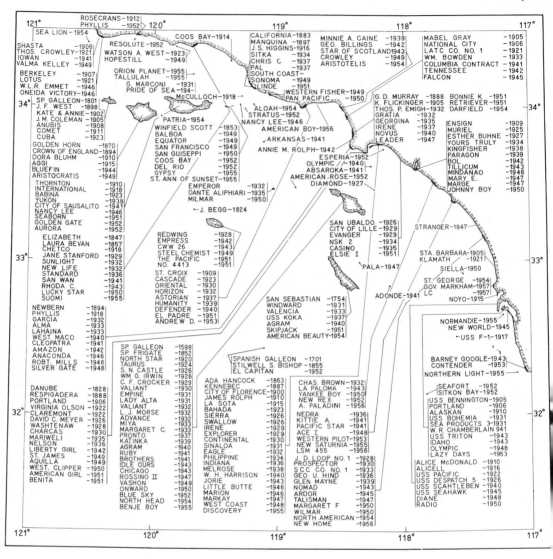

Figure 238. Names, dates, and distribution of shipwrecks. Taken from Mason (1955) and Gibbs (1957) supplemented by some data from Coffman (1957) and other sources. Only a dozen ships are known to have been salvaged.

larger pleasure craft in the region. A map of the geographical distribution of wrecks (Fig. 238) shows that 45 per cent are within 30 miles (48 km) of Los Angeles–Long Beach Harbor, suggesting a correlation between number of wrecks and density of shipping. A second concentration of 25 per cent occurs in Santa Barbara Channel and on the islands and mainland on either side of it. Traffic is heavy in this area, and several collisions have taken place in which both ships that were involved sank at the site; however, poor navigation is probably the cause of most of the other losses through stranding, generally on the islands. The remaining 30 per cent of the wrecks are fairly evenly distributed throughout the rest of the region.

Some of the wrecks have been salvaged or partly stripped, whereas others remain untouched and are for the most part of uncertain position and depth dangerous to divers. In addition, hundreds of additional derelicts have slowly sunk and rotted away at anchorages in the quite waters of San Pedro, Newport, and San Diego harbors.

Table 30
SHIPWRECKS PER DECADE OFF SOUTHERN
CALIFORNIA

Decade	Number of Wrecks
Later	11
1946–1955	90
1936–1945	67
1926–1935	53
1916–1925	23
1906–1915	21
1896–1905	6
1886–1895	5
Earlier	14
Total	290

Many were buried during land-fill enlargement of Terminal Island in Los Angeles Harbor. Whether any of the wrecks, recent or ancient, in harbors or open sea, treasure-laden or empty, are worth the trouble and expense of salvage is an open question, but their very existence serves as a perennial invitation to the poor but romantic landsman, as indicated by occasional newspaper stories of the departure from port of another party of eager treasure seekers. No mention is ever made of their successful return!

Shorelines

Landslides

The rugged nature of much of the coast of southern California is reflected in numerous landslides along its sea cliffs (Fig. 20). Deep valleys that have been eroded into the coastal areas behind these cliffs are such great obstacles to building of roads that in some areas highways have been built at the foot of sea cliffs, in spite of the danger from landslides and from wave erosion. This danger has been increased by the removal of ancient slides and talus slopes in order to provide space for a right of way and some material for a road bed. The three chief areas where highways lie between cliff and sea are the east half of the Santa Monica Mountains at Pacific Palisades west of Santa Monica, the west end of Santa Monica Mountains west of Point Dume,

and midway between Dana Point and San Clemente.

By far the most dangerous of the three areas is the one immediately west of Santa Monica where cliffs about 60 meters high consist of Pleistocene alluvium at the east and soft Middle Miocene shales at the west. The alluvium is poorly consolidated, and most slides in it are of the soil or debris fall and the slump types (Sharpe, 1938; Varnes, 1958). Not only are the shales poorly consolidated but they dip seaward so that most of the slides in them probably start as block glides that soon become thoroughly broken up and transformed into slumps. Both ancient and modern slides have occurred (Fig. 20, Section 7) and, although they have not been the largest in the region, they are especially destructive, owing to steepness of the slopes. In 1932 two slides, one of 30,000 cu meters and the other of 45,000 cu meters, covered the highway. Control was established by digging tunnels for drying with hot air (Hill, 1934). After about 6 years of operation the blowers were stopped and the tunnels and equipment allowed to deteriorate. At present the shales have again become saturated, largely through the heavy watering of lawns, so that renewed movement can soon be expected. About 1 km farther west a slide of about 40,000 cu meters occurred as a slump in the Miocene shale during March 1958. The debris partly blocked the highway but was soon cleared up. Just as the last of the debris was being moved another slide of more than 80,000 cu meters took place, burying an engineer and some of the equipment used on the first slide (Fig. 239). It was decided that removal of the new slide might cause still more slides, so instead the highway was rebuilt around the toe of the second slide. These and many other smaller landslides west of Santa Monica have been examined by Roth (1959), who found most to be of the slump type, with smaller ones of the soil avalanche type. Although it is evident that lubrication and weighting by water is a prime factor in original and subsequent movements, intensive watering of lawns by residents and municipalities occurs at an in-

Figure 239. Landslide of April 1958 at Pacific Palisades west of Santa Monica which cut off coastal traffic for several weeks. It occurred just as a previous slide (to its left) had been nearly cleared up by dumping along the shore. Movement was so unexpected that it caused one death and the destruction of several pieces of earth-moving equipment. Compare with Figure 20, Section 7. Photograph by Pacific News Pictures.

creasing rate. Escape of water at the base of the sea cliffs is noticeable at many places, carrying with it the certainty of renewed movement.

Fewer and smaller slides characterize the other two areas where highways lie at the foot of sea cliffs. West of Point Dume (Fig. 20, Section 6) many of the rocks are well consolidated, and the scarcity of residences has protected the area from excessive watering. Between Dana Point and San Clemente the cliffs are very steep and consist of poorly consolidated shales and mudstones of the Capistrano formation (Late Miocene or Early Pliocene). Fortunately the dip here is landward, so that most of the movements have taken the form only of rock falls that do not destroy the highway and menace

only an occasional motorist. With the continuing development of the cliff top as a residential district and the consequent watering of lawns, larger slides here may well occur.

In addition to blocking highways landslides have caused a huge destruction of residential property in southern California, and an even larger future destruction can be predicted. In the area immediately west of Santa Monica at least fifteen residences have been destroyed by movements along the sea cliffs and along the sides of valleys incised into them. As pointed out by McGill (1954), these slides have been promoted by improper excavation and by building atop or below loose fill. Excessive watering of lawns, seepage from septic tanks, leakage from swimming pools, and breakage of water and sewer pipes are important causes of movement (Roth, 1959). In spite of the warning and denial of grading and building permits by the Department of Building and Safety of the City of Los Angeles, owners have insisted on building in dangerous areas, with past and future damages amounting to millions of dollars. In areas such as that between Dana Point and San Clemente some homes have been built at the very edge of the cliff so as to provide the best view, but so far the main losses have been the slow undermining of the houses followed by their removal before falling down the cliff.

The situation with respect to residences has been especially serious along the south side of the Palos Verdes Hills. Near Point Fermin a slide began in 1929 (Miller, 1931) where Middle Miocene shales dip seaward toward a vertical cliff. A dozen or so houses atop the slide block had to be moved. Renewed movement in 1940, 1941, and probably subsequently has so broken up the strata that slump has produced backward rotation. This slide is a classic one, being pictured in many textbooks of geology (for example, Emmons, Thiel, Stauffer, and Allison, 1955, Fig. 125) and in technical studies of slides (Varnes, 1958). Farther west on the same coast is the largest slide of southern California from the point of view of area. This one, known as the Portuguese Bend slide, began in ancient times as a block glide down seaward-dipping bentonitic Middle Miocene shales. Movement of an area of about 2.5 sq km produced a hummocky topography that is easily recognized as of slide origin even on a topographic map of 1916 (Nelson, Zinn, Strahorn, Watson, and Dunn, 1919), and was described as such by Miller (1931) and by Woodring, Bramlette, and Kew (1946) in their geological study of Palos Verdes Hills. In some of the depressions lake sediments accumulated with internal unconformities that bear witness to repeated movements of the slide. Doubtlessly each movement continued until a toe pushed into the ocean was large enough to provide sufficient resistance to counterbalance the weight of the moving mass. With the great residential development of Los Angeles, the area of the slide became subdivided, owing to its gentle slope and beautiful view. About August 1956 renewed movement of the eastern half of the ancient slide began. Whether the cause was the just-completed dumping of about 175,000 tons of rock at the top of the slide during road building or whether it was due to excessive watering and leakage from septic tanks, or both, has not been legally estabished. Nevertheless, after 2 years the movement has reached about 16 meters horizontally with a 6-meter drop at the top and a bulge at the toe (Merriam, in preparation). Of 156 houses in the area, only 40 remained occupied in January 1959, the others having been moved away or ruined through shear at the west side and compression at the toe. Continued movement of the original area removed support from surrounding areas so that additional movement has occurred both to the west and north, with still more areas likely to be involved in the near future. Movement at the head (north) resulted in the identification as ancient slide of areas not originally recognized as such; these areas are not shown on Figure 20. An attempt to stop the movement of this mass of about 50 million tons by insertion of a score of steel and concrete pilings across the slip plane merely caused them to be broken or rotated with no appreciable effect on the slide. Slides of this type are known elsewhere in the world (MacPherson, 1952), but there seems to be no effective way of stopping them. Presumably therefore future use of the area will be restricted to park or golf course.

Beaches

The excellent sand beaches of southern California are a notable resource of the region, primarily for recreation. The sunbathing, swimming, and surf fishing are internationally known. On hot summer days as many as a million people have been estimated to visit the beaches, particularly those near the larger cities. Crowds from Los

Angeles populate the 75 km of beaches between Point Dume and Newport Beach. Others from Santa Barbara and San Diego use beaches near those cities for the most part. Where the beaches receive no care, they soon become unsightly, as exemplified by "tin can beach" south of Long Beach. Recognizing the public interest in beaches and the need for public access and continuous maintenance, the State of California has established 31 State Park Beaches along the coast with an aggregate length of about 64 km, about 15 per cent of the mainland shore. This property alone had an original purchase value of about $17 million. Still other public beaches are maintained by various counties and coastal cities. Maintenance includes mechanical raking up of cans and bottles, protection by lifeguards and police, and for some of them the providing of fireplaces, toilets, and showers. Most are free except for parking charges, and they are supported by taxes.

In addition to their recreational value beaches serve as barriers to attack of shore installations by waves. Where beaches have become narrowed through man's interference with natural beach processes, waves have cut into the shore behind them. At Santa Barbara, Port Hueneme, Malibu, Santa Monica, Redondo Beach, and Surfside (east of Seal Beach), and possibly elsewhere damage to shore structures has resulted from loss of beaches. At Venice, Newport Beach, Oceanside, and other places the beaches have become alarmingly narrowed. The cause of narrowing can be seen in an examination of the sand budget and of longshore movements of sand.

Beaches along the 480 km mainland shore of southern California average about 55 meters wide. At an assumed average thickness of 4 meters the total volume of sand landward of the low tide line is thus about 100,000,000 cu meters. By assuming an equal volume of sand beyond the low tide line, the total amount of beach sand is about 200,000,000 cu meters. At the estimated annual rate of supply of sand by streams, 2.4 million cu meters, the entire beach could be replaced in only 85 years if

there were no losses from it. That natural losses do occur is indicated by the fact that beaches have not widened greatly during historical time and by the known movements of beach sand down submarine canyons to basin floors. Longshore movement of beach sand amounts to more than 200,000 cu meters per year at Santa Barbara, Port Hueneme, and Santa Monica. If no sand passed these breakwaters and the sand at their lee sides continued to move, the annual loss would be equivalent to a complete disappearance of beach for an average distance of about 0.5 km leeward of each obstacle. In practice, of course, depletion occurs in a long tapering wedge that reaches a far greater distance.

The damage to property and loss of recreational areas produced by narrowing of beaches down-coast from breakwaters have been remedied in two ways, replenishment of sand and protection of what remains. Replenishment has frequently consisted of pumping sediment from the harbors that had intercepted it, where it was not wanted. This procedure is advantageous to both harbor and beach. It has been done at least eight times at Santa Barbara since construction of the harbor there in 1929 (Johnson, 1953) with a total dredging of perhaps 6,000,000 cu meters. About 310,000 cu meters were pumped from the harbor at Port Hueneme in 1953. Plans have been made to establish permanent and continuous by-pass sand pumps at the entrances of both harbors. Sand from the artificial small boat harbor at Santa Monica has been released three times: 46,000 cu meters in 1940, 76,000 cu meters in 1950, and 420,000 cu meters in 1958. In 1947 about 920,000 cu meters were pumped to the beach at Surfside from between the nearby jetties at Anaheim Bay constructed in 1944. At Oceanside 610,000 cu meters were pumped from the boat basin at the nearby Camp Pendleton in 1957. Another source of sand was tapped for Santa Monica Bay when in 1947–1948 about 11,000,000 cu meters of dune sand was sluiced to the beaches to provide space in the dune area for the Hyperion Sewage Treatment Plant. In other areas, notably Venice, San Pedro, Long Beach, Newport Beach, and Coronado, sediment has been pumped to the beach from nearby lagoon floors. These replenishment actions fall far short of the 2,400,000 cu meters annually contributed by streams, but they are approximately equal to the amount of beach sand trapped by artificial structures. Thus we might expect the beaches to remain except for local and intermittent losses. Unfortunately, however, the character of the beaches made by artificial dumping is different from that of the original natural beaches. For example, the artificially nourished beaches at Santa Monica Bay and Newport Beach have been built so far seaward that their foreshores are steep and waves break almost at the shore, spoiling the areas for swimming. Differences in grain size of the original beaches and the ones artificially formed of dune sand and lagoon floor sediments have also locally produced steeper than normal slopes.

The second method of keeping beaches is that of building groins, structures normal to the beach. Some of these are of rock, and others are of wood or steel piling. All intercept the longshore flow of sand and thus cause its deposition. However, this same interception creates a steadily worsening beach situation at their lee so that ever more expensive measures are required. Basically the problems of narrowed beaches are related to the construction of boat harbors in places where nature never intended them to be. The best-situated artificial harbor of the entire coast is that at Redondo Beach located near the head of a submarine canyon toward which sand moves along beaches both from north and south. Any sand that it intercepts would have been lost to the canyon anyway. Other favorable places, at least so far as beach sand losses are concerned, are around the Palos Verdes Hills, at Laguna, La Jolla, and Point Loma. The suitability of these sites was recognized by nature because natural harbors occur near several of the sites, obviating the need for artificial harbors there. By the same token, the two worst-situated artificial harbors, with respect to down-beach losses, are

doubtlessly Santa Barbara and Santa Monica, but the population pressure in both areas may justify their existence.

Harbors

Harbors can be classified into five main types, commercial, military, recreational, fishing, and refuge (Peel, 1951). The two largest harbors of southern California, Los Angeles–Long Beach and San Diego, are used for all five purposes. The harbors of intermediate size, Santa Barbara, Port Hueneme, and Newport Bay, are used for most of them. Smaller ones are less versatile with Anaheim Bay and Camp Pendleton chiefly military, and Santa Monica, Playa del Rey (under construction), Redondo Beach, Alamitos Bay, Sunset Bay–Bolsa Chica, and Mission Bay chiefly recreational, and most of the ones around the islands are used chiefly for refuge. Most of the harbors used chiefly for recreation are of artificial origin or at least have been extensively modified by man. Except for the largest cities, the population centers of southern California formed independently of harbor facilities; later, when recreational needs arose, small harbors had to be built to serve the need. Thus the large cities developed because of the presence of large harbors, but many of the small recreational harbors developed because of the presence of cities. Because of increased interest in boating, additional harbors are being considered at Goleta Lagoon, Carpinteria Lagoon, Point Dume, Malibu Lagoon, Malaga Cove, Portuguese Bend, Dana Point, Agua Hedionda Lagoon, San Elijo Lagoon, Batiquitos Lagoon, and Imperial Beach.

As pointed out in the previous section, some of the small harbors are well placed to intercept the longshore drift of beach sands with consequent narrowing of beaches at their lee. At the same time, the intercepted sediments serve to block the entrances of harbors such as Santa Barbara, Port Hueneme, Anaheim Bay, and Mission Bay and to fill the interior of ones such as Santa Monica Harbor (Fig. 240). Both processes decrease the usefulness of the harbors and

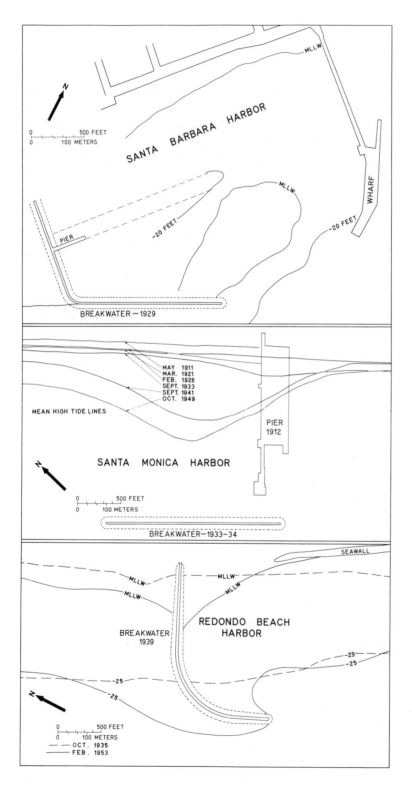

Figure 240. Top, Santa Barbara Harbor. Accretion of sediment against and within the breakwater, based on survey of February 1958 by U. S. Army Engineers. MLLW is mean lower low water.

Middle, Santa Monica Harbor. Accretion of sediment next to the Amusement Pier and within the detached breakwater. Mean high-tide shorelines for approximately 8-year intervals are taken from Handin and Ludwick (1950) and unpublished records of the City Engineers of Los Angeles and Santa Monica.

Bottom, Redondo Beach Harbor. Accretion of sediments against both sides of the landward end of the breakwater between 1935 and 1953. Redrawn from compilation by R. L. Patterson of data from Los Angeles County Surveyor's Office (Marlette, 1954).

require continuous or intermittent removal. Studies of problems of filling of the various harbors have been sponsored by the Army Beach Erosion Board: Santa Barbara (Trask, 1952), Port Hueneme (Savage, 1957), Santa Monica (Grant and Shepard, 1939; Handin and Ludwick, 1950), and Anaheim Bay (Caldwell, 1956). Published studies by other organizations and individuals have for the most part been related to other aspects of the harbor sediments than rates of filling.

The two large harbors, Los Angeles–Long Beach and San Diego, have had little difficulty with silting up, owing to their positions on the lee sides of submarine canyons which reach close to shore and on the lee side of large rocky points. Artificial modification has consisted of construction of a multimillion-dollar breakwater and mole at Los Angeles–Long Beach (McQuat, 1951), dredging of deep ship channels, and erection of wharves and warehouses (Board of Harbor Commissioners, 1957).

All the harbors are subject to oceanographic and geologic influences other than sediments, some of which are more easily controlled than others. A common factor introduced by organisms is the destruction of wooden pilings by certain isopods and mollusks. In some of the harbors, such as Los Angeles–Long Beach, discharges of industrial and sewage wastes during the past have been greater than could be effectively diluted by circulation, so the oxygen content of the water dropped to zero and hydrogen sulfide formed. Under these conditions borers could not become established and the pilings were safe (Barnard, 1958). When fishing and other interests required the waste discharge to be improved, the borers appeared along with some of the fish that were desired. Reducing the effects of borers, concrete has sometimes been used as a substitute for wooden pilings, as well as for sea walls, breakwaters, outfalls, and other marine structures. Tests of concrete blocks at San Pedro showed no deterioration by sea water in a period of 27 years (Mather, 1957). Similarly, a pozzolanic concrete pier from near Naples, Italy, was found to be in excellent condition, despite centuries of immersion in sea water (Drury, 1954). In fact, sea water has been used in mixing of concrete (Narver, 1954; Krynine and Judd, 1957) with satisfactory results.

Waves have several interesting effects on sea walls and breakwaters. At Redondo Beach erosion caused by depletion of the beach resulting from construction of the partial breakwater was offset by construction of a sea wall using blocks of granodiorite (Fig. 240). The blocks, set loosely atop the sand, pebble, and cobble foreshore, were repeatedly undermined by wave action so that they settled a meter or two during winters and the waves hurled cobbles and even small boulders over the sea wall and into adjacent houses. Repeated rebuilding and addition to the sea wall were necessary from 1945 to completon of the harbor breakwater in 1958. The ability of storm waves to move huge blocks of breakwaters and sea walls is attested by studies of Cornish (1912), Johnson (1919), and others. In the southern California region storm waves of September 1939 destroyed the lighthouse at what was then the Long Beach end of the main breakwater in San Pedro Bay, about 1 km of a small breakwater at the mouth of Los Angeles River, and several piers at Seal Beach, Huntington Beach, Laguna Beach, and San Clemente. Other storms have torn large gaps in the breakwaters at Santa Monica and Redondo Beach. Measurements of the forces exerted by waves in the region are scanty, although computations have been made of wave power from measurements of wave length, height, and period (Luplow, 1950; Johnson, 1953). Some tank studies were made by O'Brien and Morison (1952). Dynamometer measurements (Fig. 241) by Lindsay (1957a) showed that waves averaging about 50 cm high at Zuma Beach (west of Point Dume) produced forces of as much as 10 pounds per square foot (5 gm/sq cm). Forces developed by storm waves are enormously greater. For example, Johnson (1919, pp. 63–65) reported that impact forces of storm waves at Scotland reached 6000 pounds per square foot, 600 times the forces measured by Lindsay.

One of the most interesting problems con-

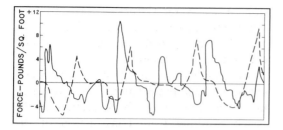

Figure 241. Dynamometer records of 50-cm waves at Zuma Beach. Solid line shows measurements about 0.6 meter below the surface; dashed line those 1.5 meters below the surface a few hours later. From Lindsay (1957a).

fronting a harbor is that of subsidence at Los Angeles–Long Beach (Gilluly and Grant, 1949; Grant, 1954; Jones, 1955). Beginning about 1937 an elliptical area of Terminal Island and adjacent mainland began to sink. By 1941 subsidence in the middle of the area had reached 1.2 feet; by 1947, 6 feet; by 1951, 16 feet; and by 1958, 25 feet (Fig. 242). According to Jones the ultimate subsidence may reach 35 feet unless water injection is practiced. The annual rate attained a peak of 2.5 feet in 1951, decreasing thereafter to about half in 1958. Accompanying the vertical movements are radially inward horizontal displacements amounting to as much as 5 feet. Also associated with the subsidence are local earthquakes and shear along small faults, one of which in 1947 resulted in destruction or damage to about 100 oil wells. The contours of subsidence correspond closely to the outline of the Wilmington Oil Field. As of August 1958 the total crude-oil production of the field (the fourth largest of the United States) amounted to about 750 million barrels, or about 4.2 billion cubic feet (0.12 billion cu meters). The volume of subsidence is less well known, owing to incomplete data on the position and nature of the outer margin of the affected area. However, a reasonable extrapolation of the areas of the various contours of Figure 242 yields a figure of subsidence of about 5 billion cubic feet (0.14 billion cu meters), not far from the volume of oil produced. The similarity of shape, volume, and time of subsidence to oil production leads naturally to the belief that the two are related. Probably the subsidence resulted from compaction of shales interbedded with the thick sequence of oil sands when fluid pressure was decreased during recovery of oil from the field. Repressuring with water injection wells will reduce the rate of subsidence and the ultimate amount of subsidence as well as increase the ultimate amount of oil to be recovered, but political and ownership problems conspired against effective repressuring until late 1958. The effect of subsidence reduces the amount of dredging needed to keep ship channels clear, but this advantage is more than offset by serious results of subsidence. Bridges have had to be jacked up and straightened, dikes have been built around low-lying areas that would have become submerged, buildings have been damaged and probably some will require lifting, and a large navy drydock is in danger of being flooded according to press releases. Although the value of the oil produced is great, the ultimate costs of combating effects of subsidence are also great.

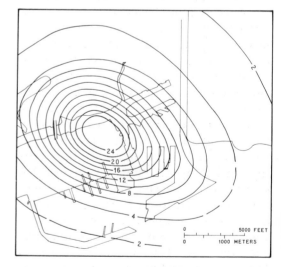

Figure 242. Contours of subsidence (2-foot interval) in area of Wilmington Oil Field for period between 1928 and 1958. Redrawn from survey of August 1958 by Harbor Department, City of Long Beach.

Sea Floor

Mining

Every cubic kilometer of sea water contains about 40,000,000 tons of dissolved solids such as sodium, calcium, magnesium, bromine, iodine, copper, silver, and gold. At 1940 prices these materials would have a value of about a billion dollars if they could be extracted (Smith, 1940). The two most abundant elements in sea water, sodium and chlorine, are separated as salt deposited on the floors of three areas of evaporation ponds in California. The largest of these is at the south end of San Francisco Bay where about 1,000,000 tons is produced annually. In southern California salt is also produced in salt ponds at the heads of San Diego Bay and Newport Bay where the annual production is about 80,000 and 10,000 tons, respectively. The chief uses of the salt produced in southern California are water softening, refrigeration, and stock feeding (ver Planck, 1958). The third most abundant dissolved solid in sea water is magnesium, constituting about 0.13 per cent, or 0.011 pounds per gallon. Most of the commercial production from sea water is at Freeport, Texas, where the easy availability of salt, sulfur, lime, and fuel promotes cheap extraction. Smaller-scale extraction of this important metal has also been developed in California at Moss Landing in Monterey Bay. Along with the magnesium, several thousand tons of bromine, the seventh most abundant element in sea water, has been extracted (Stewart, 1934). Since 1928, iodine, formerly obtained from algae, has been produced from oil field brines of the Los Angeles Basin, the only commercial source in the United States, with an annual production of possibly 400 tons (ver Planck, 1957).

Some mining of beaches has also been done. Beaches at Redondo Beach, consisting of sands having an average of 7 per cent ilmenite, have supplied about 15,000 tons of concentrates mined mostly in 1927–1928 (Lydon, 1957). Some beach sands, but mostly dune sands, of El Segundo are mined and used for sand blasting and foundry sand. Beach gravels between Carlsbad and Encinitas (Fig. 157) were extensively mined between 1915 and 1948 for grinding stones and as filter aids at $65/ton (Troxel, 1957).

Turning to the deeper ocean floor, we find two potential resources, neither of which is yet mined. The first of these is phosphorite which occurs in estimated quantities of about 1 billion tons—on bank tops, shelves, and other high areas. This reserve is about 70 times the total 1954 production of the United States, mostly from Florida, Tennessee, Idaho, and Montana. At the going price of phosphate rock ($5/ton) the sea floor phosphorite probably cannot be mined for many years yet. Similar submerged deposits occur off Florida (Pepper, 1958). Possibly the layers and nodules of manganese with their included copper, nickel, and cobalt will be mined from the deep sea floor before phosphorite is mined from the continental borderland. Comparatively negligible amounts of manganese occur on the continental borderland.

The second potential resource from the sea floor is the basin sediment itself. This is present in inexhaustible quantities, probably at least 3×10^{12} tons in Santa Barbara Basin alone with a probable 4 per cent average organic matter and other small amounts of inorganic nutrients. One possible use for these sediments is as fertilizer —to return the nutrients that have been washed from the land to the sea floor during past centuries. A rather simple test of the value of basin sediments for growth of plants was made by spreading about 10 kg of it over a square meter of lawn. After the salts had been leached out, the grass became a fine dark green, appearing to be healthier than the untreated surrounding area. A second possible use is that of distillation by pyrolysis. Tests showed, however, that only about 0.5 per cent of oil by dry weight could be produced, much less than from oil shales. Whether either use will be realized cannot be foretold now, but use will never be prevented by insufficient supply of sediment.

Petroleum

In 1769 the Portola expedition en route from San Diego to Monterey came upon the tar springs later to be known as La Brea near the site of the pueblo of Los Angeles. The tar proved to be a good fuel for their camp fires. Later, when a land grant that included La Brea was made to Antonio José Rocha in 1828, it was stipulated that the people of the region were to have an un-molested right to carry away such tar as they needed for waterproofing their abode houses (Clover, 1932, pp. 19, 21). Studies by Stock (1949) and others revealed the presence of many remarkably well-preserved skeletons of mastodons, saber-toothed tigers, and other Pleistocene vertebrates that had been caught in the sticky mass. Indians of the region had earlier known of the tar springs here and along the coast near Carpinteria where in 1770 Fray Crespi made special mention of an Indian village near a tar seep (Bolton, 1927, p. 164). Among the uses that the Indians found for the tar was cement for sticking together pieces of shell to form ornaments, waterproofing of baskets and caulking material for boats (Heizer, 1943) (Fig. 243). Analyses of tar from a seep at the south shore of Palos Verdes Hills by Richfield Oil Corporation showed it to have a melting point of 87°C and a specific gravity of 1.06, to be 63 per cent soluble in ether, and to contain 7.9 per cent sulfur and 0.14 per cent ash of which one-third consists of vanadium and nickel.

Indians also collected and used tar that was washed up on shore then as now according to accounts by Spanish explorers (Heizer, 1943). Where the tar masses encounter boulders or bedrock along the shore, they stick to the surface and become a semipermanent feature, in some instances remaining so long as to protect the underlying

Figure 243. Indian canoe planks showing asphalt caulking in holes and (lower) asphalt plugs remaining after wood has decayed. Asphalt for caulking boats and setting of tools and ornaments was used as early as 7000 years ago but reached its greatest popularity during the Early Canaliño cultural period about 2500 to 3000 years ago. Photograph by Phil C. Orr, Santa Barbara Museum of Natural History (×0.6).

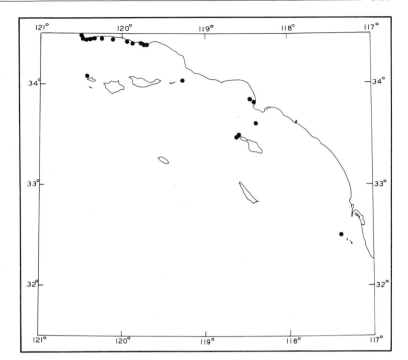

Figure 244. Positions of known offshore oil seeps.

rock from erosion and causing the tar-splotched areas to stand out in relief as much as 3 mm. Tar-splotched rock has been noted at nearly all places along the coast where rock is exposed. More common, however, is the finding of small sticky masses of soft black tar on sand beaches, where they enclose sand grains, dry out, and become buried or are carried back out to sea. Because the fresh soft tar is most easily found on the feet of bathers and others who walk on the beaches, it is notorious in well-frequented beaches such as Santa Barbara, Santa Monica, Huntington Beach, Oceanside, La Jolla, and San Diego. The latter areas are remote from known offshore seeps, and some of the tar may have come from tankers. In areas closer to the seeps, such as Carpinteria, Summerland, Coal Oil Point, Goleta Point, and Elwood, the tar is much more common per unit area of beach and is frequently associated with oil that gives the water an appearance of a brown emulsion smelling strongly of petroleum.

Navigational charts published by the U. S. Coast and Geodetic Survey indicate oil seeps at the head of Redondo Submarine Canyon and on the shelf west of San Miguel Island. Many other seeps are readily evident from aboard ships by odor and by smooth slicks on the sea surface. They have been observed in abundance in the nearshore area from Point Conception to about 8 km east, near Coal Oil Point, Summerland, and Elwood, and a few kilometers east of Anacapa Island (Fig. 244). In some of these seeps large bubbles of gas and masses of tar can be seen rising to the surface of the water—the gas to escape into the air, the oil to spread atop the water, and the tar to be carried away by currents. A deep seep was found at 304 fathoms (556 meters) on the north slope of San Pedro Basin, where a sample (no. 5905) contained slabs of tar as much as 20 × 12 × 2 cm, droplets of oil, and a petroleum odor.

Floating pieces of tar have been noted far from known seeps, some even in the deep-sea area 60 km west of Northeast Bank. Most are brown and the larger ones are flat and round (5 mm thick and 15 cm in diameter). Their rims are slightly scalloped and folded back on themselves as though by the buffeting action of wavelets. Some samples of the shelf sediments near the areas of active seeps contain bits of tar and globules of oil. In deeper basin sediments small masses of tar (Fig. 245) have sometimes been found. These were probably included in the asphaltic fraction analyzed in the cores, but they should not have affected the hydrocarbon analyses.

The obvious presence of submarine oil seeps off known oil fields on land led to early exploitation of the seaward parts of the fields. The first wells drilled in the off-shore region were in 1896 at Summerland, 30 years after the first well was drilled on land in southern California near Ventura (Carter, 1954). Several offshore rigs were built atop pilings and wharves extended out from shore. Most offshore production, however, has been from wells drilled at the shore and whipstocked seaward so that their bottoms are located as far as 4 km from the well heads. Spectacular numbers of closely spaced wells lined up along the shore may be seen at Huntington Beach and Wilmington. Since 1950 use has been made of drilling barges, Texas towers (Fig. 246), and man-made islands (Monterey Oil Company's 1954 island 2.5 km off Seal Beach, Richfield Oil Corporation's 1958 island 0.8 km off Rincón, and Standard-Humble's 1958 platform 3.5 km off Summerland). Although the islands cost 3 or 4

million dollars each, there is enough space on each to drill 25 to 70 wells. In 1958 the ultimate method was approached when patents were issued to a group of four companies (Continental, Union, Shell, and Superior) for a method of drilling wells in very deep water. This method has been used to depths of nearly 500 meters, and it involves positioning the drilling equipment (including blowout preventers and mud pumps) on the sea floor and guiding the drill bit to the desired location with flexible cables (Fig. 247). In contrast to the 11 per cent success of wildcat wells on land in the United States, a much higher percentage of success has been attained in drilling the off-shore region of southern California (98 per cent), Louisiana (27 per cent), and Texas (23 per cent), owing largely to the great care required by the high cost.

Total production in the offshore area to the end of 1957 amounted to 549 million 42-gallon barrels (Table 31), more than four times the total offshore production in the Gulf of Mexico (Thomasson, 1958). Production for the year 1957 was 31.9 million barrels, or 9.4 per cent of the total production of California—339.1 million barrels (Popenoe, 1958), or 1.2 per cent of the total United States production (Bureau of Mines, 1958). Reserves for California are about

Figure 245. Small masses of tar found occasionally in basin cores. These are believed to have floated from distant seep areas and, after partial oxidation, to have sunk to the bottom. Diameters are about 2 mm.

Figure 246. Texas tower type of offshore drilling platform being used off Huntington Beach in 1957. Courtesy of Howard C. Pyle, Monterey Oil Company.

eleven times annual production, and those for the whole United States about twelve times annual production. Figures for offshore reserves total at least 150 million barrels (Hortig, 1958), but doubtlessly the ultimate reserves are enormously greater. Any estimate of them can be little more than a guess because to date all production has been only from extensions of known fields on land, although the artificial island off Seal Beach is producing from a distant extension of the Wilmington oil field. Almost certainly there exist oil accumulations on the outer part of the shelves that are unrelated to structures present on the adjacent land.

Inspection of Table 31 and Figure 248 shows that most of the offshore production has been from only two fields, Wilmington and Huntington Beach. Peak production for Wilmington was reached in 1951, for Elwood in 1930, and for Rincón in 1946. Peak production has probably not yet been reached at Huntington Beach. Maximum production to date was reached in 1957 for each of several new fields: Alamitos, Seal

Beach, Montalvo, Newport Beach, and Redondo Beach; but peaks for all are probably several or many years hence. Although early fame touched Summerland, Coal Oil Point, and Capitan, their productions have been relatively negligible.

Table 31

CUMULATIVE PRODUCTION OF PETROLEUM
FROM OFFSHORE—TO JANUARY 1, 1958

Field	First Reported Date of Off-shore Production	Millions of Barrels of Crude Oil
Wilmington	1939	233.5
Huntington Beach	1932	225.6
Elwood	1929	72.0
Rincón	1928	11.6
Alamitos	1955	1.7
Seal Beach	1947	1.6
Montalvo	1953	1.3
Newport Beach	1953	1.0
Redondo Beach	1956	0.4
Summerland	1896	0.3
Capitan	1931	0.07
Coal Oil Point	1947	0.001
Total		549.1

Figure 247. Schematic drawing of method developed by Continental, Union, Shell, and Superior Oil Companies for test drilling in water depths as great as 1500 feet. From Bauer, Crooke, and Stratton (1958). Modification of the method has permitted Global Marine Exploration Company to drill producing wells in a water depth of 350 feet and a total completion depth of 6250 feet.

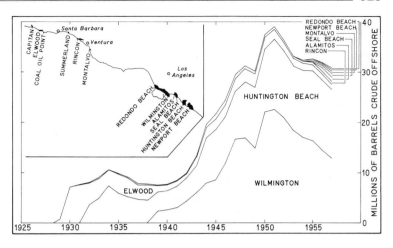

Figure 248. Annual production of crude oil cumulated by years for each of the major offshore oil fields. Data from California State Lands Commission, Port of Long Beach, City of Redondo Beach, and Monterey Oil Company.

Some idea of the value of the offshore oil resources is given by the fact that the total value of production to date is nearly a billion dollars, and this is only from extensions of known oil fields of the coastal area.

Ownership

For centuries international disputes have arisen over fishing rights, shipping lanes, and naval intrusions near national coasts. By tacit understanding national control has been assumed to a distance of 3 statute miles from shore, the "hypothetical range of an imaginary gun" in the late eighteenth century, or simply a unit of 1 league (Mouton, 1952, pp. 192–200). This distance became meaningless for control of the sea in 1958 when missiles were fired thousands of miles over the ocean and even into orbit around the earth. Because no formal agreements as to the seaward limits of nations have been made, incidents have arisen through occasional claims to greater distance from shore such as those since 1945 for fishing rights by Chile (to 200 nautical miles), Ecuador, and Iceland in 1958, for military purposes by Communist China in 1958, and for oil claims by several Middle East countries. A compilation of many such claims made before 1952 and of protests against them is given by Mouton (1952), who says that ". . . an epidemic has broken out, characterized by an insatiable thirst for salt water and a great gusto for fish."

In addition to basing territorial claims on a particular distance from shore, consideration has also been given to claims extending to the edge of the continental shelf. Such is reasonable in view of the fact that exploitation of the sea floor beyond the range of slant drilling is more limited by depth than by distance from shore; for example, oil was produced 50 miles (80 km) from shore in the Gulf of Mexico in 1958. Legal definition of the true edge of the continental shelf, however, raises many difficulties, owing to the varied depth of the shelf-break from place to place, to its commonly unsounded nature, and to the question of classification of shelf indentations such as submarine canyons, troughs, depressions, and deep basins (Mouton, 1952, pp. 6–32; Guilcher, Kuenen, Shepard, and Zenkovitch, 1957). It has even been suggested that the legal problem of classification can be avoided by redefining the continental shelf as extending to a depth of 1000 fathoms (1829 meters); however, not only does such a definition conflict with geological and other scientific considerations, but for southern California it would also leave spots of "no-man's sea" within the shelf over the deep areas of Santa Cruz, San Clemente, Velero, and other basins.

Since fishing and transportation are transient in nature, more complex questions are brought up by mining at and below the sea floor because of the more permanent nature of the mining facilities, blocking of free ship movements, and pollution dangers from runaway oil wells (Mouton, 1952; Thomasson, 1958). With these questions in consideration, the United States provided for the administration of the outer part of its continental shelf by enactment of the Outer Continental Shelf Lands Act in 1953 (Public Law 212, 83rd Congress, 1st Session, 67, Statute 462). This act claims the subsoil and sea bed of the outer continental shelf as subject to the jurisdiction, control, and disposition of the United States government, but it does not affect the international rights of navigation and fishing. Similar rights for all coastal nations were approved by a United Nations Conference on the Law of the Sea in April 1958. The whole question of precise legal definition of the shelf edge as a seaward limit for national territorial claims may well turn out to be a useless one because of the recent development of equipment capable of drilling in water depths much greater than those of the continental shelf. Clearly, a new concept of territorial limit is necessary.

Extraction of petroleum and natural gas started at the shore and subsequently proceeded farther seaward. Leases for production from tidelands and submerged lands were first issued by states, namely, California, Texas, and Louisiana. When the large size of the revenues became obvious, legal disputes arose over whether the states or the federal government had the right to license and tax these operations. A long series of legislative and judicial maneuvers ended with the Submerged Lands Act of 1953 (Public Law 31, 83rd Congress, 1st Session, 67, Statute 29). The act determined that title, ownership, and the right to manage, administer, lease, develop, and use the lands and natural resources of the sea floor to a distance of 3 statute miles (4.8 km) from the coast belongs to the states. Thus exploitation of the shelf beyond a line 3 statute miles from the coastline is controlled by the federal government and inshore of that line by state governments. There, of course, remain many legal questions for particular

areas as to what constitutes the coast. For example, does the coastline extend around or across the mouth of bays? San Diego Bay represents no problem, but what about San Pedro and Santa Monica Bays? More important, the State of California holds that the coastline should be taken as a line joining the seaward sides of the farthest offshore islands, whereas the United States government considers that the coastline follows the mainland; this question will also be settled in time by the courts.

Locally along the coast petroleum has been found off the shores of various cities. These properties, extending to various distances from shore, have been assigned by the State of California to some of the cities, so that offshore oil is controlled by Redondo Beach, Long Beach, and Newport Beach. Thus the sizes of sea floor areas controlled by various governmental units vary in proportion to the size and power of the unit, municipal, state, and federal. To date, the state-controlled lands are the most interesting because they are much larger than municipally controlled lands and are far more exploited than federally controlled lands owing to their nearness to shore. The history of offshore leasing by the State of California has been well summarized by Krueger (1958). Until 1921 California's policy was one of silent acquiescence toward offshore exploitation. A 1921 California statute and its 1923 amendment authorized the Surveyor-General to issue 2-year prospecting leases on 640-acre units of submerged land. If valuable deposits of oil or gas were discovered, the permittee was entitled to lease 160 acres of the land for 20 years at 5 per cent royalty. Proven property was leased for 20-year periods at one-eighth royalty plus a bonus bid factor. For various reasons, including an unfavorable court decision in 1929, leasing under the 1921 act was ended after about 100 permits and leases had been issued.

The State Lands Act of 1938 was the next major action, creating the State Lands Commission and giving it authority to administer, control, and lease all tidelands and submerged lands owned by the State. Leases were awarded at first on the basis of sliding royalty bids with minimums of one-eighth from 1938 to 1942 and one-sixth from 1942 to 1955. Actual royalties averaged about 35 per cent. In 1955 several leases were awarded on the basis of cash bonus payments plus royalty, whereas others were based on royalty bids. The four parcels at Huntington Beach and Summerland put up on a bonus basis received total successful bids of $5.25 million, or $1440/acre. The act also permitted the construction of offshore islands such as Monterey Oil Company's island off Seal Beach; municipal restrictions were overruled by provisions of the State Lands Act.

As a result of increased municipal opposition to construction of drilling islands, the Cunningham-Shell Act of 1955 restricted offshore leasing to areas of known potential and to areas subject to drainage by wells on adjacent land. The question of known potential required for granting leases, however, could be solved only through costly exploration by the State Lands Commission or by requiring the operators to submit copies of all exploration results. The latter alternative was chosen. Royalties were set in unproven areas at a flat rate of one-eighth and in proven areas at a sliding scale beginning at one-sixth. Bids were to be granted on the basis of the highest cash bonus in addition to royalty and rental requirements of $1/acre. Because of the great difference in royalty between wildcat and proven submerged lands and the natural reluctance of operators to part with costly information, leasing was soon suspended. Only one lease was awarded, one for 5500 acres off Summerland for $7.75 million, or $1410/acre.

The question of relative revenue of wildcat and proven leases formed the basis for the Amendment of 1957. By this amendment royalty was set at a sliding scale beginning at one-sixth for all tideland and submerged land. The State Land Commission was also empowered to choose between royalty and bonus as the bid determinant, with the probable choice of royalty for proven lands and bonus for wildcat land. In July 1958 cash bonus bids totaling $54 million were accepted for four offshore parcels near Gaviota. The high royalty for wildcat land plus the 1958 excess of oil production and importation over consumption and the consequent 50-cent decrease in price of crude oil in October 1958 have subsequently decreased interest in offshore exploration on the part of operators. Doubtlessly, this is only temporary.

Altogether the offshore production of petroleum has added revenue to the State from bonus and royalty amounting to nearly $200 million up to 1958 and additional millions to cities such as Long Beach. Eventually, additional fields farther from shore should add additional revenues to the State and probably also to the United States Treasuries.

References

Abelson, P. H., 1956, Paleobiochemistry: *Sci. American,* vol. 195, pp. 83–92.

Abelson, P. H., 1957, Some aspects of paleobiochemistry: *Ann. New York Acad. Sciences,* vol. 69, pp. 276–285.

Ahrens, L. H., K. Rankama, and S. K. Runcorn, 1956, *Physics and Chemistry of the Earth:* McGraw-Hill Book Company, New York, 317 pp.

Albritton, E. C., editor, 1953, Standard values in nutrition and metabolism: Wright Air Development Center, Tech. Rept. 52–301, 380 pp.

Alldredge, L. R., and F. Keller, Jr., 1949, Preliminary report on magnetic anomalies between Adak, Alaska, and Kwajalein, Marshall Islands: *Trans. Amer. Geophys. Union,* vol. 30, pp. 494–500.

Allee, W. C., A. E. Emerson, O. Park, T. Park, and K. P. Schmidt, 1949, *Principles of Animal Ecology:* W. B. Saunders, Philadelphia, 837 pp.

Allen, E. T., J. L. Crenshaw, J. Johnston, and E. S. Larsen, 1912, The mineral sulfides of iron: *Amer. Jour. Science,* vol. 33, pp. 169–236.

Allen, W. E., 1939, Methods of field and laboratory procedure in phytoplankton research at the Scripps Institution of Oceanography of the University of California: *Proc. Pacific Science Congress, 6th,* vol. 3, pp. 525–528.

Allen, W. E. 1941, Twenty years' statistical studies of marine plankton dinoflagellates of southern California: *Amer. Midland Naturalist,* vol. 26, pp. 603–635.

Allen, W. E., 1945, Vernal distribution of marine plankton diatoms offshore in southern California in 1940: *Bull. Scripps Inst. of Oceanography, Univ. Calif.,* vol. 5, pp. 335–370.

Allen, W. E., 1946, "Red water" in La Jolla Bay in 1945: *Trans. Amer. Microscopical Society,* vol. 65, pp. 149–153.

Allison, L. E., 1935, Organic carbon by reduction of chromic acid: *Soil Science,* vol. 40, pp. 311–320.

Anonymous, 1940, Monthly and annual mean heights of sea-level: *Assoc. d'oceanographie physique, Union geodesque et Geophysique internationale, Publ. 5,* 255 pp.

Anonymous, 1944, Breakers and surf: Principles in forecasting: *U. S. Hydrographic Office Bull. 234,* 52 pp.

Anonymous, 1950, Monthly and annual mean heights of sea-level, 1937–1946: *Assoc. d'oceanographie physique, Union geodesque et geophysique internationale, Publ. 10.*

Anonymous, 1955, Tide tables West Coast North and South America: *U. S. Coast and Geodetic Survey, Serial 781,* 226 pp.

Anonymous, 1956a, Surface water temperatures of tide stations, Pacific coast: *U. S. Coast and Geodetic Survey, Special Publ. 260,* 74 pp.

Anonymous, 1956b, *Forecaster's Handbook,* U. S. Fleet Weather Central, San Diego.

Antevs, E. V., 1953, Geochronology of the Deglacial and Neothermal ages: *Jour. Geology,* vol. 61, pp. 195–230.

Arnal, R. E., 1955, Some occurrences of abnormal Foraminifera: *The Compass,* vol. 32, pp. 185–194.

Arrhenius, G., 1952, Sediment cores from the east Pacific: *Swedish Deep-Sea Expeditions 1947–1948, Reports,* vol. 5, fasc. 1, 227 pp.

Arrhenius, G. O. S., in press, Sedimentation on the ocean floor, *Symposium on Geochemistry,* Carnegie Inst., Washington.

Arthur, R. S., 1954, Oscillations in sea temperature at Scripps and Oceanside Piers: *Deep-Sea Research,* vol. 2, pp. 107–121.

Ayres, E., and C. A. Scarlott, 1952, *Energy Sources—The Wealth of the World:* McGraw-Hill Book Company, New York, 344 pp.

Babcock, B. A., 1957, Analysis of wind blown sediment: Univ. Southern California, unpubl. rept. in sedimentation, 16 pp.

Bache, A. D., 1856, Notice of earthquake waves on the western coast of the United States, on the 23d and 25th December, 1854: Rept. Supt. Coast Survey for 1855, pp. 342–347.

Bader, R. G., 1955, Carbon and nitrogen relations in surface and subsurface marine sediments: *Geochimica et Cosmochimica Acta,* vol. 7, pp. 205–211.

Bailey, E. H., 1941, Mineralogy, petrology, and geology of Santa Catalina Island, California: Stanford Univ., unpubl. doctoral dissertation, 193 pp.

Bailey, H. P., 1954, Climate, vegetation, and land use in southern California: *Calif. Div. Mines, Bull. 170,* ch. 1, pp. 31–44.

Bailey, T. L., and R. H. Jahns, 1954, Geology of the Transverse Range province, southern California: *Calif. Div. Mines, Bull. 170,* ch. 2, pp. 83–106.

Baldwin, E. Joan, 1956, Distribution of rocks derived from a point source on a marine beach: Univ. Southern California, unpubl. rept. in sedimentation, 5 pp.

Baldwin, E. Joan, 1959, Pliocene turbidity current deposits in Ventura Basin, California: Univ. Southern California, unpubl. master's thesis, 66 pp.

Ball, J. S., M. L. Whisman, and W. J. Wenger, 1951, Nitrogen content of crude petroleums: *Ind. and Eng. Chemistry,* vol. 43, pp. 2577–2581.

Bancroft, H. H., 1884, *History of the Pacific States,* vol. 12: *California,* vol. 1—*1542–1800,* The History Company, San Francisco, 744 pp.

Bandy, O. L., 1953a, Ecology and paleoecology of some California Foraminifera. Part I. The frequency distribution of Recent Foraminifera off California: *Jour. Paleontology,* vol. 27, pp. 161–182.

Bandy, O. L., 1953b, Ecology and paleoecology of some California Foraminifera. Part II. Foraminiferal evidence of subsidence rates in the Ventura Basin: *Jour. Paleontology,* vol. 27, pp. 200–203.

Bandy, O. L., 1958, Dominant molluscan faunas of the San Pedro Basin, California: *Jour. Paleontology,* vol. 32, pp. 703–714.

Bandy, O. L., in press, The geological significance of coiling ratios in the foraminifer *Globigerina pachyderma* (Ehrenberg): *Jour. Paleontology.*

Banks, H. O., R. C. Richter, and J. Harder, 1957, Sea water intrusion in California: *Jour. Amer. Water Works Assoc.,* vol. 49, pp. 71–88.

Barnard, J. L., 1955, The wood boring habits of *Chelura terebrans* Philippi in Los Angeles Harbor, *Essays in the Natural Sciences in Honor of Captain Allen Hancock:* Univ. Southern California Press, Los Angeles, pp. 87–95.

Barnard, J. L., 1958, Amphipod crustaceans as fouling organisms in Los Angeles–Long Beach Harbors, with reference to the influence of seawater turbidity: *Calif. Fish and Game,* vol. 44, pp. 161–170.

Barnhart, P. S., 1936, *Marine Fishes of Southern California:* Univ. California Press, Berkeley, 209 pp.

Barrows, A. L., 1917, The geologic significance of fossil rock-boring animals: *Bull. Geol. Soc. America,* vol. 28, pp. 965–972.

Bartholomew, G. A., Jr., R. D. Collyer, and W. R. Dawson, 1951, The sea lion population of Santa Barbara Island, California in the 1950 breeding season: *Calif. Fish and Game,* vol. 37, pp. 65–68.

Bartholomew, G. A., Jr., and C. L. Hubbs, 1952, Winter population of pinnipeds about Guadalupe, San Benito, and Cedros Islands, Baja California: *Jour. Mammalogy,* vol. 33, pp. 160–171.

Bartrum, J. A., 1935, Shore-platforms: *Proc. Aust. and N. Z. Assoc. Adv. Science,* vol. 22, pp. 135–143.

Bascom, W. N., 1951, The relationship between sand size and beach-face slope: *Trans. Amer. Geophys. Union,* vol. 32, pp. 866–874.

Bauer, R. F., R. C. Crooke, and H. Stratton, 1958, Drilling from a floating vessel: Second Annual Joint Meeting of the Northern and Southern California Sections of Soc. North Amer. Mech. Engineers, Santa Barbara, October 10.

Baumann, P., and F. B. Laverty, 1956, Biennial report on hydrologic data, seasons of 1953–54 and 1954–55: Los Angeles County Flood Control Project, 472 pp.

Beal, C. H., 1948, Reconnaissance of the geology and the oil possibilities of Baja California, Mexico: *Geol. Soc. America, Memoir 31,* 138 pp.

Bell, H. S., 1942, Density currents as agents for transporting sediments: *Jour. Geology,* vol. 50, pp. 512–547.

Berry, S. S., 1912, A review of the cephalopods of western North America: *Bull. U. S. Bureau Fisheries,* vol. 30, pp. 267–336.

Bittinger, C., 1933, Experiences over a submarine epicenter: *Trans. Amer. Geophys. Union,* vol. 14, p. 260.

Blackwelder, E., 1916, The geologic role of phosphorus: *Amer. Jour. Science, Proc.,* 4th. ser., vol. 42, pp. 285–298.

Blake, W. P., 1856, Observations on the physical geography and geology of the coast of California, from Bodega Bay to San Diego; Ann. Report U. S. Coast Survey 1855, app. 65, pp. 376–398, pls. 57–60.

Board of Harbor Commissioners, City of Los Angeles, 1957, 48th Annual Report, Fiscal Year 1956–57: Los Angeles Harbor Department, 48 pp.

Boden, B. P., 1950, Plankton organisms in the deep scattering layer: U. S. Navy Electronics Laboratory Rept. 186, 29 pp.

Boden, B. P., and E. M. Kampa, 1957, Records of bioluminescence in the ocean: *Pacific Science,* vol. 11, pp. 229–235.

Bolin, R. L., 1954, Report on a fatal attack by a shark: *Pacific Science,* vol. 8, pp. 105–108.

Bolton, H. E., 1916, *Spanish Exploration in the Southwest, 1542–1706:* Charles Scribner's Sons, New York, 487 pp.

Bolton, H. E., 1927, *Fray Juan Crespi, Missionary Explorer on the Pacific Coast 1769–1774:* Univ. California Press, Berkeley, 402 pp.

Bonnot, P., 1951, The sea lions, seals and sea otter of the California coast: *Calif. Fish and Game,* vol. 37, pp. 371–389.

Bonnot, P., and W. E. Ripley, 1948, The California sea lion census for 1947: *Calif. Fish and Game,* vol. 34, pp. 89–92.

Bookman, M., 1957, Report on Watermaster Service in West Coast Watermaster Service Area, Los Angeles, California for period June 1, 1956 through May 31, 1957: Calif. Dept. of Water Resources, 39 pp. plus appendices.

Bourcart, J., 1938, La marge continentale: Essai sur les régressions et transgressions marines: *Bull. soc. géol. France,* pp. 393–474.

Bradley, W. C., 1956, Carbon-14 date for a marine terrace at Santa Cruz, California: *Bull. Geol. Soc. America,* vol. 67, pp. 675–678.

Bramlette, M. N., 1958, Significance of coccolithophorids in calcium-carbonate deposition: *Bull. Geol. Soc. America,* vol. 69, pp. 121–126.

Branner, J. C., 1900, The origin of beach cusps: *Jour. Geology,* vol. 8, pp. 481–484.

Bremner, C. St. J., 1932, Geology of Santa Cruz Island, Santa Barbara County, California: *Santa Barbara Museum Nat. History, Occ. Paper 1,* 33 pp.

Bremner, C. St. J., 1933, Geology of San Miguel Island, Santa Barbara County, California: *Santa Barbara Museum Nat. History, Occ. Paper 2,* 23 pp.

Brice, D. B., M. R. Dusbabek, and C. R. Townsend, 1958, Study of the applicability of combining nuclear reactors with saline water distillation processes: U. S. Dept. of Interior, Office of Saline Water, Research and Development Progress Rept. 19, 66 pp. and appendices.

Briggs, R. D., 1950, Mechanical analysis of a gravel beach: Univ. Southern California, unpubl. rept. in sedimentation, 8 pp.

Brisbin, W. C., 1957, Regional gravity studies in southern California: Univ. California at Los Angeles, unpubl. doctoral dissertation.

Broecker, W. S., M. Ewing, K. Gerard, and B. C. Heezen, in press, Natural radiocarbon in the oceans: *Jour. Geophysical Research.*

Broecker, W. S., and J. L. Kulp, 1957, Lamont natural radiocarbon measurements, IV: *Science,* vol. 126, pp. 1324–1334.

Broecker, W. S., K. K. Turekian, and B. C. Heezen, 1958, The relation of deep-sea sedimentation to variations in climate: *Amer. Jour. Science,* vol. 256, pp. 503–517.

Bromery, R. W., K. O. Emery, and J. R. Balsley, Jr., in press, Reconnaissance airborne magnetometer survey off southern California: U. S. Geol. Survey, Geophys. Investig. Map GP.

Brooks, B. T., 1952, Evidence of catalytic action in petroleum formation: *Ind. and Eng. Chemistry,* vol. 44, pp. 2570–2577.

Bruff, S. C., 1946, The paleontology of the Pleistocene molluscan fauna of the Newport Bay area, California: *Univ. Calif. (Berkeley), Publs. in Geol. Sciences,* vol. 27, pp. 213–240.

Bryson, D. K., 1956, The measurement of directional permeability of some beach sand: Univ. Southern California, unpubl. rept. in sedimentation, 13 pp.

Bucher, W. H., 1940, Submarine valleys and related geologic problems of the North Atlantic: *Bull. Geol. Soc. America,* vol. 51, pp. 489–512.

Buffington, E. C., 1951, Gullied submarine slopes off southern California (abst.): *Bull. Geol. Soc. America,* vol. 62, p. 1497.

Buffington, E. C., 1952, Submarine "natural levees": *Jour. Geology,* vol. 60, pp. 473–479.

Bureau of Mines, 1958, *Minerals Yearbook 1955:* Bureau of Mines, Division of Minerals, Division of Petroleum, vols. 1–3, 3017 pp.

Burst, J. F., 1958, "Glauconite" pellets: Their mineral nature and applications to stratigraphic interpretations: *Bull. Amer. Assoc. Petrol. Geologists,* vol. 42, pp. 310–327.

Burton, V. L., and G. R. Sullivan, 1951, Carbon content and radioactivity of marine rocks: *Trans. Amer. Geophys. Union,* vol. 32, pp. 881–884.

Butcher, W. S., 1951, Foraminifera, Coronado Bank and vicinity, California, pt. 2: Scripps Inst. Oceanography, Submarine Geology Rept. 19, ref. 51–21, 9 pp. (mimeographed).

Butschli, O., 1880–1882, *Dr. H. G. Bronn's Klassen und Ordnungen des Their-Reichs: I Abth.: Sarkodina und Sporozoa:* Winter'sche Verlagshandlung, Leipzig, 616 pp.

Butschli, 0., 1883–1887, *Dr. H. G. Bronn's Klassen und Ordnungen des Their-Reichs: II Abth.: Mastigophora:* Winter'sche Verlagshandlung, Leipzig, pp. 617–1097.

Caldwell, J. M., 1956, Wave action and sand movement near Anaheim Bay, California: Dept. of Army, Corps of Engineers, Beach Erosion Board, Tech. Memo. 68, 21 pp.

California Cooperative Oceanic Fisheries Investigations, 1955, Progress Report, 1 July 1953 to 31 March 1955: Calif. Dept. Fish and Game, 52 pp.

Cameron, F. K., 1915, Potash from kelp, 1. Pacific kelp beds as a source of potassium salts: *U. S. Dept. Agriculture, Rept. 100,* pp. 9–46.

Carritt, D. E., D. F. Bumpus, J. H. Carpenter, W. A. Chipmen, J. H. Harley, B. C. Heezen, B. H. Ketchum, and R. O. Reid, 1958, The feasibility of the disposal of low level radioactive wastes into the inshore waters of the Atlantic and Gulf coasts of the United States: Natl. Research Council, 37 pp. plus 10 appendices (multilithed).

Carsey, J. B., 1950, Geology of Gulf coastal area and continental shelf: *Bull. Amer. Assoc. Petrol. Geologists,* vol. 34, pp. 361–385.

Carsola, A. J., and R. S. Dietz, 1952, Submarine geology of two flat-topped northeast Pacific seamounts: *Amer. Jour. Science,* vol. 250, pp. 481–497.

Carter, F. B., 1954, Oil and gas production in California: *Calif. Div. Mines, Bull. 170,* ch. 9, pp. 21–28.

Carter, G. F., 1955, On submarine archaeology about San Diego: *The Masterkey,* vol. 29, pp. 21–27.

Carter, G. F., 1957a, *Pleistocene Man at San Diego:* Johns Hopkins Press, Baltimore, 400 pp.

Carter, G. F., 1957b, The American civilization puzzle: *Johns Hopkins Magazine,* 6 pp.

Chapman, V. J., 1938–1941, Studies in salt-marsh ecology: *Jour. Ecology,* vol. 26, pp. 144–179; vol. 27, pp. 160–201; vol. 28, pp. 118–152; vol. 29, pp. 69–82.

Charlesworth, J. K., 1957, *The Quaternary Era, with Special Reference to Its Glaciation:* London, Edward Arnold, Ltd., 1700 pp.

Chave, K. E., 1954, Aspects of the biogeochemistry of magnesium: *Jour. Geology,* vol. 62, pp. 266–283, 587–599.

Chilingar, G. V., 1953, Use of Ca/Mg ratio in limestones as a geologic tool: *The Compass,* vol. 30, pp. 202–209.

Chilingar, G. V., 1956, Relationship between Ca/Mg ratio and geologic age: *Bull. Amer. Assoc. Petrol. Geologists,* vol. 40, pp. 2256–2266.

Clark, B. L., 1921, The marine Tertiary of the west coast of the United States: Its sequence, paleogeography, and the problems of correlation: *Jour. Geology,* vol. 29, pp. 583–614.

Clarke, F. W., 1920, The data of geochemistry: *U. S. Geol. Survey, Bull. 695,* 832 pp.

Clarke, J. M., 1918, Strand and undertow markings of

upper Devonian time as indications of the prevailing climate: *New York State Museum Bull.,* vol. 196, pp. 199–239.

Clemens, W. A., and G. V. Wilby, 1946, Fishes of the Pacific coast of Canada: *Fisheries Research Board of Canada, Bull. 68,* 367 pp.

Clements, T., 1955, The Pleistocene history of the channel island region, southern California, *Essays in the Natural Sciences in Honor of Captain Allan Hancock:* Univ. Southern California Press, Los Angeles, pp. 311–323.

Clements, T., and L. Clements, 1953, Evidence of Pleistocene man in Death Valley, California: *Bull. Geol. Soc. America,* vol. 64, pp. 1189–1204.

Clements, T., and S. W. Dana, 1944, Geologic significance of a coarse marine sediment from near Santa Catalina Island, California: *Jour. Geology,* vol. 52, pp. 351–354.

Clements, T., and K. O. Emery, 1947, Seismic activity and topography of the sea floor off southern California: *Bull. Seismol. Soc. America,* vol. 37, pp. 307–313.

Clothier, C. R., and E. C. Greenhood, 1956, Jack mackerel and sardine yield per area from California waters, 1946–47 through 1954–55: *Calif. Dept. Fish and Game, Fish Bull. 102,* pp. 7–16.

Cloud, P. E., 1954, Superficial aspects of modern organic reefs: *Sci. Monthly,* vol. 79, pp. 195–208.

Cloud, P. E., 1955, Physical limits of glauconite formation: *Bull. Amer. Assoc. Petrol. Geologists,* vol. 39, pp. 484–492.

Clover, S. T., 1932, *A Pioneer Heritage:* Saturday Night Publishing Company, Los Angeles, 291 pp.

Cockerell, T. D. A., 1938, Studies of island life: *Colorado Univ. Studies,* vol. 26, pp. 3–20.

Cockerell, T. D. A., 1940, The marine invertebrate fauna of the California islands: *Proc. Pacific Science Congress, 6th,* vol. 3, pp. 501–504.

Coe, W. R., 1955, Ecology of the bean clam *Donax gouldi* on the coast of southern California: *Ecology,* vol. 36, pp. 512–514.

Coffman, F. L., 1957, *Atlas of Treasure Maps:* Thomas Nelson & Sons, New York, 124 pp.

Cohee, G. V., 1938, Sediments of the submarine canyons off the California coast: *Jour. Sedimentary Petrology,* vol. 8, pp. 19–33.

Committee on Origin of Oil, 1958, The modern theory of origin of oil: Report to Organization Committee of the U. S. S. R. Natl. Acad. Science, 59 pp.

Conrey, B. L., 1959, Sedimentary history of the Lower Pliocene in the Los Angeles Basin, California: Univ. Southern California, unpubl. doctoral dissertation, 268 pp.

Corey, W. H., 1954, Tertiary basins of southern California: *Calif. Div. Mines, Bull. 170,* ch. 3, pp. 73–83.

Cornish, V., 1912, *Waves of the Sea and Other Water Waves:* Open Court Publishing Company, Chicago, 374 pp.

Correns, C. W., 1939, Pelagic sediments of the North Atlantic Ocean, *Recent Marine Sediments:* Amer. Assoc. Petroleum Geologists, Tulsa, pp. 373–395.

Craig, H., 1953, The geochemistry of the stable carbon isotopes: *Geochimica et Cosmochimica Acta,* vol. 3, pp. 53–92.

Craig, H., 1954, Carbon 13 in plants and the relationships between carbon 13 and carbon 14 variations in nature: *Jour. Geology,* vol. 62, pp. 115–149.

Craig, H., 1957, Isotopic tracer techniques for measurement of physical and chemical processes in the sea and the atmosphere, in The effects of atomic radiation on oceanography and fisheries: *Natl. Acad. Sciences–Natl. Research Council, Publ. 551,* pp. 103–120.

Crandall, W. C., 1912, The kelps of the southern California coast, *in* Appendix N of Fertilizer resources of the United States: Senate Doc. 190, 62nd Congress, 2nd Session, pp. 209–213.

Crouch, R. W., 1952, Significance of temperature on Foraminifera from deep basins off southern California coast: *Bull. Amer. Assoc. Petrol. Geologists,* vol. 36, pp. 807–843.

Crouch, R. W., 1954, Paleontology and paleoecology of the San Pedro Shelf and vicinity: *Jour. Sedimentary Petrology,* vol. 24, pp. 182–190.

Crowell, J. C., 1952, Submarine canyons bordering central and southern California: *Jour. Geology,* vol. 60, pp. 58–83.

Crowell, J. C., 1955, Directional-current structures from the prealpine flysch, Switzerland: *Bull. Geol. Soc. America,* vol. 66, pp. 1351–1384.

Crowell, J. C., 1957, Origin of pebbly mudstones: *Bull. Geol. Soc. America,* vol. 68, pp. 993–1010.

Cupp, E. E., 1943, Marine plankton diatoms of the west coast of North America: *Bull. Scripps Inst. Oceanography, Univ. Calif.,* vol. 5, pp. 1–238.

Curray, J. R., 1956, Dimensional grain orientation studies of Recent coastal sands: *Bull. Amer. Assoc. Petrol. Geologists,* vol. 40, pp. 2440–2456.

Cushman, J. A., 1940, *Foraminifera, Their Classification and Economic Use:* Harvard Univ. Press, Cambridge, Mass., 425 pp.

Cushman, J. A., R. Todd, and R. J. Post, 1954, Recent Foraminifera of the Marshall Islands: *U. S. Geol. Survey, Prof. Paper 260-H,* pp. 319–384.

Daly, R. A., 1936, Origin of submarine "canyons": *Amer. Jour. Science,* 5th ser., vol. 31, pp. 401–420.

Daly, R. A., 1940, *Strength and Structure of the Earth:* Prentice-Hall, New York, 434 pp.

Daly, R. A., 1942, *The Floor of the Ocean—New Light on Old Mysteries:* Univ. North Carolina Press, Chapel Hill, 177 pp.

Dana, J. D., 1863, *Manual of Geology,* 1st ed.: Trübner & Co., London, 798 pp.

Dana, J. D., 1890, Long Island Sound in the Quaternary era, with observations on the submarine Hudson River channel: *Amer. Jour. Science,* 3rd ser., vol. 40, pp. 425–437.

Dana, R. H., 1945, *Two Years Before the Mast:* Random House, New York, 423 pp. (first published in 1840).

David, Lore R., 1943, Miocene fishes of southern California: *Geol. Soc. America, Special Paper 43,* 193 pp.

David, Lore R., 1944, Use of fossil fish scales in micropaleontology: *Carnegie Inst. Washington, Publ. 551,* pp. 25–43.

David, Lore R., 1947, Significance of fish remains in Recent deposits off coast of southern California: *Bull. Amer. Assoc. Petrol. Geologists,* vol. 31, pp. 367–370.

Davidson, G., 1872, Minutes of meeting, October 7, 1872: *Proc. Calif. Acad. Sciences,* vol. 4, pp. 267–269.

Davidson, G., 1875, The abrasions of the continental shores of N. W. America, and the supposed ancient sea levels: *Proc. Calif. Acad. Sciences,* vol. 5 (1873–1874), pp. 90–97.

Davidson, G., 1887, Submarine valleys on the Pacific coast of the United States: *Calif. Acad. Sciences, Bull. 2,* pp. 265–268.

Davidson, G., 1897, The submerged valleys of the coast of California, U. S. A., and of Lower California, Mexico: *Proc. Calif. Acad. Sciences,* 3rd ser., (geol) vol. 1, pp. 73–103.

Davis, C. C., 1955, *The Marine and Fresh-water Plankton:* Michigan State Univ. Press, 562 pp.

Davis, J. B., and R. M. Squires, 1954, Detection of microbially produced hydrocarbons other than methane: *Science,* vol. 119, pp. 381–382.

Davis, W. M., 1933, Glacial epochs of the Santa Monica Mountains, California: *Bull. Geol. Soc. America,* vol. 44, pp. 1041–1133.

Davis, W. M., 1934, Submarine mock valleys: *Geograph. Review,* vol. 24, pp. 297–308.

Dawson, E. Y., 1945, An annotated list of the marine algae and marine grasses of San Diego County, California: *San Diego Soc. Nat. History, Occ. Paper 7,* 87 pp.

Dawson, E. Y., 1946, A guide to the literature and distributions of the marine algae of the Pacific Coast of North America: Memoirs *Southern Calif. Acad. Sciences,* vol. 3, 134 pp.

Dawson, E. Y., 1956, *How to Know the Seaweeds:* W. C. Brown Company, Dubuque, Iowa, 197 pp.

de Andrade, C. F., 1937, Os vales submarinos portugueses e o diastrofismo das Berlengas e da Estremadura: *Serv. Geol. (Portugal),* 235 pp.

Deevey, G. B., 1956, Zooplankton: in Oceanography of Long Island Sound, 1952–1954: *Bull. Bingham Oceanographic Collection,* vol. 15, pp. 113–155.

Defant, A., 1950a, On the origin of internal tide waves in the open sea: *Jour. Marine Research,* vol. 9, pp. 111–119.

Defant, A., 1950b, Reality and illusion in oceanographic surveys: *Jour. Marine Research,* vol. 9, pp. 120–138.

Demarest, D. F., 1947, Rhomboid ripple marks and their relationship to beach slope: *Jour. Sedimentary Petrology,* vol. 17, pp. 18–22.

Department of Fish and Game, 1953, Biological survey of Lower Newport Bay: Report to Santa Ana Regional Water Pollution Control Board, 9 pp. (mimeographed).

Dietrich, G., 1939, Das Amerikanische Mittlemeer: *Zeit. Gesellschaft für Erdkunde zu Berlin,* pp. 108–130.

Dietz, R. S., 1941, Clay minerals in recent marine sediments: Univ. Illinois, unpubl. doctoral dissertation, 68 pp.

Dietz, R. S., 1948, Deep scattering layer in the Pacific and Antarctic Oceans: *Jour. Marine Research,* vol. 7, pp. 430–442.

Dietz, R. S., 1952, Geomorphic evolution of continental terrace (continental shelf and slope): *Bull. Amer. Assoc. Petrol. Geologists,* vol. 36, pp. 1802–1819.

Dietz, R. S., 1953, Possible deep-sea turbidity-current channels in the Indian Ocean: *Bull. Geol. Soc. America,* vol. 64, pp. 375–378.

Dietz, R. S., 1955, Manganese deposits on the northeast Pacific sea floor: *Jour. Calif. Mines and Geology,* vol. 51, pp. 209–220.

Dietz, R. S., 1958, Point d'impact des astéroides comme origine des bassins océaniques: une hypothèse: La topographie et la Géologie des profondeurs océaniques, *Centre natl. de la recherche scientifique,* vol. 83, 13 pp.

Dietz, R. S., K. O. Emery, and F. P. Shepard, 1942, Phosphorite deposits on the sea floor off southern California: *Bull. Geol. Soc. America,* vol. 53, pp. 815–848.

Dietz, R. S., and H. W. Menard, 1951, Origin of abrupt change in slope at continental shelf margin: *Bull. Amer. Assoc. Petrol. Geologists,* vol. 35, pp. 1994–2016.

Dill, R. F., 1952, Environmental analysis of sediment from the sea floor off Point Artuello, California: Univ. Southern California, unpubl. master's thesis, 64 pp.

Dill, R. F., R. S. Dietz, and H. Stewart, 1954, Deep-sea channels and delta of the Monterey Submarine Canyon: *Bull. Geol. Soc. America,* vol. 65, pp. 191–194.

Dobbs, P. H., 1958, Effects of wave action on the shape of beach gravel: *The Compass,* vol. 35, pp. 269–275.

Doty, P., 1957, Proteins: *Sci. American,* vol. 197, pp. 173–184.

Downs, T., 1956, A new pinniped from the Miocene of southern California: with remarks on the Otariidae: *Jour. Paleontology,* vol. 30, pp. 115–131.

Drury, F. W., Jr., 1954, Pozzolans in California: *Calif. Div. Mines, Mineral Information Service,* vol. 7, no. 10, pp. 1–6.

Duerksen, J. A., 1949, Pendulum gravity data in the United States: *U. S. Coast and Geodetic Survey, Special Publ. 244,* 218 pp.

Dunham, J. W., 1951, Refraction and diffraction diagrams, *Proceedings 1st Conference on Coastal Engineering:* Univ. California Press, Berkeley, pp. 33–49.

Dunkle, M. B., 1950, Plant ecology of the Channel Islands of California: *Allan Hancock Pacific Expedition,* vol. 13, no. 3, 386 pp.

Durham, J. W., 1950, Cenozoic marine climates of the Pacific Coast: *Bull. Geol. Soc. America,* vol. 61, pp. 1243–1264.

Durham, J. W., 1954, The marine Cenozoic of southern California: *Calif. Div. Mines, Bull. 170,* ch. 3, pp. 23–31.

Durrell, C., 1954, Geology of the Santa Monica Mountains, Los Angeles and Ventura Counties: *Calif. Div. Mines, Bull. 170,* Map Sheet 8.

Eastman, C. R., 1903, Sharks' teeth and cetacean bones from the red clay of the tropical Pacific: *Museum Comp. Zool., Harvard College Memoir,* vol. 26, pp. 179–191.

Eckis, R., 1934, Geology and ground water storage capacity of valley fill: South Coastal Basin investigation: *Calif. Div. Water Resources, Bull. 45,* 273 pp.

Edwards, E. C., 1951, Possible future oil provinces of North America: Los Angeles region: *Bull. Amer. Assoc. Petrol. Geologists,* vol. 35, pp. 241–248.

Ekholm, G. F., 1953, A possible focus of Asiatic influence in the late classic cultures of Mesoamerica, *in* Asia and North America transpacific contacts: *Memoirs Soc. Amer. Archaeology,* no. 9 (Suppl. to *Amer. Antiquity,* vol. 18, no. 3, pt. 2), pp. 72–89.

Ekman, S., 1953, *Zoogeography of the Sea:* Sidgwick & Jackson, Ltd., London, 417 pp.

Ellis, A. J., and E. H. Lee, 1919, Geology and ground waters of the western part of San Diego County, California: *U. S. Geol. Survey, Water Supply Paper 446,* 321 pp.

Emery, K. O., 1941*a,* Rate of surface retreat of sea cliffs based on dated inscriptions: *Science,* vol. 93, pp. 617–618.

Emery, K. O., 1941*b,* Transportation of rock particles by sea-mammals: *Jour. Sedimentary Petrology,* vol. 11, pp. 92–93.

Emery, K. O., 1944, Beach markings made by sand hoppers: *Jour. Sedimentary Petrology,* vol. 14, pp. 26–28.

Emery, K. O., 1945*a,* Entrapment of air in beach sand: *Jour. Sedimentary Petrology,* vol. 15, pp. 39–49.

Emery, K. O., 1945*b,* Transportation of marine beach sand by flotation: *Jour. Sedimentary Petrology,* vol. 15, pp. 84–87.

Emery, K. O., 1946, Marine solution basins: *Jour. Geology,* vol. 54, pp. 209–228.

Emery, K. O., 1948, Submarine geology of Ranger Bank, Mexico: *Bull. Amer. Assoc. Petrol. Geologists,* vol. 32, pp. 790–805.

Emery, K. O., 1950*a,* A suggested origin of continental slopes and of submarine canyons: *Geol. Magazine,* vol. 87, pp. 102–104.

Emery, K. O., 1950*b,* Ironstone concretions and beach ridges of San Diego County, California: *Jour. Calif. Mines and Geology,* vol. 46, pp. 213–221.

Emery, K. O., 1950*c,* Contorted Pleistocene strata at Newport Beach, California: *Jour. Sedimentary Petrology,* vol. 20, pp. 111–115.

Emery, K. O., 1951, Continental shelf—southern California, *in* Symposium on future oil provinces: *Bull. Amer. Assoc. Petrol. Geologists,* vol. 35, pp. 249–252.

Emery, K. O., 1952*a,* Submarine photography with the benthograph: *Sci. Monthly,* vol. 75, pp. 3–11.

Emery, K. O., 1952*b,* Continental shelf sediments of southern California: *Bull. Geol. Soc. America,* vol. 63, pp. 1105–1108.

Emery, K. O., 1953, A newly surveyed submarine basin off Mexico: *Amer. Jour. Science,* vol. 251, pp. 656–660.

Emery, K. O., 1954*a,* The Painted Cave, Santa Cruz Island: *Sea and Pacific Motorboat,* vol. 46, pp. 37–39, 91, 92.

Emery, K. O., 1954*b,* Transparency of water off southern California: *Trans. Amer. Geophys. Union,* vol. 35, pp. 217–220.

Emery, K. O., 1954*c,* Source of water in basins off southern California: *Jour. Marine Research,* vol. 13, pp. 1–21.

Emery, K. O., 1954*d,* General geology of the offshore area, southern California: *Calif. Div. Mines, Bull. 170,* ch. 2, pp. 107–111.

Emery, K. O., 1954*e,* Some characteristics of southern California sediments: *Jour. Sedimentary Petrology,* vol. 24, pp. 50–59.

Emery, K. O., 1955*a,* Grain size of marine beach gravels: *Jour. Geology,* vol. 63, pp. 39–49.

Emery, K. O., 1955*b,* Transportation of rocks by driftwood: *Jour. Sedimentary Petrology,* vol. 25, pp. 51–57.

Emery, K. O., 1956*a,* Sediments and water of Persian Gulf: *Bull. Amer. Assoc. Petrol. Geologists,* vol. 40, pp. 2354–2383.

Emery, K. O., 1956*b,* Deep standing internal waves in California basins: *Limnology and Oceanography,* vol. 1, pp. 35–41.

Emery, K. O., 1958*a,* Shallow submerged marine terraces of southern California: *Bull. Geol. Soc. America,* vol. 69, pp. 39–60.

Emery, K. O., 1958*b,* Southern California basins, *Habitat of Oil:* Amer. Assoc. Petrol. Geologists, Tulsa pp. 955–967.

Emery, K. O., W. S. Butcher, H. R. Gould, and F. P. Shepard, 1952, Submarine geology off San Diego, California: *Jour. Geology,* vol. 60, pp. 511–548.

Emery, K. O., and R. S. Dietz, 1941, Gravity coring instrument and mechanics of sediment coring: *Bull. Geol. Soc. America,* vol. 52, pp. 1685–1714.

Emery, K. O., and R. S. Dietz, 1950, Submarine phosphorite deposits off California and Mexico: *Calif. Div. Mines and Geology,* vol. 46, pp. 7–15.

Emery, K. O., and J. F. Foster, 1948, Water tables in marine beaches: *Jour. Marine Research,* vol. 7, pp. 644–653.

Emery, K. O., and J. F. Gale, 1951, Swash and swash mark: *Trans. Amer. Geophys. Union,* vol. 32, pp. 31–36.

Emery, K. O., D. S. Gorsline, E. Uchupi, and R. D. Terry, 1957, Sediments of three bays of Baja California: Sebastian Viscaino, San Cristobal, and Todos Santos: *Jour. Sedimentary Petrology,* vol. 27, pp. 95–115.

Emery, K. O., and D. Hoggan, 1958, Gases in marine sediments: *Bull. Amer. Assoc. Petrol. Geologists,* vol. 42, pp. 2174–2188.

Emery, K. O., W. L. Orr, and S. C. Rittenberg, 1955, Nutrient budgets in the ocean, *Essays in the Natural Sciences in Honor of Captain Allan Hancock:* Univ. Southern California Press, Los Angeles, pp. 299–309.

Emery, K. O., and S. C. Rittenberg, 1952, Early diagenesis of California basin sediments in relation to origin of oil: *Bull. Amer. Assoc. Petrol. Geologists,* vol. 36, pp. 735–806.

Emery, K. O., and F. P. Shepard, 1945, Lithology of the sea floor off southern California: *Bull. Geol. Soc. America,* vol. 56, pp. 431–478.

Emery, K. O., and R. E. Stevenson, 1950, Laminated beach sand: *Jour. Sedimentary Petrology,* vol. 20, pp. 220–223.

Emery, K. O., and R. D. Terry, 1956, A submarine slope of southern California: *Jour. Geology,* vol. 64, pp. 271–280.

Emery, K. O., J. I. Tracey, Jr., and H. S. Ladd, 1954,

Geology of Bikini and nearby atolls: Part I, Geology: *U. S. Geol. Survey, Prof. Paper 260-A,* 265 pp.

Emery, K. O., and R. H. Tschudy, 1941, Transportation of rock by kelp: *Bull. Geol. Soc. America,* vol. 52, pp. 855–862.

Emiliani, C., 1955, Pleistocene temperatures: *Jour. Geology,* vol. 63, pp. 538–578.

Emiliani, C., and S. Epstein, 1953, Temperature variations in the lower Pleistocene of southern California: *Jour. Geology,* vol. 61, pp. 171–181.

Emmons, W. H., G. A. Thiel, C. R. Stauffer, and I. S. Allison, 1955, *Geology, Principles and Processes,* 4th ed.: McGraw-Hill Book Company, New York, 638 pp.

Ericson, D. B., W. S. Broecker, J. L. Kulp, and G. Wollin, 1956, Late-Pleistocene climates and deep-sea sediments: *Science,* vol. 124, pp. 385–389.

Ericson, D. B., and G. Wollin, 1956*a,* Correlation of six cores from the equatorial Atlantic and the Caribbean: *Deep-Sea Research,* vol. 3, pp. 104–125.

Ericson, D. B., and G. Wollin, 1956*b,* Micropaleontological and isotopic determinations of Pleistocene climates: *Micropaleontology,* vol. 2, pp. 257–270.

Esterly, C. O., 1912, The occurrence and vertical distribution of the Copepoda of the San Diego region, with particular reference to nineteen species: *Univ. Calif. (Berkeley) Publs. in Zoology,* vol. 9, pp. 253–340.

Esterly, C. O., 1928, The periodic occurrence of Copepoda in the marine plankton of two successive years at La Jolla, California: *Bull. Scripps Inst. Oceanography, Univ. Calif.,* tech. ser., vol. 1, pp. 247–345.

Evans, O. F., 1938, Floating sand in the formation of swash marks: *Jour. Sedimentary Petrology,* vol. 8, p. 71.

Ewing, G., 1950, Slicks, surface films and internal waves: *Jour. Marine Research,* vol. 9, pp. 161–187.

Ewing, M., B. C. Heezen, D. B. Ericson, J. Northrop, and J. Dorman, 1953, Exploration of the Northwest Atlantic Mid-Ocean Canyon: *Bull. Geol. Soc. America,* vol. 64, pp. 865–868.

Ewing, M., and R. D. Gerard, 1956, Radiological studies in the investigation of ocean circulation, Proceedings Natl. Acad. Sciences Symposium on Aspects of Deep-sea Research: *Natl. Acad. Sciences–Natl. Research Council, Publ. 473,* pp. 58–66.

Ewing, M., and J. L. Worzel, 1954, Gravity anomalies and structure of the West Indies, Pt. I: *Bull. Geol. Soc. America,* vol. 65, pp. 165–174.

Fairbanks, H. W., 1897, Oscillations of the coast of California during the Pliocene and Pleistocene: *Amer. Geologist,* vol. 20, pp. 213–245.

Fairbridge, R. W., 1946, Submarine slumping and location of oil bodies: *Bull. Amer. Assoc. Petrol. Geologists,* vol. 30, pp. 84–92.

Fairchild, H. L., 1901, Beach structure in Medina sandstone: *Amer. Geologist,* vol. 28, pp. 9–14.

Fast, T. N., 1955, Second known shark attack on a swimmer in Monterey Bay: *Calif. Fish and Game,* vol. 41, pp. 348–351.

Faughn, J. L., T. R. Folsom, J. D. Isaacs, F. D. Jennings, D. Martin, L. E. Miller, and R. L. Wisner, 1957, A preliminary radioactivity survey along the California coast through disposal areas: Presented at 9th Pacific Science Congress, Bangkok, Thailand, November 18–30.

Fergusson, G. J., 1955, Radiocarbon dating system: *Nucleonics,* vol. 13, pp. 18–23.

Fisher, R. L., and G. Shor, 1956, Topography and structure of the Acapulco Trench, *20th International Geological Congress, Mexico City, Abstracts,* p. 263.

Fisk, H. N., 1939, Depositional terrace slopes in Louisiana: *Jour. Geomorphology,* vol. 2, pp. 181–200.

Fitch, J. E., 1953, Common marine bivalves of California: *Calif. Dept. Fish and Game, Fish Bull. 90,* 102 pp.

Flint, R. F., 1947, *Glacial Geology and the Pleistocene Epoch:* John Wiley & Sons, New York, 589 pp.

Ford, W. L., and A. R. Miller, 1952, The surface layer of the Gulf Stream and adjacent waters: *Jour. Marine Research,* vol. 11, pp. 267–280.

Fowler, G. A., 1957, The relationship between hydrogen-ion concentration and oxidation-reduction potentials within a marsh environment: Univ. Southern California, unpubl. rept. in sedimentation, 10 pp.

Fowler, G. A., 1958, Submarine topography and geology of Lasuen Seamount, southern California: Univ. Southern California, unpubl. rept. in marine geology, 11 pp.

Fox, D. L., 1957, Particulate organic detritus: *Geol. Soc. America, Memoir 67,* vol. 1, pp. 383–389.

Fox, D. L., and W. R. Coe, 1943, Biology of the California sea-mussel (*Mytilus californianus*): *Jour. Experimental Zoology,* vol. 93, pp. 205–249.

Fox, D. L., D. M. Updegraff, and G. D. Novelli, 1944, Carotenoid pigments in the sea floor: *Arch. of Biochem.,* vol. 5, pp. 1–23.

Frye, T. C., G. B. Rigg, and W. C. Crandall, 1915, The size of kelps on the Pacific coast of North America: *Bot. Gazette,* vol. 60, pp. 473–482.

Galliher, E. W., 1931, Collophane from Miocene brown shales of California: *Bull. Amer. Assoc. Petrol. Geologists,* vol. 15, pp. 257–269.

Galliher, E. W., 1935, Geology of glauconite: *Bull. Amer. Assoc. Petrol. Geologists,* vol. 19, pp. 1569–1601.

Ganssle, D., and H. B. Clemens, 1953, California-tagged albacore recovered off Japan: *Calif. Fish and Game,* vol. 39, pp. 443.

Gibbs, J. A., Jr., 1957, *Shipwrecks of the Pacific Coast:* Binfords & Mort, Portland, Ore., 312 pp.

Gilluly, J., 1949, Distribution of mountain building in geologic time: *Bull. Geol. Soc. America,* vol. 60, pp. 561–590.

Gilluly, J., and U. S. Grant, 1949, Subsidence in the Long Beach Harbor area, California: *Bull. Geol. Soc. America,* vol. 60, pp. 461–529.

Gilmore, R. M., 1956*a,* The California gray whale: *Zoonooz,* San Diego Zoological Magazine, February, 4 pp.

Gilmore, R. M., 1956*b,* Rare right whale visits California: *Pacific Discovery,* vol. 9, pp. 20–25.

Gilmore, R. M., and G. Ewing, 1954, Calving of the California grays: *Pacific Discovery,* vol. 7, no. 3, pp. 13–15.

Goddard, E. N., chairman, 1948, Rock-color chart: Natl. Research Council, Washington, D. C.

Goldberg, E. D., 1954, Marine geochemistry. I. Chemical scavengers of the sea: *Jour. Geology,* vol. 62, pp. 249–265.

Goldberg, E. D., and G. O. Arrhenius, 1958, Chemistry of Pacific pelagic sediments: *Geochimica et Cosmochimica Acta,* vol. 13, pp. 153–212.

Goodrich, L. C., 1938, China's first knowledge of the Americas: *Geograph. Review,* vol. 28, pp. 400–411.

Gorsline, D. S., 1954, Suspended sediments in sea water: Univ. Southern California, unpubl. rept. in sedimentation, 13 pp.

Gorsline, D. S., 1958, Marine geology of San Pedro and Santa Monica basins and vicinity, California: Univ. Southern California, unpubl. doctoral dissertation, 301 pp.

Gorsline, D. S., and K. O. Emery, 1959, Turbidity current deposits in San Pedro and Santa Monica Basins off southern California: *Bull. Geol. Soc. America,* vol. 70, pp. 279–280.

Gould, H. R., 1953, Lake Mead sedimentation: Univ. Southern California, unpubl. doctoral dissertation, 333 pp.

Gould, H. R., 1954, Sedimentology, *in* Lake Mead Comprehensive Survey of 1948–49: U. S. Depts. of Interior and Navy, advance rept., 366 pp. (mimeographed).

Grady, J. R., in preparation, Submarine geology of Santa Barbara Island and vicinity: Univ. Southern California, unpubl. master's thesis.

Graham, R. D., 1950, Divergence and vorticity of the southern California coastal winds: U. S. Weather Bureau, Los Angeles Office, Special Rept., 9 pp.

Grant, U. S., 1943, Waves as a sand transporting agent: *Amer. Jour. Science,* vol. 241, pp. 117–123.

Grant, U. S., 1954, Subsidence of the Wilmington Oil Field, California: *Calif. Div. Mines, Bull. 170,* ch. 10, pp. 19–24.

Grant, U. S., and F. P. Shepard, 1939, Shallow-water sediment-shifting processes along the southern California coast: *Proc. Pacific Science Congress, 6th,* vol. 2, pp. 801–805.

Gray, J., 1957, How fishes swim: *Sci. American,* vol. 197, no. 2, pp. 48–54.

Green, C. K., 1946, Seismic sea wave of April 1, 1946, as recorded on tide gauges: *Trans. Amer. Geophys. Union,* vol. 27, pp. 490–500.

Grim, R. E., 1951, The depositional environment of red and green shales: *Jour. Sedimentary Petrology,* vol. 21, pp. 226–232.

Grim, R. E., 1953, *Clay Mineralogy:* McGraw-Hill Book Company, New York, 384 pp.

Grim, R. E., R. S. Dietz, and W. F. Bradley, 1949, Clay mineral composition of some sediments from the Pacific Ocean off the California coast and the Gulf of California: *Bull. Geol. Soc. America,* vol. 60, pp. 1785–1808.

Grinnell, J., J. S. Dixon, and J. M. Linsdale, 1937, *Fur-bearing Mammals of California,* vol. 2: Univ. California Press, Berkeley, pp. 452–471.

Guilcher, A., P. H. Kuenen, F. P. Shepard, and V. P. Zenkovitch, 1957, Scientific considerations relating to the continental shelf: United Nations Educational, Scientific and Cultural Organization, Conference on the Law of the Sea 13/2, 20 pp.

Gunnerson, C. G., 1956, Summary report on oceanographic investigations of Santa Monica Bay, July: Unpubl. rept. in files of Bureau of Sanitation, City of Los Angeles, California.

Gunnerson, C., 1957a, Cruise report, offshore survey of 26 June 1957: Unpubl. memo in files of Bureau of Sanitation, City of Los Angeles, California.

Gunnerson, C. G., 1957b, Cruise report, offshore survey, October 5, 1957: Unpublished memo in files of Bureau of Sanitation, Dept. of Public Works, City of Los Angeles, 19 pp.

Gunnerson, C. G., 1958a, Sewage disposal in Santa Monica Bay, California: *Proc. Amer. Soc. Civil Engineers,* vol. 84, Paper 1534, 28 pp.

Gunnerson, C. G., 1958b, Sanitary engineering and oceanography in Santa Monica Bay, California: Limnology and Oceanography, Annual Meeting of Pacific Section at Logan, Utah, June.

Gunter, G., R. H. William, C. C. Davis, and F. G. W. Smith, 1948, Catastrophic mass mortality of marine animals and coincident phytoplankton bloom on the west coast of Florida, November 1946 to August 1947: *Ecol. Monographs,* vol. 18, pp. 309–324.

Gutenberg, B., 1941a, Changes in sea level, postglacial uplift, and mobility of the earth's interior: *Bull. Geol. Soc. America,* vol. 52, pp. 721–772.

Gutenberg, B., 1941b, Mechanism of faulting in southern California indicated by seismograms: *Bull. Seismol. Soc. America,* vol. 31, pp. 263–302.

Gutenberg, B., 1952, Waves from blasts recorded in southern California: *Trans. Amer. Geophys. Union,* vol. 33, pp. 427–431.

Gutenberg, B., and C. F. Richter, 1942, Earthquake magnitude, intensity, energy, and acceleration: *Bull. Seismol. Soc. America,* vol. 32, pp. 163–191.

Gutenberg, B., and C. F. Richter, 1946, Seismic waves from atomic bomb tests: *Trans. Amer. Geophys. Union,* vol. 27, p. 776.

Gutenberg, B., and C. F. Richter, 1949, *Seismicity of the Earth and Associated Phenomena:* Princeton Univ. Press, Princeton, 273 pp.

Hack, J. T., 1957, Submerged river system of Chesapeake Bay: *Bull. Geol. Soc. America,* vol. 68, pp. 817–830.

Hadaway, R. B., 1957, Course zero nine five: *Proc. U. S. Naval Inst.,* vol. 83, pp. 40–48.

Hamilton, E. L., 1956, Low sound velocities in high-porosity sediments: *Jour. Acoustical Soc. America,* vol. 28, pp. 16–19.

Hamilton, E. L., G. Shumway, H. W. Menard, and C. J. Shipek, 1956, Acoustic and other physical properties of shallow-water sediments off San Diego: *Jour. Acoustical Soc. America,* vol. 28, pp. 1–15.

Handin, J. W., 1951, The source, transportation, and deposition of beach sediment in southern California:

Dept. of Army, Corps of Engineers, Beach Erosion Board, Tech. Memo. 22, 113 pp.

Handin, J. W., and J. C. Ludwick, 1950, Accretion of beach sand behind a detached breakwater: Dept. of Army, Corps of Engineers, Beach Erosion Board, Tech. Memo. 16, 13 pp.

Häntzschel, W., 1955, Rezente und fossile Lebensspuren, ihre Deutung und geologische Auswertung: *Experientia,* vol. 11, pp. 373–382.

Hardy, A. C., 1956, *The Open Sea:* Houghton Mifflin Company, Boston, 335 pp.

Harrison, J. C., G. L. Brown, and F. N. Spiess, 1957, Gravity measurements in the northeastern Pacific Ocean: *Trans. Amer. Geophys. Union,* vol. 38, pp. 835–840.

Hartman, O., 1955a, Quantitative survey of the benthos of San Pedro Basin, southern California, Part I, Preliminary results: *Allan Hancock Pacific Expeditions,* vol. 19, 185 pp.

Hartman, O., 1955b, Endemism in the North Pacific Ocean, with emphasis on the distribution of marine annelids, and descriptions of new or little known species, *Essays in the Natural Sciences in Honor of Captain Allan Hancock:* Univ. Southern California Press, Los Angeles, pp. 39–55.

Hartman, O., 1956, Contributions to a biological survey of Santa Monica Bay, California: Final Report to Hyperion Engineers, Inc., from Geology Dept., Univ. Southern California, 161 pp. (multilithed).

Hartman, O., and J. L. Barnard, 1957, Summary of results of a biological survey of the shallow offshore ocean bottoms from Point Arguello, California, to the Mexican border: Interim Report to California State Water Pollution Board, from Hancock Foundation, Univ. Southern California, 87 pp. (multilithed).

Hartman, O., and J. L. Barnard, 1958, The benthic fauna of the deep basins off southern California: *Allan Hancock Pacific Expeditions,* vol. 22, 67 pp.

Hartman, O., and K. O. Emery, 1956, Bathypelagic coelenterates: *Limnology and Oceanography,* vol. 1, pp. 304–312.

Harvey, H. W., 1950, On the production of living matter in the sea off Plymouth: *Jour. Marine Biol. Assoc.,* vol. 29, pp. 97–137.

Harvey, H. W., 1955, *The Chemistry and Fertility of Sea Waters:* Cambridge Univ. Press, England, 224 pp.

Heacock, J. G., Jr., and J. L. Worzel, 1955, Submarine topography west of Mexico and Central America: *Bull. Geol. Soc. America,* vol. 66, pp. 773–776.

Heck, N. H., 1947, List of seismic sea waves: *Bull. Seismol. Soc. America,* vol. 37, pp. 269–286.

Hedgpeth, J. W., 1957, Classification of marine environments: *Geol. Soc. America, Memoir 67,* pp. 93–100.

Heezen, B. C., and M. Ewing, 1952, Turbidity currents and submarine slumps, and the 1929 Grand Banks Earthquake: *Amer. Jour. Science,* vol. 250, pp. 849–873.

Heizer, R. F., 1943, Aboriginal use of bitumen by the California Indians: *Calif. Div. Mines, Bull. 118,* p. 74.

Helland-Hansen, B., and F. Nansen, 1909, The Norwegian Sea. Its physical oceanography based upon the Norwegian researches 1900–1904: *Report on Norwegian Fishery and Marine Investigations,* vol. 2, no. 2, 390 pp.

Hendricks, S. B., and C. S. Ross, 1941, Chemical composition and genesis of glauconite and celadonite: *Amer. Mineralogist,* vol. 26, pp. 683–708.

Hertlein, L. G., and U. S. Grant, IV, 1944, The geology and paleontology of the marine Pliocene of San Diego, California: *Memoirs San Diego Soc. Nat. History,* vol. 2, 72 pp.

Hess, H. H., 1948, Major structural features of the Western North Pacific: an interpretation of H. O. 5485, Bathymetric chart, Korea to New Guinea: *Bull. Geol. Soc. America,* vol. 59, pp. 417–446.

Hess, H. H., and P. MacClintock, 1936, Submerged valleys on continental slopes and changes of sea-level: *Science,* vol. 83, pp. 332–334.

Hill, C. L., and C. A. Kofoid, 1927, Marine borers and their relation to marine construction on the Pacific coast: Final Report of the San Francisco Bay Marine Piling Committee: Univ. California Press, Berkeley, 357 pp.

Hill, M. L., and T. W. Dibblee, Jr., 1953, San Andreas, Garlock, and Big Pine Faults, California: *Bull. Geol. Soc. America,* vol. 64, pp. 443–458.

Hill, R. A., 1934, Clay stratum dried out to prevent landslips: *Civil Engineering,* vol. 4, pp. 403–407.

Hillinger, C., 1958, *The California Islands:* Academy Publishers, Los Angeles, 165 pp.

Hinton, C., 1958, Atomic power in Britain: *Sci. American,* vol. 198, pp. 29–35.

Holder, C. F., 1910, *The Channel Islands of California:* A. C. McClurg & Company, Chicago, 397 pp.

Holmes, R. W., 1957, Surface chlorophyll A, surface primary production, and zooplankton volumes in the northeastern Pacific Ocean: Symposium on Measurement of Primary Production in the Sea, Conseil International pour l'Exploration de la Mer, Bergen, September 1957.

Holzman, J. E., 1952, Submarine geology of Cortes and Tanner Banks: *Jour. Sedimentary Petrology,* vol 22, pp. 97–118.

Hoots, H. W., 1931, Geology of the eastern part of the Santa Monica Mountains, Los Angeles County, California: *U. S. Geol. Survey, Prof. Paper 165-C,* pp. 83–134.

Horrer, P., and R. Revelle, 1956, The ocean off the California coast: *California and the Southwest,* ch. 9: John Wiley & Sons, New York, pp. 80–96.

Hortig, F. J., 1958, California offshore oil, present and future: 35th Annual Meeting Pacific Section Amer. Assoc. Petrol. Geologists, Los Angeles, November 6.

Hough, J. L., 1953, Pleistocene climatic record in a Pacific ocean core sample: *Jour. Geology,* vol. 61, pp. 252–262.

Howe, E. D., 1952, Fresh water from salt water: *Trans. Amer. Geophys. Union,* vol. 33, pp. 417–422.

Howe, E. D., 1958, Status of sea water conversion research: Annual Pacific Southwest Regional Meeting Amer. Geophys. Union, California Inst. of Technology, Pasadena, February 6 and 7.

Hubbs, C. L., 1948, Changes in the fish fauna of western North America correlated with changes in ocean temperature: *Jour. Marine Research,* vol. 7, pp. 459–482.

Hume, N. B., R. D. Bargman, C. G. Gunnerson, and C. E. Imel, 1958, Progress report on operation of a 7-mile digested sludge outfall: Annual Convention Amer. Soc. Civil Engineers, New York, October 13, 20 pp. (mimeographed preprint).

Hunt, J. M., 1953, Composition of crude oil and its relation to stratigraphy in Wyoming: *Bull. Amer. Assoc. Petrol. Geologists,* vol. 37, pp. 1837–1872.

Hunt, J. M., F. Stewart, and P. A. Dickey, 1954, Origin of hydrocarbons of Uinta Basin, Utah: *Bull. Amer. Assoc. Petrol Geologists,* vol. 38, pp. 1671–1698.

Inman, D. L., 1949a, Sorting of sediments in the light of fluid mechanics: *Jour. Sedimentary Petrology,* vol. 19, pp. 51–70.

Inman, D. L., 1949b, Sediment trap studies of suspended material near the surf zone: Scripps Inst. Oceanography, Quarterly Progress Report 2 to Beach Erosion Board, pp. 5–6.

Inman, D. L., 1950, Submarine topography and sedimentation in the vicinity of Mugu submarine canyon, California: Dept. of Army, Corps of Engineers, Beach Erosion Board, Tech. Memo. 19, 45 pp.

Inman, D. L., 1952, Measures for describing the size distribution of sediments: *Jour. Sedimentary Petrology,* vol. 22, pp. 125–145.

Inman, D. L., 1953, Areal and seasonal variations in beach and nearshore sediments at La Jolla, California: Dept. of Army, Corps of Engineers, Beach Erosion Board, Tech. Memo. 39, 82 pp.

Inman, D. L., 1957, Wave-generated ripples in nearshore sands: Dept. of Army, Corps of Engineers, Beach Erosion Board, Tech. Memo. 100, 42 pp.

Inman, D. L., and T. K. Chamberlain, in press, Tracing beach sand movement with irradiated quartz: *Trans. Amer. Geophys. Union.*

Inman, D. L., and N. Nasu, 1956, Orbital velocity associated with wave action near the breaker zone: Dept. of Army, Corps of Engineers, Beach Erosion Board, Tech. Memo. 79, 43 pp.

Inman, D. L., and G. A. Rusnak, 1956, Changes in sand level on the beach and shelf at La Jolla, California: Dept. of Army, Corps of Engineers, Beach Erosion Board, Tech. Memo. 82, 30 pp.

Irwin, W. P., 1957, Franciscan group in Coast Ranges and its equivalents in Sacramento Valley, California: *Bull. Amer. Assoc. Petrol. Geologists,* vol. 41, pp. 2284–2297.

Issatchenko, B. L., 1929, Zür Frage nach der biogenen Bildung des Pyrite: *Intern. Rev. d. ges. Hydrobiol. u. Hydrographie,* vol. 22, pp. 99–101.

Jakosky, J. J., and J. Jakosky Jr., 1956, Characteristics of explosives for marine seismic exploration: *Geophysics,* vol. 21, pp. 969–991.

Jefferson, M. S. W., 1899, Beach cusps: *Jour. Geology,* vol. 7, pp. 237–246.

Jenkins, D. S., 1957, Fresh water from salt: *Sci. American,* vol. 196, pp. 37–45.

Jenkins, D. S., director, 1958, Saline Water Conservation Report for 1957: U. S. Dept. of Interior, 128 pp.

Johnson, C. H., and R. B. Galeski, 1949, Offshore seismic problems affecting geologic evaluation (abstracts): *Bull. Amer. Assoc. Petrol. Geologists,* vol. 33, pp. 2059–2060.

Johnson, D. S., and H. H. York, 1915, The relation of plants to tide-levels: *Carnegie Inst. Washington, Publ. 206,* 162 pp.

Johnson, D. W., 1919, *Shore Processes and Shoreline Development:* John Wiley & Sons, New York, 584 pp.

Johnson, D. W., 1925, *The New England-Acadian Shoreline:* John Wiley & Sons, New York, 608 pp.

Johnson, D. W., 1938–1939, Origin of submarine canyons: *Jour. Geomorphology,* vol. 1, pp. 111–129, 230–243, 324–340; vol. 2, pp. 42–60, 133–158, 213–236.

Johnson, H. R., R. H. Backus, J. B. Hersey, and D. M. Owen, 1956, Suspended echo-sounder and camera studies of midwater sound scatterers: *Deep-Sea Research,* vol. 3, pp. 266–272.

Johnson, J. W., 1953, Sand transport by littoral currents: Proceedings Fifth Hydraulics Conference, *Iowa Univ., Coll. of Engineering, Studies in Engineering, Bull. 34,* pp. 89–109.

Johnson, J. W., 1956, Dynamics of nearshore sediment movement: *Bull. Amer. Assoc. Petrol. Geologists,* vol. 40, pp. 2211–2232.

Johnson, M. E., and H. J. Snook, 1935, *Seashore Animals of the Pacific Coast:* Macmillan Company, New York, 659 pp.

Johnson, M. W., 1948, Sound as a tool in marine ecology, from data on biological noises and the deep scattering layer: *Jour. Marine Research,* vol. 7, pp. 443–458.

Johnson, M. W., and W. M. Lewis, 1942, Pelagic larval stages of the sand crabs *Emerita analoga* (Stimpson), *Blepharipoda occidentalis* Randall, and *Lepidopa myops* Stimpson: *Biol. Bull.,* vol. 83, pp. 67–87.

Jones, C. S., 1955, Subsidence and oil production—an indisputable and irrevocable trust: Richfield Oil Corporation pamphlet, 20 pp.

Jordan, D. S., and J. Z. Gilbert, 1919, Fossil fishes of the (Miocene) Monterey Formations of Southern California: *Leland Stanford Junior Univ. Publ., Univ. Series 2,* pp. 13–64.

Jutson, J. T., 1939, Shore platforms near Sydney, New South Wales: *Jour. Geomorphology,* vol. 2, pp. 236–250.

Kampa, E. M., and B. P. Boden, 1956, Light generation in a sonic-scattering layer: *Deep-Sea Research,* vol. 4, pp. 73–92.

Keesling, Stuart, 1953, Rhomboid beach markings: Univ. Southern California, unpubl. rept. in sedimentation, 10 pp.

Keller, G. H., 1957, Distribution of brown sand off the coast of California and Baja California: Univ. Southern California, unpubl. rept. in marine geology, 19 pp.

Keller, W. D., 1953, Illite and montmorillonite in green

sedimentary rocks: *Jour. Sedimentary Petrology,* vol. 23, pp. 3–9.

Kellogg, R., 1931, Pelagic mammals from the Temblor formation of the Kern River region, California: *Proc. Calif. Acad. Sciences,* ser. 4, vol. 19, pp. 217–397.

Kemnitzer, L. E., 1933, Geology of San Nicolas and Santa Barbara Islands, California: California Inst. Technology, unpubl. master's thesis, 45 pp.

Kerr, A. R., 1938, Littoral erosion and deposition of Santa Monica Bay: Univ. California at Los Angeles, unpubl. master's thesis, 49 pp.

Kew, W. S. W., 1927, Geologic sketch of Santa Rosa Island, Santa Barbara County, California: *Bull. Geol. Soc. America,* vol. 38, pp. 645–654.

King, E. J., 1946, United States Navy at war: Final official report to the Secretary of the Navy: *Proc. U. S. Naval Inst.,* vol. 72, pp. 129–204.

Knapp, R. T., 1952, Wave-produced motion of moored ships, *Proceedings 2nd Conference on Coastal Engineering,* Univ. California Press, pp. 48–61.

Kofoid, C. A., and J. Grinnell, 1929, A conspectus of the marine and fresh-water ciliata belonging to the suborder Tintinnoinea, with descriptions of new species principally from the Agassiz Expedition to the Eastern Tropical Pacific 1904–1905: *Univ. Calif. (Berkeley), Publs. in Zoology,* vol. 34, pp. 1–402.

Kramsky, M., and others, 1952, Draft of report of referee, Case 506806 in the Superior Court of the State of California in and for the County of Los Angeles: Calif. Dept. of Public Works, 175 pp.

Krauskopf, K. B., 1955, Sedimentary deposits of rare metals: *Econ. Geology,* 50th ann. vol., pp. 411–463.

Kropotkin, P. N., 1957, The geological conditions for the appearance of life on the earth, and the problems of petroleum genesis, *The Origin of Life on the Earth* (a symposium): Publishing House of Academy of Sciences of U.S.S.R., Moscow, pp. 44–54.

Krueger, R. D., 1958, State tidelands leasing in California: *Univ. Calif. (Los Angeles) Law Review,* vol. 5, no. 3, pp. 427–490.

Krumbein, W. C., 1941, Measurement and geological significance of shape and roundness of sedimentary particles: *Jour. Sedimentary Petrology,* vol. 11, pp. 64–72.

Krumbein, W. C., and R. M. Garrels, 1952, Origin and classification of chemical sediments in terms of *p*H and oxidation-reduction potentials: *Jour. Geology,* vol. 60, pp. 1–33.

Krumholz, L. A., and R. F. Foster, 1957, Accumulation and retention of radioactivity from fission products and other radiomaterials by fresh-water organisms, *in* The effects of atomic radiation on oceanography and fisheries: *Natl. Acad. Sciences–Natl. Research Council, Publ. 551,* pp. 88–95.

Krynine, P. D., 1948, The megascopic study and field classification of sedimentary rocks: *Penn State College, Mineral Ind. Exp. Station, Tech. Paper 130,* pp. 130–165.

Krynine, P. D., and W. R. Judd, 1957, *Principles of Engineering Geology and Geotechnics:* McGraw-Hill Book Company, New York, 730 pp.

Kuenen, P. H., 1943, Collecting of the samples and some general aspects: *The Snellius-Expedition,* vol. 5, part 3, sec. 1, 46 pp., E. J. Brill Company, Leiden.

Kuenen, P. H., 1948, The formation of beach cusps: *Jour. Geology,* vol. 56, pp. 34–40.

Kuenen, P. H., 1950, *Marine Geology:* John Wiley & Sons, New York, 568 pp.

Kuenen, P. H., 1951, Properties of turbidity currents of high density: *Soc. Econ. Paleontologists and Mineralogists, Special Publ. 2,* pp. 14–33.

Kuenen, P. H., 1953*a,* Origin and classification of submarine canyons: *Bull. Geol. Soc. America,* vol. 64, pp. 1295–1314.

Kuenen, P. H., 1953*b,* Significant features of graded bedding: *Bull. Amer. Assoc. Petrol. Geologists,* vol. 37, pp. 1044–1066.

Kuenen, P. H., 1954, Eustatic changes of sea-level: *Geologie en Mijnbouw,* new ser., vol. 16, pp. 148–155.

Kullenberg, B., 1947, The piston core sampler: *Svenska Hydrograf. Biol. Komm. Skrifter, Tredje Ser., Hydr.,* vol. 1, no. 2, 46 pp.

Kullenberg, B., 1952, On the salinity of the water contained in marine sediments: *Medd. Oceanographic Inst. Göteborg,* vol. 21, 38 pp.

Kulp, J. L., 1953, Carbon-14 measurements on geological samples: *Atomics,* vol. 4, 4 pp.

Kulp, J. L., H. W. Feely, and L. E. Tryon, 1951, Lamont natural radiocarbon measurements, I: *Science,* vol. 114, pp. 565–568.

Kulp, J. L., L. E. Tryon, W. R. Eckelman, and W. A. Snell, 1952, Lamont natural radiocarbon measurements, II: *Science,* vol. 116, pp. 409–414.

Kulp, J. L., K. Turekian, and D. W. Boyd, 1952, Strontium content of limestones and fossils: *Bull. Geol. Soc. America,* vol. 63, pp. 701–716.

Ladd, H. S., J. W. Hedgpeth, and R. Post, 1957, Environments and facies of existing bays on the Central Texas Coast: *Geol. Soc. America, Memoir 67,* pp. 599–639.

LaFond, E. C., 1939*a,* Variations of sea level on the Pacific Coast of the United States: *Jour. Marine Research,* vol. 2, pp. 17–29.

LaFond, E. C., 1939*b,* Sand movements near the beach in relation to tides and waves: *Proc. Pac. Sci. Congress, 6th,* vol. 2, pp. 795–799.

LaFond, E. C., and R. P. Rao, 1954, Beach erosion cycles near Waltair on Bay of Bengal: *Andhra Univ. Memoirs on Oceanography,* vol. 1, pp. 1–15.

Landergren, S., 1954, On the relative abundance of the stable carbon isotopes in marine sediments: *Deep-Sea Research,* vol. 1, pp. 98–120.

Lane, B., 1956, The movement of chitins: Univ. Southern California, unpubl. rept. in oceanography, 12 pp.

Lane, F. K., 1958, *Kingdom of the Octopus, a Life History of the Cephalopoda:* Jarrolds, Publishers, Ltd., London, 287 pp.

Lawson, A. C., 1893*a,* The geology of Carmelo Bay: *Univ. Calif., Publs. in Geology,* vol. 1, pp. 1–59.

Lawson, A. C., 1893*b,* The post-Pliocene diastrophism of

the coast of southern California: *Univ. Calif., Publs. in Geology,* vol. 1, pp. 115–160.

Lawson, A. C., 1950, Sea bottom off the coast of California: *Bull. Geol. Soc. America,* vol. 61, pp. 1225–1242.

Le Calvez, J., 1951, Déréglement du métabolisme ferrugineux chez les Formainifères: *Vie et milieu,* vol. 2, pp. 335–337.

Le Conte, J., 1891, Tertiary and post-Tertiary changes of the Atlantic and Pacific coasts: *Bull. Geol. Soc. America,* vol. 2, pp. 323–330.

Leipper, D. F., 1955, Sea temperature variations associated with tidal currents in stratified shallow water over an irregular bottom: *Jour. Marine Research,* vol. 14, pp. 234–252.

Leypoldt, H., 1937, California seiches and Philippine typhoons: *Proc. U. S. Naval Inst.,* vol. 63, pp. 775–788.

Light, S. F., R. I. Smith, F. A. Pitelka, D. P. Abbott, and F. M. Weesner, 1954, *Intertidal Invertebrates of the Central California Coast:* Univ. California Press, Berkeley, 446 pp.

Limbaugh, C., and F. P. Shepard, 1957, Submarine Canyons: *Geol. Soc. America, Memoir 67,* vol. I, pp. 633–640.

Lindenkohl, A., 1885, Geology of the sea-bottom in the approaches to New York Bay: *Amer. Jour. Science,* 3rd ser., vol. 29, pp. 475–480.

Lindenkohl, A., 1891, Notes on the sub-marine channel of the Hudson River and other evidences of postglacial subsidence of the Middle Atlantic coast region: *Amer. Jour. Science,* 3rd ser., vol. 41, pp. 489–499.

Lindsay, J. B., 1957*a,* Experiment—undertow: Univ. Southern California, unpubl. rept. in oceanography, 6 pp.

Lindsay, J. B., 1957*b,* Analysis and history of a small intermittent stream sediment deposited on a sandy beach: Univ. Southern California, unpubl. rept. in sedimentation, 10 pp.

Link, T. A., 1957, Whence came the hydrocarbons?: *Bull. Amer. Assoc. Petrol. Geologists,* vol. 41, pp. 1387–1402.

Llano, G. A., 1957, Sharks v. men: *Sci. American,* vol. 196, no. 6, pp. 54–61.

Lochman, Christina, 1957, Paleoecology of the Cambrian in Montana and Wyoming: *Geol. Soc. America, Memoir 67,* vol. 2, pp. 117–162.

Loel, W., and W. H. Corey, 1932, The Vaqueros formation, lower Miocene of California. I. Paleontology: *Univ. Calif. (Berkeley), Publs. in Geol. Sciences,* vol. 22, pp. 31–410.

Los Angeles–Long Beach Harbor Pollution Control Committee, 1956, Second Annual Report to Regional Water Pollution Control Board 4, 16 pp. (mimeograped).

Lüders, K., 1939, Sediments of the North Sea, *Recent Marine Sediments,* Amer. Assoc. Petrol. Geologists, Tulsa, pp. 322–341.

Ludwick, J. C., Jr., 1950, Deep water sand layers off San Diego California: Univ. California at Los Angeles, unpubl. doctoral dissertation, 56 pp.

Luplow, W. D., 1950, Beach-erosion control report on cooperative study of Pacific coast line of the state of California, Point Mugu to San Pedro breakwater: Dept. of Army, Corps of Engineers, 114 pp. plus 12

appendices (same as House Doc. 277, 83rd Congress, 2nd Session, App. 2, 1953, 178 pp.)

Luskin, B., B. C. Heezen, M. Ewing, and M. Landisman, 1954, Precision measurement of ocean depth: *Deep-Sea Research,* vol. 1, pp. 131–140.

Lydon, P. A., 1957, Titanium: in Mineral Commodities of California: *Calif. Div. Mines, Bull. 176,* pp. 647–654.

Lyell, C., 1850, *Principles of Geology,* 8th ed.: John Murray, London, 811 pp.

Lyman, J., 1948, The sea's phantom bottom: *Sci. Monthly,* vol. 66, pp. 87–88.

Ma, T. Y. H., 1952, *The Shiftings in Pole-positions with Diastrophisms Since the End of the Cretaceous, and the Accompanying Drift of Continents:* World Book Company, Ltd., Taipeh, Taiwan, 176 pp.

MacGinitie, G. E., and N. MacGinitie, 1949, *Natural History of Marine Animals:* McGraw-Hill Book Company, New York, 473 pp.

Mackin, J. H., 1948, Concept of the graded stream: *Bull. Geol. Soc. America,* vol. 59, pp. 463–512.

MacNeil, F. S., 1949, Pleistocene shore lines in Florida and Georgia: *U. S. Geol. Survey, Prof. Paper 221-F,* pp. 95–107.

MacPherson, E. O., 1952, The stratigraphy and bentonitic shale deposits of Kekerangu and Blue Slop, Marlborough: *New Zealand Jour. of Science and Technology,* vol. 33, pp. 258–286.

Mandelbaum, H., 1956, Evidence for a critical wind velocity for air-sea boundary processes: *Trans Amer. Geophys. Union,* vol. 37, pp. 685–690.

Mansfield, G. R., 1927, Geography, geology, and mineral resources of part of southeastern Idaho: *U. S. Geol. Survey, Prof. Paper 152,* pp. 1–409.

Mansfield, G. R., 1940, Phosphate deposits of the United States: *Econ. Geology,* vol. 35, pp. 405–429.

Marine Research Committee, 1958, Progress report, 1 July 1956 to 1 January 1958: California Cooperative Oceanic Fisheries Investigations, Calif. Dept. Fish and Game, 57 pp.

Marlette, J. W., 1954, The breakwater at Redondo Beach, California, and its effects on erosion and sedimentation: Univ. Southern California, unpubl. master's thesis, 82 pp.

Marmer, H. A., 1926, *The Tide*: D. Appleton & Company, New York, 282 pp.

Marmer, H. A., 1932, Tides and tidal currents: *Bull. Natl. Research Council 85,* pp. 229–309.

Marmer, H. A., 1949, Sea level changes along the coasts of the United States in recent years: *Trans. Amer. Geophys. Union,* vol. 30, pp. 201–204.

Martin, D., Jr., 1957, The uptake of radioactive wastes by benthic organisms: Presented at 9th Pacific Science Congress, Bangkok, Thailand, November 18–30.

Martin, W. E., 1955, Seasonal infections of the snail, *Cerithidea californica* Haldeman, with larval trematodes, *Essays in the Natural Sciences in Honor of Captain Allan Hancock!* Univ. Southern California Press, Los Angeles, pp. 203–210.

Mason, W. A., 1955, Strandings and wrecks of vessels on

the coasts of California, Oregon, and Washington: Graphic Specialties Company, San Pedro, chart.

Mather, B., 1957, Factors affecting the durability of concrete in coastal structures: Dept. of Army, Corps of Engineers, Beach Erosion Board, Tech. Memo 96, 27 pp. plus appendices.

Mattox, N. T., 1955, Observations on the brachiopod communities near Santa Catalina Islands, *Essays in the Natural Sciences in Honor of Captain Allan Hancock:* Univ. Southern California Press, Los Angeles, pp. 73–83.

Maury, M. F., 1855, *The Physical Geography of the Sea:* Harper & Brothers, New York, 287 pp.

McAllister, R. F., 1957, Photography of submerged vertical structures: *Trans Amer. Geophys. Union,* vol. 38, pp. 314–319.

McCulloh, T. H., 1957, Simple Bouguer gravity and generalized geologic map of the northwestern part of the Los Angeles Basin, California: U. S. Geol. Survey, Geophys. Investig. Map GP 149.

McEwen, G. F., 1916, Summary and interpretation of the hydrographic observations made by the Scripps Institution for Biological Research of the University of California 1908–1915: *Univ. Calif. (Berkeley), Publs. in Zoology,* vol. 15, pp. 255–356.

McEwen, G. F., 1935, Destructive high waves along the southern California coast: *Shore and Beach,* vol. 3, pp. 61–64.

McGill, J. T., 1954, Residential building-site problems in Los Angeles, California: *Calif. Div. Mines, Bull. 170,* ch. 10, pp. 11–18.

McGlasson, R. H., 1957, Foraminiferal biofacies around Santa Catalina Island: Univ. Southern California, unpubl. master's thesis, 106 pp.

McKinney, T. C., 1956, Ye true map of reported facts and tales: Miller Brothers Printing, Burbank, Calif., chart.

McQuat, H. W., 1951, History of Los Angeles Harbor: *Proceedings 1st Conference on Coastal Engineering,* Univ. California Press, Berkeley, pp. 259–270.

Menard, H. W., 1955, Deep-sea channels, topography, and sedimentation: *Bull. Amer. Assoc. Petrol. Geologists,* vol. 39, pp. 236–255.

Menard, H. W. 1956, Deformation of the northeastern Pacific basin and the west coast of North America: *Bull. Geol. Soc. America,* vol. 66, pp. 1149–1198.

Menard, H. W., and R. S. Dietz, 1951, Submarine geology of the Gulf of Alaska: *Bull. Geol. Soc. America,* vol. 62, pp. 1263–1286.

Menard, H. W., R. F., Dill, E. L. Hamilton, D. G. Moore, G. Shumway, M. Silverman, and H. B. Stewart, 1954, Underwater mapping by diving geologists: *Bull. Amer. Assoc. Petrol. Geologists,* vol. 38, pp. 129–147.

Menard, H. W., and J. C. Ludwick, 1951, Applications of hydraulics to the study of marine turbidity currents: *Soc. Econ. Paleontologists and Mineralogists, Special Publ. 2,* pp. 2–13.

Mendenhall, W. C., 1905, Development of underground waters in the western coastal plain region of southern California: *U. S. Geol. Survey, Water Supply and Irrigation Paper 139,* 103 pp.

Menzies, R. J., 1951, The phylogeny, systematics, distribution and natural history of *Limnoria:* Univ. Southern California, unpubl. doctoral dissertation, 520 pp.

Merriam, Patricia D., 1949, Geology of the El Segundo sand hills: Univ. Southern California, unpubl. master's thesis, 42 pp.

Merriam, R. H., in preparation, *Landslide at Portuguese Bend, Palos Verdes Hills, California.*

Mertz, H., 1953, *Pale Ink: Two Ancient Records of Chinese Exploration in America:* Published by author, Box 207, Old Post Office Sta., Chicago, 158 pp.

Miller, H. E., and I. Nusbaum, 1952, The oxygen resources of San Diego Bay, *in* Extent, effects and limitations of waste disposal into San Diego Bay: San Diego Regional Water Pollution Control Board, pp. 83–94.

Miller, L., 1940, Observations on the black-footed albatross: *The Condor,* vol. 42, pp. 229–238.

Miller, W. J., 1931, The landslide at Point Fermin, California: *Sci. Monthly,* vol. 32, pp. 464–469.

Moody, J. D., and M. J. Hill, 1956, Wrench-fault tectonics: *Bull. Geol. Soc. America,* vol. 67, p. 1207–1246.

Moore, D. G., 1951, Rhomboid ripple marks and their relationship to beach characteristics: Univ. Southern California, unpubl. rept. in marine geology, 16 pp.

Moore, D. G., 1954a, Submarine geology of San Pedro shelf: *Jour. Sedimentary Petrology,* vol. 24, pp. 162–181.

Moore, D. G., 1954b, Origin and development of sea caves: *Amer. Caver, Natl. Speleological Soc. Bull.,* vol. 16, pp. 71–76.

Moore, D. G., 1956, Vane shear strength, porosity, and permeability relationships of some sieved cohesionless sands: 20th International Geological Congress, Mexico City, September 4, 1956.

Moore, D. G., 1957, Acoustic sounding of Quaternary marine sediments off Point Loma, California: U. S. Navy Electronics Laboratory, San Diego, Rept. 815, 17 pp.

Moore, D. G., and G. Shumway, in press, Sediment thickness and physical properties: Pigeon Point Shelf, California: *Trans. Amer. Geophys. Union.*

Mortimer, C. H., 1951, Water movements in stratified lakes: *International Association Hydrology, General Assembly of International Union of Geodesy and Geophysics, Brussels,* vol. 3, pp. 335–349.

Mouton, M. W., 1952, *The Continental Shelf:* Martinus Nijhoff, The Hague, 367 pp.

Munk, W. H., 1947a, A critical wind speed for air-sea boundary processes: *Jour. Marine Research,* vol. 6, pp. 203–218.

Munk, W. H., 1947b, Increase in the period of waves traveling over large distances: With applications to tsunamis, swell, and seismic surface waves: *Trans. Amer. Geophys. Union,* vol. 28, pp. 189–217.

Munk, W. H., 1947c, Tracking storms by forerunners of swell: *Jour. Meteorology,* vol. 4, pp. 45–57.

Munk, W. H., 1949a, The solitary wave theory and its application to surf problems: *Ann. New York Acad. Sciences,* vol. 51, pp. 376–424.

Munk, W. H., 1949b, Surf beats: *Trans. Amer. Geophys. Union,* vol. 30, pp. 849–854.

Munk, W. H., 1953, Small tsunami waves reaching California from the Japanese earthquakes of March 4, 1952: *Bull. Seismol. Soc. America,* vol. 43, pp. 219–222.

Munk, W., and R. Revelle, 1952, Sea level and the rotation of the earth: *Amer. Jour. Science,* vol. 250, pp. 829–833.

Munk, W. H., and M. Traylor, 1947, Refraction of ocean waves, a process linking underwater topography to beach erosion: *Jour. Geology,* vol. 55, pp. 1–26.

Murray, J., and J. Hjort, 1912, *The Depths of the Ocean:* Macmillan & Company, London, 821 pp.

Murray, J., and A. F. Renard, 1891, *Deep Sea Deposits: H.M.S. Challenger, Scientific Results,* London, 525 pp.

Nanz, R. H., 1955, Grain orientation in beach sands: a possible means for predicting reservoir trend (abst.): 29th Annual Meeting, Soc. Econ. Paleontologists and Mineralogists, New York.

Narver, D. L., 1954, Good concrete made with coral and sea water, II Sea water for concrete: *Civil Engineering,* vol. 24, pp. 725–728.

Natland, M. L., 1933, The temperature and depth-distribution of some recent and fossil Foraminifera in the southern California region: *Bull. Scripps Inst. Oceanography, Univ. Calif.,* vol 3, pp. 225–230.

Natland, M. L., 1957, Paleoecology of West Coast Tertiary Sediments: *Geol. Soc. America, Memoir 67,* pp. 543–572.

Natland, M. L., and P. H. Kuenen, 1951, Sedimentary history of the Ventura Basin, California, and the action of turbidity currents: *Soc. Economic Paleontologists and Mineralogists, Special Publ. 2,* pp. 76–107.

Natland, M. L., and W. T. Rothwell, Jr., 1954, Fossil Foraminifera of the Los Angeles and Ventura regions, California: *Calif. Div. Mines, Bull. 170,* ch. 3, pp. 33–42.

Nelson, J. W., C. J. Zinn, A. T. Strahorn, E. B. Watson, and J. E. Dunn, 1919, Soil survey of the Los Angeles area, California: U. S. Dept. Agriculture, Bureau of Soils, 78 pp.

Norris, K. S., 1958, The big one got away: *Pacific Discovery,* vol. 11, no. 5, pp. 3–13.

Norris, K. S., and D. H. Brown, in press, *Observations on the Natural History of Captive and Wild Cetaceans:* Univ. California Press, Berkeley.

Norris, R. M., 1951, Marine geology of the San Nicolas Island region, California: Scripps Inst. Oceanography, unpubl. doctoral dissertation, 124 pp.

Norris, R. M., 1952, Recent history of a sand spit at San Nicolas Island, California: *Jour. Sedimentary Petrology,* vol. 22, pp. 224–228.

North, W., 1954, Size distribution, erosive activities, and gross metabolic efficiency of the marine intertidal snails, *Littorina planaxis* and *L. scutulata: Biol. Bull.,* vol. 106, pp. 185–197.

Nuclear Science and Engineering Corporation, 1956, Radioactive tracer study of sewage field in Santa Monica Bay: Report to Hyperion Engineers, 21 pp.

Oakwood, T. S., D. S. Shriver, H. H. Fall, W. J. McAleer, and P. R. Wunz, 1952, Optical activity of petroleum: *Ind. and Eng. Chemistry,* vol. 44, pp. 2568–2570.

O'Brien, J. T., and D. I. Kuchenreuther, 1958, Waves in and around Port Hueneme, California associated with the tsunami of 9 March 1957: Annual Pacific Southwest Regional Meeting, Amer. Geoph. Union, Pasadena, February 7.

O'Brien, M. P., and J. R. Morison, 1952, The forces exerted by waves on objects: *Trans. Amer. Geophys. Union,* vol. 33, pp. 32–38.

Orr, P. C., 1956, Radiocarbon dates from Santa Rosa Island, I: *Santa Barbara Museum Nat. History, Dept. Anthopology, Bull. 2,* 10 pp.

Orr, P. C., 1958, Items of interest: Western Speleological Inst., Inc.: Santa Barbara Museum Nat. History, no. 2, 3 pp. (mimeographed).

Orr, W. L., and K. O. Emery, 1956a, Composition of organic matter in marine sediments: Preliminary data on hydrocarbon distribution in basins off southern California: *Bull. Geol. Soc. America,* vol. 67, pp. 1247–1258.

Orr, W. L., and K. O. Emery, 1956b, Progress report I concerning studies of organic matter in recent marine sediments off southern California: Hydrocarbon separations: Univ. Southern California, Report to Shell Development Company, 64 pp. (multilithed).

Orr, W. L., K. O. Emery, and J. R. Grady, 1958, Preservation of chlorophyll derivatives in sediments off southern California: *Bull. Amer. Assoc. Petrol. Geologists,* vol. 42, pp. 925–962.

Orr, W. L., and J. R. Grady, 1957, Determination of chlorophyll derivatives in marine sediments: *Deep-Sea Research,* vol. 4, pp. 263–271.

Parks, R., 1957, Carbon isotope fractionation and photosynthesis: Calif. Inst. Technology, Dept. Geol. Sciences, unpubl. doctoral dissertation.

Parr, A. E., 1937, A contribution to the hydrography of the Caribbean and Cayman Seas based upon the observations made by the research ship Atlantis, 1933–34: *Bull. Bingham Oceanographic Collection,* vol. 5, 110 pp.

Patterson, R. L., 1950, Report upon the improvement of Upper Newport Bay, Newport Bay Harbor, Orange County, California: Orange County Board of Supervisors and Harbor Commission, 100 pp.

Pattullo, J., W. Munk, R. Revelle, and E. Strong, 1955, The seasonal oscillation in sea level: *Jour. Marine Research,* vol. 14, pp. 88–155.

Pearse, A. S., 1936, *The Migrations of Animals from Sea to Land:* Duke Univ. Press, 176 pp.

Peel, K. P., 1951, Location of harbors: *Proc. 1st Conference on Coastal Engineering,* Univ. California Press, Berkeley, pp. 179–185.

Pepper, J. F., 1958, Potential mineral resources of the continental shelves of the western hemisphere, *in* An introduction to the geology and mineral resources of the continental shelves of the Americas: *U. S. Geol. Survey, Bull. 1067,* pp. 43–65.

Pequegnat, W. E., 1958, Whales, plankton and man: *Sci. American,* vol. 198, pp. 84–90.

Pérès, J. M., 1958, Trois plongées dans le canyon du Cap Sicié, affectuées avec le bathyscaphe *F.N.R.S. III* de la Marine Nationale: *Bull. de l'institut océanographique,* no. 1115, 21 pp.

Pérès, J. M., J. Picard, and M. Ruivo, 1957, Résultats de la Campagne de Recherches du Bathyscaphe *F.N.R.S. III: Bull. l'institut océanographique,* no. 1092, 29 pp.

Pérès, J. M., and J. Piccard, 1956, New biological observations made with the bathyscaphe *FNRS-3* and comments on the aphotic regime of the Mediterranean: *Bull. Inst. Oceanography (Monaco),* no. 1075, 10 pp.

Pettijohn, F. J., 1957, *Sedimentary Rocks,* 2nd ed.: Harper & Brothers, New York, 718 pp.

Phleger, F. B., 1951, Displaced Foraminifera faunas: *Soc. Econ. Paleontologists and Mineralogists, Special Publ.* 1, pp. 66–75.

Piccard, J., and R. S. Dietz, 1957, Oceanographic observations by the bathyscaphe *Trieste* (1953–1956): *Deep-Sea Research,* vol. 4, pp. 221–229.

Pierce, R. L., 1956, Upper Miocene Foraminifera and fish from the Los Angeles area, California: *Jour. Paleontology,* vol. 30, pp. 1288–1314.

Pierson, W. J., 1951, The interpretation of crossed orthogonals in wave refraction phenomena: Dept. of Army, Corps of Engineers, Beach Erosion Board, Tech. Memo. 21, 83 pp.

Pinkas, L., 1951, Yield per area of the California sardine fishing grounds 1937–1949: *Calif. Dept. Fish and Game, Fish Bull. 80,* pp. 9–14.

Plass, G. N., 1956, Carbon dioxide and the climate: *Amer. Scientist,* vol. 44, pp. 302–316.

Poland, J. F., A. A. Garrett, and A. Sinnott, 1948, Geology, hydrology, and chemical character of the ground waters in the Torrance-Santa Monica area, Los Angeles County, California: U. S. Geol. Survey, Ground Water Branch, pp. 1–472 (duplicated).

Poland, J. F., A. M. Piper, and others, 1945, Geologic features in the coastal zone of the Long Beach-Santa Ana area, California, with particular respect to ground-water conditions: U. S. Geol. Survey, Ground Water Branch, pp. 1–328 (duplicated).

Poland, J. F., A. M. Piper, and others, 1956, Ground-water geology of the coastal zone Long Beach-Santa Ana Area, California: *U. S. Geol. Survey, Water Supply Paper 1109,* 162 pp.

Pollack, M. J., 1951, The sources of the deep water of the eastern Mediterranean Sea: *Jour. Marine Research,* vol. 10, pp. 128–152.

Polski, W., 1957, Varved sediments in a core from the Santa Barbara Basin off the California coast: Univ. Southern California, unpubl. rept. in sedimentation, 15 pp.

Popenoe, H. L., 1958, Developments in West coast area in 1957: *Bull. Amer. Assoc. Petrol. Geologists,* vol. 42, pp. 1394–1412.

Pora, E. A., 1946, Problèmes de Physiologie animals dans la Mer Noire: *Bull. l'institut océanographique,* vol. 903, pp. 1–43.

Porfiriev, V. B., 1955, Methods and factors in origin of petroleum, *Symposium on the Problem of Origin and Migration of Petroleum:* Acad. Ukranian SSR, Inst. Economic Geology, Kiev, pp. 169–195 (in Russian).

Pratt, W. L., 1956, Glauconite casts in some bottom sediments from Santa Monica Bay and Santa Rosa Ridge off southern California: Univ. Southern California, unpubl. rept. in marine geology, 19 pp.

Press, F., 1956, Determination of crustal structure from phase velocity of Rayleigh waves. Part I: Southern California: *Bull. Geol. Soc. America,* vol. 67, pp. 1647–1658.

Price, W. A., 1947, Equilibrium of form and forces in tidal basins of coast of Texas and Louisiana: *Bull. Amer. Assoc. Petrol. Geologists,* vol. 31, pp. 1619–1663.

Purer, E. A., 1942, Plant ecology of the coastal salt marshlands of San Diego County, California: *Ecol. Monographs,* vol. 12, pp. 81–111.

Putnam, J. A., 1949, Loss of wave energy due to percolation in a permeable sea bottom: *Trans. Amer. Geophys. Union,* vol. 30, pp. 349–356.

Putnam, J. A., W. H. Munk, and M. A. Traylor, 1949, The prediction of longshore currents: *Trans. Amer. Geophys. Union,* vol. 30, pp. 337–345.

Putnam, W. C., 1942, Geomorphology of the Ventura region, California: *Bull. Geol. Soc. America,* vol. 53, pp. 691–754.

Putnam, W. C., 1950, Moraine and shoreline relationships at Mono Lake, California: *Bull. Geol. Soc. America,* vol. 61, pp. 115–122.

Rabinovitz, D., 1958, Directional permeability and dimensional orientation of beach sands: Univ. Southern California, unpubl. rept. in sedimentation, 8 pp.

Rafter, T. A., 1953, The preparation of carbon for C[14] age measurements: *New Zealand Jour. of Science and Technology,* Sect. B, vol. 35, pp. 64–89.

Rafter, T. A., 1955a, ^{14}C variations in nature and the effect on radiocarbon dating: *New Zealand Jour. of Science and Technology,* Sect. B., vol. 37, pp. 20–38.

Rafter, T. A., 1955b, Carbon dioxide as a substitute for solid carbon in ^{14}C age measurements: *New Zealand Jour. of Science and Technology,* Sect. B., vol. 36, pp. 363–370.

Raitt, R. W., 1949, Studies of ocean-bottom structure off southern California with explosive waves (abst): *Bull. Geol. Soc. America,* vol. 60, p. 1915.

Raitt, R. W., 1952, Geophysical measurements: Oceanographic instrumentation: *Natl. Acad. Sciences–Natl. Research Council Publ. 309,* pp. 70–84.

Rand, W. W., 1933, The geology of Santa Cruz Island, California: Univ. California, unpubl. doctoral dissertation, 175 pp.

Rand, W. W., 1951, Ventura Basin: *Bull. Amer. Assoc. Petrol. Geologists,* vol. 35, pp. 231–240.

Rankama, K., and T. G. Sahama, 1950, *Geochemistry:* Univ. Chicago Press, 912 pp.

Redwine, L. E., (chairman), 1952, Cenozoic correlation section paralleling north and south margins western Ventura Basin from Point Conception to Ventura and Channel, California: Pacific Section Amer. Assoc. Petrol. Geologists, chart.

Ree, W. R., 1958, Radiological monitoring—January to June, 1958: City of Los Angeles, Dept. of Water and Power, Sanitary Engin. Div., unpubl. memo, 3 pp.

Reed, R. D., 1928, The occurrence of feldspar in California sandstones: *Bull. Amer. Assoc. Petrol. Geologists,* vol. 12, pp. 1023–1024.

Reed, R. D., 1933, *Geology of California:* Amer. Assoc. Petrol. Geologists, Tulsa, 355 pp.

Reed, R. D., and J. S. Hollister, 1936, *Structural Evolution of Southern California:* Amer. Assoc. Petrol. Geologists, Tulsa, 157 pp.

Reid, J. L., Jr., 1956, Observations of internal tides in October 1950: *Trans. Amer. Geophys. Union,* vol. 37, pp. 278–286.

Reid, J. L., Jr., G. I. Roden, and J. G. Wyllie, 1958, Studies of the California current system: California Cooperative Oceanic Fisheries Investigations, Calif. Dept. Fish and Game, pp. 27–56.

Reish, D. J., 1956, An ecological study of Lower San Gabriel River, California, with special reference to pollution: *Calif. Fish and Game,* vol. 42, pp. 51–61.

Reish, D. J., and H. A. Winter, 1954, The ecology of Alamitos Bay, California, with special reference to pollution: *Calif. Fish and Game,* vol. 40, pp. 105–121.

Reiter, M., 1957, Seasonal variations in intertidal Foraminifera of Santa Monica Bay: Univ. Southern California, unpubl. master's thesis, 101 pp.

Resig, Johanna M., 1958, Ecology of Foraminifera of the Santa Cruz Basin, California: *Micropaleontology,* vol. 4, pp. 287–308.

Revelle, R., 1941, Criteria for recognition of sea water in ground-water: *Trans. Amer. Geophys. Union,* vol. 3, pp. 593–597.

Revelle, R. R., 1944, Marine bottom samples collected in the Pacific Ocean by the Carnegie on its seventh cruise: *Carnegie Inst. Washington, Publ. 556,* 180 pp.

Revelle, R., M. Bramlette, G. Arrhenius, and E. D. Goldberg, 1955, Pelagic sediments of the Pacific: *Geol. Soc. America, Special Paper 62,* pp. 221–235.

Revelle, R., and K. O. Emery, 1951, Barite concretions from the ocean floor: *Bull. Geol. Soc. America,* vol 62, pp. 707–724.

Revelle, R., and K. O. Emery, 1957, Chemical erosion of beach rock and exposed reef rock: *U. S. Geol. Survey, Prof. Paper 260-T,* pp. 699–709.

Revelle, R., and F. P. Shepard, 1939, Sediments off the California coast: *Recent Marine Sediments,* Amer. Assoc. Petrol. Geologists, Tulsa, pp. 245–282.

Revelle, R., and H. E. Suess, 1957, Carbon dioxide exchange between atmosphere and ocean and the question of an increase of atmospheric CO_2 during the past decades: *Tellus,* vol. 9, pp. 18–27.

Rex, R. W., and E. D. Goldberg, 1958, Quartz contents of pelagic sediments of the Pacific Ocean: *Tellus,* vol. 10, pp. 153–159.

Rich, J. L., 1950, Flow markings, groovings, and intrastratal crumplings as criteria for recognition of slope deposits: *Bull. Amer. Assoc. Petrol. Geologists,* vol. 34, pp. 717–741.

Rich, M., 1956, Seiche study in Los Angeles Harbor and adjoining channel: Univ. Southern California, unpubl. rept. in oceanography, 11 pp.

Richter, R. C., and E. C. Marliave, 1952, Ground water basins in California: Calif. Div. Water Resources, Water Quality Investigation, Rept. 3, 44 pp.

Ricketts, E. F., and J. Calvin, 1952, *Between Pacific Tides,* 3rd ed., revised by J. W. Hedgpeth: Stanford Univ. Press, Stanford, 502 pp.

Riley, G. A., 1941, Plankton studies III. Long Island Sound: *Bull. Bingham Oceanographic Collection,* vol. 7, no. 3, 93 pp.

Riley, G. A., 1951, Oxygen, phosphate and nitrate in the Atlantic Ocean: *Bull. Bingham Oceanographic Collection,* vol. 13, pp. 1–126.

Rittenberg, S. C., 1956, Studies on coliform bacteria discharged from the Hyperion outfall: Final bacteriological report: Report to Hyperion Engineers, Inc., from Geology Dept., Univ. Southern California, 51 pp. (multilithed).

Rittenberg, S. C., K. O. Emery, and W. L. Orr, 1955, Regeneration of nutrients in sediments of marine basins: *Deep-Sea Research,* vol. 3, pp. 23–45.

Rittenberg, S. C., T. Mittwer, and D. Ivler, 1958, Coliform bacteria in sediments around three marine sewage outfalls: *Limnology and Oceanography,* vol. 3, pp. 101–108.

Rittenhouse, G., 1943, A visual method of estimating two dimensional sphericity: *Jour. Sedimentary Petrology,* vol. 13, pp. 79–81.

Ritter, W. E., 1901, Some observations bearing on the probable subsidence during recent geological time of the island of Santa Catalina off the coast of southern California: *Science,* new ser., vol. 14, pp. 575–577.

Ritter, W. E., 1902, A summer's dredging on the coast of southern California: *Science,* new ser., vol. 15, pp. 55–65.

Roedel, P. M., 1953, Common ocean fishes of the California coast: *Calif. Dept. Fish and Game, Fish Bull. 91,* 184 pp.

Romanovsky, V., 1948, Recherches sur les propriétés physiques des sédiments: Institut Technique du Batiment, Paris, Thèse Ing. Doct. 175, 32 pp.

Roth, E. R., 1959, Landslides between Santa Monica and Point Dume: Univ. Southern California, unpubl. master's thesis, 184 pp.

Rubin, M., and H. E. Suess, 1955, U. S. Geological Survey radiocarbon dates II: *Science,* vol. 121, pp. 481–488.

Russell, R. D., 1950, Research in submarine geology sponsored by the U. S. Navy: 18th International Geological Congress, Great Britain, Rept. pt. 8, pp. 63–68.

Ryther, J. H., 1957, On the efficiency of primary production in the Ocean: Proceedings 9th Pacific Science Congress, Bangkok, Thailand. 29 pp. (mimeographed).

Sanders, H. L., 1956, Oceanography of Long Island Sound, 1952–1954: X. The biology of marine bottom communities: *Bull. Bingham Oceanographic Collection,* vol. 15, pp. 345–414.

Sargent, M. C., and T. J. Walker, 1947, Diatom populations associated with eddies off southern California in 1941: *Jour. Marine Research,* vol. 7, pp. 490–505.

Savage, R. P., 1957, Sand bypassing at Port Hueneme, California: Dept. of Army, Corps of Engineers, Beach Erosion Board, Tech. Memo. 92, 34 pp.

Scammon, C. M., 1874, *The Marine Mammals of the Northwest Coast of North America:* J. H. Carmony & Company, San Francisco, 319 pp.

Schäfer, W., 1956, Wirkungen der Benthos-Organismen auf den jungen Schichtverband: *Senckenbergiana Lethaea,* vol. 37, pp. 183–263.

Schoellhamer, J. E., and A. O. Woodford, 1951, The floor of the Los Angeles Basin, Los Angeles, Orange, and San Bernardino Counties, California: U. S. Geol. Survey, Oil and Gas Investigations, Map OM 117.

Scholl, D. W., 1959, Geology and surrounding recent marine sediments of Anacapa Island: Univ. Southern California, unpubl. master's thesis, 105 pp.

Schollenberger, C. J., 1927, A rapid approximate method for determining soil organic matter: *Soil Science,* vol. 24, pp. 63–68.

Schott, G., 1902, Oceanographie und maritime Meteorologie: *Wiss. Ergeb. Deutschen Tiefsee-Expedition auf dem Dampfer "Valdiva" 1898–1899,* vol. 1, p. 153 and Atlas Chart 21.

Schott, G., 1928, Die Wasserbewegungen im Gebiete der Gibralterstrasse: *Jour. du Conseil,* vol. 3, pp. 139–175.

Schupp, R. D., 1953, A study of the cobble beach cusps along Santa Monica Bay, California: Univ. Southern California, unpubl. master's thesis, 131 pp.

Scott, T., 1954, Sand movement by waves: Dept. of Army, Corps of Engineers, Beach Erosion Board, Tech. Memo. 48, 37 pp.

Scripps Institution of Oceanography, 1949–1952, Physical and chemical data: Marine Life Research Program, Division 3, Physical Oceanography, Division of Chemical Oceanography, Cruise reports 1–36. (mimeographed).

Seilacher, A., 1953, Die geologische Bedeutung fossiler Lebensspuren: *Zeit. deutschen geologischen gesellschaft,* vol. 105, pp. 214–227.

Sharpe, C. F. S., 1938, *Landslides and Related Phenomena: A Study of Mass-movements of Soil and Rock:* Columbia Univ. Press, New York, 136 pp.

Shattuck, G. B., 1906, The Pliocene and Pleistocene deposits of Maryland: *Maryland Geol. Survey Bull.,* pp. 21–137.

Shelton, J. S., 1954, Miocene volcanism in coastal southern California: *Calif. Div. Mines, Bull. 170,* ch. 7, pp. 31–36.

Shepard, F. P., 1935, Gravel cusps on the California coast related to tides: *Science,* new ser., vol. 82, pp. 251–253.

Shepard, F. P., 1941, Nondepositional physiographic environments off the California coast: *Bull. Geol. Soc. America,* vol. 52, pp. 1869–1886.

Shepard, F. P., 1948, *Submarine Geology:* Harper & Brothers, New York, 348 pp.

Shepard, F. P., 1949, Terrestrial topography of submarine canyons revealed by diving: *Bull. Geol. Soc. America,* vol. 60, pp. 1597–1612.

Shepard, F. P., 1950a, Longshore current observations in southern California: Dept. of Army, Corps of Engineers, Beach Erosion Board, Tech. Memo. 13, 54 pp.

Shepard, F. P., 1950b, Beach cycles in southern California: Dept. of Army, Corps of Engineers, Beach Erosion Board, Tech. Memo. 20, 26 pp.

Shepard, F. P., 1951a, Mass movements in submarine canyon heads; *Trans. Amer. Geophys. Union,* vol. 31, pp. 196–212.

Shepard, F. P., 1951b, Transportation of sand into deep water: *Soc. Econ. Paleontologists and Mineralogists, Special Publ. 2,* pp. 53–65.

Shepard, F. P., 1952, Composite origin of submarine canyons: *Jour. Geology,* vol. 60, pp. 84–96.

Shepard, F. P., 1954, Nomenclature based on sand-silt-clay ratios: *Jour. Sedimentary Petrology,* vol. 24, pp. 151–158.

Shepard, F. P., and C. N. Beard, 1938, Submarine canyons: Distribution and longitudinal profiles: *Geograph. Review,* vol. 28, pp. 439–451.

Shepard, F. P., and G. V. Cohee, 1936, Continental shelf sediments off the mid-Atlantic states: *Bull. Geol. Soc. America,* vol. 47, pp. 441–458.

Shepard, F. P., and K. O. Emery, 1941, Submarine topography off the California coast: Canyons and tectonic interpretations: *Geol. Soc. America, Special Paper 31,* 171 pp.

Shepard, F. P., and K. O. Emery, 1946, Submarine photography off the California coast: *Jour. Geology,* vol. 54, pp. 306–321.

Shepard, F. P., K. O. Emery, and H. R. Gould, 1949, Distribution of sediments on East Asiatic continental shelf: *Allan Hancock Foundation Publ., Occ. Paper 9,* 64 pp.

Shepard, F. P., K. O. Emery, and E. C. LaFond, 1941, Rip currents: a process of geological importance: *Jour. Geology,* vol. 49, pp. 337–369.

Shepard, F. P., and U. S. Grant, IV, 1947, Wave erosion along the southern California coast: *Bull. Geol. Soc. America,* vol. 58, pp. 919–926.

Shepard, F. P., and D. L. Inman, 1950, Nearshore water circulation related to bottom topography and wave refraction: *Trans. Amer. Geophys. Union,* vol. 31, pp. 196–212.

Shepard, F. P., and D. L. Inman, 1951a, Sand movement on the shallow inter-canyon shelf at La Jolla, California: Dept. of Army, Corps of Engineers, Beach Erosion Board, Tech. Memo. 39, 29 pp.

Shepard, F. P., and D. L. Inman, 1951b, Nearshore circulation: *Proceedings 1st Conference on Coastal Engineering,* Univ. California Press, Berkeley, pp. 50–59.

Shepard, F. P., and D. L. Inman, 1953, Areal and seasonal variations in beach and nearshore sediments at La Jolla, California: Dept. of Army, Corps of Engineers, Beach Erosion Board, Tech. Memo. 39, 82 pp.

Shepard, F. P., and E. C. LaFond, 1940, Sand movements along the Scripps Institution pier: *Amer. Jour. Science,* vol. 238, pp. 272–285.

Shepard, F. P., and G. A. Macdonald, 1938, Sediments of Santa Monica Bay, California: *Bull. Amer. Assoc. Petrol. Geologists,* vol. 22, pp. 201–216.

Shepard, F. P., G. A. Macdonald, and D. C. Cox, 1950, The tsunami of April 1, 1946: *Bull. Scripps Inst. Oceanography, Univ. Calif.,* vol. 5, pp. 391–528.

Shepard, F. P., and D. G. Moore, 1954, Sedimentary environments differentiated by coarse-fraction studies: *Bull. Amer. Assoc. Petrol. Geologists,* vol. 38, pp. 1792–1802.

Shepard, F. P., R. Revelle, and R. S. Dietz, 1939, Ocean-bottom currents off the California coast: *Science,* vol. 89, pp. 488–489.

Shepard, F. P., and H. E. Suess, 1956, Rate of postglacial rise of sea level: *Science,* vol. 123, pp. 1082–1083.

Shepard, F. P., and W. F. Wrath, 1937, Marine sediments around Catalina Island: *Jour. Sedimentary Petrology,* vol. 7, pp. 41–50.

Shirshov, P. P., 1940, *Bottom Relief in Central Water Mass of the Northwest Arctic Ocean.* Scientific results of the drifting station "North Pole": Acad. Sci. U. S. S. R., Oceanic Laboratory, pp. 110–140.

Shor, G. G., Jr., and R. W. Raitt, 1956, Seismic studies in the southern California continental borderland: *20th International Geological Congress, Mexico City, Abstracts,* p. 167.

Shor, G. G., Jr., and R. W. Raitt, 1958, Seismic studies in the southern California continental borderland: Marine Physical Laboratory of Scripps Institution of Oceanography, Scripps Inst. Oceanography, Ref. 58–78, 17 pp. (mimeographed).

Shumway, G., 1956, A resonant chamber method for sound velocity and attenuation measurements in sediments: *Geophysics,* vol. 21, pp. 305–319.

Silverman, S. R., and S. Epstein, 1958, Carbon isotopic compositions of petroleums and other sedimentary organic materials: *Bull. Amer. Assoc. Petrol. Geologists,* vol. 42, pp. 998–1012.

Simpson, G. G., 1947, A continental Tertiary time chart: *Jour. Paleontology,* vol. 21, pp. 480–483.

Slater, W. R., and R. C. Richter, 1952, Sea-water intrusion into ground water basins, Paper presented December 3, 1952 before the Pacific Southwest Federal Inter-Agency Technical Committee at Riverside, California: Calif. State Div. of Water Resources, 27 pp. (mimeographed).

Slosson, J. E., 1958, Lithofacies and sedimentary-paleogeographic analysis of the Los Angeles Repetto Basin: Univ. Southern California, unpubl. doctoral dissertation, 128 pp.

Smith, C. L., 1941, The solubility of calcium carbonate in tropical sea water: *Jour. Marine Biol. Assoc.,* vol. 25, pp. 235–242.

Smith, E. H., F. M. Soule, and O. Mosby, 1937, *Marion and General Green Expeditions to Davis Strait and Labrador Sea under the Direction of the U. S. Coast Guard 1928–1931–1933–1934–1935:* Washington, 259 pp.

Smith, G. M., 1944, *Marine Algae of the Monterey Peninsula:* Stanford Univ. Press, Stanford, 622 pp.

Smith, J. R., and H. S. Yoder, Jr., 1956, Variations in X-ray powder diffraction patterns of plagioclase feldspars: *Amer. Mineralogist,* vol. 41, pp. 632–647.

Smith, P. H., 1940, Metal from the sea: *Sci. American,* vol. 163, pp. 62–64.

Smith, P. V., Jr., 1952, The occurrence of hydrocarbons in recent sediments from the Gulf of Mexico: *Science,* vol. 116, pp. 437–439.

Smith, P. V., Jr., 1954, Studies on origin of petroleum: Occurrence of hydrocarbons in recent sediments: *Bull. Amer. Assoc. Petrol. Geologists,* vol. 38, pp. 377–404.

Smith, W. S. T., 1897, The geology of Santa Catalina Island: *Calif. Acad. Proc. Sciences,* 5th ser., Geology, vol. 1, pp. 1–71.

Smith, W. S. T., 1898, A geological sketch of San Clemente Island: *U. S. Geol. Survey, 18th Ann. Rept.,* pt. 2, pp. 459–496.

Smith, W. S. T., 1900, A topographic study of the islands of southern California: *Univ. Calif. (Berkeley), Publs. in Geology,* vol. 2, pp. 179–230.

Smith, W. S. T., 1902, The submarine valleys of the California coast: *Science,* new ser., vol. 15, pp. 670–672.

Smith, W. S. T., 1933, Marine terraces on Santa Catalina Island: *Amer. Jour. Science,* 5th ser., vol. 25, pp. 123–136.

Smitter, Y. H., 1955, An investigation of littoral "Warm Spots": *The Compass,* vol. 32, pp. 211–215.

Snodgrass, J. M., and J. H. Cawley, Jr., 1957, Bathythermometer telemeters ocean data: *Electronics,* May 1, 4 pp.

Sommer, H., W. F. Whedon, C. A. Kofoid, and R. Stohler, 1937, Relation of paralytic shell-fish poison to certain plankton organisms of the genus Gonyaulax: *Arch. of Pathology,* vol. 24, pp. 537–559.

Spencer, J. W., 1903, Submarine valleys off the American coast and in the North Atlantic: *Bull. Geol. Soc. America,* vol. 14, pp. 207–226.

Staff of Bureau of Marine Fisheries, 1949, The commercial fish catch of California for the year 1947 with an historical review 1916–1947: *Calif. Dept. Fish and Game, Fish Bull. 74,* 267 pp.

Staff of Marine Fisheries Branch, 1956, The marine fish catch of California for the years 1953 and 1954: *Calif. Dept. Fish and Game, Fish Bull. 102,* 99 pp.

Staff, South Pacific Fishery Investigations, 1953, Zooplankton volumes off the Pacific coast, 1952: *U. S. Fish and Wildlife Service, Spec. Sci. Rept.: Fisheries Ser. 100,* 41 pp.

Staff, South Pacific Fishery Investigations, 1954, Zooplankton volumes off the Pacific coast, 1953: *U. S. Fish and Wildlife Service, Spec. Sci. Rept.: Fisheries Ser. 132,* 38 pp.

Staff, South Pacific Fishery Investigations, 1955, Zooplankton volumes off the Pacific coast, 1954, *U. S. Fish and Wildlife Service, Spec. Sci. Rept.: Fisheries Ser. 161,* 35 pp.

Staff, South Pacific Fishery Investigations, 1956, Zooplankton volumes off the Pacific coast, 1955: *U. S. Fish and Wildlife Service, Spec. Sci. Rept.: Fisheries Ser. 177,* 32 pp.

Stearns, H. T., 1935, Pleistocene shore-lines on the islands of Oahu and Maui, Hawaii: *Bull. Geol. Soc. America,* vol. 46, pp. 1927–1956.

Stearns, H. T., 1945, Eustatic shore lines in the Pacific: *Bull. Geol. Soc. America,* vol. 56, pp. 1071–1078.

Stevens, N. P., 1956, Origin of petroleum—A review: *Bull. Amer. Assoc. Petrol. Geologists,* vol. 40, pp. 51–61.

Stevens, N. P., E. E. Bray, and E. D. Evans, 1956, Hydrocarbons in sediments of Gulf of Mexico: *Bull. Amer. Assoc. Petrol. Geologists,* vol. 40, pp. 975–983.

Stevenson, R. E., 1954, The marshlands at Newport Bay, California: Univ. of Southern California, unpubl. doctoral dissertation, 199 pp.

Stevenson, R. E., and K. O. Emery, 1958, Marshlands at Newport Bay, California: *Allan Hancock Foundation Publ., Occ. Paper 20,* 109 pp.

Stevenson, R. E., and D. S. Gorsline, 1956, A shoreward movement of cool subsurface water: *Trans. Amer. Geophys. Union,* vol. 37, pp. 553–557.

Stevenson, R. E., and J. R. Grady, 1956, Plankton and associated nutrients in the waters surrounding three sewer outfalls in southern California: Report to Hyperion Engineers, Inc., from Geology Dept., Univ. Southern California, 48 pp. (multilithed).

Stevenson, R. E., and R. D. Terry, 1957, Bottom materials and topography of the shelf between Point Conception and San Diego, *in* Oceanography and marine geology of the southern California shelf: Interim Report to State Water Pollution Control Board by Hancock Foundation, Univ. Southern California, pp. 24–74.

Stevenson, R. E., R. B. Tibby, and D. S. Gorsline, 1956, The oceanography of Santa Monica Bay, California: Report to Hyperion Engineers, Inc., from Geology Dept., Univ. Southern California, 268 pp. (multilithed).

Stewart, G. R., 1945, *Names on the Land:* Random House, New York, 418 pp.

Stewart, H. B., Jr., 1956, Sediments and the environment of deposition in a coastal lagoon: Univ. California at Los Angeles, unpubl. doctoral dissertation, 355 pp.

Stewart, H. B., Jr., 1957, Oceanographic surveys for the city of San Diego, 1956–1957: Geological Diving Consultants, Inc., San Diego, 202 pp. (duplicated).

Stewart, H. B., Jr., B. D. Zetler, and C. B. Taylor, 1958, Recent increases in coastal water temperatures and sea level—California to Alaska: *U. S. Coast and Geodetic Survey, Tech. Bull. 3,* 11 pp.

Stewart, L. C., 1934, Commercial extraction of bromine from sea water: *Ind. and Eng. Chemistry,* vol 26, pp. 361–369.

Stock, C., 1935, Exiled elephants of the Channel Islands, California: *Sci. Monthly,* vol. 41, pp. 205–214.

Stock, C., 1949, Rancho La Brea, a record of Pleistocene life in California: *Los Angeles Museum Publ. 13,* 4th ed., 81 pp.

Strakhov, N. M., 1958, Forms of iron in the deposits of the Black Sea: *Doklady Akad. Nauk S.S.S.R.,* vol. 118, pp. 803–806 (in Russian).

Ström, K. M., 1936, Land-locked waters. Hydrography and bottom deposits in badly ventilated Norwegian fjords with remarks upon sedimentation under anaeobic conditions: *Norske Videnskaps Akad. 1. Mat.-Nat. Klasse,* no. 7, 85 pp.

Suda, K., 1932, On the bottom of the Japan Sea (preliminary report): *Jour. Oceanography,* vol. 4, pp. 221–240.

Suess, H., 1954, U. S. Geological Survey radiocarbon dates I: *Science,* vol. 120, pp. 167–173.

Suess, H., 1956, Absolute chronology of the last glaciation: *Science,* vol. 123, pp. 355–357.

Sugawara, K., T. Koyama, and A. Kozawa, 1953, Distribution of various forms of sulphur in lake-, river- and sea-muds: *Jour. Earth Sciences, Nagoya Univ.* (Japan), vol. 1, pp. 17–23.

Sugawara, K., T. Koyama, and A. Kozawa, 1954, Distribution of various forms of sulphur in lake-, river- and sea-muds (II): *Jour. Earth Sciences, Nagoya Univ.* (Japan), vol. 2, pp. 1–4.

Sverdrup, H. U., 1947, Period increase of ocean swell: *Trans. Amer. Geophys. Union,* vol. 28, pp. 407–417.

Sverdrup, H. U., and W. E. Allen, 1939, Distribution of diatoms in relation to the character of water masses off southern California in 1938: *Jour. Marine Research,* vol. 2, pp. 131–144.

Sverdrup, H. U., and R. H. Fleming, 1941, The waters off the coast of southern California, March to July 1937: *Bull. Scripps Inst. Oceanography, Univ. Calif.,* vol. 4, pp. 261–378.

Sverdrup, H. U., M. W. Johnson, and R. H. Fleming, 1942, *The Oceans:* Prentice-Hall, New York, 1087 pp.

Sverdrup, H. U., and Staff, 1942, Oceanographic observations in the "E. W. Scripps" cruises of 1938: *Records of Observations, Scripps Inst. Oceanography,* vol. 1, no. 1, pp. 1–64.

Sverdrup, H. U., and Staff, 1943, Oceanographic observations on the "E. W. Scripps" cruises of 1939: *Records of Observations, Scripps Inst. Oceanography,* vol. 1, no. 2, pp. 65–160.

Sverdrup, H. U., and Staff, 1944, Oceanographic observations on the "E. W. Scripps" cruises of 1940: *Records of Observations, Scripps Inst. Oceanography,* vol. 1, no. 3, pp. 161–248.

Sverdrup, H. U., and Staff, 1947, Oceanographic observations on the "E. W. Scripps" cruises of 1941: *Records of Observations, Scripps Inst. Oceanography,* vol. 1, no. 4, pp. 249–408.

Sykes, G., 1937, *The Colorado Delta:* Carnegie Inst. of Washington, Publ. 460, 193 pp.

Taber, S., 1927, Fault troughs: *Jour. Geology,* vol. 35, pp. 577–606.

Takahashi, J-I., 1939, Synopsis of glauconitization, *Recent Marine Sediments:* Amer. Assoc. Petrol. Geologists, Tulsa, pp. 503–512.

Taliaferro, N. L., 1943, Franciscan-Knoxville problem: *Bull. Amer. Assoc. Petrol. Geologists,* vol. 27, pp. 109–219.

Tatel, H. E., and M. A. Tuve, 1955, Seismic exploration of a continental crust: *Geol. Soc. America, Special Paper 62,* pp. 35–50.

Terry, R. D., 1951, Suspended sediment study of surf at Huntington Beach, California: Univ. Southern California, unpubl. rept. in sedimentation, 21 pp.

Terry, R. D., 1955, Bibliography of marine geology and oceanography, California coast: *Calif. Div. Mines, Special Rept. 44,* 131 pp.

Terry, R. D., S. A. Keesling, and E. Uchupi, 1956, Submarine geology of Santa Monica Bay, California: Report to Hyperion Engineers, Inc., from Geology Dept., Univ. Southern California, 177 pp. (multilithed).

Terry, R. D., and R. E. Stevenson, 1957, Microrelief of the Santa Monica Shelf, California: *Bull. Geol. Soc. America,* vol. 68, pp. 125–128.

Terzaghi, K., and R. B. Peck, 1948, *Soil Mechanics in Engineering Practice:* John Wiley & Sons, New York, 566 pp.

Thomas, R. G., E. C. Marliave, L. B. James, and R. T. Bean, 1954, Geology and hydrology of Ventura County: *Calif. Div. Mines, Bull. 170,* ch. 6, pp. 19–28.

Thomasson, E. M., 1958, Problems of petroleum development on the continental shelf of the Gulf of Mexico, *in* An introduction to the geology and mineral resources of the continental shelves of the Americas: *U. S. Geol. Survey, Bull. 1067,* pp. 67–92.

Thompson, E. F., 1939a, The general hydrography of the Red Sea: *John Murray Expedition, 1933–34,* vol. 2, no. 3, pp. 83–103.

Thompson, E. F., 1939b, The exchange of water between the Red Sea and the Gulf of Aden over the "sill": *John Murray Expedition, 1933–34,* vol. 2, no. 4, pp. 105–119.

Thompson, T. G., and K. H. Nelson, 1954, Desalting of sea water by freezing: *Refrigerating Engineering,* vol. 62, pp. 44–48.

Thompson, W. C., 1957, Continental shelf structure and sediments west of Santa Barbara, California: Proceedings International Association for Quaternary Research, Barcelona, Spain, August-September 1957.

Thompson, W. O., 1937, Original structures of beaches, bars, and dunes: *Bull. Geol. Soc. America,* vol 48, pp. 723–751.

Tibby, R. B., 1939, Report on returns of drift bottles released off southern California, 1937: *Bull. Div. Fish and Game of California,* no. 55, pp. 1–36.

Todd, D. K., and R. L. Wiegel, 1952, Near-coastal storms and associated waves: *Trans. Amer. Geophys. Union,* vol. 33, pp. 217–225.

Tolman, C. F., 1937, *Ground Water:* McGraw-Hill Book Company, New York, 593 pp.

Townley, S. D., and M. W. Allen, 1939, Descriptive catalogue of earthquakes of the Pacific Coast of the United States, 1769–1928: *Bull. Seismol. Soc. America,* vol. 29, pp. 1–297.

Trask, P. D., 1931, Sedimentation in the Channel Islands Region, California: *Econ. Geology,* vol. 26, pp. 24–43.

Trask, P. D., 1932, *Origin and Environment of Source Sediments of Petroleum:* Gulf Publishing Company, Houston, 323 pp.

Trask, P. D., 1937, Inferences about the origin of oil as indicated by the composition of the organic constituents of sediments: *U. S. Geol. Survey, Prof. Paper 186,* pp. 147–157.

Trask, P. D., 1939, Organic content of recent marine sediments, *Recent Marine Sediments:* Amer. Asso. Petrol. Geologists, Tulsa, pp. 428–453.

Trask, P. D., 1952, Source of beach sand at Santa Barbara, California as indicated by mineral grain studies: Dept. of Army, Corps of Engineers, Beach Erosion Board, Tech. Memo. 28, 24 pp.

Trask, P. D., 1955, Movement of sand around southern California promontories: Dept. of Army, Corps of Engineers, Beach Erosion Board, Tech. Memo. 76, 60 pp.

Trask, P. D., and H. W. Patnode, 1942, *Source Beds of Petroleum:* Amer. Assoc. Petrol. Geologists, Tulsa, 566 pp.

Trask, P. D., and C. C. Wu, 1930, Does petroleum form in sediments at time of deposition?: *Bull. Amer. Assoc. Petrol. Geologists,* vol. 14, pp. 1451–1463.

Trégouboff, G., 1958, Prospection biologique sous-marine dans la région de Villefranche-sur-Mer au cours de l'année 1957. I. Plongées en bathyscaphe: *Bull. de l'institut océanographique,* no. 1117, 37 pp.

Treibs, A., 1934, Chlorophyll- and Hämin-Derivate in bituminösen Gesteinen, Erdölen, Erdwachsen und Asphalten: *Annalen d. Chemie,* vol. 510, pp. 42–62.

Troxel, B. W., 1954, Geologic guide for the Los Angeles Basin, southern California: *Calif. Div. Mines, Bull. 170,* Guide 3, 46 pp.

Troxel, B. W., 1957, Abrasives, *in* Mineral commodities of California: *Calif. Div. Mines, Bull. 176,* pp. 23–28.

Troxell, H. C., and others, 1942, Floods of March 1938 in southern California: *U. S. Geol. Survey, Water Supply Paper 844,* 399 pp.

Tseng, C. K., 1944, Agar: a valuable seaweed product: *Sci. Monthly,* vol. 58, pp. 24–32.

Tseng, C. K., 1946, Seaweed products and their uses in America: *Jour. New York Botanical Garden,* vol. 47, pp. 1–10, 32–39.

Tsuboi, C., 1956, Crustal structure in northern and middle California from gravity-pendulum data: *Bull. Geol. Soc. America,* vol. 67, pp. 1641–1646.

Tucker, G. H., 1951, Relation of fishes and other organisms to the scattering of underwater sound: *Jour. Marine Research,* vol. 10, pp. 215–238.

Tuthill, C., and A. A. Allanson, 1954, Ocean-bottom artifacts: *The Masterkey,* vol. 28, pp. 222–232.

Twenhofel, W. H., 1932, *Treatise on Sedimentation:* Williams & Wilkins Company, Baltimore, 926 pp.

Uchupi, E., 1954, Submarine geology of the Santa Rosa-Cortes Ridge: Univ. Southern California, unpubl. master's thesis, 72 pp.

Uda, M., 1951, On the fluctuations of the main stream axis and its boundary line of Kuroshio: *Jour. Oceanography (Japan),* vol. 6, pp. 181–189.

Ufford, C. W., 1947a, Internal waves in the ocean: *Trans. Amer. Geophys. Union,* vol. 28, pp. 79–86.

Ufford, C. W., 1947b, Internal waves measured at three stations: *Trans, Amer. Geophys. Union,* vol. 28, pp. 87–95.

Ufford, C. W., 1947c, The theory of internal waves: *Trans. Amer. Geophys. Union,* vol. 28, pp. 96–101.

Umbgrove, J. H. F., 1947, *The Pulse of the Earth:* Martinus Nijhoff, The Hague, 358 pp.

Upson, J. E., 1949, Late Pleistocene and recent changes of sea level along the coast of Santa Barbara County, California: *Amer. Jour. Science,* vol. 247, pp. 94–115.

Upson, J. E., 1951a, Former marine shore lines of the Gaviota quadrangle, Santa Barbara County, California: *Jour. Geology,* vol. 59, pp. 415–446.

Upson, J. E., 1951b, Geology and ground-water resources of the south-coast basins of Santa Barbara County, California: *U. S. Geol. Survey, Water Supply Paper 1108,* 144 pp.

Urey, H. C., H. A. Lowenstam, S. Epstein, and C. R. McKinney, 1951, Measurement of paleotemperatures and temperatures of the upper Cretaceous of England, Denmark, and the southeastern United States: *Bull. Geol. Soc. America,* vol. 62, pp. 399–416.

U. S. Public Health Service, 1946, Public Health Service drinking water standards: *Publ. Health Repts. (U. S.),* vol. 61, pp. 371–384.

Valentine, J. W., 1955, Upwelling and thermally anomalous Pacific coast Pleistocene molluscan faunas: *Amer. Jour. Science,* vol. 253, pp. 462–474.

Valentine, J. W., 1956, Upper Pleistocene mollusca from Potrero Canyon, Pacific Palisades, California: *Trans. San Diego Soc. Nat. History,* vol. 12, pp. 181–205.

Valentine, J. W., 1957, Late Pleistocene faunas from the northwestern coast of Baja California, Mexico: *Trans. San Diego Soc. Nat. History,* vol. 12, pp. 289–308.

van Andel, T., and H. Postma, 1954, Recent sediments of the Gulf of Paria, Reports of the Orinoco Shelf Expedition, vol. 1: *Verhandel. Koninklijke Nederlandse Akademie van Wetenschappen, Afdeel. Natuurkunde,* vol. 20, no. 5, 245 pp.

Vanoni, V. A., and J. H. Carr, 1951, Harbor surging: *Proceedings 1st Conference on Coastal Engineering,* Univ. California Press, pp. 60–68.

van Riel, P. M., 1934, The bottom configuration in relation to the flow of the bottom water: *The Snellius Expedition,* vol. 2, pt. 2, ch. 3, 60 pp.

van Riel, P. M., H. C. Hamaker, L. van Eyck, 1950, Serial and bottom observations. Temperature, salinity, and density: *The Snellius Expedition,* vol. 2, pt. 6, 44 pp.

Varnes, D. J., 1958, Landslide types and processes, *in* Landslides and engineering practice: Highway Research Board Special Rept. 29, *Natl. Acad. Sciences–Natl. Research Council, Publ. 544,* pp. 20–47.

Veatch, A. C., and P. A. Smith, 1939, Atlantic submarine valleys of the United States and the Congo Submarine Valley: *Geol. Soc. America, Special Paper 7,* 101 pp.

Vening Meinesz, F. A., 1954, Indonesian archipelago: a geophysical study: *Bull. Geol. Soc. America,* vol. 65, pp. 165–174.

ver Planck, W. E., 1957, Iodine, *in* Mineral Commodities of California: *Calif. Div. Mines, Bull. 176,* pp. 241–243.

ver Planck, W. E., 1958, Salt in California: *Calif. Div. Mines, Bull. 175,* 168 pp.

Vining, E. P., 1885, *An Inglorious Columbus; or Evidence that Hwui Shan and a Party of Buddhist Monks from Afghanistan Discovered America in the Fifth Century, A. D.:* D. Appleton & Company, New York, 788 pp.

Vinogradov, A. P., 1953, The Elementary Chemical Composition of Marine Organisms: *Sears Foundation for Marine Research, Memoir 2,* 647 pp.

Volkmann, G., J. Knauss, and A. Vine, 1956, The use of parachute drogues in the measurement of subsurface ocean currents: *Trans. Amer. Geophys. Union,* vol. 37, pp. 573–577.

von Arx, W. S., 1950, An electromagnetic method for measuring the velocity of ocean currents from a ship under way: *Papers Phys. Oceanography and Meteorology,* vol. 11, 62 pp.

von Arx, W. S., D. F. Bumpus, and W. S. Richardson, 1955, On the fine structure of the Gulf Stream front: *Deep-Sea Research,* vol. 3, pp. 46–65.

Wagner, H. R., 1937, *The Cartography of the Northwest Coast of America to the Year 1800:* Univ. California Press, Berkeley, 543 pp.

Waksman, S. A., C. L. Carey, and H. W. Reuszer, 1933, Marine bacteria and their role in the cycle of life in the sea: *Biol. Bull.,* vol. 65, pp. 57–79.

Walker, B. W., 1947, The beach-spawning grunion: *Aquarium Journal,* Nov., pp. 8–12, 31.

Walker, B. W., 1952, A guide to the grunion: *Calif. Fish and Game,* vol. 38, pp. 409–420.

Wallace, E. T., and G. Kritzman, 1956, A shell-encrusted artifact: *Newsletter of the Archaeological Survey Assoc. of Southern California,* vol. 3, no. 1, pp. 11–12.

Warren, E., Jr., 1958, Off Santa Barbara: California's ranches in the sea: *Natl. Geograph. Magazine,* vol. 114, pp. 234–284.

Watts, G. M., 1953, Field investigation of suspended sediment in the surf zone: *Proceedings 4th Conference on Coastal Engineering,* Univ. California Press, pp. 181–199.

Wellman, P. E., 1950, Secrets of a hundred sunken ships: *Saturday Evening Post,* vol. 223, pp. 19–21, 51, 54, 59–60, 62, 64, 66, 68–69.

Wentworth, C. K., 1938, 1939, Marine bench-forming processes: Water-level weathering: *Jour. Geomorphology,* vol. 1, pp. 6–32; vol. 2, pp. 3–25.

Wertheim, G. K., 1954, Studies of the electric potential between Key West, Florida, and Havana, Cuba: *Trans. Amer. Geophys. Union,* vol. 35, pp. 872–886.

West, P. J., 1950, Preferred orientation of beach pebbles: Univ. Southern California, unpubl. rept. in sedimentation, 24 pp.

White, R. T., chairman, 1952, Cenozoic correlation section across Los Angeles Basin from Palos Verdes Hills to San Gabriel Mts., California: Pacific Section Amer. Assoc. Petrol. Geologists, 1 chart.

White, W. A., 1949, Atterberg plastic limits of clay minerals: *Illinois State Geol. Survey, Rept. of Investigations 144,* pp. 508–512.

Whitehead, W. L., 1950–1951, Studies of the effect of radioactivity in the transformation of marine organic materials into petroleum hydrocarbons, *Fundamental Research on Occurrence and Recovery of Petroleum,* Amer. Petrol. Inst., pp. 115–157.

Wickman, F. E., 1956, The cycle of carbon and the stable carbon isotopes: *Geochimica et Cosmochimica Acta,* vol. 9, pp. 136–153.

Wiegel, R. L., 1953, Waves, tides, currents and beaches: Glossary of terms and list of standard symbols: Council on Wave Research, The Engineering Foundation, Univ. California, Berkeley, 113 pp.

Wilbur, M. E., 1954, *Vancouver in California, 1792–1794,* vol. 2: Dawson, Los Angeles, pp. 135–274.

Wilson, D. M., 1956, Quantitative survey of the benthic mollusca of San Pedro Basin area, southern California: Univ. Southern California, unpubl. master's thesis, 96 pp.

Wimberley, C. S., 1955, Marine sediments north of Scripps Submarine Canyon, La Jolla, California: *Jour. Sedimentary Petrology,* vol. 25, pp. 24–37.

Wohnus, J. F., 1942, The kelp resources of southern California: *Calif. Fish and Game,* vol. 28, pp. 199–205.

Wood, H. O., 1947, Earthquakes in southern California with geologic relations: *Bull. Seismol. Soc. America,* vol. 37, pp. 107–157, 217–256.

Wood, H. O., M. W. Allen, and N. H. Heck, 1934, Destructive and near-destructive earthquakes in California and western Nevada, 1769–1933: *U. S. Coast and Geodetic Survey, Special Publ. 191,* 24 pp.

Woodford, A. O., 1924, The Catalina metamorphic facies

of the Franciscan series: *Univ. Calif. (Berkeley), Publs. in Geol. Sciences,* vol. 15, pp. 49–68.

Woodford, A. O., 1925, The San Onofre breccia; its nature and origin: *Univ. Calif. (Berkeley), Publs. in Geol. Sciences,* vol. 15, pp. 159–280.

Woodford, A. O., 1935, Rhomboid ripple mark: *Amer. Jour. Science,* 5th ser., vol. 29, pp. 518–525.

Woodford, A. O., 1951, Stream gradients and Monterey Sea Valley: *Bull. Geol. Soc. America,* vol. 62, pp. 799–852.

Woodford, A. O., J. E. Schoellhamer, J. G. Vedder, and R. F. Yerkes, 1954, Geology of the Los Angeles Basin: *Calif. Div. Mines, Bull. 170,* ch. 2, pp. 56–81.

Woodring, W. P., M. N. Bramlette, and W. S. W. Kew, 1946, Geology and paleontology of Palos Verdes Hills, California: *U. S. Geol. Survey, Prof. Paper 207,* 145 pp.

Woollard, G. P., 1949, Gravity anomalies and the nature of the earth's crust: *Trans. Amer. Geophys. Union,* vol. 30, pp. 189–201.

Woollard, G. P., chairman, 1955, Report of the special committee on the geophysical and geological study of continents, 1952–1954: *Trans. Amer. Geophys. Union,* vol. 36, pp. 695–708.

Worzel, J. L., and M. Ewing, 1954, Gravity anomalies and structure of the West Indies, Part 2: *Bull. Geol. Soc. America,* vol. 65, pp. 195–200.

Worzel, J. L., and G. L. Shurbet, 1955, Gravity anomalies at continental margins: *Proc. Natl. Acad. Sciences, U. S.,* vol. 41, pp. 458–469.

Worzel, J. L., G. L. Shurbet, and M. Ewing, 1955, Gravity measurements at sea, 1952 and 1953: *Trans. Amer. Geophys. Union,* vol. 36, pp. 326–334.

Yalkovsky, R., 1957, The relationship between paleotemperature and carbonate content in a deep-sea core: *Jour. Geology,* vol. 65, pp. 480–496.

Yates, L. G., 1890, Stray notes on the geology of the Channel Islands: Calif. State Min. Bur., 9th Ann. Rept. State Mineralogist, pp. 171–174.

Young, R. E., H. K. Pratt, and J. B. Biale, 1951, Identification of ethylene as a volatile product of the fungus Penicillium digitatum: *Plant Physiology,* vol. 26, pp. 304–310.

Young, R. T., Jr., 1939, Measurements on the transparency of sea-water off the coast of southern California: *Jour. Marine Research,* vol. 2, pp. 117–125.

Zalesny, E. R., 1956, Foraminiferal ecology of Santa Monica Bay: Univ. Southern California, unpubl. master's thesis, 78 pp.

Zenkevitch, L., 1947, *Fauna and Biological Productivity of the Sea,* vol. 2, Soviet Science, Leningrad, 588 pp.

ZoBell, C. E., 1945, The role of bacteria in the formation and transformation of petroleum hydrocarbons: *Science,* vol. 102, pp. 364–369.

ZoBell, C. E., 1946a, Studies on redox potential of marine sediments: *Bull. Amer. Assoc. Petrol. Geologists,* vol. 30, pp. 477–513.

ZoBell, C. E., 1946b, Action of microorganisms on hydrocarbons: *Bacterial Review,* vol. 10, pp. 1–49.

ZoBell, C. E., 1946c, *Marine Microbiology:* Chronica Botanica Company, Waltham, Mass., 240 pp.

Author Index

Subject Index